SCIENCEPOWER™ 10

McGraw-Hill Ryerson SCIENCEPOWER™ Program

SCIENCEPOWER™ 7
SCIENCEPOWER™ 8
SCIENCEPOWER™ 9
SCIENCEPOWER™ 10

Chenelière/McGraw-Hill OMNISCIENCES Program

OMNISCIENCES 7
OMNISCIENCES 8
OMNISCIENCES 9
OMNISCIENCES 10

This program is available directly from Chenelière/McGraw-Hill.

Teacher Support for Each Grade Level
Teacher Resource Binder
Blackline Masters
Assessment and Evalution Handbook
Computerized Assessment Bank
Web site: *http//www.mcgrawhill.ca*
Videotape series

Our cover Like scientists, photographers need patience and perseverance to meet their goals. Think about our cover photograph, for example. To "freeze" one stunning moment in time, the photographer waited calmly, for hours. At last, a kingfisher arrivd. As it splashed in the sparkling water, the photograher snapped frame after frame of photographs. Forty rolls of film later, he carried away a mere seven good photographs. You see one of these photographs on our cover.

In this textbook, you will explore living moments in ecosystems across Canada and throughout the world. You will consider how we can sustain these ecosystems for the future. You will investigate reactions that involve water and other important chemical compounds. You will explore the nature of motion and the technologies we use to move around. Finally, you will examine the factors that produce Earth's weather systems, and the impact of these weather systems on life on Earth.

SCIENCEPOWER™ 10
SCIENCE • TECHNOLOGY • SOCIETY • ENVIRONMENT

Author Team

Eric Grace
Professional Writer
Victoria, British Columbia

Frank Mustoe
University of Toronto Schools
Toronto, Ontario

John Ivanco
Former Head of Science
Anderson Collegiate and Vocational Institute
Whitby, Ontario

David Gue
Crescent Heights High School
Medicine Hat, Alberta

Frederick D. Brown
Former Assistant Head of Science
Applewood Heights Secondary School
Mississauga, Ontario

Lois Edwards
Professional Writer
Cochrane, Alberta

Rick Bello
Associate Professor
Department of Geography
York University
Toronto, Ontario

Senior Program Consultants

Malisa·Mezenberg
Loyola Catholic Secondary School
Mississauga, Ontario

Douglas A. Roberts
University of Calgary
Calgary, Alberta

McGraw-Hill Ryerson

Toronto   Montréal   New York   Burr Ridge   Bangkok   Bogotá   Caracas
Lisbon   London   Madrid   Mexico City   Milan   New Delhi
Seoul   Singapore   Sydney   Taipei

McGraw-Hill Ryerson Limited
A Subsidiary of The McGraw·Hill Companies

SCIENCEPOWER™ 10
Science • Technology • Society • Environment

The information and activities in this textbook have been carefully developed and reviewed by professionals to ensure safety and accuracy. However, the publishers shall not be liable for any damages resulting, in whole or in part, from the reader's use of the material. Although appropriate safety procedures are discussed in detail and highlighted throughout the textbook, safety of students remains the responsibility of the classroom teacher, the principal, and the school board/district.

0-07-560364-0

http://www.mcgrawhill.ca

1 2 3 4 5 6 7 8 9 0 GTC 0 9 8 7 6 5 4 3 2 1 0

Printed and bound in Canada

Care has been taken to trace ownership of copyright material contained in this textbook. The publishers will gladly take any information that will enable them to rectify any reference or credit in subsequent printings. Please note that products shown in photographs in this textbook do not reflect an endorsement by the publisher of those specific brand names.

Canadian Cataloguing in Publication Data
Main entry under title:

Sciencepower 10: science, technology, society, environment

Includes index.
ISBN 0-07-560364-0

1. Science. I. Grace, Eric, date. II. Title: Sciencepower ten.

Q161.2.S387 2000   500   C00-930901-2

The *SCIENCEPOWER*™ Development Team
SCIENCE PUBLISHER: Trudy Rising
SENIOR DEVELOPMENTAL EDITORS: Tom Gamblin, Lois Edwards, Dan Kozlovic, Jonathan Bocknek, Gerry De Iuliis
SENIOR SUPERVISING EDITOR: Linda Allison
PROJECT CO-ORDINATOR: Nancy Landry
ASSISTANT PROJECT CO-ORDINATOR: Janie Reeson
EDITORIAL ASSISTANT: Joanne Murray
SPECIAL FEATURES: Trudee Romanek, Elma Schemenauer
COPY EDITOR: Paula Pettitt-Townsend
PERMISSIONS EDITOR: Ann Ludbrook
PRODUCTION CO-ORDINATOR: Brad Madill
PROOFREADER: Carolann Freeman
COVER AND INTERIOR DESIGN: Pronk & Associates
ELECTRONIC PAGE MAKE-UP: ArtPlus Limited/Valerie Bateman
ART DIRECTION: ArtPlus Limited/Kristi Moreau
SET-UP PHOTOGRAPHY: Ian Chrysler
SET-UP PHOTOGRAPHY CO-ORDINATOR: Jane Affleck
TECHNICAL ILLUSTRATIONS: Imagineering Scientific and Technical Artworks Inc.
ILLUSTRATORS: Tina Holdcroft, Renné Benoit

Acknowledgements

We sincerely thank our consultant, Dr. Penny McLeod, for her constant input of valuable ideas and recommendations for the development of SCIENCEPOWER™ 10. We also wish to thank the following people: William Webb, who granted us permission to use, with modifications, his activity "An Interdisciplinary Deer and Human Population Study"; Mr. Jim Lewko, who authored the Unit 1 Project; Grace Price, who wrote SkillPower 3; Craig Jackson, who produced activities and special features for Unit 4; and Dr. William Rees, from the University of British Columbia, who developed the concept of "ecological footprint" and so willingly gave us updates on his work, while also reviewing this part of our textbook. As well, we are deeply indebted to each and every reviewer from across the country, and our highly experienced safety reviewer, who brought different perspectives to our project, based on their special interests, their regions, and their own teaching expertise. The authors, editors, senior program consultants, and publisher sincerely thank them all. We extend sincere thanks to Exclusive Educational Games of Excellence Inc. and Boreal Laboratories Ltd. for supplying us with equipment gratis for use in our photographs of students conducting various investigations.

Consultant

Dr. Penny McLeod
Thornhill Secondary School
Thornhill, Ontario

Pedagogical and Academic Reviewers

Jane Alexander
Canterbury High School
Ottawa, Ontario

Marietta Alibranti
Elia Middle School
North York, Ontario

Anthony Amirault
Halifax West High School
Halifax, Nova Scotia

David Arthur
Ontario Society for Environmental Education
Toronto, Ontario

Ray Bowers
North York Board of Education
North York, Ontario

Mike Calcutt
Holy Heart of Mary Regional High School
St. John's, Newfoundland

Brian Cochrane
Cove Harbour District High School
Dartmouth, Nova Scotia

Cliff Coveyduc
Former Physics Teacher
Testing Specialist
Atlantic Provinces Education Foundation
Dartmouth, Nova Scotia

Gail de Souza
St. Joseph Secondary School
Mississauga, Ontario

Nancy Flood
University College of the Cariboo
Kamloops, British Columbia

Steve Gosse
Queen Elizabeth High School
Halifax, Nova Scotia

Bruce Hickey
Holy Spirit High School
Conception Bay, Newfoundland

Craig Jackson
Kapuskasing District High School
Kapuskasing, Ontario

David Knox
Canterbury High School
Ottawa, Ontario

Ping Lai
University of Toronto Schools
Toronto, Ontario

Jim Lewko
Toronto District School Board
Toronto, Ontario

Wayne Lincoln
Charles P. Allen High School
Bedford, Nova Scotia

Peter MacDonald
Science Co-ordinator
Charles P. Allen High School
Bedford, Nova Scotia

Henry Pasma
Cawthra Park Secondary School
Mississauga, Ontario

Terry Price
Huron Heights Secondary School
Thornhill, Ontario

Wayne Purcell
Queen Elizabeth High School
Halifax, Nova Scotia

Terry Quinlan
Vice-Principal
Charles P. Allen High School
Bedford, Nova Scotia

Clifford Sampson, Ph.D.
Appleby College
Oakville, Ontario

Beth Savan, Ph.D., M.C.I.P.
University of Toronto
Toronto, Ontario

Mario Simon
Holy Heart of Mary Regional High School
St. John's Newfoundland

Susan Tanner
Queen Elizabeth High School
Halifax, Nova Scotia

Paul Weese
Former Head of Science
Lambton-Kent Composite School
Dresden, Ontario

Sandy Wohl
Hugh Boyd Secondary School
Richmond, British Columbia

Safety Reviewer

Margaret Redway
Fraser Scientific & Business Services
Delta, British Columbia

Contents

Unit 1 Sustainability of Ecosystems

Unit 2 Chemistry in Action

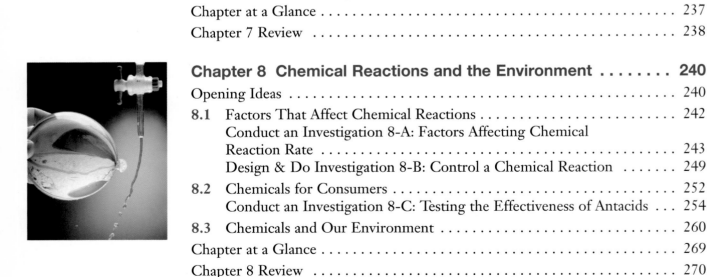

Unit 3 The Physics of Motion

Unit 4 Weather Dynamics

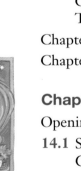

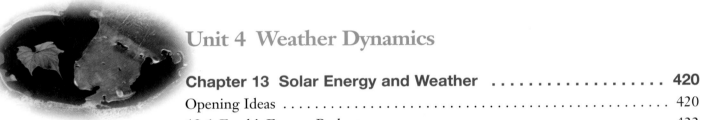

To the Teacher

We are very pleased to have been part of the team of experienced science educators and editors working together to bring you and your students this new program — the *SCIENCEPOWER*™ *7-10* series of textbooks and its French equivalent, *OMNISCIENCES 7-10*. The *SCIENCEPOWER*™ and *OMNISCIENCES* student and teacher resources were specifically developed to provide 100 percent congruence with the curriculum. As the titles *SCIENCEPOWER*™ and *OMNISCIENCES* suggest, these resources are designed to foster an appreciation of the power of scientific explanation as a way of understanding our world. They are also designed to empower students to examine societal issues critically, using their knowledge of science concepts and processes.

SCIENCEPOWER™ *10* and *OMNISCIENCES 10* provide three primary emphases:

- A science inquiry emphasis, in which students address questions about the nature of science involving broad explorations as well as focussed investigations. Skill areas that are emphasized include careful observing; questioning; proposing ideas; predicting; hypothesizing; making inferences; designing experiments; gathering, processing, and interpreting data; and explaining and communicating.

- A technological problem-solving emphasis, in which students seek answers to practical problems. Problem solving may either precede knowledge acquisition or provide students with opportunities to apply their newly acquired science knowledge in novel ways. Skill areas that are emphasized include understanding the problem; setting and/or understanding criteria; developing a design plan; carrying out the plan; evaluating; and communicating.

- A societal decision-making emphasis, in which students draw upon those science and technology concepts and skills that will inform the question or issue under consideration. Students are encouraged to give particular attention to sustainability and stewardship. Skill areas that are emphasized include identifying the issue; identifying alternatives; researching, reflecting, and deciding; taking action; evaluating; and communicating.

The particular emphases within a unit are, in part, suggested by the topic itself. The primary and secondary emphases for *SCIENCEPOWER*™ *10* and *OMNISCIENCES 10* are listed in the table opposite.

Scientific literacy has become the goal in science education throughout the world. This goal has been given expression, in Canada, in the *Common Framework of Science Learning Outcomes, K-12: Pan-Canadian Protocol for Collaboration on School Curriculum* (Council of Ministers of Education, Canada, 1997).

> Scientific literacy is an evolving combination of the science-related attitudes, skills, and knowledge students need to develop inquiry, problem-solving, and decision-making abilities, to become lifelong learners, and to maintain a sense of wonder about the world around them. To develop scientific literacy, students require diverse learning experiences which provide opportunity to explore, analyze, evaluate, synthesize, appreciate, and understand the interrelationships among science, technology, society, and the environment that will affect their personal lives, their careers, and their future.

SCIENCEPOWER™ 10/ OMNISCIENCES Unit	Primary Emphasis	Secondary Emphasis or Emphases
Unit 1 Sustainability of Ecosystems	Societal Decision Making	Science and Science Inquiry
Unit 2 Chemistry in Action	Technological Problem Solving	Science and Science Inquiry
Unit 3 The Physics of Motion	Science and Science Inquiry	Technological Problem Solving
Unit 4 Weather Dynamics	Science and Science Inquiry	Societal Decision Making, Technological Problem Solving

Through varied features, **SCIENCEPOWER™ 10** enables students to understand and develop skills in the processes of scientific inquiry, and in relating science to technology, society, and the environment.

Like the other textbooks in our series, **SCIENCEPOWER™ 10** builds on the three basic goals of the curriculum. It reflects the essential triad of knowledge, skills, and the ability to relate science to technology, society, and the environment (STSE). Science is approached both as an intellectual pursuit and as an activity-based enterprise operating within a social context.

Our extensive *Teacher's Resource Binder* provides planning and implementation strategies that you will find helpful and practical. Our *Blackline Masters* include materials that you can use for vocabulary building, skill building, and concept clarification, as well as alternative activities for multiple learning styles, and forms for performance task assessment of student achievement that are specific to the unit of study. Our *Assessment and Evaluation Handbook* provides strategies and forms for assessment that focus on the larger, encompassing skills of science, technology, and societal decision making. Our *Computerized Assessment Bank* will assist you in your full implementation of the **SCIENCEPOWER™ 10** program. Many of our teacher support materials can be found at our web site: *http//www.mcgrawhill.ca*

We feel confident that we have provided you with the best possible program to help your students achieve excellence and a high degree of scientific literacy through their course of study.

The Authors and Senior Program Consultants

A TOUR OF YOUR TEXTBOOK

Welcome to **SCIENCEPOWER™ 10**. This textbook introduces you to the interactions among organisms and their environments, the chemicals and chemical reactions that occur around and within us, the principles of how and why things move, and the factors that help to determine weather. To understand the book's structure, begin by taking a brief tour on the following pages.

UNIT OPENER

- *SCIENCEPOWER™ 10* has four major units.
- Each unit opener provides a clear overview of the unit's contents.
- The unit opener stimulates interest in the topic by suggesting a problem to think about, presenting science concepts to consider, or outlining a societal issue to explore.
- The unit opener identifies each chapter in the unit.

CHAPTER OPENER

- Each chapter opener gives you a clear idea of what this chapter is about.
- **Opening Ideas ...** gives you a chance to think about what you already know (or do not know) about the topic.
- **Science Log** suggests various ways to answer the *Opening Ideas* questions, and provides an opportunity to keep a record of what you learn in the same way that scientists log their observations and the results of their findings. (Your teacher may call this record a *Science Journal* instead of a *Science Log.*)
- The **Starting Point Activity** launches each chapter in a variety of ways. Like the *Opening Ideas*, the *Starting Point Activity* helps you think about what you already know (or do not know) about the chapter's main topics.
- **Key Concepts, Key Skills,** and **Key Terms** focus your attention on the major concepts, skills, and terms that you will be expected to know by the time you have completed the chapter.
- The **introductory paragraphs** of each chapter invite you to learn more about the topic and clearly tell you what you will be studying in the chapter.

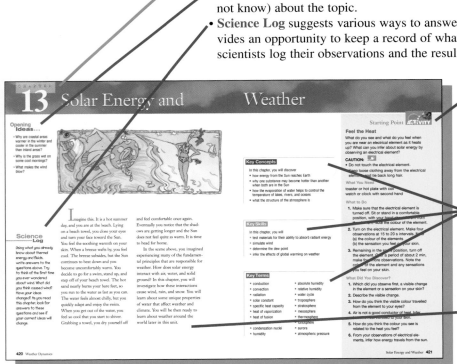

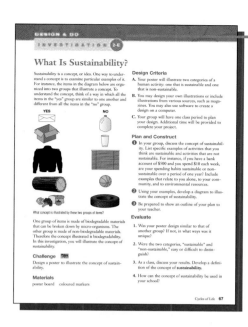

DESIGN & DO INVESTIGATION

- These investigations set challenges to design and construct your own models, systems, or products.
- The co-operative group work icon shows that you will be doing these investigations in a team.
- The Design Criteria provide a framework for evaluating your results.
- You and your team members are then on your own to design and construct!

OUTSIDE LINK ACTIVITY

- These are short, informal inquiry activities to do outside of class.
- They involve simple materials and equipment.

CONDUCT AN INVESTIGATION

- One- to six-page "formal" labs provide an opportunity to develop science inquiry skills using various apparatus and materials.
- These investigations provide a chance to ask questions about science, to make observations, and to obtain results.
- You then analyze your results to determine what they tell you about the topic you are investigating.
- Safety icons and Safety Precautions alert you to any special precautions you should take.

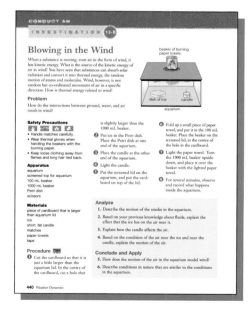

WordCONNECT

- Word origins and a variety of language activities provide links to language arts.

SCIENCE INQUIRY ACTIVITY

- These short, informal inquiry activities provide practice in science inquiry skills: predicting, estimating, hypothesizing, and so on.

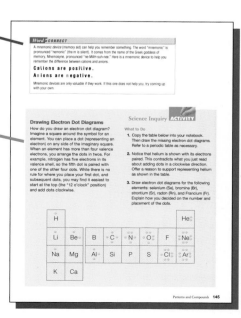

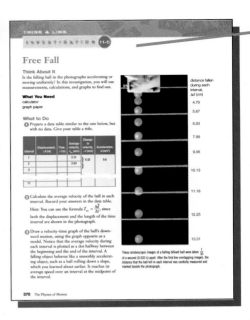

THINK & LINK INVESTIGATION

- These one- to six-page "thought" or "paper-based" investigations enable you to explore concepts or ideas that might be impractical and/or dangerous in the science classroom.
- These investigations emphasize a variety of skills, such as analyzing data, interpreting a diagram or flowchart, analyzing an issue, etc.

Across Canada

- These "mini-essays" feature information on Canadian scientists involved in important research and discoveries.
- *Across Canada* features increase your awareness and appreciation of the work of Canadian scientists. As well, they provide role models for those of you interested in careers or further study in science.

CHECK YOUR UNDERSTANDING

- A set of review questions appears at the end of each numbered section in a chapter.
- These questions provide opportunities for ongoing self-assessment.
- "Apply" and "Thinking Critically" questions present additional challenges.

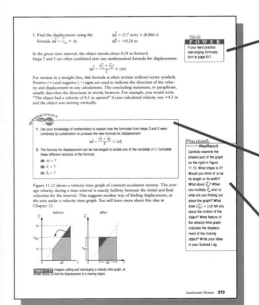

Skill POWER

- Skill development tips refer you to the *Science Skills Guide* at the back of the textbook.
- These tips provide specific skill development strategies and activities as they are needed. Topics include using the microscope and scientific drawing.

Stretch Your Mind

- These brain teasers are often related to mathematics.
- They draw upon your problem-solving skills and your imagination.

Pause & Reflect

- These features supply opportunities for you to reflect on what you know and to make connections among ideas throughout the textbook.
- This recurring feature encourages you to construct your own learning on an ongoing basis and to keep track of how your knowledge is building.

DidYou**Know**?

- These features present interesting facts related to science, technology, nature, and the universe.

InternetCONNECT

- This feature encourages productive use of the Internet by offering content-appropriate sites.
- Web site suggestions will save you time as you do research.

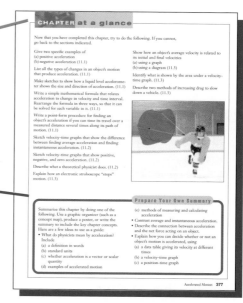

CHAPTER AT A GLANCE

- Located at the end of each chapter, this page provides self-assessment opportunities as you look back at the chapter as a whole.
- It gives parents or guardians an overview of what you have accomplished.
- **Prepare Your Own Summary** encourages you to summarize your understanding in a variety of ways: using diagrams, flowcharts, concept maps, artwork, and writing.

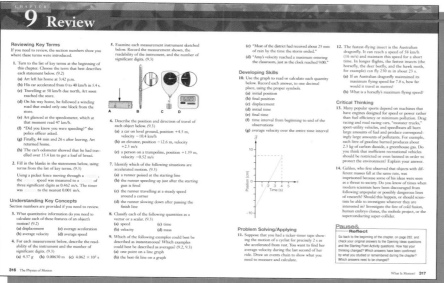

CHAPTER REVIEW

- This final wrap-up of each chapter reviews basic concepts, skills of inquiry and communication, and skills relating science to technology, society, and the environment.
- These questions help you recall, think about, and apply what you have learned.

END OF UNIT FEATURES

ASK AN EXPERT

- Experts in every area of science and technology are working to understand better how the world "works" and to try to find solutions to difficult problems. The *Ask an Expert* feature at the end of each unit is an interview with one of these experts.
- After the interview, you will have a chance to do an activity that is related to the kind of work the expert does.

UNIT ISSUE ANALYSIS

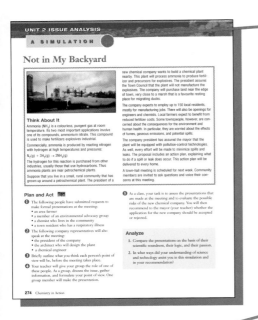

- You, your community, and society in general face complex issues in today's world. Science and technology cannot provide a "correct" answer to the problems these issues present, but understanding will lead to more informed decisions. A *Unit Issue Analysis* gives you a chance to start thinking now about how you can help make the best decisions for yourself and your community, today and in the future.
- The *Unit Issue Analysis* takes the form of a simulation or a debate.

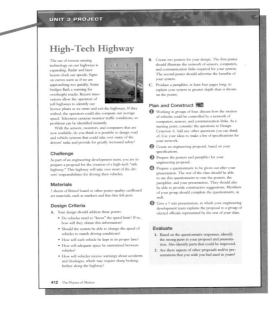

UNIT PROJECT

- A *Unit Project* gives you a chance to use key concepts and skills from the unit to build a device, system, or model of your own.
- Your teacher might ask you to begin to consider, early in the unit, how you might design, plan, and build your wrap-up project.
- You will complete the project as part of a team.

UNIT REVIEW

- Appearing at the end of each unit, a four-page *Unit Review* gives you one more opportunity to assess your understanding of the entire unit.

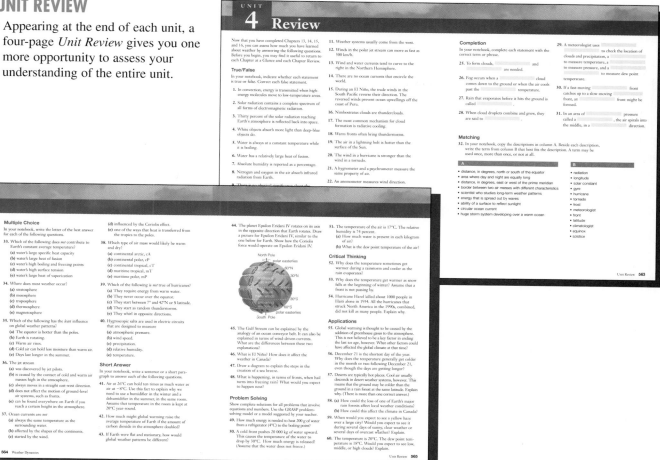

OTHER IMPORTANT FEATURES

- These features present intriguing situations, discrepant events, and weird facts.
- Ideas for connecting science with other curriculum areas are often included.

Tools of Science

- These features provide information about some of the instruments and equipment invented to help us explore the unknown.
- The information is often related to a variety of occupations and situations.

Design Your Own

- Opportunities are given in investigations, activities, *Pause & Reflect* features, *Check Your Understanding* sections, and *Chapter Reviews* for you to plan, design, and conduct your own experimental investigations.

Math CONNECT

- These features review mathematics skills that are required to do activities.
- They make connections between your science studies and your mathematics studies.

Computer CONNECT

- These features highlight opportunities where using spreadsheet or data base applications would be helpful.

Career CONNECT

- People with various levels of education are shown making practical use of science and technology in their jobs.

WRAPPING UP THE TOUR

At the back of **SCIENCEPOWER™ 10,** you will find some additional features to help you review and develop skills and knowledge that you will need to be successful in this course. Are you having trouble with graphing? Would you like help setting up a data table? Have you forgotten how to make a concept map? Do you need a reminder about scientific notation? The *Science Skills Guide* will help you review and/or develop your skills. A *Glossary* provides all the key vocabulary for the whole course. An *Index* will help you find your way to a topic.

Special Icons

The co-operative group work icon alerts you to opportunities to work within a group. The safety icons are extremely important because they alert you to any safety precautions you must take: for example, the need for safety glasses or a lab apron. Other safety icons that are used in this book are shown on page 608. Make sure that you become familiar with what they mean. Also make sure that you follow their precautions.

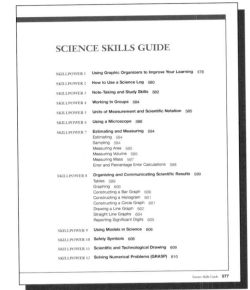

SCIENCE SKILLS GUIDE

Safety in Your Science Classroom

Become familiar with the following safety rules and procedures. It is up to you to use them and your teacher's instructions to make your activities and investigations in *SCIENCEPOWER™ 10* safe and enjoyable. Your teacher will give you specific information about any other special safety rules to be used in your school.

1. General Rules

- Listen carefully to any instructions your teacher gives you.
- Inform your teacher if you have any allergies, medical conditions, or other physical problems that could affect your work in the science classroom. Tell your teacher if you wear contact lenses or a hearing aid.
- Obtain your teacher's approval before beginning any activity or investigation you have designed yourself.
- Know the location and proper use of the nearest fire extinguisher, fire blanket, first aid kit, and fire alarm.

2. Before Each Activity or Investigation

- Before starting any activity or investigation, read all of it carefully. If you do not understand how to do a step, ask your teacher for help.
- Be sure you have read and understand the *Safety Precautions*.
- Begin an activity only after your teacher tells you to start.

3. Special Dress Precautions

- When you are directed to do so, wear protective clothing, such as a lab apron, safety glasses, and/or safety gloves. Always wear protective clothing when you are using materials that could pose a safety problem: for example, when you are using unidentified materials or when you are heating anything.
- Tie back long hair. Avoid wearing scarves, ties, long necklaces, and dangling earrings.

4. Doing Activities and Investigations

- Work carefully with a partner. Make sure your work area is clear.
- Handle apparatus and materials carefully.
- Make sure stools and chairs are resting securely on the floor.
- If other students are doing something that you consider dangerous, report it to your teacher.
- Do not chew gum, eat, or drink in your science classroom.
- Do not taste any substances. Do not draw any material into a tube with your mouth.
- Make sure you understand all safety labels on school materials or materials you bring from home. Familiarize yourself, as well, with the WHMIS symbols and the special safety symbols used in this textbook. They are listed on page 608.
- Be careful when carrying apparatus for an activity or investigation. Carry only one object or container at a time.
- Be aware of others during activities and investigations. Make room for students who may be carrying apparatus to their work station.

5. Sharp Object Precautions

- Always cut away from yourself and others when using a knife or razor blade.
- Always keep the pointed end of scissors, or any other pointed object, facing away from yourself and others if you have to walk with such objects.
- If you notice sharp or jagged edges on any equipment, take special care. Report it to your teacher.
- Dispose of broken glass as your teacher directs.

6. Electrical Equipment Precautions

- Make sure your hands are dry when touching electrical cords, plugs, or sockets.
- Pull the plug, not the cord when unplugging electrical equipment. Report damaged equipment or frayed cords to your teacher.
- Place electrical cords in places where people will not trip over them.

7. Heat Source Precautions

- When heating any item, wear safety glasses, heat-resistant safety gloves, and any other safety equipment that the textbook or your teacher suggests.
- Always use heat-proof containers.
- Do not use broken or cracked containers.
- Point the open end of a container that is being heated away from yourself and others.
- Do not allow a container to boil dry unless specifically directed to do so.
- Handle hot objects carefully. Be especially careful with a hot plate that might look as though it has cooled down.
- If you use a Bunsen burner, make sure you understand how to light and use it safely.
- If you do receive a burn, inform your teacher. Apply cold water to the burned area immediately.

Use this method to smell a substance in the laboratory

8. Chemical Precautions

- If any part of your body comes in contact with a potentially dangerous substance, wash the area immediately and thoroughly with water. If you get anything in your eyes, do not touch them. Wash them immediately and continuously for 15 min. Inform your teacher.
- Always handle substances carefully. If you are asked to smell a substance, never smell it directly. Hold the container slightly in front of and beneath your nose. Waft the fumes toward your nostrils, as shown here.
- Hold containers away from you when pouring liquids, as shown on the next page.

9. Working with Living Things

On a field trip:

- Try not to disturb the area any more than is absolutely necessary.
- If you move something, do it carefully. Always replace it carefully.
- If you are asked to remove plant material, remove it gently. Take as little as possible.

In the classroom:

- Treat living creatures with respect.
- Make sure that living creatures receive humane treatment while they are in your care.
- If possible, return living creatures to their natural environment when your work is complete.

10. Cleaning Up in the Science Classroom

- Clean up any spills, according to your teacher's instructions.
- Clean equipment before you put it away.
- Wash your hands thoroughly after doing an activity or an investigation.
- Dispose of materials as directed by your teacher. Never discard materials in the sink unless your teacher requests it.

11. Technology Projects

- Use tools safely to cut, join, and shape objects.
- Handle modelling clay correctly. Wash your hands after using modelling clay.
- Follow proper procedures when comparing mechanical systems and their operations.
- Use special care when observing and working with objects in motion: for example, objects that spin, swing, bounce, or vibrate; gears and pulleys; and elevated objects.
- Do not use power equipment (such as drills, sanders, saws, and lathes) unless you have specialized training in handling such tools. Make sure you obtain information and support from a specialist teacher when necessary. This is important for all *Design & Do Investigations* and *Unit Projects* that ask you to design and build models and/or devices or structures.

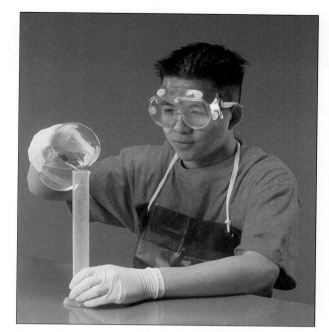

Hold containers away from you while pouring liquids.

Skill POWER

To help you become familiar with all the safety icons used in this textbook and in workplaces, turn to page 608.

onsider this. As we begin the new millenium, you can be in touch, almost instantly, with friends or relatives — even if they are on the other side of Earth's surface. Contrast this with the situation at the turn of the last century, when making a telephone call was a big event! Today doctors are perfecting the use of keyhole surgical techniques, as shown in the photograph on the left. These techniques allow heart bypass surgery without the need to open the chest cavity. Only a few decades ago, any kind of heart surgery was a risky procedure.

What is science? What is technology? How are they related? What do they mean to each of us, to society, and to the environment in which we live? In your Grade 10 program, you will be actively involved in science investigations, gaining new skills and knowledge. You will be looking at relationships among science, technology, society, and the environment (abbreviated STSE). Today science and technology affect everyone. You may decide to become a scientist or a technologist yourself. On the other hand, you may be more interested in other areas — from public service to journalism, from carpentry to sales. In either case, you will need to know the basic concepts and skills that you will develop in this program. Start with the Instant Practice below to consider what you already know about the nature of science and technology.

Instant Practice

Working in groups, examine the photograph on the right. Come up with five ideas that relate to science and five ideas that relate to technology, based on what you can see in the photograph. Then consider how these ideas relate to each other, to society, and to the environment. Use your ideas to devise definitions for science and for technology.

Science, Technology, and Society

You and your classmates probably thought of a number of important ideas about what the terms "science" and "technology" mean. Because everyone comes from a slightly different background, there were probably a number of different opinions about the meanings of these terms.

Some people think of science as a body of knowledge or facts. It *is* that, but it is more than that. Science is also a way of thinking, a "mindset," which you will explore throughout this course. Likewise, many people think of technology as applied science, and it certainly can be that. Again, however, technology is also a process. People used technology long before they understood the scientific principles behind the technological processes they were using. Early humans, for example, developed processes for producing stone tools. Examples of such tools are shown in the photograph below. These tools were efficient implements with varied functions, such as cutting and scraping. They greatly helped early humans obtain and prepare food. Scientists have studied how these tools were made. They have discovered that the people who made the tools had a very good understanding of the features of the rocks with which they worked. This means that early humans had developed a knowledge of the way that rocks respond to fracturing many thousands of years before the structure of rocks was understood by science.

Basically, science asks questions that aim to increase our understanding of the physical universe and our ability to explain nature. Technology aims to design and develop devices and processes for practical purposes. How can you easily grasp what science, technology, and society are, especially in terms of issues surrounding our environment? The diagram on the right presents one way to think about the meanings of these words and the interrelationships among these concepts.

Science
a way of knowing about nature that values knowledge for its own sake and depends on observation and experiment, logical argument, and sceptical review

Technology
the designing and use of devices, processes, and materials to solve practical problems and to satisfy human needs and wants

Issue
a problem with two or more possible resolutions, any one of which may be satisfactory to most members of society, while at the same time affecting all of society

Society
a group, large or small, of people in a particular place and time who are linked by common goals and interests

Science, technology, and society are separate, and yet intimately interconnected, human inventions.

Science and Science Inquiry

Science involves understanding and explaining nature. When you think about nature, however, science is probably not the first thing that comes to mind. You might think about gazing up at the sky on a warm moonlit night. You might think of crickets chirping or the rustling of a raccoon. An artist or a poet may try to capture the beauty of this scene in a painting or a verse. A scientist will ask questions about the same scene and then seek answers using methods of science inquiry. Why do crickets chirp? Why are owls more active at night? Why does day become night? No one can possibly learn all the answers to all the questions that scientists have wondered about over the centuries. Since there is so much to learn, where do you start?

Scientific knowledge is divided into logical categories. Each category can, in turn, be further divided. The work of scientists itself follows this pattern. A scientist is usually an expert in only one field of knowledge. This is one reason why teams of scientists in different fields often work together to make discoveries.

Science can be divided into life topics, Earth topics, and physical topics. You can use these categories of knowledge to help you find answers to questions about nature. As you examine the photographs on these pages, think about how varied science is. Keep in mind that even though scientists may research very different topics, they all share a genuine interest in how the world "works."

People who study life sciences are known as biologists. A botanist is a biologist who studies plants. A zoologist studies animals. A biologist who specializes in the interactions between living organisms and their environments is known as an ecologist.

Earth topics can be subdivided into various other fields. Geology includes the study of the structure and dynamics of Earth, such as the causes and effects of volcanic eruptions. Meteorology, on the other hand, deals with the causes and effects of weather and climate, such as hurricanes.

Science also includes topics about the physical world, such as chemistry and physics. Chemistry involves the study of the structure and properties of matter. It also involves the chemical reactions that occur between the components (atoms and molecules) of matter. Physics is the field of science that deals with many different aspects of the natural world, such as motion and energy. In one branch of physics, known as quantum physics, scientists are trying to unlock the mysteries of the tiny particles that make up atoms. They use particle accelerators, such as the one shown below on the right.

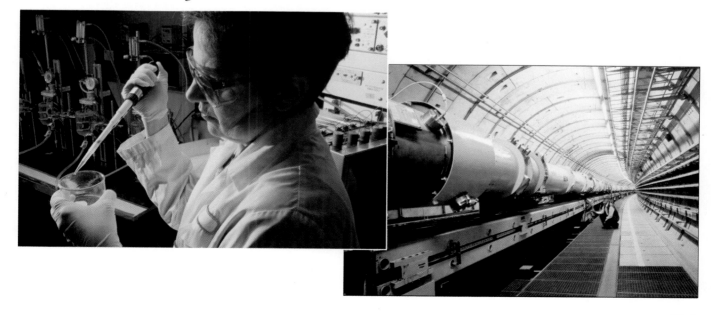

No one can possibly hope to learn all there is to know about science. Everyone, however, can learn enough about the basic concepts of science to gain a general understanding of the world around them. In this course, you will focus on the four categories that are represented by the following photographs.

In the first unit of this textbook, you will learn how organisms interact among themselves and with their environment. You will study how human activities affect Earth and how nutrient cycles help to maintain nature's balance. As well, you will consider factors that influence Earth's productivity. In this satellite image, the amount of plant productivity is indicated by different colours. On land, for example, the areas in darkest green indicate the highest productivity.

In the second unit, you will learn about the substances that make up matter. You will gain knowledge about some of the chemical reactions that occur around you and within your body. Chemicals and chemical reactions are used to make many common products, such as soap. They are also important in industries, such as those that produce food and beverages, plastics, wood and paper, and textiles.

In the third unit, you will investigate motion. You already possess a good deal of intuitive knowledge about motion. For example, your ability to observe the speed of a car and to predict its position allows you to cross the street safely. The scientific study of motion will help you achieve a deeper understanding of how and why objects move as they do. As well, it will introduce you to methods that allow you to accurately describe and predict the movement of objects.

Finally, in the fourth unit, you will learn about Earth's weather. What factors do you think might influence the weather? You will have the opportunity to learn about some of these factors, such as the distribution of solar energy and the movement of ocean currents and air masses. These and other factors can produce major weather events, such as hurricanes. Also, they can lead to localized events, such as the wonderful rainbow shown in the photograph.

You may find that one of these topics interests you more than the others. As you learn more about a topic, you might find that you wish to pursue a career in this field. Whether you choose a career in science, or not, knowing more about the topics you investigate in this course will be important to you in your understanding of how the world works.

Science Inquiry

How do scientists begin their search for answers to the questions they pose? What methods have they used to accumulate the scientific knowledge we now have? The starting place for this knowledge is curiosity, with someone asking "How?" or "Why?" As scientists over the centuries began accumulating this knowledge, they were also developing logical procedures for conducting scientific inquiry. Scientists realized the need to ask precise, focussed questions and design experiments to give clear answers to their questions.

Knowledge begins with observation and curiosity. For example, plants are so familiar that you have probably observed them for as long as you can remember. Think of the plants you saw on your way to school. Examine the photograph, and use it to help you make a list of the features of plants that you observe.

What features did you observe? Perhaps you noticed that the leaves are green and the trunks are woody. Did you notice that plants grow upward? This may seem obvious, but a scientist or another curious person might wonder why it is so. The first step in arriving at an answer is to ask a question.

A question often helps to clarify the problem. Asking "Why do plants grow upward?" suggests that there might be factors that influence the direction that a plant grows. In other words, "Does the plant respond to some stimulus during its growth?"

WHY DOES A PLANT GROW UPWARD?

The next step is to *gather information*. This can be done in several ways. It can involve library or Internet research and making observations. For example, review the background information that relates to your question. Also, consider other relevant information, such as any pattern of events that you have observed. As you will see, this step is very important.

Once you have recorded your observations and data, analyze the results from your experiment. This will allow you to draw *conclusions* as to whether the data support your hypothesis. If they do, *repeat* the experiment several times to check your results. When you are confident that your hypothesis is supported by experimental results, *communicate* your results.

What if the results do not support your hypothesis? This means that you may need to revise your hypothesis. Then you will need to test your new hypothesis by experimentation. The design of your experiment will probably have to be changed to accommodate your new hypothesis.

The next step is to test your hypothesis on the proposed relationship between light and plant growth by doing experiments or investigations. A hypothesis is tested by making a prediction about what you will observe in an *experiment*. Suppose your hypothesis is that a plant grows upward in response to the overhead light of the Sun. You might predict that a plant will grow toward light no matter which direction the light is coming from. A possible experimental design to test your prediction would involve light shining on a plant from different directions. Set up and conduct this experiment.

From the information you gathered, you might discover that light is very important to plants. This is because plants use energy from the Sun's light for photosynthesis. This knowledge allows you to suggest a general statement or explanation about what the relationship between light and plant growth might be. Such a statement or explanation is called a *hypothesis*.

HYPOTHESIS:
A plant grows upward because it grows toward light.

Scientific Laws

There are several concepts and definitions in science that help all curious people find answers to questions about nature. You have probably learned about various laws in your past studies of science. In science, a **law** describes a condition that has been observed so consistently that scientists are convinced it will always happen. A law has no theoretical basis, although it often leads to new theories. An example is the law of universal gravitation. This law predicts that any two masses attract each other.

Objects fall toward Earth because the object and Earth exert an attractive force on each other. The larger the object is, the greater the attractive force. This explains why things fall but says nothing about how they fall. What are the factors that influence the way an object falls? To answer this question, you would have to narrow your investigation down to one factor that you can control.

Variables

Consider an investigation to find out whether two objects fall to Earth at the same rate. Examine the figure of the student shown on the left, and list some of the factors that might affect the motion of the objects if they fell. Each factor that may influence the outcome of an investigation is known as a **variable**.

When you perform an investigation, you must control all the variables except one. Suppose you are interested in finding out whether height affects the rate at which objects fall. Then the objects must all be the same size, shape, and mass. If you change more than one variable at the same time, you cannot be sure which variable was responsible for any differences you might obtain in your results. If your investigation is to be valid and unbiased (a **fair test**), you must carry out the procedure in precisely the same way more than once. You must change only the variable you are measuring. Many experiments have a **control**. This is a treatment or experiment that you can compare with the results of your test groups. The variable that you change is called the **independent** (or **manipulated**) **variable** — in this case, height. The variables that might change as a result of the **independent** variable are known as the **dependent** (or **responding**) **variables**.

What if you are interested in finding out whether a light object and a heavy object fall at the same rate? You will have to use objects that have different masses. They will need to be the same size and shape, however, to control the variable of air resistance. In addition, you will have to drop them from the same height.

Observations

Next, use any information and **observations** that you have to make a hypothesis. At some time, for example, you may have observed a feather floating gently to the ground. At another time, you may have noticed a heavy rock falling straight and quickly to the ground. There are two kinds of observations that can be made.

Hypothesis

Use the information you have gathered through research and observations to formulate a **hypothesis:** a possible explanation for a question or an observation. In other words, a hypothesis is a statement that suggests what the link is between the variables.

Prediction

A hypothesis can lead to a **prediction**. A prediction states what you would expect to observe based on the hypothesis. Making a prediction allows you to test a hypothesis.

TITLE:
Investigation SSI-1: The Rate of Falling Objects

QUESTION:
Do objects of different masses fall to Earth at the same or different rates?

INDEPENDENT VARIABLE:
    -the mass of the objects

DEPENDENT VARIABLE:
    -the rates at which the objects fall.

HYPOTHESIS:
    -The objects of different masses will fall to Earth at different rates.

PREDICTION:
    -the heavier object will fall more quickly than the lighter object,
    -the heavier object will hit the ground first

An experiment is an investigation or procedure that attempts to falsify the hypothesis.

Experiment

Design an **experiment** to test your hypothesis. An experiment is an investigation or a procedure that is designed to falsify a hypothesis. It may seem strange to attempt to prove something wrong. It is not possible, however, to prove something to be absolutely true because there always might be one more experiment that would show the hypothesis to be wrong. Only one experiment is needed to falsify a hypothesis. If you do not falsify a hypothesis, then the results support it. If a hypothesis survives repeated attempts to falsify it, then your confidence in the hypothesis, as the true explanation for an observation, increases.

RESULTS:

Qualitative observations:
→ the objects both fell quickly to the ground and hit the ground at the same time.

Quantitative results:
→ the objects fell through 6 m at nearly identical times.
→ the 4 kg object took 1.6 s to fall 6 m.
→ the 2 kg mass took 1.6 s to fall the same distance.

CONCLUSION:

The results of the experiment did not support the hypothesis that the objects would fall at different rates. Therefore, the hypothesis is falsified and objects of different masses fall to Earth at the same rate.

Conclusion

When you have gathered data from your experiment, you may draw a **conclusion**. A conclusion is an interpretation of the results, as they apply to the hypothesis being tested. In this case, the results do not support the hypothesis.

The final step in a scientific inquiry is to write a report on your experiment. The report should state the procedures and the results clearly. Someone who reads the report should be able to repeat your experiment. In the report, include a discussion of your interpretation of the results.

Model

The example you just read is a **model** of science inquiry designed to show you how scientific knowledge accumulates. However, this model is just the first stage in a broader process. When many different scientists make observations based on the same hypothesis, and come to the same conclusions, the hypothesis gains more and more support. Eventually, scientists agree that the hypothesis has been tested so thoroughly that it should be universally accepted. At this point, the hypothesis has earned the status of a **theory**.

In science, a model can be a mental image, diagram, structure, or mathematical expression that attempts to explain a concept or hypothesis. You may, for example,  have made a working model of a volcano in your earlier studies. Such a model can be made from clay, a small amount of baking soda, vinegar, and a bottle cap. A model is often used to visualize a concept. An example is the "rubber sheet model" used to simulate Albert Einstein's idea of curved space. Examine the diagram to see how a central mass can cause the space around the mass to curve. Space is represented by a thin rubber sheet. Placing a mass, such as bowling ball, in the middle of the sheet causes the sheet to lower and curve.

Theory

A theory is an explanation of an observation or event that has been supported by consistent, repeated experimental results, and has therefore been accepted by a majority of scientists. In earlier studies, you learned about the particle theory of matter. Another theory that you may have heard of is Einstein's theory of special relativity. One part of this theory states that the speed of light, c, is the only thing in the universe that is constant. All other measurements are relative, depending on the observer's point of view. A famous formula that is associated with this theory is $E = mc^2$. It tells us that mass and energy are different forms of the same thing. In other words, matter is energy standing still!

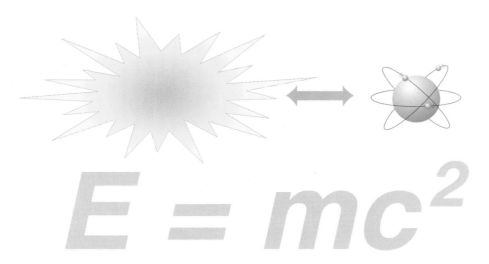

$$E = mc^2$$

Technology and Technological Problem Solving

The lives of ordinary people have undergone profound changes since prehistoric times. As mentioned earlier, early humans learned how to make tools by shaping elements from their environment. These tools helped them solve practical problems. Such innovations have continued to the present day. Their pace has increased tremendously, however. Numerous examples can be given of modern devices and processes designed to solve practical problems. The ability to travel into deep space, the use of radiation therapy in cancer treatments, and the development of modern farm equipment are just three. These innovations can be classified as technology. Technology is the designing of devices or processes to solve practical problems and to satisfy human needs and desires.

Most people see technology as closely tied with science. In our modern world, this is often the case. Scientific principles are usually required to develop sophisticated technologies. For example, scientists discovered lasers while researching light. Their knowledge of lasers was later applied to produce a technology that uses precision lasers in eye surgery.

Technology is not the same as science, though. It does not always require a knowledge of science. Sometimes everyday experiences are sufficient to develop technology. A pick, for example, is a simple technology that makes moving soil and rocks easier. Its invention did not require scientific knowledge. A fork is another example of a common, everyday technological development.

Science, in the modern sense of the word, goes back only about 500 years. Before this, complex structures were produced even though people did not grasp the scientific principles behind the technology. Think of the aqueducts that were built by the ancient Romans some 2000 years ago. These structures stretched great distances — some as far as 80 km — to transport water to cities. A number of these aqueducts, such as the one shown below, are still standing. Many other complex structures were built, as well. The Cathedral of Notre-Dame in Reims, France, shown in the photograph to the right was built between 1211 and the end of the thirteenth century. This was at least 400 years before the physics of engineering was understood.

Technological Problem Solving

Engineers, architects, technologists, and designers use technological problem-solving skills to guide them in their efforts. When a new device is designed and built, engineers and inventors usually go through a lot of trial and error. The device is built according to all the information that is available. Then the device is tested. The first attempt may not be successful. It may, however, provide new information for continued refinement of the device. As a child, perhaps you were involved in building a tree house. What would be an effective way to bring materials up to where you were building a tree house? One way would be using a bucket and rope to help haul the materials. Although this seems to be a trivial solution, it is a technology specifically designed to solve a problem. It requires prior experience with different materials and the ways they might be combined to perform a specific function. The same basic idea is used for the cranes that are needed to build skyscrapers.

Instant Practice

1. Explain the similarities and differences between science inquiry and technological problem solving.

2. The forces that building materials can withstand before breaking must be known before a structure can be designed and built. Explain whether this knowledge is the result of scientific inquiry or technological problem solving.

3. Suppose that a 3 m² wooden platform can hold no more than four adults. Explain whether this knowledge results from scientific inquiry, technological problem solving, or both.

Solving a Technological Problem

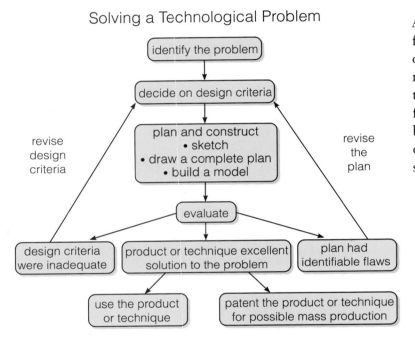

As you probably know from experience, an orderly problem-solving method can save you time and effort. The flow chart shows some basic steps in a process of technological problem solving.

Instant Practice

Imagine that you are travelling across unknown country. You come to a crevasse, about 4 m wide, that you must cross. Use the flowchart to work through the following questions.

1. Explain how the nature of the problem will change depending on the factors that you must consider. For example, will the type of device you construct depend on who will have to use it? If you are alone, you might be able to use a simple rope. A rope would not be suitable, however, if there are elderly people who must also cross or if you need to move equipment or supplies across the crevasse.

2. Come up with four different scenarios for the problem. These scenarios will determine your design criteria. One of your scenarios must include working only with materials that are available locally.

3. Design a device for each of your four scenarios.

4. Choose two of your designs. Explain how you might evaluate them.

Societal Decision Making

At the dawn of the last century, powered flight was still in the future. Automobiles were just beginning to have an impact on transportation. By the close of the century, space walks on shuttle missions had become common. Space probes had been sent hundreds of millions of kilometres to explore the planets in our solar system. In addition, the *International Space Station* was only a few short years away.

Science and technology have helped to improve our quality of life in many ways. Advancements in medicine have allowed many diseases to be treated. This has decreased suffering and prolonged life. Computers have made communication and information accessible to more people than ever before. As science and technology provide us with new ways to meet the challenging problems we all face, they often lead to new challenges. In your science course this year, you will be asked to think about the interactions among science, technology, society, and the environment (abbreviated STSE). STSE interactions often lead to important issues, both public and personal. Dealing with an issue usually means making a choice among several options. Choosing which (if any) of the options is the best solution is not always clear.

Fossil fuels pollute in both the production of electricity and the mining process.

Consider society's dependence on energy. Canada's population and economy continue to expand. So, too, does the need to increase the production of electrical energy. The additional energy may be obtained by increasing traditional methods of production or by developing alternative methods. At present, most of our energy needs are met through three main sources of energy: nuclear energy, fossil fuels, and hydroelectric power. Alternative, and renewable, sources of energy — such as wind, geothermal, and solar energy — are seen as either impractical or too expensive to be viable alternatives.

We are already using most of the sites that can provide large amounts of hydroelectric energy, which is a renewable source. It seems, therefore, that additional electrical energy must be obtained by increasing our use of non-renewable resources — either fossil fuels or nuclear energy. Technology has made these sources cost-effective. There are problems associated with them however. Fossil fuel reserves are finite. As well, both the mining and burning of fossil fuels have environmental consequences. Nuclear power is also limited. It produces radioactive wastes that cannot yet be disposed of satisfactorily.

During your study of science this year, you will encounter various situations that involve science, technology, society, and the environment. When these elements come together, we need to consider how they interact and influence each other and the world in which we live. This is important because we all belong to the same society. What each of us does has an impact on others and on the environment.

Your *SCIENCEPOWER™ 10* textbook promotes an understanding of issue analysis. As well, two special features are specifically designed to help enhance your decision-making

There is no satisfactory system for the disposal of spent fuel rods, which are highly radioactive. They are stored in deep pools of water.

skills. Many of the *Think & Link Investigations* deal with issues. At the end of each unit, the *Issue Analysis* provides an issue to debate or a simulation to role-play. These will provide you with an opportunity to participate in critical thinking and decision making.

Science can provide basic information to help you evaluate risks. Thus it can guide the decision-making process. It can help you weigh the advantages and disadvantages of any particular decision. Science alone, however, does not and cannot make the decisions for us, at either the personal or the public level. There are many other factors — such as art, history, philosophy, religion, and culture — that play a role in shaping how each person interprets the world. All viewpoints must be considered with respect.

As you work through the following Instant Practice, use the accompanying flow chart to help you analyze the issues.

Instant Practice

1. Work in groups. Discuss whether fossil fuels, nuclear energy, or another source of energy should be used to meet increased electrical demand.

2. Research the possible methods for producing electrical power and their relative costs. Use print and electronic media resources.

3. (a) Identify the potential of each method for environmental harm.
   (b) Prepare a quick survey to find out how society might react to higher costs for less harmful electrical sources. For example, you could ask a few home-owners and businesspeople whether they would be prepared to pay double or triple the amount they now pay.

4. Based on the information your group has gathered, discuss the risks and benefits for each alternative.

5. As a group, decide on one of the alternatives as the best possible choice for increasing electrical production.

Identify the issue.

Gather relevant information.

Identify all the alternatives.

Weigh each alternative by clarifying its consequences.

Make a decision.

Evaluate the decision.

The decision is the best alternative based on risks and benefits and, therefore, on probable consequences.

Take action. Communicate the decision.

One or more of the steps in the decision-making process were faulty. No action should be taken. The process should be repeated to eliminate the faulty steps and replace them with improved thinking.

Errors of judgement may have been made at any of these steps in the decision-making process.

Sustainability of Ecosystems

How can a tiny insect, less than half a centimetre in length, threaten the life of a tree and affect the economy of Canada? A bark beetle can — its scientific name, *Dendroctonus*, means "tree killer." For the bark beetle, the tree is a source of food and shelter. The mother beetle chews through the tree bark and makes tunnels between the bark and the wood, where she lays her eggs. Larvae hatch from the eggs and eat out their own tunnels between the bark and the wood. This destroys tree tissues and causes branches to wither and die. During some years, the populations of bark beetles increase rapidly. They damage or kill vast areas of usable trees, increasing the price of lumber and, in turn, the price we pay for a home.

Bark beetles and people are only two of the hundreds of thousands of species that use the resources of forests. Each species continually interacts with its environment and responds to changes in conditions. For example, bark beetles cause the death of many trees. When there are fewer trees to feed on, the number of bark beetles rapidly declines. A smaller beetle population allows the forest to recover. The numbers of most organisms are limited by various factors, such as food supply, space, climate, predators, and disease. People, however, continue to increase in number and increase their demand for resources. We behave as if there were no limits.

Are people an exception to the processes that affect the survival of all other organisms? Our technology helps us overcome limits. Biotechnology, computers, satellites, and other modern developments seem to set us apart from nature. Technology demands more of Earth's resources, however, and adds more waste materials to the environment. In this unit, you will explore the concept of sustainability. What effect does our technology have on cycles of materials and flows of energy? Why do many of our social beliefs encourage increasing consumption? Will future technology help us to correct our past mistakes and maintain the resources on which our survival depends?

Unit Contents

1 Connecting Links

Opening Ideas...

- How is your brain powered by the Sun?
- Why are rabbits more common than foxes?
- Why might overfishing of herring lead to an increase in populations of sea urchins?

Science Log

In your Science Log, answer the above questions. Recall what you know about how plants and animals obtain and use energy and how they interact with each other. When you finish this chapter, review your answers and make any changes or additions based on what you have learned.

Why do we need to eat? Eating food is one of the main activities of most animals. Imagine a spider sucking juices from a fly, a rabbit nibbling dandelion leaves, or a crab scooping up dead matter from a beach. Imagine youself munching a piece of cheese. The everyday act of eating transfers materials and energy from one organism to another. These transfers keep organisms alive. By eating and being eaten, organisms form links in food chains. In this chapter, you will investigate the flow of energy through food chains. Energy flows through living systems by being transferred from one organism to another. You will also see how this affects such things as the numbers, types, and even sizes of organisms living in an area.

The original source of the energy in food is the Sun. Radiant energy from the Sun is captured through photosynthesis by green plants, algae, and some bacteria, and used to make food. When we cut down trees in a forest or harvest crops in a field, we are taking this energy for our own use. The birds, beetles, and other animals that live in forests and fields also use this energy. How much energy does an organism or a group of organisms need to survive? Is the supply of energy unlimited? Does the amount of energy that is captured by plants differ from place to place? Many of our environmental problems are caused by people changing the flow of energy among organisms.

Skill
P O W E R

For tips on how to use a Science Log, turn to page 580.

Key Concepts

In this chapter, you will discover

- why the ultimate source of energy for most ecosystems is the Sun
- how radiant energy from the Sun is converted by plants into chemical energy
- how the energy in ecosystems is channelled through food chains
- how the position of an organism in a food chain may determine its mass and population size
- why people consume a large part of all the radiant energy that is converted into living material

Key Skills

In this chapter, you will

- assess energy flow in agricultural ecosystems
- study a community of organisms and analyze the relative abundance of each type
- investigate the growth of a population of paramecia over time
- determine which climatic variables can influence the productivity of ecosystems
- determine how pesticides enter food chains and affect organisms at each level
- design your own experiment to study the effects of different factors on a population

Key Terms

- ecosystem
- producers
- primary consumers
- secondary consumers
- trophic levels
- detritivores
- decomposers
- pyramid of numbers
- biomass
- pyramid of biomass
- pyramid of energy flow
- carrying capacity
- competition
- intraspecific competition
- interspecific competition
- population density
- density-dependent factors
- density-independent factors
- productivity
- biological magnification

You and Food Chains

Think about the last meal you ate. Whatever it was, its main ingredients were once part of living organisms. The plant matter in your food was made by plants, from sunlight, carbon dioxide, water, and nutrients in the soil. The animal matter was made from items the animal ate (which may have included plants, animals, or both). By eating, you become another link in this chain of life.

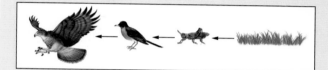

What to Do

1. Make a list of all the food items in your last two meals.

2. For processed food (anything made from two or more ingredients), list all the ingredients that come from living things.

3. Divide your list into animal matter and plant matter. Include eggs, milk, butter, and cheese as animal matter.

4. Divide the animal matter into herbivores (plant-eaters, such as cows) and carnivores (meat-eaters, such as tuna). Record omnivores (animals, such as chickens, that eat both plant and animal matter) in both groups.

5. From your data, draw three food chains to which you are linked.

What Did You Discover?

1. What kinds of organisms are at the start of every food chain?

2. Do any of your food chains have more than three links? Suggest a reason why.

3. **Thinking Critically** For what species might you become a source of food?

1.1 Capturing Energy from the Sun

What do all organisms need in order to carry out their daily activities? Examine Figures 1.1A to 1.1D, and read the captions that describe the activities taking place. Think of something that the four activities have in common.

Figure 1.1A In a forest, young spruce trees grow in a patch of sunlight.

Figure 1.1B In a lake, a pike hides among the weeds, waiting to capture a smaller fish.

Figure 1.1C In a desert, a desert pocket mouse stores plant seeds in its underground burrow.

Figure 1.1D At the edge of a farmer's field, a monarch butterfly lays eggs on a milkweed.

To understand nature, scientists look for patterns or concepts that can explain a wide variety of observations. Figures 1.1A to 1.1D show four different places where organisms live: a forest, a lake, a desert, and a field. The photographs include plants and animals. They show growth, feeding, and reproduction. Despite their differences, however, they can be analyzed in the same way if you think of organisms as being consumers of energy. Energy is what makes it possible for a tree to grow, a pike to catch its food, a mouse to dig a burrow, and a butterfly to lay eggs. Energy is what makes the activities of all organisms, including you, possible.

An **ecosystem** includes all the organisms in an area that interact with each other and with their environment of energy and matter. The "fuel" for ecosystems is energy from the Sun. Sunlight is captured by green plants during photosynthesis and stored as chemical energy in carbohydrate molecules. The energy then passes through the ecosystem from species to species when herbivores eat plants and carnivores eat the herbivores (see Figure 1.2). These interactions form food chains.

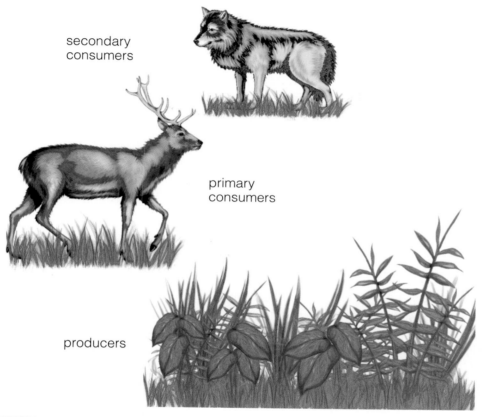

secondary consumers

primary consumers

producers

Figure 1.2 Food chains begin with producers.

Because green plants convert radiant energy into chemical energy for ecosystems, they are called **producers**. Animals, such as rabbits and deer, that eat plants are called **primary consumers**. Animals, such as foxes and wolves, that feed on the plant-eaters are called **secondary consumers**. The energy is used by organisms to carry out their life processes. To maintain an ecosystem, there must be a continual input of energy from the Sun.

Does one ecosystem hold more energy than another? How is energy stored and transferred within an ecosystem? How does it leave the ecosystem? These questions are important because the energy that is captured by plants through photosynthesis determines the amount of energy that is available for all the other organisms in the ecosystem. Human survival depends on the amount of energy that is stored in agricultural ecosystems. Can we increase this amount of energy and provide more food for ourselves?

From Land to Mouth

A field of corn contains a certain amount of food energy. If cattle eat the corn, they will gain some of the food energy. How does the amount of energy in the corn compare with the amount of energy in the cattle? Is it more efficient for people to feed on corn or beef? In this activity, you will compare the energy content of some familiar human foods. Then you will relate the data to the flow of energy in an agricultural ecosystem.

What You Need

graph paper   calculator
coloured pencils   metre stick

What to Do

1. The table below lists the average amount of energy, in kilojoules (kJ) per square metre of land per year, in different organisms that people use for food. Study the data, then make a bar graph to compare the relative amounts of usable kilojoules produced by each organism. Arrange the organisms in terms of least energy produced to most produced. Use different

Energy Produced by Different Organisms

Organism	Energy (kJ/m²/year)
wheat cereal	3 400
oranges and grapefruit (fresh)	4 200
peanut butter	3 850
rice or rice cereal	5 200
potatoes	6 700
carrots	3 400
other vegetables	840
apples	6 300
peaches and pears	3 800
beet sugar	8 300
cane sugar	14 650
corn cereal	6 700
milk	1 800
eggs	840
chicken	800
pork	800
beef (feedlot)	550
fish fillets	8

colours to identify the producers (plants) and the consumers (animals and their products).
Note: Units of energy in food are usually given in joules. A kilojoule is 1000 J.

2. Calculate the average kJ/m²/year in producers and in consumers.

3. Choose one plant organism (such as rice) and one animal organism (such as beef) from the table.

4. Assume that 800 kJ of each organism is consumed in one meal. Calculate the area of land needed to produce 800 kJ of each organism per year. For example, rice yields 5200 kJ/m²/year. To produce 800 kJ, $\frac{800}{5200} = 0.15$ m² of land is required.

5. To visualize the difference in land area needed to produce the plant and animal organisms, measure and mark out these areas with a metre stick on a lawn or your classroom floor. For example, a 1m × 0.15 m strip of land has an area of 0.15 m².

What Did You Discover?

1. What is the ratio of average energy/m²/year for producers compared with consumers? Suggest an explanation for this ratio.

2. Would you say that plants vary a little or a lot in their efficiency at producing joules for human consumption? Suggest reasons for the variation.

3. Is it more efficient for people to eat plant products or animal products? Why?

Extension

4. Calculate the total area of land needed to support the student population of your school for one year on a diet of
(a) rice (b) chicken
Assume a daily intake of 2400 KJ per person.

Compared with animals, green plants produce more energy per unit of land area. Thus most of the energy in an agricultural ecosystem is found in the crops, such as the field of corn shown in Figure 1.3A. Only a portion of this energy is transferred to the livestock that eat the plants (see Figure 1.3B). As a result, animals and animal products contain less energy than plants and plant products that are raised on the same amount of land. Why is only some of the original energy transferred to plant-eaters? What happens to it? In the next section, you will learn how energy passes through food chains and how this affects population sizes.

Figure 1.3A This field of corn produces a certain amount of energy.

Skill
P O W E R
For tips on how to make a bar graph, turn to page 600.

Skill
P O W E R
For tips on solving numerical problems using the GRASP method, turn to page 610.

Figure 1.3B How much energy do livestock get from the plants they eat?

Check Your Understanding

1. What is the source of energy for an ecosystem?

2. How does this energy enter the ecosystem?

3. Sketch a food chain that begins with a green plant.

4. Distinguish between producers and consumers.

5. Which has the greater total amount of energy available: the duckweed, cattails, and other producers of a pond ecosystem or the frogs, minnows, and other consumers of that ecosystem?

6. **Apply** What kind of food would you produce if you wanted to obtain the maximum amount of usable energy from a field?

7. **Thinking Critically** Suppose that volcanic eruptions send tonnes of particles high into the atmosphere. The particles create clouds of dust that filter out part of the sunlight for a period of one year. Explain what might happen to various organisms in an ecosystem following such an event.

1.2 Feeding Levels

Word CONNECT

The word "trophic" is derived from the Greek word *trophe*, meaning "nourishment." Use a dictionary to find other words that contain the root "troph".

How can we compare food chains in different ecosystems? Try to think of ecosystems as being made up of several feeding levels, or **trophic levels**, instead of the eating habits of individual species. Each trophic level may include a variety of species, as you can see in Figure 1.4. Producers make up the first trophic level. Primary consumers feed at the second trophic level. Secondary consumers feed at the third trophic level, and so on. Many organisms eat a variety of foods and may consume organisms from more than one trophic level. For example, a bear eats both berries and fish. The concept of trophic levels is useful for thinking about how the energy in food resources is distributed in an ecosystem.

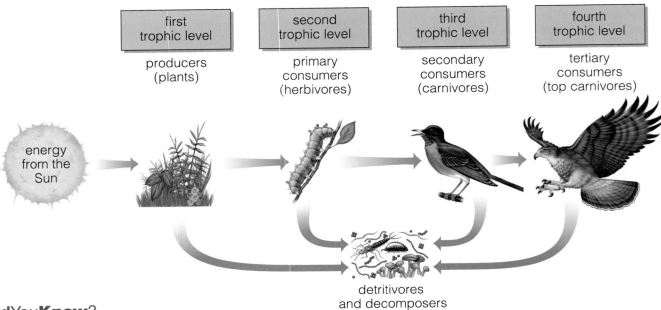

first trophic level	second trophic level	third trophic level	fourth trophic level
producers (plants)	primary consumers (herbivores)	secondary consumers (carnivores)	tertiary consumers (top carnivores)

energy from the Sun

detritivores and decomposers

Figure 1.4 This food web shows the structure of an ecosystem. Different organisms obtain their food and energy at different trophic levels.

DidYou**Know**?

Energy is stored and transformed in ecosystems and mechanical systems, such as an automobile, in similar ways. Scientists describe the principles of energy flow in the laws of thermodynamics. The first law states that energy cannot be created or destroyed. The second law states that every time energy is transformed from one state to another, useful energy is reduced due to the loss of thermal energy from the system.

Most of the energy that enters each trophic level is used by the organisms at this level just to stay alive. The organisms need energy to move from place to place, grow, reproduce, and carry out other activities. Some of the energy cannot be used and passes out of the organisms as waste. Only a small percentage of the energy remains stored in each organism as body tissues. This energy is available as potential food for consumers in the next trophic level. For example, for every 100 kJ of plant energy consumed by a mouse, only about 10 kJ is left to make new tissue. The rest is converted to thermal energy and waste matter by the mouse's activities (see Figure 1.5A). Similarly, if the mouse is eaten by a snake at the next trophic level, most of the usable energy in the mouse is converted to thermal energy. The amount of energy that is transferred from one trophic level to the next varies from about 5 to 20 percent, with 10 percent commonly used as a rough average (see Figure 1.5B).

Many organisms do not get eaten — at least, they do not get eaten until after they have died. When they die, energy still remains in the tissues of their bodies. Consumers known as scavengers feed on the bodies of larger dead animals. Vultures, bald eagles, ravens, hyenas, and some species of ants and beetles are examples of scavengers. The bodies of smaller dead animals, dead plant matter, and animal dung are food for **detritivores**. These organisms include crabs, earthworms, wood beetles, and carpenter ants. Detritivores also include various **decomposers**, such as bacteria and fungi, which consume any remaining dead plant and animal matter. Decomposers break down the cells and extract the last remaining energy.

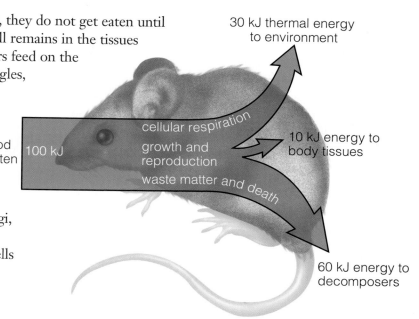

30 kJ thermal energy to environment

food eaten 100 kJ

cellular respiration
growth and reproduction
waste matter and death

10 kJ energy to body tissues

60 kJ energy to decomposers

energy from the Sun

thermal energy and wastes

producer

primary consumer

secondary consumer

Figure 1.5A Food energy that is taken in by a consumer is used in all the processes shown. Only about 10 percent is converted to new tissues.

Figure 1.5B There is less energy available at each successive trophic level in a food chain.

Detritivores feed at every trophic level and make up their own important food chains. In fact, food chains based on dead plant and animal matter actually outnumber food chains based on living plants and animals. In a field of cows, for instance, detritivores, such as earthworms and beetles, feed on dead plant matter and cow dung, which is mainly undigested plant matter. Other organisms, such as birds, feed on the detritivores. Like all food chains, these pathways originate with the Sun's energy. You will examine different ways that energy can flow through an ecosystem in the next activity.

Figure 1.6 Fungi are decomposers. These mushrooms are obtaining their food from a fallen tree trunk.

It is estimated that 80 percent of plants become dead matter and are consumed by detritivores. In a field of cows, the mass of the detritivores in the soil far exceeds the mass of the cows eating the living grass.

What Eats What?

Ecosystems are composed of many different food chains. In this activity, you will study some possible pathways of energy flow among organisms in a mixed-forest ecosystem.

What You Need
12 labels or pieces of small notepaper
pencil

What to Do

1. Work in a group of four. On each piece of paper, print the name of one of the following organisms:

grass	common raven
red fox	willow tree
bacteria/fungi	ruffed grouse
grasshopper	bunch berries
cottontail rabbit	red-tailed hawk
red squirrel	maple seeds

2. Sort the pieces of paper into three groups: producers, consumers, and detritivores.

3. Arrange the organisms into four food chains. Each food chain should be only three links long.

What Did You Discover?

1. To which trophic level does each organism belong?

2. How many producers did you identify? How many consumers?

3. Which organisms were at the start of each food chain?

4. Which organisms can consume food from more than one trophic level? Which organisms can consume food from other food chains?

5. Compare your food chains with those of the other groups. In what ways did your food chains differ? In what ways were they similar?

Extensions

6. Rearrange your organisms to make four new food chains, each three links long.

7. How are these new food chains different from your original food chains? How are they similar?

INVESTIGATION 1-A

Seeing Patterns in Nature

You can now appreciate a pond or river, forest, park, or coastland in a new way — as an ecosystem fuelled by energy from the Sun. In this investigation, you will look for clues to how this energy affects the numbers and types of living things in a local ecosystem.

Problem

Which trophic level has most living matter, and which has least?

Safety Precautions

- During the field trip, follow the safety instructions provided by your teacher.
- In your science lab, wear safety equipment (including an apron, goggles, and rubber gloves) when appropriate.
- Do *not* harm any organisms. Minimize your disturbance of the study area, and return the organisms to their natural environment after completing your investigation.

Apparatus

plant and animal field guides or checklists
binoculars
hand lens
tape measure

Optional

camera
collecting nets
collecting jars or bags
labels
tweezers
microscope
microscope slides
cover slips
medicine dropper

Materials

map of study area
notebook

Procedure

❶ Your teacher will give you a map and some introductory information about the area you will study on the field trip.

❷ To prepare for the trip, work in groups of four for 5 min to produce a list of all the different types of organisms that you think live in the study area. Share information about species you know about or may have seen in your community. Be as specific as possible. For example, write down "blue jay" instead of "bird."

❸ Include your list of organisms in a class list. When the class list is complete, discuss ways of organizing this information. For instance, in which trophic level does each organism belong? In your discussion, start to think about energy relationships between different trophic levels of the ecosystem.

Skill
POWER

To review the safety symbols used in this book, turn to page 608.

CONTINUED ▶

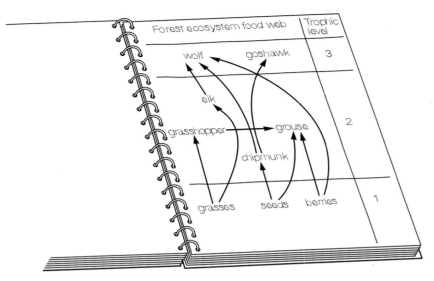

A simple food web

Producers	Primary consumers	Secondary consumers	Detritivores

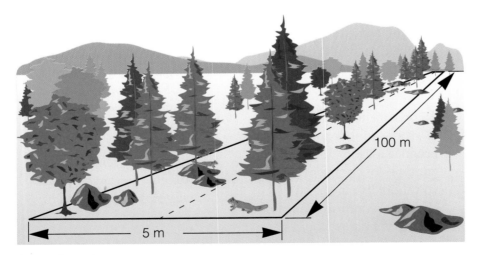

A survey transect

4 Use the class list and discussion to draw a food web for the ecosystem, as shown in the illustration. Place the organisms in their different trophic levels. Keep your food web to use on the field trip.

5 Your class has two main goals:
- to survey the organisms living in the study area
- to obtain quantitative estimates of the relative numbers of organisms there

6 Make a table like the one shown to record your observations on the field trip. Give your table a title.

7 To conduct the survey, your group will walk along a straight line through the study area. This line is called a *transect*. It is a common sampling method used by biologists. Your transect will be approximately 5 m wide and 100 m long. Determine how many paces you need to walk to cover a distance of 100 m. Walk this number of paces when you are in the field during your survey. Each group should start their transect in a different part of the study area. (Your map should include a line showing the position of your transect within the study area.)

8 Record the numbers and types of organisms you encounter along your transect. If possible, identify different plants and animals using field guides or checklists provided by your teacher. You may also make sketches or take photographs to help you record and identify the different species. Record only the organisms within your transect. You can include species that cross your transect, such as a flying bird or insect.

9 During your survey, list each different species you observe in the appropriate column of your table. If you do not know which column to place an animal in, try to infer its eating habits from what it looks like or where you found it.

10 For each species, note where you saw it. For example, is a particular species found throughout the transect or only in certain parts of it?

11 As a group, devise methods to estimate the number of one plant species and one animal species along your transect. Carry out your method, and record your population estimates. Wash your hands on returning from the field trip.

Analyze

1. Review the food web you created before the field trip. Add to it any organisms that your class observed during the trip.

2. As a class, make a table to record the population estimates of each group. List the species in order of abundance. Beside each species, indicate the trophic level in which it obtains its energy. Discuss what patterns, if any, are revealed by these data. In which trophic level are most organisms found? Which level has fewest organisms? Write a brief a summary of your findings.

Conclude and Apply

3. As a class, discuss why different organisms might prefer living in different places (with different amounts of light, different temperatures, and so on) within the ecosystem.

4. What problems did you encounter while conducting your survey? How might you solve these problems in future surveys?

Extend Your Knowledge

5. What other sampling methods do biologists use to survey organisms? How might different surveying methods affect which organisms are found? For instance, is time of day important when surveying singing birds?

Pyramid of Numbers

Why do you think some organisms are very common while others are rare? The study of trophic levels in ecosystems gives clues. Look at the organisms in Figure 1.7. At which trophic level does each organism obtain its energy? Which level has the most energy, and which has the least? Which organisms are most common?

As you have learned, there is less energy at each step along a food chain. The greatest amount of energy is in the first trophic level — the producers. They are the first organisms to use the energy of the Sun. In the second trophic level, there is less energy available. In the third level, there is still less

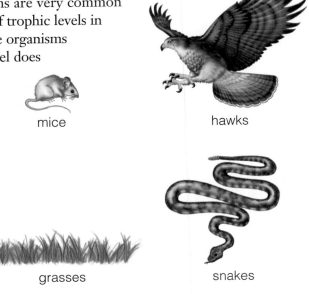

Figure 1.7 Each of these organisms occupies a different trophic level in an ecosystem.

energy, and so on. Considering Figure 1.7, for example, there is more energy available for mice than snakes, and more energy for snakes than hawks. As a result, there are generally more mice than snakes and more snakes than hawks in an ecosystem. This pattern results in a **pyramid of numbers,** as shown in Figure 1.8.

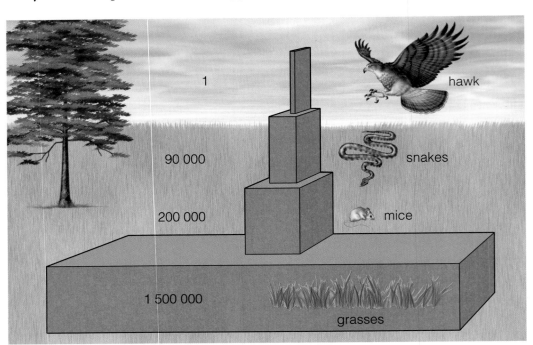

Figure 1.8 This pyramid of numbers, for a grassland ecosystem, shows the relative population sizes of organisms at each link in a food chain.

Counting organisms is a useful way to estimate the energy that is present in each trophic level, but organisms come in different sizes. Why do you think some animals are large and others are small? One reason is that most animals are larger than the food they eat. A robin would find it difficult to ingest a worm larger than itself. Similarly, large fish tend to eat smaller fish (see Figures 1.9A and 1.9B).

Figure 1.9A Great white sharks are relatively large and rare.

There are many exceptions to this pattern, however. For instance, a pine bark beetle is much smaller than the pine tree on which it feeds. On the other hand, many thousands of beetles can feed on a single tree. The beetles and the tree turn the pyramid of numbers upside down. The result is a reversed pyramid of numbers, as shown in Figure 1.10.

Figure 1.9B Herring are much smaller and more common.

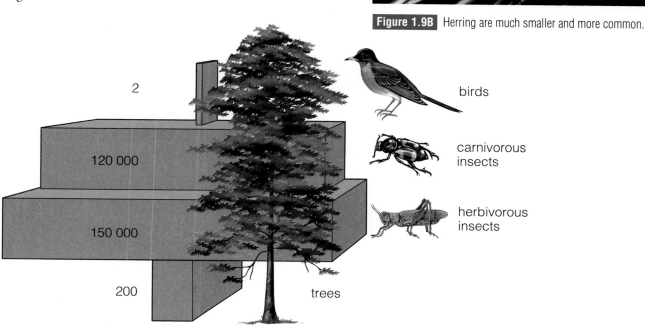

2   birds

120 000   carnivorous insects

150 000   herbivorous insects

200   trees

Figure 1.10 In this reversed pyramid of numbers, a single tree may feed thousands of plant-eating insects.

Pyramid of Biomass

Using numbers of organisms to make a pyramid of numbers does not take into account the sizes of the individual organisms. An alternative measure of energy combines the number with the size of an organism. This measure, called **biomass**, indicates how much of a particular organism there is in an ecosystem. Biomass is often calculated as the total dry mass of a given population of organisms. It may include a few large organisms or a larger number of small organisms. In general, biomass is a good indicator of the amount of energy that is present in living matter. A **pyramid of biomass** shows that biomass decreases from each trophic level to the one above (see Figure 1.11).

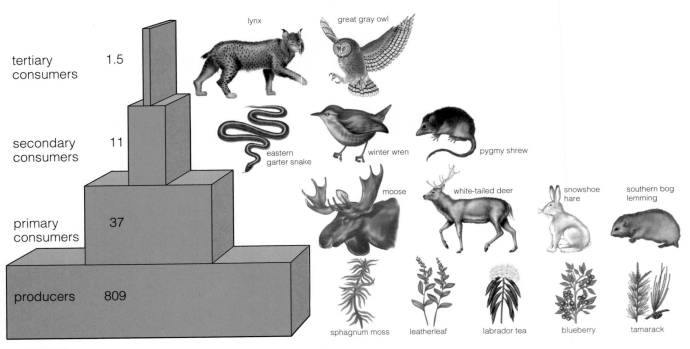

tertiary consumers	1.5
secondary consumers	11
primary consumers	37
producers	809

Figure 1.11 This pyramid of biomass shows the relative dry mass, in grams per square metre, of organisms in a bog food chain. Some examples of organisms at each trophic level are shown.

Once again, there are a few exceptions to this pattern. For example, the producers in an ocean ecosystem are microscopic algae, which float in the open water. These plant organisms are food for masses of small animals called zooplankton. At any given time, the biomass of the zooplankton may be greater than the biomass of the algae they are eating (see Figure 1.12). Why does this ecosystem not collapse? The reason is that the algae grow and reproduce at a much faster rate than the zooplankton. They double in numbers every few days, reproducing as fast as they are eaten. Thus they produce enough energy to support a larger population of zooplankton. There is a similar relationship between the biomass and reproductive rate of the zooplankton and the fish that feed on them.

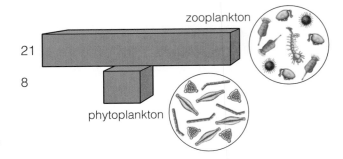

Figure 1.12 In this inverted pyramid of biomass for an ocean ecosystem, the mass of zooplankton (g/m²) is greater than the mass of the phytoplankton they feed on.

Pyramid of Energy Flow

A third type of pyramid can be used to eliminate the exceptions that may occur in a pyramid of numbers or a pyramid of biomass. A **pyramid of energy flow** measures the total chemical energy that flows through each trophic level. Why is it impossible to invert a pyramid of energy flow? Remember there is always less energy available for each successive trophic level in a pyramid. Therefore pyramids of energy flow are always upright, as shown in Figure 1.13.

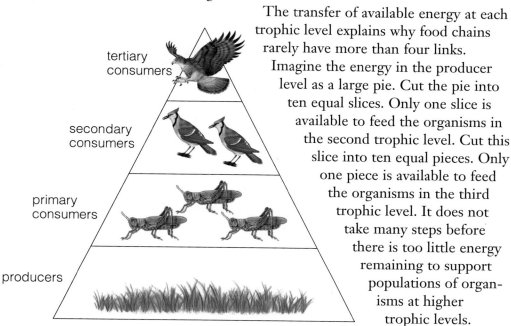

tertiary consumers

secondary consumers

primary consumers

producers

The transfer of available energy at each trophic level explains why food chains rarely have more than four links. Imagine the energy in the producer level as a large pie. Cut the pie into ten equal slices. Only one slice is available to feed the organisms in the second trophic level. Cut this slice into ten equal pieces. Only one piece is available to feed the organisms in the third trophic level. It does not take many steps before there is too little energy remaining to support populations of organisms at higher trophic levels.

Figure 1.13 A pyramid of energy flow shows the decrease in energy that is available to each successive trophic level.

Check Your Understanding

1. Give an example of an organism in the second trophic level of an ecosystem.

2. Why are there rarely more than four links in a food chain?

3. What is a pyramid of numbers?

4. Which would you expect to have the greatest biomass, a population of rabbits or a population of foxes living in the same ecosystem? Explain your answer.

5. **Thinking Critically** To study the transfer of food energy from dogs to fleas, would you use a pyramid of numbers or a pyramid of biomass? Sketch an example to show how each pyramid might look, and give a reason for your choice.

6. **Thinking Critically** Ecosystem A has a plant biomass of x. Ecosystem B has a plant biomass of $2x$. Suggest which ecosystem has the largest populations of consumers, giving reasons for your answer.

Math CONNECT

Devise your own graphic organizer to illustrate how energy is transferred at each trophic level. Remember that only about ten percent of the energy in each trophic level is available to consumers in the next trophic level. How will you represent the energy that is present in the producers?

Pause&
Reflect

Why do you think large carnivores, such as wolves and polar bears, are in greater danger of extinction than small herbivores, such as deer and rabbits?

1.3 Populations

During the 1990s, the number of sea otters (see Figure 1.14) living near the Aleutian Islands off the coast of Alaska fell sharply, by about 90 percent. Looking for an explanation, scientists discovered that killer whales had started eating sea otters. Killer whales usually eat seals and sea lions, not the much smaller otters. Study Figure 1.15 to find out why the whales changed their feeding habits, and what the effects were.

Figure 1.14 Sea otters are aquatic mammals that feed on sea urchins.

A Perch and herring populations are reduced by overfishing, changes in water temperature, and shortages of food.

B Seal and sea lion populations also decrease because there are fewer fish to eat.

C Killer whales, which usually feed on seals and sea lions, must search for other sources of food. They move from the open ocean into coastal waters and begin to feed on sea otters.

D Sea otters become the main food for killer whales. The otter population drops by 90 percent.

E The sea urchin population increases dramatically because there are so few otters to feed on the sea urchins.

F Kelp forests are eaten by large numbers of sea urchins.

G A variety of species that depend on the kelp forest for their survival are affected. These species include ducks, gulls, eagles, fishes, sea stars, and mussels.

ocean ecosystem ← → kelp forest ecosystem

Figure 1.15 Changes in the feeding habits of killer whales in the Pacific Ocean

The story of the sea otters shows how changes in a population in one part of a food web affects populations in other parts of the web. A linked series of events extended all the way from the fish to the seals, to the killer whales, to the otters, to the kelp forest. In a food web, each organism survives by gaining food energy from the trophic level below it. This organism, in turn, may be used as food by species in the trophic level above it. The population size of each species is continually adjusted by the species' interactions with both its food supply and the consumers that use it as food. In addition, each species may compete for food resources with others in its own trophic level.

INTERNET CONNECT

www.school.mcgrawhill.ca/resources/

What happens if a new species is introduced into a food web? How does an introduced species reach its new home? What effects does it have on other species in the ecosystem? Should people control the movements of species? Find out about introduced species by going to the web site above. Go to **Science Resources**, then to **SCIENCEPOWER 10** to know where to go next. Choose one species that has been introduced into an ecosystem in Canada, and prepare a brief report of your findings.

Carrying Capacity

Can any population of organisms keep growing forever? What might limit its numbers? The largest population of a species that an environment can support is called the **carrying capacity** of the environment for this species. You have already discovered how food supply, competition, and predators affect population size. Here is a summary of the four main factors that determine carrying capacity.

- *Materials and Energy* All populations of organisms are ultimately limited by the amount of usable energy from the Sun, as well as the supply of water, carbon, and other essential materials.

- *Food Chains* The population sizes at any trophic level are limited by the population sizes (or the biomass) in all the levels below it. In other words, populations are limited by their food supply. Populations are also limited by organisms in the levels above them, which use them as food. Thus animal populations are limited by their predators and plant populations are limited by herbivores.

- *Competition* Each organism has the same needs as other organisms of its species. The demand for resources (such as food, water, mates, and space) results in **competition** among individuals for these resources (see Figure 1.16). For example, each wolf in an area may use deer as its main source of food. If the deer population is low and the wolf population is high, competition for food among wolves increases.

Figure 1.16B Wolves compete with other predators for food.

Figure 1.16A Male elk compete for mates.

Competition among members of the same species is called **intraspecific competition**. The wolves may also compete with other predators, such as pumas and coyotes, that live in the area and also feed on deer. Competition between species is called **interspecific competition**. Both intraspecific and interspecific competition can limit population growth.

- *Density* Depending on their size, environment, and way of life, different species have different needs for space. The need for space can determine an organism's **population density**: how many individuals can live in an area at one time. Think of animals that live close together and animals that live far apart (see Figures 1.17A and 1.17B). How might you explain this difference between them?

Figure 1.17A Some species live in crowded conditions, such as this colony of northern gannets at Cape St. Mary, Newfoundland.

Figure 1.17B Grizzly bears need to space themselves far apart.

Figure 1.18 Overcrowding leads to stress, with increased death rate and decreased birth rate.

If population density increases beyond a suitable level for a particular species, it produces conditions that tend to limit further growth in numbers. For example, overcrowding may increase stress and promote the spread of diseases or parasites. Among some animals, overcrowding leads to increased aggression and neglect of offspring. These factors increase death rate and decrease birth rate, which together reduce the population size (see Figure 1.18). Factors that increase in significance as a population grows are called **density-dependent factors**.

Other factors can limit a population, regardless of its size. For example, a forest fire may kill most of the snakes in an area of forest, whether there are ten or ten thousand of them. Such factors are called **density-independent factors** because their effect on population size does not depend on how many individuals there are in the population. What other density-independent factors might limit population size?

Regulating Population Size

Paramecia are unicellular organisms commonly found in fresh-water ponds and marshes. They are covered by fine hairs that they use to move themselves around and to sweep bacteria and other small food particles into their mouths. In this investigation, you will study the factors that limit the growth of a paramecium (singular) population in a given volume of water over three weeks.

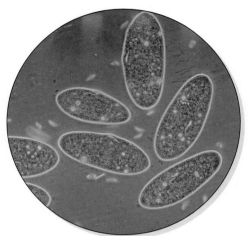

Paramecia

Problem

How is population size related to food supply?

Safety Precautions

- Wear appropriate safety equipment, such as an apron and rubber gloves.
- Remember the proper techniques for using a microscope. Handle microscope slides with care.

Apparatus

50 mL graduated cylinder
medicine dropper
scissors
tweezers
6 microscope slides
6 cover slips
microscope

Materials

paramecium culture
2 plastic cups
labels
felt marker
yeast culture
toothpick
methyl cellulose
30 cm cotton thread
plastic wrap
2 rubber bands
distilled water

Procedure

① Make two copies of the data table below. Title one "Added Food" and the other "Limited Food."

② Using the graduated cylinder, carefully measure 10 mL of paramecium culture into each plastic cup. Label one cup "added food" and the other "limited food."

③ Using the marker, draw a line on each cup to indicate the level of the water.

④ Add one drop of yeast culture to the cup labelled "added food."

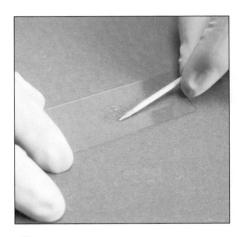

⑤ Using the toothpick, smear a small amount of methyl cellulose in the middle of each of three slides. The methyl cellulose should cover an area roughly the size of the cover slip.

Data Table for Paramecium Population Growth

Day	Number of paramecia in sample			Average number of paramecia
	Slide 1	Slide 2	Slide 3	
1				
3				
5				
7				

CONTINUED ▶

6 Cut the thread into 12 pieces, each about 5 mm long.

7 Using the tweezers, place four pieces of cotton thread on each of the slides. These threads, together with the methyl cellulose, will be obstacles for the paramecia and slow down their movement enough to allow you to count them. Number each slide.

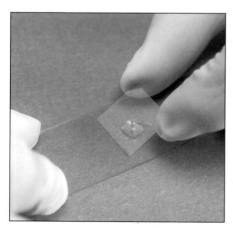

8 Place one drop of paramecium culture from the cup labelled "added food" on each slide, then put a cover slip over each drop.

9 Using the low power of your microscope, count the number of paramecia in one field of view on each slide.

10 Record your counts in your data table. Calculate and record the average.

11 Repeat steps 5 to 10 for the culture in the cup labelled "limited food."

12 Cover each cup with plastic wrap, and secure the plastic wrap with a rubber band. Make several small holes in the plastic wrap to allow air to enter.

13 Clean your slides and cover slips in preparation for the next samples. Repeat steps 5 to 11 every two or three days for three weeks.

14 Add distilled water to each cup every few days to keep the water level constant.

15 After three weeks, make a line graph of your data for each culture. Put "Average number of paramecia" on the *y*-axis and "Time (days)" on the *x*-axis. Always wash your hands after completing the procedure.

Analyze

1. Why did you count three samples of each culture, rather than one sample?

2. Compare the shapes of the graphs. What can you infer about the role of food in limiting population growth?

Conclude and Apply

3. Predict the effect of doubling the amount of food added to your paramecium culture. Explain your answer.

4. Suggest the factors that are most important in limiting human population growth today. Do you think that the human population can continue to grow indefinitely? Explain your answer.

5. You counted the paramecia in one field of view to measure changes in population size over time. Outline a method that you could use to estimate the size of the entire population of paramecia in each cup.

Extend Your Knowledge

6. The graphs below show the results of an experiment on two species of paramecia. This experiment was first carried out by population biologist G. F. Gause. He observed the growth of populations of these two species when each was grown alone and when they were mixed together. Study the two graphs, and answer the following questions.

(a) Describe the population growth curve of *Paramecium aurelia* when grown alone. Compare it with the population growth curve of *Paramecium caudatum* when grown alone.

(b) Describe what happened to the population of *Paramecium aurelia* when the two species were mixed.

(c) Describe what happened to the population of *Paramecium caudatum* when the two species were mixed.

(d) Suggest an explanation for any differences between the two populations after mixing.

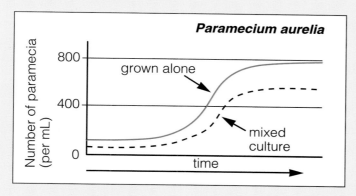

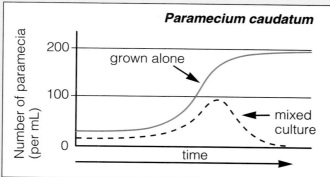

Increase in paramecium populations grown alone (solid line) and in a mixed culture (dashed line).

Skill
P O W E R

To review proper microscope handling techniques, turn to page 588.

Skill
P O W E R

For tips on how to make a line graph, turn to page 602.

Lemmings do not intentionally jump off cliffs to drown in the sea, as some people may think. Mass movements of these near-sighted little rodents may result in their accidental drowning, however. University of British Columbia ecologist Dr. Deborah Wilson went to Nunavut in Canada's Far North to study lemmings. As part of her study, she looked at their population peaks and crashes, which have led to the cliff-jumping myth.

"Lemming numbers fluctuate quite regularly," Deborah explains, "with peaks in the population every three years. We place small radio transmitters on individual lemmings and follow their movements. This helps us learn whether they become food for predators or whether some other factor is responsible for the steep declines in numbers. Predators (such as arctic foxes and ermine) are responsible for most lemming deaths, but that's not the whole story. Lemmings reproduce at a lower rate when they are very abundant. Whether their lower reproduction is a response to the population density or to a shortage of food or space to live in is not known."

Deborah Wilson

One great thing about working in the North, Deborah reports, "was getting to know the Inuit who lived near our remote field station. Some helped with our field study, and we were able to learn about their culture and the difficulties they face living in an arctic environment."

Deborah started her working life as a computer programmer but later realized that she would rather be an ecologist. This meant more years of study, but it was worthwhile. "Keep striving to do what you love," she advises students. "It took me a long time to be able to work in the field of ecology, where my real interest lies. It is much less lucrative than working in business, but that doesn't matter to me at all."

Check Your Understanding

1. Give one example of each of the following types of limiting factors.
   (a) density-dependent
   (b) density-independent

2. What is meant by the term "carrying capacity"?

3. Give an example of
   (a) interspecific competition
   (b) intraspecific competition

4. How might overcrowding lead to a reduction in population size?

5. **Thinking Critically** How might an increase in the population of plants in an area lead to an increase in the population of hawks?

6. **Thinking Critically** How might an increase in the population of hawks in an area lead to an increase in the population of plants?

1.4 Feeding People

Consider a field of vegetables growing in New Brunswick and, far to the south, a tropical rain forest in Guatemala (see Figures 1.19A and 1.19B). Beneath the sunlight, the vegetables in the field and the trees in the forest carry out photosynthesis and grow. Do you think that a hectare of a Canadian field and a hectare of a tropical forest produce the same amount of biomass during a given period of time? If not, what might make their production different?

Figure 1.19A Potatoes growing in a field in New Brunswick

Figure 1.19B A tropical rain forest in Guatemala

Figure 1.20 shows **productivity** (the average amounts of new plant biomass produced each year per unit area) in a number of different ecosystems. Compare the productivity of agricultural land with the productivity of a tropical rain forest. Could we increase food production for people by farming in regions with tropical rain forests? Find out the factors that can influence productivity in the following activity.

Ecosystem

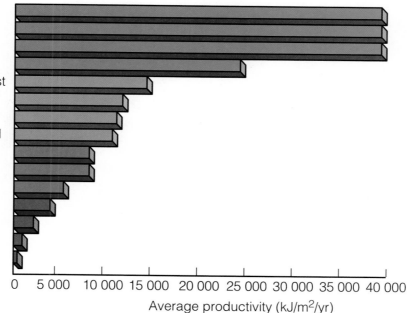

Estuary
Swamp and marsh
Tropical rainforest
Temperate forest
Northern coniferous forest
Savanna
Agricultural land
Woodland and shrubland
Temperate grassland
Lakes and streams
Continental shelf
Open ocean
Tundra
Desert scrub
Extreme desert

0   5 000   10 000 15 000   20 000 25 000 30 000 35 000 40 000
Average productivity (kJ/m^2/yr)

Figure 1.20 Average productivity of major ecosystems.

Which Factors Influence Productivity?

In addition to sunlight, what else do plants need for growth? In this activity, you will compare climatic variables for areas of Earth that are least productive with climatic variables for areas that are most productive. What climatic variables have the greatest impact on productivity of plant biomass?

What You Need
atlas with climate maps of the world

What to Do

1. Work with a partner. Using the information in Figure 1.20 on page 25, locate the deserts on the satellite image shown below. (Hint: Deserts have the lowest productivity of all terrestrial ecosystems.)

2. Choose three deserts, and find out their names.

3. Using the climate maps, determine the average annual temperature and precipitation for each desert. Based on these averages, define the term "desert."

4. Repeat steps 1 to 3 for three tropical rain forests — areas of highest productivity.

What Did You Discover?

1. What climatic variables do deserts have in common?

2. What climatic variables do tropical rain forests have in common?

3. How do deserts and tropical rain forests differ in terms of the climatic variables you studied?

4. Why do deserts occur in different parts of the world? What climatic variables are responsible for this pattern?

5. Refer to Figure 1.20 to find out how the productivity of agricultural land compares with the productivity of deserts and tropical rain forests. Based on your findings, estimate the average temperature and rainfall for areas of agricultural land.

Extensions

6. Are there any deserts in Canada? Explain why or why not, with reference to climate. (Hint: Think carefully. Are all deserts hot?)

7. Could deserts be used to produce food for people? What technology might help to make this possible?

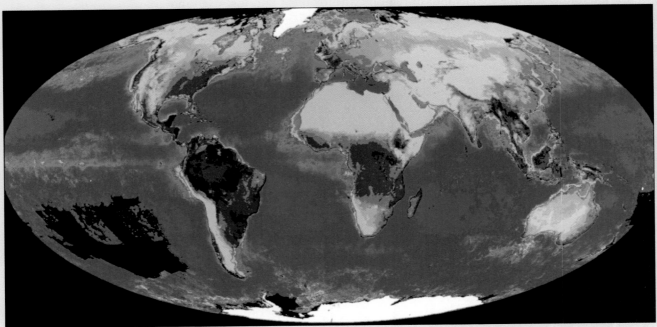

This satellite image shows Earth's production of plant biomass. The most productive areas of land are dark green and the least productive are yellow. Productivity in the oceans is indicated by the amount of phytoplankton (plants) present, ranging from red (greatest) to orange, yellow, green, and blue (lowest).

Plant Productivity and Climate

Plant growth does not depend on sunlight alone. Plants need water and carbon dioxide to make the food (carbohydrates) they require to grow. They also need nutrients, such as nitrogen and phosphorus, to help them grow. As well, the rate of plant growth is affected by temperature. Warm conditions allow plants to grow faster than cold conditions. As a result of differences in these and other factors, the production of plant biomass varies from one ecosystem to another. Warm, wet areas of Earth tend to have the highest levels of productivity. Areas with low temperatures and little water have the lowest levels of productivity.

Figure 1.21 Adding water and fertilizer to deserts could increase food production for people.

Deserts have abundant sunlight and warmth, but they lack water and mineral nutrients for plant growth. Careful use of irrigation and fertilizers could increase plant productivity and make these areas suitable for crop production in some parts of the world (see Figure 1.21). These methods can be costly and can create problems, however. What environmental and social issues might arise from the use of irrigation?

Figure 1.22 This tropical rain forest is being cleared for agriculture.

Observing the lush growth and abundant animal life of tropical forests, people have believed that these forests could provide productive farmland. In practise, this is not always the case. Farm plants and animals that are introduced from different parts of the world do not always survive well in new environments. They may be vulnerable to pests, diseases, and weather fluctuations. In addition, replacing a forest ecosystem with an agricultural ecosystem may create other problems. For instance, clearing a forest results in a loss of habitats for plants and animals. Consequently there is a decrease in species diversity. The loss of certain organisms can change the flow of energy in an ecosystem. How do you think a pyramid of energy flow would be affected by a decrease in the biomass of producers? As well, changes in the flow of energy in an ecosystem can affect such variables as soil composition and the cycling of water.

In tropical forests, there is very little decomposing organic matter in the soil. Detritivores quickly consume the dead and waste materials on the forest floor. As a result, these materials do not build up into the thick layers of soil found in cooler climates where the process of decomposition is slower. The trees in a tropical forest contain most of the biomass in the ecosystem. If the trees are cut and burned to clear land for crops, all that is left is a thin, poor soil. The soil and the few nutrients that it contains are quickly washed away by the heavy tropical rainfalls (see Figure 1.22).

STRETCH Your Mind

One of the most serious problems that face people today is *desertification*. It results from human activities that degrade the land and cause deserts to expand. How much of Earth's land surface is affected by desertification? How many people are threatened by it? What kinds of human activities contribute to desertification, and how can this process be prevented? Are there any regions of Canada that might be affected by it? To answer these questions, conduct research at your local library and/or on the Internet. Present your findings in a brief report.

Food and Population Size

At the start of this chapter, you considered some food chains to which you are linked and you analyzed the different energy content of different foods. The typical meal of a Canadian, however, is not typical of what most people around the world eat. How do you think it is different?

On average, Canadians consume more joules each day and eat more meat than most people. About 80 percent of the global human population eats mainly grains and vegetables, and consumes very little meat or other animal products. From your study of ecological pyramids, recall which trophic level of consumers has access to the greatest amount of usable food energy. Figure 1.23 shows how much energy is available to people in food chains of different lengths.

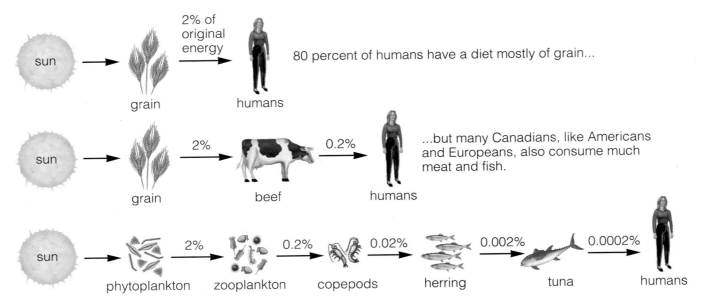

Figure 1.23 The longer a food chain is, the smaller the amount of the Sun's energy that is available to humans at the end of the chain. Each farm animal consumes plant energy that could otherwise be eaten directly by people.

Recall what you discovered in the activity on page 6. Which type of farm can support a larger human population on a given area of farmland — a farm that produces plants alone or a farm that produces plants and animals? If all people ate only plant material, could we increase our agricultural production? How many times more people do you think could be fed on this diet? Think of some reasons why such a change in diet is unlikely to occur.

Food and Competitors

How do food chains in agricultural and natural ecosystems compare? In natural ecosystems, there may be hundreds of species connected, by many links, into complex food webs. The goal of agriculture is to produce short, simple food chains that usually have no more than two links leading directly from plants to people. To accomplish this, a single crop (such as wheat, corn, or rice) is often grown on huge areas of land. This practice is called monoculture. How might monoculture affect populations of primary consumers?

Although we consider a field of wheat or corn to be *our* food, we are not the only species that eats wheat or corn. Many insects, birds, and other organisms also feed on crop plants. A huge supply of crop plants in one place naturally tends to increase the population size of these organisms, which then compete with people for the food. We call these organisms pests, but it is important to realize that pest populations are affected by our manipulation of the food supply. Many insect pests are species that specialize in feeding on a particular type of plant. They typically have a rate of reproduction that allows them to increase in numbers very rapidly (see Figure 1.24). In nature, many plants grow in patches that are spaced far apart. Therefore the populations of insects that feed on them are kept in check.

Figure 1.24 Aphids are small insects that feed on plants. When they encounter an abundant food supply, they reproduce and increase in numbers very quickly.

Poisons in Food Chains

To keep pests from damaging crops, many farmers spray their fields with poisonous chemicals, called *pesticides*, as shown in Figure 1.25. These pesticides are designed to kill the insects but not harm other animals, in small doses. Problems occur, however, when pesticides enter food chains and pass from one trophic level to another. You can discover how pesticides enter an ecosystem by analyzing a food web in the next investigation.

Figure 1.25 How can spraying crops with pesticides affect food chains?

DDT in a Food Chain

Think About It

DDT is an example of a persistent pesticide that can remain in the environment for long periods of time. The longer a pesticide is present in the environment, the greater the chance that it will be consumed by organisms. Pesticides can accumulate in the bodies of organisms. As a result, they can increase in concentration in specific tissues or organs. How do pesticides, such as DDT, enter food chains? In this investigation, you will trace the path of DDT in a north Pacific Ocean food chain.

What to Do

1 Study the following food web. Below the name of each organism is a number that indicates the amount of DDT in the organism's tissues, in parts per billion (ppb). One ppb is equivalent to 1 mg/1000 L.

2 Use the food web and the information about DDT on page 31 to answer the questions that follow.

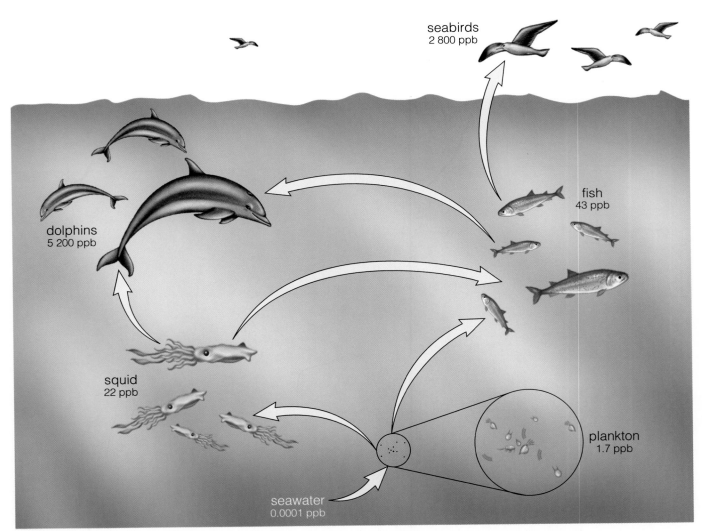

seabirds
2 800 ppb

fish
43 ppb

dolphins
5 200 ppb

squid
22 ppb

plankton
1.7 ppb

seawater
0.0001 ppb

DDT in a north Pacific Ocean food web, in parts per billion (ppb). Arrows show the flow of energy from one trophic level to another.

The DDT Story

The risks of using powerful pesticides in ecosystems first became widely known during the 1950s and 1960s, when the toxic effects of the insecticide DDT were recorded. DDT was one of the first and most powerful insecticides developed. During World War II, it was used to control populations of insects (such as body lice, fleas, and mosquitoes) that can transmit deadly diseases to people. As a result, the rate of death from malaria, bubonic plague, typhus, and yellow fever fell dramatically. DDT was also used widely on crops to control damage caused by insect pests.

In 1962 biologist and writer Rachel Carson published a book entitled *Silent Spring*, which described how pesticides had spread through the environment. As a result of her scientific evidence and the demands from an alarmed public, the use of DDT was restricted in Canada after 1969.

About ten years after the first use of DDT, signs of trouble appeared. Dead birds, fish, frogs, and other animals were found in areas that had been heavily sprayed with DDT. The fat in their bodies contained high levels of the insecticide. Harmless or beneficial insects, such as butterflies and honeybees, also started to disappear from areas that had been sprayed.

Tests of soil and water showed that DDT remained in the environment for many years. For example, DDT was still found in the soil of some heavily sprayed orchards ten years after the spraying was stopped. DDT was also found in the bodies of many different organisms in areas around the world where the insecticide

Rachel Carson

had never been used. It also began showing up in the tissues of people.

An unexpected outcome of using DDT was its effect on populations of birds of prey. Numbers of hawks, eagles, and ospreys on farmlands across North America and Europe fell sharply during the 1950s and 1960s. Scientists discovered that DDT reduced the ability of these birds to produce normal eggshells. Affected birds laid eggs with thin shells that broke in the nest, so they were unable to produce the usual number of young. The adult birds had accumulated DDT in their bodies from the fish they ate. The amount of DDT had accumulated in the bodies of organisms, moving from producers to primary consumers, to secondary consumers, and so on. This process is called **biological magnification**. Eventually concentrations of DDT became large enough in birds of prey to affect their reproduction. Unfortunately, DDT continues to be used in some tropical countries because it is such an effective pesticide. It not only affects species that live in these countries but also species that live elsewhere in the world, including people who consume food products imported from the tropics.

Math CONNECT

One percent is equal to 10 000 000 ppb. What percent is 5200 ppb?

DidYou**Know**?

DDT is the abbreviation for the chemical named dichlorodiphenyltrichloroethane. It was first made in 1874.

Pesticides can severely affect the reproduction of birds of prey, such as this osprey.

CONTINUED ▶

Analyze

1. How does DDT enter a food web?

2. Which organisms contain the most DDT?

3. At what trophic level are these species?

4. What is the relationship between the trophic level of an organism and the concentration of DDT in its body?

5. How many times greater is the concentration of DDT in the fish than in the seawater? How many times greater is it in the dolphins than in the seawater?

6. In your own words, explain why animals at the top of a food chain are particularly at risk from poisons in the environment.

Conclude and Apply

7. Use an example to explain how an animal living hundreds of kilometres from an area sprayed with DDT might get DDT in its body.

8. DDT is stored in body fat and remains toxic for many years. Explain why these characteristics are undesirable in a pesticide. What characteristics would you want in a pesticide to make it less harmful to non-pest organisms?

Extend Your Knowledge and Skills

9. After spraying crops with DDT for several years, farmers found that populations of insect pests rebounded. One reason was that the insects had developed resistance to the insecticide. Suggest another reason, based on what you know about populations, pyramids, predators, and competitors.

10. When Rachel Carson published her book about the effects of pesticides on food chains and people, she had many opponents. Use your local library and/or the Internet to research Rachel Carson. How did she present her ideas to the general public and the scientific community? What methods would you use to inform people of a threat to the environment? Why were Rachel Carson's ideas initially opposed?

11. The table below gives DDT levels, in parts per million (ppm), found in the eggs of three species of seabirds. The eggs were sampled from two different locations along Canada's east coast. Pesticide levels found in birds' eggs are a good indicator of pesticide levels in the environment. Study the data and answer the questions that follow.

DDT Level in Atlantic Seabird Eggs

		DDT Level in Eggs (ppm)	
Species	Year	Bay of Fundy	Atlantic Ocean
Leach's Storm-Petrel (feeds on small organisms near the surface of the water)	1968	no data	1.46
	1972	6.81	2.48
	1976	1.75	0.75
	1980	1.13	0.46
	1984	1.05	0.40
Atlantic Puffin (feeds on small fish)	1968	no data	0.89
	1972	2.57	0.76
	1976	1.27	0.59
	1980	1.03	0.55
	1984	0.74	0.30
Double-crested Cormorant (feeds on larger fish)	1972	6.51	2.85
	1976	1.49	2.18
	1980	1.91	1.34
	1984	1.07	1.88

(a) Describe general differences in pesticide levels found in birds' eggs taken from the Bay of Fundy and from the Atlantic Ocean. Suggest a reason for the differences.

(b) Describe changes in pesticide levels between the late 1960s and early 1980s. What may account for the changes?

(c) Describe any differences in pesticide levels found in different species of seabirds. Suggest a reason for the differences.

Consuming the Planet

In 1925 the global human population was about two billion. Today it is over six billion and still growing. This is more people than have ever lived together on Earth (see Figure 1.26). The rapid population growth has occurred mainly because of a decline in the death rate. This is due to improved health care and sanitation, as well as the increased production of food.

Imagine the human population in the top trophic level of many different food chains around the world. The energy of the Sun that enters large areas of farmland, forests, oceans, and lakes is eventually converted into food for people. In addition, people use both plants and animals for many purposes other than food. For example, our demands for wood, cotton, tobacco, and even domestic pets all take a share of Earth's biological productivity.

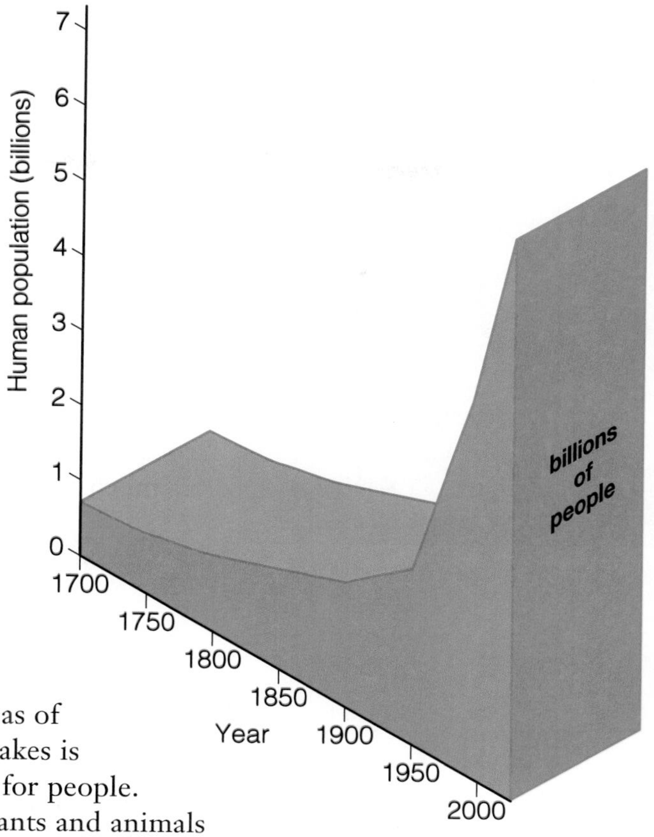

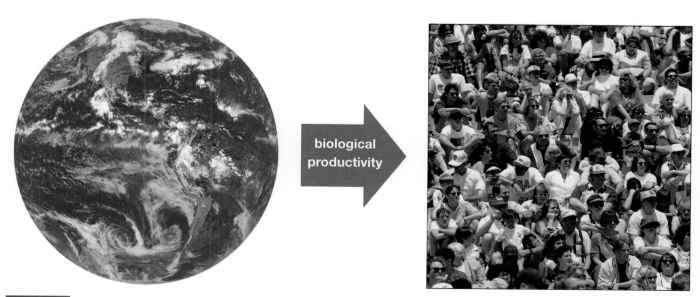

Figure 1.26 The human population tripled during the twentieth century and continues to grow.

Pause & Reflect

Do you think it is possible to develop a system of agricultural production that is not affected by pests and by crop and livestock diseases? Give reasons for your answer.

Figure 1.27 How much of Earth's energy do people consume? What effect does our use of energy have on other species that share the planet with us?

People also affect the flow of energy in ecosystems indirectly. For example, we burn forests, drain wetlands, pave over land for cities and highways, build golf courses and parks, flood land by damming rivers, and turn grasslands into deserts by overgrazing with livestock. All these activities reduce the plant biomass that is produced in natural ecosystems. As a result, less energy is available for other species. Scientists have calculated that the human population uses, converts, or diverts more than 20 percent of Earth's biomass. Probably no other species has used or affected this much of Earth's biological productivity.

Figure 1.28 Developments such as this remove energy and resources that plants and animals need to survive.

Pause&
Reflect

People affect ecosystems by harvesting trees. Canada is the largest exporter of timber in the world and the Canadian economy depends heavily on our forestry industry. How can we harvest trees yet minimize our impact on the environment? What social and economic issues might arise? Write down your thoughts about these questions. You will debate the merits of different forestry practices in the Unit 1 Issue Analysis.

Check Your Understanding

1. Name two ways in which humans have been able to increase our food supply.

2. What change in diet would allow a growing human population to be supported without any further increase in farmland? Explain your answer.

3. Give one reason why conversion of tropical forests into farmland has generally been unsuccessful.

4. Why do monocultures usually have pests?

5. Give an example to show the meaning of the term "biological magnification."

6. **Apply** Suggest one way in which the productivity of farmland could be increased. How would this impact the environment? Also consider the costs involved and the effect on local communities of people.

7. **Thinking Critically** Name a problem that must be overcome if we want to irrigate deserts. Suggest a remedy for this problem.

Now that you have completed this chapter, try to do the following. If you cannot, go back to the sections indicated.

Define the term "ecosystem." (1.1)

Describe how energy passes though an ecosystem. (1.1)

Explain why green plants are called producers (1.1)

Name the trophic levels in a food chain. Give examples of the types of organisms that might occupy each level. (1.2)

Describe how energy is transferred from organism to organism in a food chain. (1.2)

Explain the difference between a pyramid of numbers and a pyramid of biomass. (1.2)

Explain why food chains rarely have more than four links. (1.2)

List the main factors that determine carrying capacity. Briefly describe each factor. (1.3)

Distinguish between intraspecific competition and interspecific competition. (1.3)

Name two density-dependent factors that can limit population size. (1.3)

Explain why plant productivity varies from place to place. (1.4)

Explain how monocultures can affect populations of primary consumers. (1.4)

Use the example of DDT to explain the process of biological magnification. (1.4)

Describe how energy flows through food chains of different lengths. (1.4)

Skill
P O W E R

For tips on using graphic organizers, turn to page 578.

Prepare Your Own Summary

Summarize this chapter by doing one of the following. Use a graphic organizer (such as a concept map), produce a poster, or write the summary to include the key chapter concepts. Here are a few ideas to use as a guide:

- Explain how people affect the flow of energy in ecosystems.
- Describe how the feeding patterns in a food web can be altered by a change in the population size of one of the species.
- Explain why it is more efficient for people to eat plant products rather than animal products.
- Explain why mice are more abundant than owls.
- Describe how competition can affect population size.
- Identify the trophic levels shown in the illustration.

Reviewing Key Terms

If you need to review, the section numbers show you where these terms were introduced.

1. Give one example of a producer and one example of a consumer. (1.1)

2. Explain the meaning of the term "ecosystem." (1.1)

3. In your notebook, state whether each of the following statements is true or false. If the statement is false, explain why.

   (a) Productivity is the energy of producers that is available to consumers. (1.1)

   (b) The total dry mass of plant or animal matter is its biomass. (1.2)

   (c) A rabbit and a cow are in different trophic levels. (1.2)

   (d) The carrying capacity is the lowest population of a species that can live in a particular environment. (1.3)

   (e) A flood that drowns most of the animals of species X in an area is an example of density-dependent population regulation. (1.3)

Understanding Key Concepts

Section numbers are provided if you need to review.

4. By what means does energy move from the Sun to a fox? (1.1)

5. In a study area, there are 558 of species A, and 7 of species B. Which species is most likely to be a herbivore, and which is most likely to be a carnivore? Explain your answer, using the terms "energy," "trophic level," and "pyramid of numbers." (1.1, 1.2)

6. Only about 10 percent of the energy in the food that is eaten by a consumer is available to the next consumer in the food chain. What happens to the remaining energy in the food chain? (1.2)

7. If you eat a meal with a mass of 300 g, you do not increase your mass by the same amount. Explain why. (1.2)

8. Using examples, describe how the population size of a species might be affected by

   (a) intraspecific competition

   (b) interspecific competition. (1.3)

Developing Skills

9. Suppose that there is a transfer of 10 percent of biomass at each link in the following food chain:

   phytoplankton → zooplankton → small fish → medium fish → tuna → human

   What biomass of phytoplankton is required to supply a human family with 1 kg of tuna for dinner?

10. Brewer's yeast is a micro-organism that produces ethyl alcohol as a waste product of its metabolism. It is used to make beer and wine. Suppose that a wine-maker adds 500 brewer's yeast cells to a vat of grape juice. Each cell divides in two every 15 min.

    (a) How many cells are present after 3 h?

    (b) What do you think will limit the growth of this yeast population?

    (c) Is the factor you named in your answer to part (b) density-dependent or density-independent?

 Design Your Own Design an experiment to study the effects of density-independent factors on paramecium populations. What variables would you investigate? What would be your control variable(s)? What would be your experimental variable(s)? Make a hypothesis based on your knowledge of the factors that can limit population growth. After obtaining your teacher's approval and observing all safety precautions, carry out your experiment, and test your hypothesis.

Problem Solving/Applying

12. Is it a more efficient use of the Sun's energy for people to eat beef or salmon? Explain your answer.

13. A farmer wants to choose the most efficient way of producing meat. She compares the rate of food consumption of one steer and 300 rabbits (which have the same total mass). She measures their relative rates of converting the food into biomass. Copy the table below into your notebook. Make the calculations needed to complete the table, and then answer the questions that follow.

Food Consumption and Productivity of Two Domestic Animals

Animal	1 steer	300 rabbits
Total body mass	590 kg	590 kg
Food consumed per day	7.5 kg	30 kg
Gain in mass per day	0.9 kg	3.6 kg
Days taken to consume 1000 kg hay		
Total gain in mass after consuming 1000 kg hay		

(a) Is there any significant difference between the gain in mass by the steer or the rabbits?

(b) Which animal converts the hay into animal biomass faster? By how much is it faster?

(c) Based on your analysis, which animals do you think the farmer should raise? Explain your answer.

14. Describe two ways in which you might increase the carrying capacity of a backyard for singing birds.

Skill
P O W E R

For tips on solving numerical problems using the GRASP method, turn to page 610.

Critical Thinking

15. The diagram below shows a food web in the Antarctic Ocean.

(a) Why might a decline in the population of baleen whales lead to an increase in the populations of seals, penguins, and krill-eating fish?

(b) What might happen to the other species if the population of baleen whales increased but the population of krill stayed the same? Explain your answer.

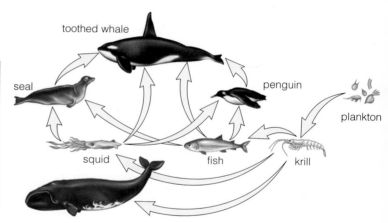

16. The productivity of different ecosystems varies. Why is the productivity of an open ocean similar to the productivity of a desert?

Pause&
Reflect

1. Go back to the beginning of the chapter, on page 2, and check your original answers to the Opening Ideas questions. How has your thinking changed? How would you answer those questions now that you have investigated the topics in this chapter?

2. Some people argue that the growing human population can be fed from the sea. If so, are people more likely to be eating salmon or algae in the future?

2 Cycles of Life

Opening Ideas...

- How are the inhabitants of Earth like the crew of a spacecraft?

- Why does your life depend on a few species of micro-organisms?

- How did the chemical elements in your body get there?

Science Log

In your Science Log, answer the questions above. State the evidence you have for each answer. If you are not sure about an answer, write down some ideas based on what you already know. Look for more ideas as you read this chapter.

During the late 1980s, a huge laboratory, called Biosphere II, was built in the Arizona desert. (Earth is "Biosphere I.") Numerous glass windows allowed energy from the Sun to enter the laboratory, but it was otherwise sealed off from the surrounding air, water, and soil. Inside the laboratory, researchers created areas of rain forest, grassland, desert, farmland, and ocean. Their aim was to learn how well people and the other living things could survive inside the laboratory without any resources from the outside. In 1991 eight men and women were locked into the miniature version of Earth for a two-year stay.

In Chapter 1, you learned that organisms need a continual supply of energy to grow and function. They also need a continual supply of chemical elements, such as carbon, oxygen, and nitrogen. These chemical elements exist on Earth in fixed amounts. To maintain the supply needed by living things, they must be recycled and re-used. They move constantly, cycling back and forth between organisms and the air, soil, and water.

A few weeks after the laboratory and its inhabitants were locked in, the composition of the air in the enclosed space began to change dramatically. Carbon dioxide levels increased by seven times. Oxygen levels decreased by nearly one third, and some species started to die. Alarmed by the changes, the researchers decided to pump in air from the outside. What do you think had happened to change the gas levels in the air?

In this chapter, you will discover how chemicals are cycled through the environment. How does our use of resources affect chemical cycles? How do changes in these cycles affect the atmosphere, water, soils, and organisms on Earth?

Build Your Own Life Dome

Space stations and undersea research labs are examples of self-contained life-support systems.

Key Concepts

In this chapter, you will discover

- how carbon, oxygen, and nitrogen are cycled through an ecosystem
- how the composition of soil affects an ecosystem
- how human activities affect natural cycles
- what the concept of sustainability means

Key Skills

In this chapter, you will

- observe non-living materials being transferred to living things, and measure the effects
- make graphs of environmental data
- relate CO_2 levels in the air to average global temperatures, and draw conclusions
- design your own investigation to measure the effects of acid precipitation on a yeast population
- draw diagrams to show how people alter nutrient cycles

Key Terms

- nutrients
- nutrient cycles
- closed system
- biotic
- abiotic
- photosynthesis
- carbon cycle
- cellular respiration
- Carboniferous Period
- nitrogen fixation
- nitrogen-fixing bacteria
- nitrifying bacteria
- nitrification
- denitrifying bacteria
- denitrification
- mycorrhizal fungi
- acid precipitation
- eutrophication
- algal bloom
- biodiversity
- sustainability
- sustainable development

Starting Point

The people and other living things must obtain everything they need to survive from within the system. How would you make a self-contained ecosystem in a sealed container?

What You Need

container that can be sealed, such as a large jar or an aquarium
soil and/or pond water
variety of small organisms

What to Do

1. You will use the container to make a model of a self-contained ecosystem. You may produce a terrestrial (land) ecosystem or an aquatic (water) ecosystem.

2. In a group, brainstorm a list of organisms to put in your ecosystem. How many of each will you include? **Note:** Handle all organisms with care.

3. Determine what each organism needs to survive and how you will meet these needs.

4. Set up your "life dome." Record any changes you observe in your ecosystem over a period of four weeks.

5. Wash your hands after setting up your ecosystem.

What Did You Discover?

1. What is the source of energy for your enclosed ecosystem?

2. Name the producers, consumers, and decomposers in your ecosystem and describe any changes you observed in their numbers. Infer a cause for each change.

3. How long can the ecosystem be maintained? Why?

2.1 A Matter of Life and Death

" . . . death, a necessary end, will come when it will come."

This quotation is from *Julius Caesar*, a play by William Shakespeare. Why do all living things eventually die? Figures 2.1A and 2.1B suggest one answer to this question. The photographs show two parts of a cycle. Could one part of the cycle exist without the other part?

Figure 2.1A What happens to the leaves that cover the ground each fall?

Figure 2.1B How do plants form each spring?

In the fall, dead leaves cover the ground. By the end of the following spring, there is little or no sign of the dead leaves. In the spring, new plants grow from the ground. Plant matter has disappeared, and plant matter has reappeared. You can probably think of an explanation for these observations. Decomposers break down the dead leaves, and new plants grow from seeds or from living roots. How can you link the two parts of this explanation together?

Decomposition and growth are evidence of the recycling of matter that life depends on. Every organism is made up of combinations of chemical elements, such as carbon, oxygen, hydrogen, and nitrogen. The chemical elements that are used by organisms to build and operate their bodies are called **nutrients.** Organisms obtain nutrients in compounds that they absorb from their environment — from soil, water, air, or other organisms. The movements of nutrients through the environment are called **nutrient cycles.**

Like Biosphere II, Earth is a **closed system.** In other words, there is little or no input of new materials from outside the system. Since early in Earth's history, Earth has had all the nutrients it will ever have. To sustain life over millions of years, nutrients are constantly recycled. When an organism dies, the materials in its body are returned to the environment where they can be used by other living things. Without death and decomposition, these materials would eventually be used up and there could be no more new life.

Building a Plant

What nutrients do plants need in order to grow? How do they obtain each nutrient? In this activity, you will compare the growth of a plant that is given light, air, water, and soil with the growth of a plant that is given only light, air, and water. You will make observations over a period of four weeks.

What You Need

2 small plants of the same species (such as *Geranium* or *Coleus*) that are similar in size
2 small, identical pots or cups
vermiculite
rich potting soil
ruler
water

What to Do

1. Make a table like the one below to record your data. Give your table a title.

	Size of plant			
	Growing in potting soil		Growing in vermiculite	
Variable	Day 1	Day 28	Day 1	Day 28
root length (mm)				
stem length (mm)				
number of leaves				

2. Carefully separate the roots of the plants from the soil. Wash off any remaining soil.

3. Measure and record the root length, stem height, and number of leaves of each plant.

4. Describe and record the characteristics of the rich potting soil and the vermiculite.

5. Fill one pot with the potting soil and the other pot with the vermiculite. Plant one plant in each pot. Label the two pots. Wash your hands.

6. List the nutrients that you think a plant obtains from air, from water, and from soil. Based on your list, write a hypothesis about how the growth rate of your two plants might differ.

7. Place both pots in the same location. Provide equal amounts of light and water over the next four weeks. At the end of this period, remove the two plants from the pots. Repeat the measurements you made in step 3, and record them in your data table.

What Did You Discover?

1. Describe any differences that you observed in the growth of the two plants. Provide an explanation for these differences.

2. Did your results support your hypothesis? Explain your answer.

3. If your results did not support your hypothesis, what reasons or sources of error might account for your observations?

4. **Thinking Critically** What nutrients that are needed by a plant might be in potting soil but not in vermiculite?

Extension

5. Many commercial greenhouses grow plants without soil, using a system called *hydroponics*. Work in a small group to research hydroponics at a local library and/or on the Internet. How does a hydroponic system recycle nutrients? What are the advantages and disadvantages of this system for producing food? Prepare a brief report of your findings.

Sustaining Life

You now know two key factors that sustain life on Earth. One is energy from the Sun, which plants use to make food. The other is nutrients, which cycle through ecosystems. In some parts of a nutrient cycle, the nutrients are in living organisms, or the **biotic** part of the environment. In other parts of a nutrient cycle, the nutrients are in the non-living or **abiotic** part of the environment, such as the air or water. Figure 2.2 shows how nutrients enter, move through, and exit all living organisms.

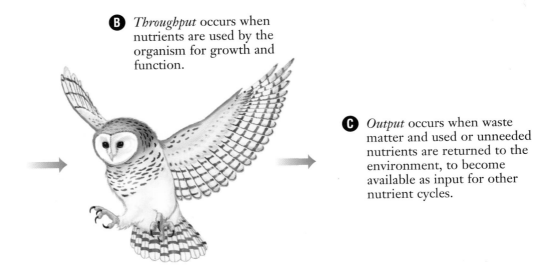

B *Throughput* occurs when nutrients are used by the organism for growth and function.

A *Input* occurs when nutrients enter a living organism. For example, there is an input of nutrients to this barn owl when it breathes in and when it eats.

C *Output* occurs when waste matter and used or unneeded nutrients are returned to the environment, to become available as input for other nutrient cycles.

Figure 2.2 The three stages of a nutrient cycle

When an organism dies, the nutrients in its body continue their endless journey through the nutrient cycles. Your own body is made up of materials that were previously used by other organisms or were once part of a rock or a lake. How did the cycling of these materials eventually reach you? In the next two sections of the chapter, you will learn more about nutrient cycles by studying two examples: the carbon cycle and the nitrogen cycle. By the end of the chapter, you will understand how human activities can alter these cycles. What can happen to living organisms if certain parts of nutrient cycles occur faster or slower than usual, or are disrupted in other ways?

Check Your Understanding

1. What is a closed system?

2. By what process do nutrients in the body of a dead mouse become part of the abiotic environment?

3. How might the elements in a living plant become part of the body of a living bear?

4. Describe one way in which a waste product from a living toad is used by a plant.

5. **Apply** How can waste products from animals benefit agriculture?

6. **Thinking Critically** What might happen if living things did not die?

2.2 The Carbon Cycle

The oak tree shown in Figure 2.3 has a mass of several tonnes. It was once a seed with a mass of only a few grams. Where did the materials that make up the large tree come from?

Figure 2.3 A tree needs nutrients in order to grow and maintain itself.

A tree can grow a trunk, branches, leaves, and roots because it can make its own food from materials in its environment. Recall that plants make carbohydrates (simple sugars) during the process of **photosynthesis**. This process can be summarized by the following equation:

$$6CO_2 + 6H_2O + energy \longrightarrow C_6H_{12}O_6 + 6O_2$$

carbon dioxide · water · carbohydrate · oxygen

Based on this equation, what three things does a tree need to make carbohydrates? Where do these things come from? In Chapter 1, you learned that the source of the energy for photosynthesis is the Sun. What are the sources of the carbon dioxide and the water? In the next investigation, you will observe evidence that plants absorb carbon dioxide from their environment.

Math CONNECT

The human body is made up of about 35 different elements. The majority of these elements occur in minute quantities. The four most common elements in your body (by percent of wet weight) are oxygen (65 percent), carbon (18 percent), hydrogen (10 percent), and nitrogen (3 percent). Hydrogen and oxygen occur mainly in the form of water (H_2O), which makes up about 60 percent of your mass. Use the values given to produce a circle graph that shows the chemical composition of your body. What percentage is made up by the other 31 elements not named?

Pause& —**Reflect**

In addition to words, the equation of photosynthesis uses chemical symbols and formulas. Which ones do you recognize? You will learn how to read and write equations like this in Chapter 5.

The Chemistry of Photosynthesis

Carbon dioxide gas dissolves in water to form a weak solution of carbonic acid. How might you use this fact to test for the presence or absence of carbon dioxide in the environment?

Problem

How can you demonstrate that plants absorb carbon dioxide?

Safety Precautions

- Follow your teacher's directions for conducting investigations safely.
- Wear appropriate safety equipment in the laboratory.
- Never taste or eat any material in the laboratory.
- Clean any spills immediately.

Apparatus

250 mL beaker
2 test tubes
2 rubber test tube stoppers
test tube rack
bench lamp
battery jar (optional)

Materials

water
phenol red solution
drinking straw
2 fresh sprigs of water plant
(*Rotela* or similar species)
black paper
masking tape

Procedure

1 Fill the beaker with water, and add three drops of phenol red. This indicator is red when the pH is 7 or higher (basic) and yellow when the pH is less than 7 (acidic).

2 Using the drinking straw, gently blow into the solution until the indicator just changes colour. **Caution:** Ensure that you blow out gently and are wearing your safety goggles.

3 Fill two test tubes with the solution.

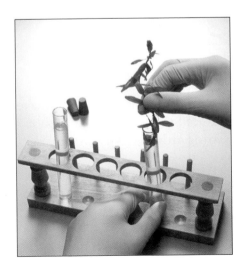

4 Add a sprig of the plant to each test tube. Seal each test tube with a stopper.

5 Tape a piece of black paper around one test tube so that no light can enter.

6 Place both test tubes in bright light for 15 to 20 min. If possible, place a battery jar filled with water between the test tubes and the lamp to absorb any heat that is given off by the lamp.

7 Record your observations. If there is no colour change, gently agitate both test tubes for a few seconds.

8 Wash your hands after completing this investigation.

Analyze

1. What gas did you add to the solution using the straw?

2. Why did this gas produce a colour change in the indicator?

3. Describe what colour changes you observed in each test tube.

4. Explain your observations, with reference to the equation for photosynthesis on page 43.

Conclude and Apply

5. Did this investigation have a control? If so, identify it. If not, suggest what control you would set up, and why.

6. How does this investigation demonstrate stages of the carbon cycle? To answer, make a simple sketch showing the flow of carbon that you observed.

Extend Your Skills and Knowledge

7. **Design Your Own** This investigation shows that plants absorb carbon dioxide for photosynthesis. Design an investigation to show that plants produce oxygen. **Note:** For tips on designing an experiment, refer to Science and Science Inquiry on page 000.

8. Knowledge of the photosynthesis reaction was built up gradually by different scientists over many years. Conduct research to find out the contributions of two of the following scientists. Write a brief report on each scientist's discovery, stating how it helped us understand photosynthesis.
   - Jan Baptista van Helmont (1577–1644)
   - Jan Ingenhousz (1730 –1799)
   - Joseph Priestley (1733–1804)
   - Jean Senebier (1742–1809)
   - Nicolas de Saussure (1767–1845)
   - Julius von Sachs (1832–1897)

DidYouKnow?

The equation for photosynthesis seems simple. In fact, to produce a sugar molecule such as sucrose, a plant requires nearly 30 distinct proteins that must carry out a complex set of physical and chemical reactions in a co-ordinated manner.

Skill POWER

For tips on how to organize and communicate scientific results, turn to page 599.

Photosynthesis, Cellular Respiration, and the Atmosphere

Photosynthesis is one stage of the **carbon cycle.** During photosynthesis, plants "capture" carbon from the atmosphere (as carbon dioxide) and combine it with water to make carbohydrates. Some of the carbon in the carbohydrate molecules is later used by the plants to build other carbon-containing compounds, such as fats and proteins. When consumers eat the plants, the carbon compounds are broken down and recombined to build animal tissues. In this way, carbon is moved through food chains, from species to species. Carbon, which is supplied by the air around us, is an important part of the structure of all living things.

Carbon dioxide makes up only 0.03 percent (by volume) of Earth's atmosphere. If plants absorb carbon dioxide during photosynthesis, why is this gas not eventually used up? There must be another process that returns the carbon dioxide to the atmosphere. Can you think of this process?

Recall that all living cells carry out a process called **cellular respiration.** It can be summarized by the following equation.

$$6O_2 \;+\; C_6H_{12}O_6 \longrightarrow 6CO_2 \;+\; 6H_2O \;+\; \text{energy}$$

oxygen   carbohydrate   carbon   water
dioxide

Compare this equation with the equation for photosynthesis, on page 43. How are they similar? Notice that photosynthesis uses carbon dioxide and produces oxygen, while cellular respiration uses oxygen and produces carbon dioxide. Together, these two processes form the two halves of the carbon cycle. In the carbon cycle, carbon and oxygen move back and forth between living things and their surrounding environment. Figure 2.4 shows the carbon cycle for a terrestrial ecosystem. Remember that only producers carry out photosynthesis, but *all* organisms, including producers, carry out cellular respiration.

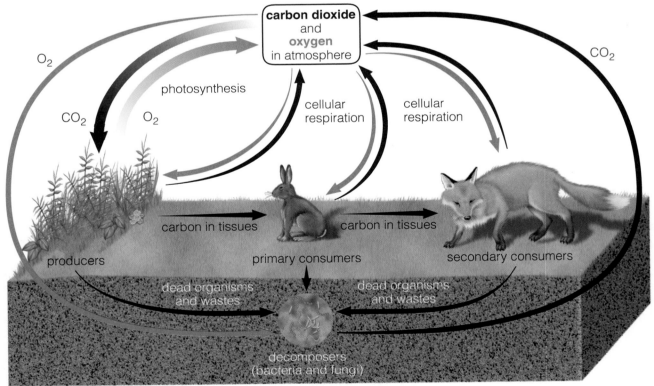

Figure 2.4 Photosynthesis and cellular respiration are the two key processes that drive the carbon cycle.

Cellular respiration breaks apart the energy-rich carbohydrate molecules in cells and releases the carbon, as carbon dioxide, back into the surrounding air or water. There it can be used once again for photosynthesis. When organisms die, however, a lot of carbon remains in their bodies. Carbon is also found in the solid and liquid waste that is released by animals. How does the carbon from these sources enter the carbon cycle? Recall, from Chapter 1, what happens to dead and waste materials in ecosystems. Decomposers, such as bacteria and fungi, use these materials as food. The carbon is released when the decomposers carry out cellular respiration.

Disrupting the Carbon Cycle

Over the centuries, the amount of carbon dioxide produced by cellular respiration has tended to equal the amount of carbon dioxide absorbed for photosynthesis. Thus the level of carbon dioxide in the atmosphere has remained fairly constant over Earth as a whole. This balance can be changed, however, if large amounts of carbon are removed from or added to parts of the carbon cycle. Figure 2.5 shows how this happened during the **Carboniferous Period.**

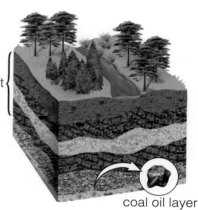

sediment

coal oil layer

A About 300 million years ago, vast areas of swamp became filled with decaying plant material.

B The plant material was buried under thick layers of sediment. Because there was no oxygen beneath these layers, the plant material could not be broken down by decomposers. As a result, a large amount of carbon was locked up in the ground.

C Over millions of years, the plant matter was compressed under the heavy layers of sediment and converted into coal and oil (also known as fossil fuels).

Figure 2.5 Coal is formed from ancient plant matter.

What happens to the carbon in coal and oil when we burn coal and oil as fuel? What effect does this have on the atmosphere? What effect does it have on the carbon cycle? In the next investigation, you will answer these questions by graphing and analyzing data, and conducting background research.

Figure 2.6 About 12 percent of Canada's domestic energy (1998) is produced by burning coal.

The Carbon Cycle and Climate

Think About It

The combustion (burning) of fossil fuels releases a number of gases, including carbon dioxide. From 1850 to 1990, the production of carbon dioxide from the combustion of fossil fuels increased about 500 times. In this investigation, you will compare changes in the production of carbon dioxide by combustion with changes in the concentration of carbon dioxide in the atmosphere, and with changes in the average global temperature.

What to Do

1 Write a hypothesis about the effect of fossil fuel combustion on levels of CO_2 in the atmosphere.

2 Based on what you already know about the *greenhouse effect*, write a second hypothesis about the effect of increased CO_2 levels on average global temperatures.

3 Use the data in the table below to make three separate line graphs, showing the relationship between

(a) year and CO_2 production

(b) year and CO_2 concentration in the atmosphere

(c) year and average global temperature change

Note: CO_2 concentration in the atmosphere is given in parts per million (ppm).

4 Describe the pattern of changes over time in

(a) the quantity of CO_2 produced by burning fossil fuels

(b) the concentration of atmospheric CO_2

(c) average global temperature change

Use terms such as "trend," "increase," "decrease," "constant," "random," and "cyclic."

CO_2 Levels and Average Global Temperature Change

Year	CO_2 production ($\times 10^9$ t)	CO_2 concentration in the atmosphere (ppm)	Temperature increase since 1850 (°C)
1850	0.01	286	0.00
1870	0.02	292	0.00
1890	0.04	298	0.05
1910	0.09	300	0.13
1930	1.20	305	0.46
1950	1.80	310	0.47
1970	4.10	320	0.23
1990	5.00	340	0.58

Skill
POWER

For tips on how to make a line graph, turn to page 602.

Analyze

1. Do the patterns of changes support or falsify each of your two hypotheses? Explain.

Extend Your Knowledge and Skills

2. To see relationships among variables more easily, all the data can be plotted on a single graph. Decide how you would do this, and then make your graph. How does your graph help you interpret the data?

3. Climate is the result of complex interactions among Earth's atmosphere, land, oceans, and organisms. Most scientists agree that CO_2 and other gases are affecting the climate. However, some critics have argued that the greenhouse effect is oversimplified. They claim that the data may be explained in other ways. Some of the ideas and arguments used in the debate are listed below. Read through the list, then use your local library and/or the Internet to research the ideas and arguments.
   - Similar trends in two measurements does not mean that one causes the other.
   - There is evidence that the quantity of atmospheric CO_2 has varied over geological time. How was the evidence obtained?
   - Historical temperature data are distorted by the locations of the measuring instruments.
   - Satellite data are providing more detailed information about climate trends.
   - Changes in temperature have produced changes in the distribution of vegetation, deserts, and glaciers, as well as changes in ocean currents and sea levels.
   - Gases other than CO_2 also contribute to the greenhouse effect.
   - Can increased growth of vegetation (forests) or increased absorption of CO_2 in ocean water compensate for increased CO_2 levels in the atmosphere?
   - Are the effects of human activities on the atmosphere and climate significant compared with long-term natural trends, such as those that have produced past ice ages?
   - Is CO_2 a pollutant or a natural compound that is essential for photosynthesis?
   - CO_2 forms only about 0.03 percent of the atmosphere. This is not very much to worry about, even if it increases by one third.
   - An increase of only one or two degrees in average temperature is not very significant.
   - A changing climate will create major changes in human society within the next 100 years.

   Form small groups to debate both sides of the issue. Does your group think there is good evidence that the combustion of fossil fuel is causing an increase in average global temperatures? Prepare a summary of your group's findings and conclusions. Include as many of the ideas listed above as possible, stating why you agree or disagree with each.

4. Make a list of all the activities you do and resources you use that produce carbon dioxide. How could you change your lifestyle to help reverse the increasing production of carbon dioxide?

Computer CONNECT

Enter the data in the table into a spreadsheet, and generate your graphs using a software program.

INTERNET CONNECT

www.school.mcgrawhill.ca/resources/

Data about climate change may be presented in many different ways, which can lead to very different conclusions. In order to assess the relationships among variables correctly, you need to be able to interpret the data properly. To examine data on climate change, visit the web site above. Go to **Science Resources**, then to **SCIENCEPOWER 10** to know where to go next. Study the data you find, and draw your own conclusions. Consider how the data are presented, and why. Do the conclusions given agree with your conclusions?

Waterworld

Living on land, we tend to focus on the importance of air in the carbon cycle. Much of the carbon cycle, however, takes place in aquatic ecosystems. In fact, the world's oceans and lakes hold over 50 times as much carbon dioxide as the atmosphere does. Carbon dioxide readily dissolves at the surface of the water to form carbonic acid, which water plants use as their source of carbon (see Figure 2.7).

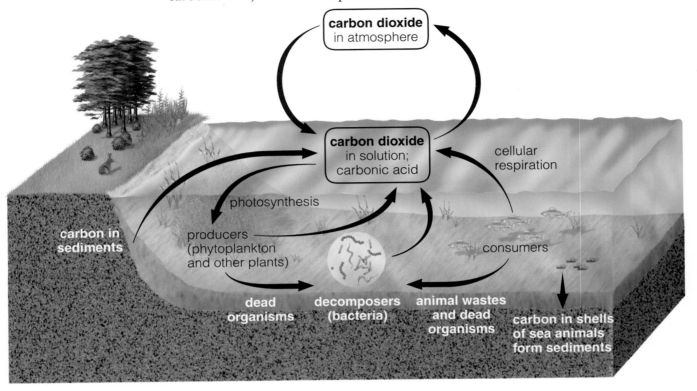

Figure 2.7 The carbon cycle for an aquatic ecosystem

Figure 2.8 Many sea animals, such as these snails, have shells that are made of calcium carbonate.

An estimated 100 billion tonnes of carbon dioxide from the air dissolve in the oceans each year. A slightly smaller amount comes out of solution at the surface of the water and returns to the atmosphere. The oceans also remove some carbon from the cycle. How does this happen? Think of the multitude of sea animals that have shells: for example, crabs, barnacles, corals, and microscopic plankton (Figure 2.8). A chief ingredient of their shells is calcium carbonate — a combination of carbon, calcium, and oxygen. When these animals die, their shells sink to the ocean floor and form thick layers that eventually harden into sedimentary rock. The carbon in this sedimentary rock may return to the cycle millions of years later. Geological forces can push the rocks to the surface, where they are slowly weathered by rain, run-off, and wind.

Tools of Science

Worldwide, the activities of humans release about 7 billion tonnes of carbon per year. Of that amount, 3 billion tonnes remain in the atmosphere and 2 billion tonnes are absorbed into the oceans. What about the other 2 billion tonnes? Scientists thought it was absorbed by land vegetation, but they were not sure. Finding an answer took the co-operation of many scientists.

The Boreal Ecosystem-Atmosphere Study (BOREAS) was a project that involved 85 science teams from five nations. The science teams selected two large regions of boreal (northern) forest in Manitoba and Saskatchewan to study. Using sophisticated sensing equipment, they collected data from the forest floor and from towers

CO_2 measuring instruments high above the canopy of the boreal forest

standing high above the forest canopy. They also collected data from remote sensors aboard aircraft and satellites. They measured such variables as soil temperature and moisture, the amount of CO_2 released from the forest floor, and the amount of cloud cover.

The scientists estimated that trees living in the boreal forest contain about 13 percent of the world's carbon. As well, the soil there, which contains a large amount of fallen leaves and spruce needles, holds about 43 percent of the world's carbon that is stored in soil. Further calculations show that the boreal forest has been building up an average of 0.6 billion tonnes of carbon per year for the last 7000 years!

Check Your Understanding

1. What three elements are carbohydrates made from?

2. Make a table with two columns. In the first column, list the processes that add CO_2 to the atmosphere. In the second column, list the processes that remove CO_2 from the atmosphere.

3. What are the reactants (left-hand side) in the equation for photosynthesis? What are the products (right-hand side)?

4. What are the reactants in the equation for cellular respiration? What are the products?

5. **Apply** What actions could you take yourself to help reduce the CO_2 levels in the atmosphere?

6. **Thinking Critically** The CO_2 levels in Biosphere II (described at the beginning of the chapter) decreased each day and increased each night. Suggest an explanation for this pattern. Why do carbon dioxide levels not fluctuate in the same way in Earth's atmosphere?

7. **Thinking Critically** Explain how extensive deforestation could increase average global temperatures.

2.3 The Nitrogen Cycle

Two neighbours enjoy growing plants. Their gardens have similar soil and receive the same amounts of sunshine and water. Neighbour A, however, always produces more flowers and vegetables than neighbour B. Neighbour A's plants grow faster and larger, as well. What do you think causes these differences between the two gardens?

Figure 2.9 How do the wildflowers, grasses, and trees in this meadow get their food?

You might guess that the secret of neighbour A's success is fertilizer. What exactly is fertilizer? Why does it make plants grow faster and larger? One of the main ingredients of fertilizer is nitrogen. After carbon, oxygen, and hydrogen, nitrogen is the most common element found in living things. It is an essential part of proteins, DNA, and other compounds. Like carbon, nitrogen passes along food chains and circulates between the biotic and abiotic parts of the environment. In this section, you will discover how plants obtain nitrogen. You will also discover how human activities, such as fertilizer use, affect the nitrogen cycle. In the next investigation, you will measure the effects of a fertilizer on plant growth and analyze the chemical ingredients in the fertilizer.

Fertilizers and Plant Growth

Does more fertilizer always produce more growth in plants? In this investigation, you will compare the growth of algae that are given different amounts of fertilizer.

Problem

How does fertilizer affect plant growth?

Safety Precautions

- To avoid skin irritation, use rubber gloves when handling fertilizers.
- Follow your teacher's instructions to dispose of fertilizers.
- Clean any spills immediately, and inform your teacher.

Apparatus

balance
scoopula
50 mL graduated cylinder
small funnel

Materials

5 plastic bottles, such as 2 L soft-drink bottles
fertilizer that contains nitrogen
algae culture
distilled water
adhesive labels
marker

Procedure

1 Number the bottles 1 through 5.

2 Add 1 L of distilled water to each bottle.

3 Add 1 g of fertilizer to bottle 1. Add 3 g of fertilizer to bottle 2. Add 5 g of fertilizer to bottle 3. Add 10 g of fertilizer to bottle 4. Bottle 5 is the control, so nothing is added.

4 Gently swirl the contents of each bottle to dissolve the fertilizer.

5 After the fertilizer has dissolved, add 10 mL of algae culture to each bottle.

6 Set the open bottles in a bright location, and observe them over the next few days. Record your observations.

7 Wash your hands after completing this investigation.

Analyze

1. Which bottle showed the greatest change in the growth of the algae? Which showed the least change?

2. From your observations, write a general statement about the effect of fertilizer on plant growth.

Conclude and Apply

3. Read the ingredients on the labels of several different containers of fertilizer. Which three elements are present in the largest amounts?

4. Suppose that a large quantity of fertilizer were added to a lake ecosystem. Suggest what might happen to the populations of
   (a) producers
   (b) consumers
   (c) decomposers

5. A farm has a pond at the bottom of a sloping meadow where cows graze. Explain why the pond water turns green in the spring.

Nitrogen Fixation

Figure 2.10 Nitrogen-fixing bacteria live in the round nodules on the roots of this legume.

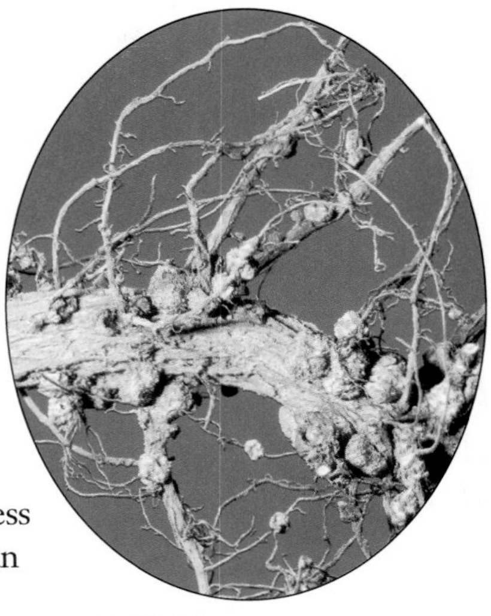

You have learned that plants use nitrogen (N), phosphorus (P), and potassium (K) for growth. These three elements are the main ingredients of commercial fertilizers. How do plants obtain their nitrogen if they are not given fertilizer? Earth's atmosphere is nearly 80 percent nitrogen gas, but most organisms cannot absorb nitrogen directly from the air. In order to be used by organisms, nitrogen atoms (like carbon atoms) must first be "fixed": that is, pulled from the air and bonded to other elements to make new compounds. This process is called **nitrogen fixation.** For example, nitrogen can combine with hydrogen or oxygen to form ions such as ammonium (NH_4^+) and nitrate (NO_3^-). You will learn more about these ions in Chapter 5. Plants then absorb these compounds through their roots. Animals can obtain nitrogen only by eating plants or other animals.

DidYouKnow?

A second, minor source of natural nitrogen fixation is lightning. A lightning flash has extremely high energy. This energy allows nitrogen to react with oxygen in the atmosphere to form nitrates. The nitrates dissolve in atmospheric moisture and fall to Earth in precipitation.

In nature, the job of nitrogen fixation is carried out by a few species of **nitrogen-fixing bacteria** that live in the soil or water. The most important of these bacteria, named *Rhizobia*, live in the nodules (rounded swellings) on the roots of legumes, such as peas, beans, alfalfa, and clover (see Figure 2.10). Before the development of artificial fertilizers, farmers planted legumes in their fields to help restore the fertility of the soil. It is estimated that a legume crop may add as much as 300 to 350 kg of nitrogen per hectare per year to the soil.

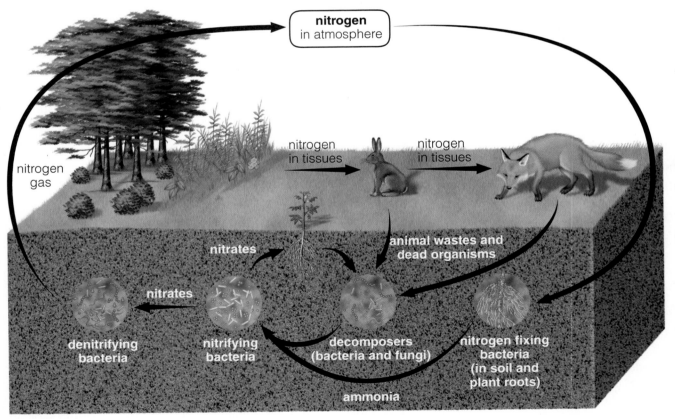

Figure 2.11 The nitrogen cycle in a terrestrial ecosystem

After nitrogen from the atmosphere has been fixed, it enters the soil and water. There it is available for living organisms to use. The nitrogen compounds that enter plants move through food chains and return to the soil and water through dead organisms and waste materials. These compounds can re-enter plants without ever being converted back into gaseous nitrogen. This route forms a subcycle in the larger nitrogen cycle, shown in Figure 2.11. Notice the importance of bacteria, which convert nitrogen-containing compounds at different stages of the cycle. Without these bacteria, the cycle could not continue and other forms of life could not survive.

Figure 2.12 shows the nitrogen cycle in an aquatic ecosystem. Here nitrogen fixation is carried out by cyanobacteria, also known as blue-green algae. How are the two ecosystems, in Figures 2.11 and 2.12, related? How might fixed nitrogen from the land enter the ocean?

Pause&
Reflect

Imagine you did not know that materials such as carbon and nitrogen move through the environment in cycles. What everyday observations might lead you to infer that they do? Think of one example to suggest that materials

(a) pass into organisms from the abiotic part of the environment

(b) pass from one organism to another

(c) pass into the abiotic part of the environment from organisms

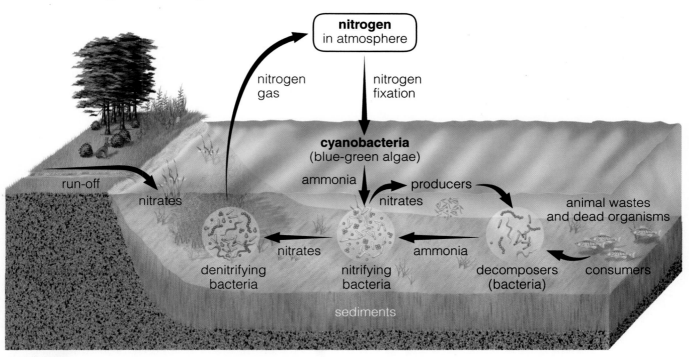

Figure 2.12 The nitrogen cycle in an aquatic ecosystem

Nitrification

Like other elements in the bodies of organisms, nitrogen is returned to the ecosystem through animal wastes and dead organisms. Decomposers, such as bacteria, break down the waste and dead materials. One of the products of this decomposition is ammonia. Have you ever smelled ammonia? It is the chemical that produces the pungent odour in a cat litter box, chicken coop, or outhouse. Ammonia is used directly by some plants as a source of nitrogen. As well, ammonia is converted back into nitrates by **nitrifying bacteria,** in a process called **nitrification.** To complete the larger cycle, the nitrates in the soil or water may be converted back into nitrogen gas by **denitrifying bacteria.** This process involves a series of chemical changes, called **denitrification.**

DidYou**Know**?

Nitrifying bacteria live in a great variety of soils, oceans, brackish water, rivers, lakes, mud, and sewage disposal systems. In some environments, such as the layers of dead leaves on a forest floor, most nitrification is carried out by fungi rather than bacteria.

Altering the Balance

abiotic environment

animal wastes and dead organisms

living organisms

Figure 2.13 Movement of an element through a typical nutrient cycle

Think of the events that happen in a store. At any one time, some people will be entering the store, some will be inside selecting items to buy, some will be paying for their items, and some will be leaving the store. What if something happens to change the balance of this cycle? Perhaps a work crew closes part of the store for renovation. Perhaps there is a giant sale, and more people than usual arrive at the same time. Perhaps a problem with the computerized cash registers slows the checkout process. Any of these things might disrupt the system and increase the overall time that people spend in the store. Other events might have the opposite effect, speeding up the flow of people through the store.

You can think about an element moving through a nutrient cycle in the same way. At any one time, some of the element is in living organisms, some is in dead organisms and waste matter, and some is in the abiotic part of the environment. In a normal cycle, the rates of movement from one part of the cycle to another are balanced. What might happen if an outside influence altered part of the cycle? You have already considered the effect of adding extra nitrogen (in a fertilizer) to a system. The immediate result is increased plant growth. How might this result, in turn, affect subsequent stages in the cycle?

What Is Organic Farming?

Some people prefer to buy foods that are labelled "organic." What are organically grown foods? How does the production of fruits and vegetables on an organic farm differ from the production on a conventional farm? How do these two methods of farming relate to balanced and unbalanced cycles?

What to Do

1. In a small group, research organically grown foods. Where are the foods produced? How are they produced? Are artificial fertilizers used on organic farms? Are other sources of nutrients used? You might like to devise tests to compare samples of organically grown foods with samples of non-organically grown foods, using such variables as appearance, taste, and cost.

2. Present a brief report of your findings to the class.

What Did You Discover?

1. Name a source of nitrates that is commonly used in organic farming.

Science Inquiry ACTIVITY

2. Explain why an organic farm could operate as a closed system, while a conventional farm could not.

3. Give two examples of ways in which organic farming reduces pollution of the soil.

4. Suggest why there is a difference in the prices of foods produced by organic farming and conventional farming.

5. What might be the health benefits of eating organically grown foods?

6. Define organic farming in your own words.

Human Impacts on the Nitrogen Cycle

Most wild plant species are adapted to thrive in the low levels of nitrogen that are usually found in soils and water. Until the early twentieth century, the supply of nitrates for plants was determined by natural processes alone. All that changed, however, when scientists developed an industrial method of fixing nitrogen and used it to manufacture artificial fertilizers. The production of artificial fertilizers soared during the second half of the twentieth century. Farmers around the world used artificial fertilizers to grow more crops for a rapidly expanding human population (see Figure 2.14). At the end of the twentieth century, the amount of nitrogen being fixed each year to make fertilizers was estimated as over half the amount being fixed in nature by micro-organisms (see Table 2.1). At the same time, expanded areas of farmland were being used to grow legume crops as a way of adding more nitrates to the soil.

Farming methods are not the only means by which people affect the nitrogen cycle. When fossil fuels are burned, the nitrogen they contain is released into the air as nitrogen compounds. Eventually these compounds dissolve in moisture in the air and fall back to Earth. Modern farming, the combustion of fossil fuels, and other human activities now move about 140 million tonnes of extra nitrogen through the environment each year. The result is nitrogen overload. More nitrogen is being added to the environment than ecosystems can absorb and use. The next few pages describe some of the effects of nitrogen overload on the world's soils, water, atmosphere, and organisms. You may want to use this information in the activity that follows.

Figure 2.14 In many parts of the world, artificial fertilizers add excess nitrogen to the environment.

Table 2.1 Global Volumes of Fixed Nitrogen

Source	Estimated amount of nitrogen fixed per year (millions of tonnes)
natural*	
micro-organisms	90–140
lightning	5–10
human	
legume crops	32–53
artificial fertilizer	80

* before the widespread planting of legume crops

Effects on the Soil

If a little fertilizer produces larger tomatoes, will a lot of fertilizer produce tomatoes the size of basketballs? As you may have discovered in an earlier activity, there are limits to how much plant growth can be increased by adding more nitrates. With a surplus of nitrogen, plant growth soon becomes limited by the scarcity of other resources, such as phosphorus, calcium, and water. The plants are unable to use more nitrogen, and further additions of fertilizer to the ecosystem produce "nitrogen saturation." When this occurs, excess nitrogen washes from the soil into streams or ground water without being absorbed by organisms.

Nitrogen saturation is a particular problem in northern Europe, where nitrogen fertilizers are used more heavily than in North America. It can affect forests as well as farmers' fields. Extra nitrogen in forest soils damages tree roots, stunts tree growth, and causes needles on spruce trees and other conifers to turn yellow and fall. These effects are due to a series of chemical changes that increase soil acidity.

Pause&
Reflect

In Chapter 1, you learned how the productivity of an ecosystem varies with climate. How might the productivity vary with nutrient levels? In which ecosystems would you expect very high or very low nutrient levels?

The acidic soil, in turn, begins to dissolve toxic metals, such as aluminum. The toxic metals cause further damage to roots and soil organisms. For example, aluminum may kill **mycorrhizal fungi** that live with roots and help trees absorb essential minerals (see Figure 2.15).

Figure 2.15 This photograph compares the growth rate of a soybean plant that does not have mycorrhizal fungi with two other plants that have mycorrhizal fungi.

Figure 2.16 The combustion of fossil fuels is a major source of nitrogen-containing gases.

Effects on the Atmosphere

Nitrogen-containing gases spew from industrial smokestacks, power plants, and vehicle exhausts. When these gases dissolve in moisture in the air, they form nitric acid. This is a component of **acid precipitation**, which includes rain or snow with higher acid levels than precipitation from unpolluted skies. During the 1970s, acid precipitation became a major problem over large areas of forests and lakes in eastern Canada. Scientists have estimated that acid precipitation has damaged about 150 000 lakes in eastern Canada. About 14 000 of these lakes are known to be acidified. This means that the acid in the water has killed fish, birds, amphibians, and other organisms.

Many scientists believe that acid precipitation has been responsible for the loss of sugar maple trees in southern Ontario and Québec. Nitric acid destroys the waxy outer layer (cuticle) of maple leaves. This layer helps to protect the trees from disease (see Figure 2.17). As well, the acid hinders tree growth by drawing essential nutrients from the soil. Sugar maple forests in Québec have been severely damaged, thus reducing harvests of maple sugar.

The global release of nitrogen-containing gases from automobiles, industries, and artificial fertilizers is about 80 million tonnes per year. In 1996 Canada and the United States

Figure 2.17 These maple leaves show damage by acid precipitation.

agreed to reduce their emissions from industries by 10 percent by the year 2000. As well, they aimed to reduce nitrogen emissions from cars built in and before 1998 by 60 percent. Despite their efforts, acid precipitation continues to be a major environmental problem, and many lakes remain acidified. The only solution, at the present time, is to add large quantities of powdered limestone to the water to neutralize the acid (see Figure 2.18).

Figure 2.18 This aircraft is dumping powdered limestone into an acidified lake.

Effects on Fresh-Water Ecosystems

In the 1970s, many lakes and streams became choked by the rapid growth of algae and weeds. The increase in plant growth was due to nitrates from fertilizers and phosphates from detergents. These chemicals had washed into waterways from farms and cities. Nitrogen-containing wastes in sewage have the same effect. The buildup of nutrients in an aquatic ecosystem is called **eutrophication.** How might an increase in the population of producers disrupt an aquatic ecosystem? Study Figure 2.19 to understand the process of eutrophication.

A Run-off carries nitrates from farms and cities into water systems.

B An increased growth of plants on the surface of the water blocks sunlight from penetrating to deeper waters.

C Plants below the surface are unable to carry out photosynthesis. They begin to die and therefore stop producing oxygen.

D As the plants die, the population of decomposers explodes, feeding on the extra decaying matter. The decomposers cause a further decline in oxygen levels through their cellular respiration.

E The altered conditions kill fish and other animals that require high oxygen levels.

Figure 2.19 Too many nutrients in a water system leads to eutrophication, causing an abundance of algal growth.

INTERNET CONNECT

www.school.mcgrawhill.ca/resources/

Lake Erie is a well-known example of a eutrophic lake. Large algal mats, up to 1 m thick, were once common along its beaches. Much of the lake bottom became deficient in oxygen, and fish began to die. Today the quality of the water is much improved. To find out about the eutrophication of Lake Erie, go to the web site above. Go to **Science Resources**, then to **SCIENCEPOWER 10** to know where to go next. Why is Lake Erie particularly vulnerable to eutrophication? What was done to make the clean-up of this lake successful? What problems have yet to be resolved? What were the environmental impacts of both the entrophication and the clean up? Also, how were local communities affected? Present your findings in an essay. In your essay, include a diagram of the nitrogen cycle and show how it was altered.

DidYouKnow?

A huge area of oxygen-depleted seawater is located in the Gulf of Mexico at the mouth of the Mississippi River. This area, known as the "dead zone," is about 18 000 km² in size. It is the result of excess nitrates in run-off from sewage and fertilizers. Some of the run-off may have originated as far away as the U.S. Midwest.

Nitrates can cause direct problems to human health when they occur in drinking water. This is a particular risk in rural areas, where nitrates from fields seep down through the soil into the ground water. Most rural residents obtain their drinking water from wells that are sunk into the ground. In the stomach, especially the stomach of an infant, nitrates are converted to nitrites. Nitrites reduce the blood's ability to carry oxygen and produce a form of anemia.

Effects on Marine Ecosystems

Scientists have found high levels of nitrogen in seawater off the west coast of Europe. They estimate that the total dissolved nitrogen, carried by rivers entering the North Atlantic Ocean, has increased 6 to 20 times since the 1950s. Most of this increase can be traced to the increased use of fertilizers and to atmospheric pollution by nitrogen-containing gases. How do you think the increased nitrogen has affected coastal marine fisheries? What impact would this have on local communities?

The added nitrates initially create a population explosion of algae in the warm surface waters (see Figure 2.20). This is called an **algal bloom.** As the algae die, they sink down to cooler waters. There they are broken down by bacteria. The process of decomposition uses the oxygen in the deeper, cold seawater. Because there is little mixing between warm and cold layers of seawater, the area near the sea floor may eventually contain little or even no dissolved oxygen. The lack of oxygen causes the death of many oxygen-requiring organisms that live in this area. The reduced life in deeper waters has an effect throughout neighbouring food chains. Algal blooms are becoming more common, for at least part of the year, in many estuaries and coastal seas on both sides of the Atlantic Ocean. They have caused significant losses of fish and shellfish.

Figure 2.20 This algal bloom along Canada's Atlantic coast is called a "red tide."

An Acid Test

Do you have acid precipitation in your neighbourhood? How could you reduce the effects of acid precipitation in a lake? You will design your own tests to answer these questions in Part 1 of this investigation. In Part 2, you will observe the effects of pH on the growth of a yeast culture. PH is a measure of acidity. You will learn more about pH in Unit 2.

Part 1
Testing Acidity

Problem

How does the pH of rainwater in your community compare with the pH of some other liquids?

Safety Precautions

- You will be working with hazardous liquids. Wear safety equipment to protect your skin, eyes, and clothing. Some of the chemicals are irritants or very corrosive.
- If you get any chemical on your skin or clothes, rinse the area with plenty of water.
- Immediately inform your teacher of any spills.
- Follow your teacher's instructions for the safe clean-up of spills.

Apparatus
test tubes
test tube rack

Materials
universal pH indicator
pH scale
rainwater
tap water
distilled water
household bleach
vinegar
lemon juice
soda water
window cleaner
dilute sodium hydroxide solution
dilute hydrochloric acid solution
labels
marker

Procedure

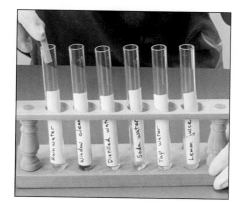

❶ Work in a small group. Different groups may collect their own samples of rainwater and tap water for comparison.

❷ Make a prediction about the pH level of each of the liquids listed.

❸ Determine the pH of each liquid.

❹ Make a table to compare the liquids. How will you organize the data?

❺ Mix 5 mL of the liquid that has the highest pH with 5 mL of the liquid that has the lowest pH. Determine the pH of the new mixture.

❻ Wash your hands after completing this investigation.

Analyze

1. How did your predictions compare with the actual pH of each liquid?

2. Unpolluted rainwater has a pH of 5.6. Is your local rainwater more acidic than this? If so, carry out research to find which sources of pollution might be responsible.

3. Distilled water, which contains no CO_2, has a pH of 7.0. It is neither acidic nor alkaline (basic). Why is unpolluted rainwater slightly acidic?

Conclude and Apply

4. What does the term "neutralization" mean? Why might acid precipitation be less of a problem in lakes where the surrounding rock is made of limestone (calcium carbonate)?

5. How might you reduce the effects of acid precipitation in a lake?

CONTINUED ▶

Part 2

pH and Population Growth

Problem

How do variations in pH affect the growth of yeast?

Safety Precautions

Handle the hot plate with care to avoid burns.

Apparatus

microscope	7 test tubes
microscope slides	balance
cover slips	thermometer
100 mL graduated cylinder	100 mL beaker hot plate

Materials

yeast culture
water
dilute acid solution
dilute base solution
sugar
labels

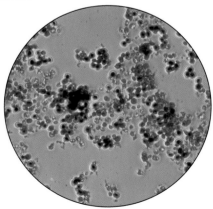

yeast cells

Skill
P O W E R

For tips on how to sample a population, turn to page 595.

Procedure

1. Work in a small group. Measure 100 mL of water into the beaker. Place the beaker on the hot place, and bring the water temperature to 30°C. **CAUTION:** Handle the hot plate with care.

2. Add 3 g of sugar and 0.5 g of yeast. Stir well.

3. Prepare seven test tubes with a pH range of 2 to 8. Label each test tube.

4. Add 10 mL of yeast culture to each test tube. Allow the test tubes to sit for 24 h.

5. Devise a sampling technique to estimate the relative population density of yeast in each test tube. Examine each sample under the microscope. Record your results.

6. Make a graph that shows the relationship between population density and pH.

7. Wash your hands after completing this investigation.

Analyze

1. At what pH did the yeast population show the most growth? At what pH did it show the least growth?

Conclude and Apply

2. The graph shows changes in the populations of various aquatic organisms in Canadian lakes and rivers in relation to pH levels. Study the graph, and answer the questions.

   (a) Which organisms appear to be most sensitive to acid conditions? Which are least sensitive?

   (b) Why might the population of a species of fish that is tolerant of high acid levels still decline in an acidified lake?

   (c) "When fish start dying, the damage has already been done." From the information on the graph, explain why you agree or disagree with this statement. Which species might be better used as an early warning of acid damage in lakes?

3. From your results, and the data presented, make a general statement about the effects of acid precipitation on organisms.

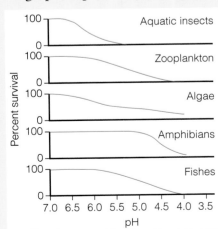

Effects on Biodiversity

Biodiversity is a measure of the variety of species on Earth. Most commonly, it is thought of as the variety of different species in an ecosystem. Biodiversity is not the same everywhere on Earth. What conditions do you think would result in high biodiversity? What conditions would result in low biodiversity?

As a rule, biodiversity is reduced by extreme conditions. For example, there tend to be fewer species in areas that are very hot, very cold, very dry, or very acidic. Very high levels of nutrients also reduce biodiversity. This is because they benefit a few species but harm the majority. For example, when nitrogen fertilizers were added to grasslands, only a few grasses were able to take full advantage of the extra nitrogen to increase their growth. These grasses became dominant (most numerous), while many other grasses and plants became rare or disappeared. In experiments, fields that were given the highest levels of nitrates had a five-fold decline in the number of plant species. Fewer plant species cause a decrease in the number of species of animals and micro-organisms that depend on them.

In fresh-water ecosystems, biodiversity has been reduced by both acidification and eutrophication. Although fish vary in their sensitivity to pH, most acidified lakes across Scandinavia, Canada, and the northeastern United States have fewer species of fish than they once did. In eutrophic waters, one or two species of algae thrive in the high levels of nutrients while most plants and animals disappear.

Figure 2.21 Marsh ecosystems have high biodiversity.

Nutrient Cycles Today

You have learned that human activities have altered the carbon and nitrogen cycles in several important ways. The cycles have become unbalanced, resulting in changes to the abiotic and biotic parts of the environment. Using the information in this chapter, how might you illustrate the nutrient cycles to include the effects of human activities?

What to Do

1. Make two concept maps: one for the carbon cycle and another for the nitrogen cycle. Follow the guidelines below.
   (a) Include both terrestrial and aquatic ecosystems in your maps, as well as the activities of people.
   (b) Show how human activities have changed each cycle.
   (c) Indicate how the changes have affected the abiotic and biotic parts of the environment.
   (d) You may include photographs or diagrams on your maps.

Science Inquiry ACTIVITY

What Did You Discover?

1. What technologies have played a major role in changing these two cycles?

2. How might tropical rain forests affect the carbon cycle in Canada?

3. How might forests in Canada affect the nitrogen cycle in the tropics?

Extensions

4. Which countries do you think have the greatest impact on the carbon and nitrogen cycles? Explain you answer.

5. What is a "carbon sink?" Why are forests and oceans considered to be carbon sinks?

Skill

P O W E R

For tips on how to make a concept map, turn to page 578.

Be an Environmental Superhero

Environmental problems are not easily solved. Climate change and loss of biodiversity may seem to be beyond your power to affect in a significant way. You do not have to be a prime minister or the head of a giant corporation, however, to make a difference in the world. For instance, if you choose local, organic produce at a store instead of imported produce, you affect events that occur hundreds or thousands of kilometres away. Fields, fertilizers, tractors, and trucks are important parts of the system that brings foods to the store. If you use a bicycle instead of a car, you reduce your demand on mining and oil-drilling operations and lessen their effects on Earth's climate. You can be an environmental superhero by simply changing your habits.

What to Do

1. Review what you have learned about the carbon and nitrogen cycles.

2. Identify three ways in which you personally affect these cycles. Carry out additional research at your local library and/or on the Internet, if necessary.

3. Choose three new habits that are easy for you to adopt but affect the planet as a whole. For example, you could stop an activity that you once did or start a new activity. Each new habit should have a clear result that benefits the cycles of which you are a part.

4. Present your choices to the class, with explanations of their significance. How might your actions reduce the cost of producing resources? How might they affect others in your community? How would your habits benefit the environment? If you can persuade others to follow your ideas, you will indeed be an environmental superhero.

What Did You Discover?

1. Name a common activity that involves the combustion of fossil fuels.

2. Student A throws an apple core in a compost bin, and student B throws an apple core in a plastic garbage bag. Explain the effects that each student has on nutrient cycles.

3. List two resources and two activities that are used to produce a can of pop.

4. Explain how a cotton shirt in your local store might be linked to water pollution in another country.

Asking the Right Questions

Imagine that you have recently earned a degree or diploma in biology, specializing in lake ecosystems. You are interested in working in the field of fish biology and notice the following advertisement in your local newspaper.

JOBS IN FISH RESEARCH

The Canada Centre for Inland Waters is one of the world's leading centres for fresh-water research. Our biologists conduct environmental research and development. As well, they monitor the waters and ecology of the Great Lakes. Currently the centre has two job openings.

Fish Habitat Biologist

The successful candidate should have a Bachelor of Science degree in biology. Responsibilities include

- reviewing proposed lakeside building and development projects to assess whether they will have a negative impact on fish or fish habitats in the area
- making recommendations for changes to the proposed plans
- presenting reports of these assessments to the developers

Fisheries Technician

The successful candidate should have a diploma in wildlife studies from a community college. Responsibilities include

- carrying out field work, often as part of a team, to monitor existing fish populations and habitats
- gathering additional field data as assigned by the project biologist
- reporting findings to the project biologist and project leader

You have the qualifications and have applied for one of the positions above. How will you prepare for your interview? Think of five questions to ask your prospective employer. Remember that insightful questions can make you stand out from the other applicants. Discuss your questions with a partner.

Check Your Understanding

1. Why do living things need nitrogen?

2. Describe the role of nitrogen-fixing bacteria in the nitrogen cycle.

3. What is nitrification?

4. What is denitrification?

5. Describe two ways of adding nitrogen to soil without using artificial fertilizers.

6. Give one example of the impact of artificial fertilizers on
   (a) the atmosphere
   (b) lakes

7. **Thinking Critically** Make a concept map to show how farming might impact a local fishery. Identify the environmental concerns and who would be affected. How could both of these industries exist together successfully?

2.4 Closing the Loop

What do you do with old clothes and empty bottles? What happens to the waste water that you flush down the sink or the plastic food wrappers that you put in the garbage? Although we seem to throw away all our waste products, on planet Earth there is no "away." Like the inhabitants of a spacecraft, we live within a closed system. There is little or no exchange of materials with the outside.

Pause&
Reflect

Nutrient cycles involve the entire planet, but you can see evidence of these cycles on a much smaller scale — in a farmer's field, a park, a garden, or an aquarium. What evidence might help you conclude that nutrient cycles are operating? Think of five examples of nutrient cycles you have seen. Describe these examples in your notebook.

Figure 2.22 Earth is a single, isolated life-support system. There is no such place as "away."

INTERNET CONNECT

www.school.mcgrawhill.ca/resources/

How are satellites being used to monitor changes on Earth? Visit the web site above. Go to **Science Resources**, then to **SCIENCEPOWER 10** to know where to go next. Select a major satellite project to investigate. Who is involved in the project, and what data are being collected? How will these data help us understand and predict how Earth's environment is changing? Prepare a poster about the satellite project you have chosen. Present your findings to the class during a poster session.

To understand the global impact of human activities, scientists around the world are using satellites to measure and monitor changes in the atmosphere, water, soils, and living organisms.

The Canadian Space Agency has an advanced Earth-observation satellite called RADARSAT. It is being used to monitor water systems and land use, such as agriculture and forestry. The U.S. National Aeronautics and Space Administration (NASA) has a long-term project called *Earth Science Enterprise*. This project involves building a database of Earth's physical and biological features. Comparing yearly records will show changing trends in biodiversity, climate, and patterns of land use (such as expanding cities and deserts, and shrinking forests).

What Is Sustainability?

Sustainability is a concept, or idea. One way to understand a concept is to examine particular examples of it. For instance, the items in the diagram below are organized into two groups that illustrate a concept. To understand the concept, think of a way in which all the items in the "yes" group are similar to one another and different from all the items in the "no" group.

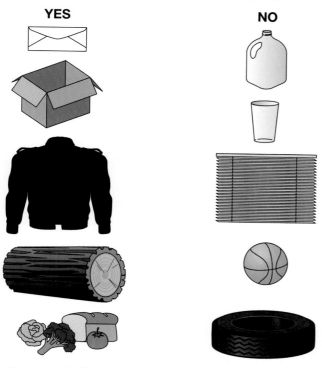

YES   **NO**

What concept is illustrated by these two groups of items?

One group of items is made of biodegradable materials that can be broken down by micro-organisms. The other group is made of non-biodegradable materials. Therefore the concept illustrated is biodegradability. In this investigation, you will illustrate the concept of sustainability.

Challenge

Design a poster to illustrate the concept of sustainability.

Materials

poster board   coloured markers

Design Criteria

A. Your poster will illustrate two categories of a human activity: one that is sustainable and one that is non-sustainable.

B. You may design your own illustrations or include illustrations from various sources, such as magazines. You may also use software to create a design on a computer.

C. Your group will have one class period to plan your design. Additional time will be provided to complete your project.

Plan and Construct

1 In your group, discuss the concept of sustainability. List specific examples of activities that you think are sustainable and activities that are not sustainable. For instance, if you have a bank account of $500 and you spend $10 each week, are your spending habits sustainable or non-sustainable over a period of one year? Include examples that relate to you alone, to your community, and to environmental resources.

2 Using your examples, develop a diagram to illustrate the concept of sustainability.

3 Be prepared to show an outline of your plan to your teacher.

Evaluate

1. Was your poster design similar to that of another group? If not, in what ways was it unique?

2. Were the two categories, "sustainable" and "non-sustainable," easy or difficult to distinguish?

3. As a class, discuss your results. Develop a definition of the concept of **sustainability.**

4. How can the concept of sustainability be used in your school?

Sustainable Development

Ecosystems are sustainable: that is, they perpetuate themselves indefinitely and require little or no additional materials each year. A key to their sustainability is the continual recycling of materials. In contrast, many human activities are not sustainable. They depend on continual growth in population and consumption. Because resources are limited, indefinite growth is not possible. As well, human demands deplete non-renewable natural resources and produce polluting wastes, which enter nutrient cycles and damage the productivity of ecosystems.

The need to change the impact of human activities on the environment is recognized in the concept of **sustainable development:** development that meets the needs of the present without compromising the ability of future generations to meet their own needs.

What does this mean for people living today? The challenge for everyone is to make decisions that will reduce our individual and collective impact on the environment. These decisions can include

- getting more from less through efficient and effective use of resources
- reducing, re-using, recycling, and recovering the materials in manufactured products, as well as the waste materials created when these products are made and used
- restoring and reclaiming damaged environments
- conserving and developing substitutes for scarce resources
- changing political and social structures to reduce human impact on the environment
- reducing consumption — do you really *need* something or do you just *want* it?

Word **CONNECT**

Prepare a case in support of the following statement: Sustainable development must be achieved by 2025, to prevent an environmental catastrophe.

Check Your Understanding

1. Define the term "sustainable."

2. Why can a population of organisms not grow indefinitely?

3. Is soil a renewable or a non-renewable resource? Explain.

4. **Apply** One of the keys to sustainability is "getting more from less." Describe an example of this principle that you can apply for yourself.

5. **Thinking Critically** Give an example to show how a local impact on the environment could affect ecosystems around the world.

6. **Thinking Critically** What is a sustainable environment? Industry? Society?

Now that you have completed this chapter, try to do the following. If you cannot, go back to the sections indicated.

Define the term "closed system." (2.1)

Name two examples of nutrient cycles. (2.1)

Explain what happens to the nutrients in a dead leaf after it falls to the ground. (2.1)

Describe the role of photosynthesis in the carbon cycle. (2.2)

Describe the role of cellular respiration in the carbon cycle. (2.2)

Explain why carbon dioxide levels in the atmosphere have increased since the mid-nineteenth century. (2.2)

Explain how the person in the photograph below is affecting the carbon cycle. (2.2)

Give an example of one activity that reduces carbon dioxide levels in the atmosphere. (2.2)

Explain how climate change can occur and how it might impact Canada's environment. (2.2)

Name two elements that are used in artificial fertilizer. (2.3)

Explain how legumes obtain nitrogen. (2.3)

Name two processes in the nitrogen cycle that depend on bacteria. (2.3)

Describe two impacts of nitrogen overload on the environment. (2.3)

Describe two human activities that affect the nitrogen cycle. (2.3)

Explain the concept of sustainable development. (2.4)

List five ways that people can reduce their impact on the environment. (2.4)

Give one example of a sustainable activity and one example of a non-sustainable activity. (2.4)

Summarize this chapter by doing one of the following. Use a graphic organizer (such as a concept map), produce a poster, or write the summary to include the key chapter concepts. Here are a few ideas to use as a guide:
- Explain how photosynthesis and cellular respiration affect the carbon cycle.
- Describe how human activities can disrupt the carbon cycle.

Prepare Your Own Summary

- Define "nitrogen fixation," and explain its importance in the nitrogen cycle.
- Explain how acid precipitation can affect producers.
- Explain how eutrophication can affect producers.
- Explain how acid precipitation and eutrophication can affect biodiversity.
- Define "sustainable development."
- Explain why ecosystems are sustainable.

2 Review

Reviewing Key Terms

If you need to review, the section numbers show you where these terms were introduced.

1. In your notebook, match the description in column A with the correct term in column B.

A

- continuous movements of chemicals between the abiotic and biotic parts of the environment
- process that uses oxygen to produce energy
- process that uses sunlight to produce carbohydrates
- process that converts nitrogen gas to ammonia or nitrates
- process that converts ammonia into nitrates
- produced when nitrogen-containing gases dissolve in moisture in the air
- produced by the buildup of nutrients in lakes

B

- eutrophication (2.3)
- nutrient cycles (2.1)
- acid precipitation (2.3)
- photosynthesis (2.2)
- cellular respiration (2.2)
- nitrogen fixation (2.3)
- nitrification (2.3)
- sustainable development (2.4)

2. In your notebook, state whether each of the following statements is true or false. If the statement is false, explain why.
   (a) Photosynthesis and cellular respiration both produce oxygen. (2.2)
   (b) Plants only use carbon dioxide and produce oxygen. (2.2)
   (c) Most plants obtain their nitrogen directly from the air by nitrogen fixation. (2.3)
   (d) Acid precipitation is caused by too much carbon dioxide in the air. (2.3)

Understanding Key Concepts

Section numbers are provided if you need to review.

3. Briefly explain why the amount of carbon dioxide in the air has remained stable over long periods of time. (2.2)

4. Why has the level of carbon dioxide in the atmosphere been steadily increasing since the mid-nineteenth century? (2.2)

5. How can changes in the carbon cycle affect Earth's climate? (2.2)

6. Draw a diagram of the nitrogen cycle by putting the following events in the correct order. (2.3)
   - nitrogen gas in the atmosphere
   - absorption of nitrates by plants
   - nitrogen fixation
   - nitrification
   - denitrification
   - release of ammonia by decomposing plants

7. Before scientists learned how to make artificial fertilizers, what key process limited the amount of nitrates available to plants in most ecosystems? (2.3)

8. Why could the term "sustainable development" be considered a conflict? (2.4)

Developing Skills

9. Use chemical equations to summarize the processes of photosynthesis and cellular respiration. Identify the sources of the reactants in each equation. Explain how the products of each process are used by organisms.

10. Copy the following diagram into your notebook. Use arrows to indicate the direction of movement of carbon in each part of the cycle. Include the following terms in your diagram: photosynthesis, cellular respiration, producers, primary consumers, secondary consumers, decomposers, atmospheric carbon dioxide and oxygen, and carbon in tissues.

11. Research the following, using your local library and/or the Internet.

    (a) changes in annual gasoline consumption in Canada during the last ten years

    (b) changes in average gasoline prices in Canada during the last ten years

    Plot your results on a graph. Analyze your graph, and write a brief comment on any trends or relationships that you observe. How do these graphs compare with those you produced in Investigation 2-B?

Problem Solving/Applying

12. Describe one problem that results when the carbon cycle is out of balance. Include the causes of the problem, and suggest a remedy.

13. How is denitrification useful for treating sewage and cleaning up nitrogen-containing pollutants?

14. As much as half of the fertilizers that are applied to fields may be lost to the air or water. This is wasteful and expensive for farmers, as well as costly for the environment. Suggest a change in technology or in farming practices that could reduce the loss.

Critical Thinking

15. Using Figure 2.4 on page 46, discuss how cutting down and burning large regions of forest would alter the carbon dioxide and oxygen levels in the atmosphere.

16. Janice knew that plants produce oxygen. One night, she added extra water plants to her aquarium to benefit her fish. The next morning, the fish were gasping at the surface of the water. Explain why.

17. Write a brief story that links a farmer growing crops to a fishing trawler going out of business.

18. Why do farmers often need to add nitrogen to the soil, but do not need to add carbon, to grow their crops.

19. How might a change in the carbon cycle affect the nitrogen cycle?

20. The government wants to put a carbon tax on gasoline to reduce fuel consumption. Argue for or against this tax by examining the environmental implications. Also consider issues of public health and the cost of buying fuel.

Pause& Reflect

1. Go back to the beginning of the chapter, on page 38, and check your original answers to Opening Ideas questions. How has your thinking changed? How would you answer those questions now that you have investigated the topics in this chapter?

2. How might the carbon cycle affect the nitrogen cycle?

3 Change and

- How might a school playing field change if it were not maintained for a year? How might it appear after ten years?

- Why do some parts of Canada have forests, while other parts have bogs, tundra, or prairie grasslands?

- How would you determine the best use of an area of land?

Science Log

In your Science Log, write your answers to the questions above. Give reasons for each answer. If you are unsure of an answer, note the additional information that you need. Look for this information as you read the chapter.

Does your school have a grass playing field where you can play soccer, baseball, and other sports? Perhaps, long ago, your playing field was a forest or meadow. Would it be possible for a forest or meadow to grow there again? In this chapter, you will look at changes in ecosystems. Humans have changed the appearance and use of the land over much of the world. We have cut down forests and drained wetlands, and we have replaced these ecosystems with towns and farms. Natural processes also change the land. For example, floods wash away river banks, droughts create deserts, and pests or diseases can kill trees in a forest or organisms in a lake.

Earth's environment is always changing. Some changes are cyclical and short-term, such as the change of seasons that occurs every year. Other changes are long-term, such as the ice ages that changed the global climate over thousands of years. How do ecosystems respond to changes in the atmosphere, water, and land?

The soil is an important part of all terrestrial (land) ecosystems. Imagine an area of land consisting of only rock. Few plants could grow there, and without plants there would be few animals. Humans depend on soil to produce food, wood, and other products. Like other parts of the environment, soil can also change over time. How do the characteristics of soil determine what grows now and what could grow in the future?

Sustainability

The School Playing Field

Is one area of land much like another area of land? If not, how and why might they differ? Would they both be suitable for the same use? In this activity, you will choose the best use of the land that is now your school playing field.

What to Do

Work with a partner. Begin by finding answers to the following questions.

Key Concepts

In this chapter, you will discover

- how the characteristics of soil affect plant growth
- how soil, organisms, and climate continually interact to change the land over time
- how human activities affect living communities
- what is being done to protect Canadian ecosystems
- how to use the resources of an area of land in a sustainable way

Key Skills

In this chapter, you will

- design an experiment to observe the effects of soil characteristics on plant growth
- study an ecosystem that is in the process of change
- conduct an Environmental Impact Assessment for making decisions about land use
- research information from various sources to investigate the protection of ecosystems
- interpret maps showing human activity and the incidence of forest fires

Key Terms

- soil
- community
- succession
- pioneer organisms
- climax community
- primary succession
- secondary succession
- remediated
- phytoremediation
- wetlands

Starting Point  ACTIVITY

(a) List some characteristics that make your school playing field suitable for its present use. If your school does not have a playing field, study a playing field or park in your community.

(b) What else might be done with the land now occupied by the field?

(c) To what climatic conditions is the playing field exposed?

(d) Is the soil of the field sandy, clay-like, or rich and crumbly in texture?

(e) Apart from grass, do any other plants grow on the playing field? If so, describe them.

(f) Do any parts of the field differ noticeably from the rest? If so, how?

(g) What activities are needed to maintain the field? List the frequency of each activity.

(h) List the uses of the land next to the field. How might each use affect the field?

What Did You Discover?

1. Why is climate important to the condition of the playing field?

2. Why is the type of soil in the field important?

3. Suggest how grass is adapted to the environment of the playing field.

4. Describe how the playing field might change if none of the activities you listed in your answer to question (g) above occurred for one year.

5. Explain what you would need to do to convert your school playing field into
   (a) a woodlot
   (b) a parking lot

   In your answer, include information about maintaining each of these uses. Consider the costs involved. Also, what might be the affect on people and the environment?

3.1 The Importance of Soil

Of all the parts of our environment, the land seems to be the most solid and unchanging. It is also the part of the environment that has the most obvious limits. If you look at a map, you can quickly see the size and characteristics of an area of land. Depending on the type of map, you may also be able to see various features covering the land, such as lakes, rivers, hills, and forests. As well, you may be able to measure the sizes of the areas used by people for different purposes, such as cities, parks, and farmland (see Figure 3.1). Because the total area of land is finite, increasing the amount of space occupied for one use causes a reduction in the amount of space available for other uses. For example, the land just north of Lake Ontario is covered partly by cities and highways and partly by farms. Because the land is level and well-drained, it is equally suitable for both uses. Over the past few decades, however, "urban sprawl" has increased the amount of space used for housing, shopping malls, industrial buildings, and highways. This has caused a reduction in the amount of farmland (see Figure 3.2).

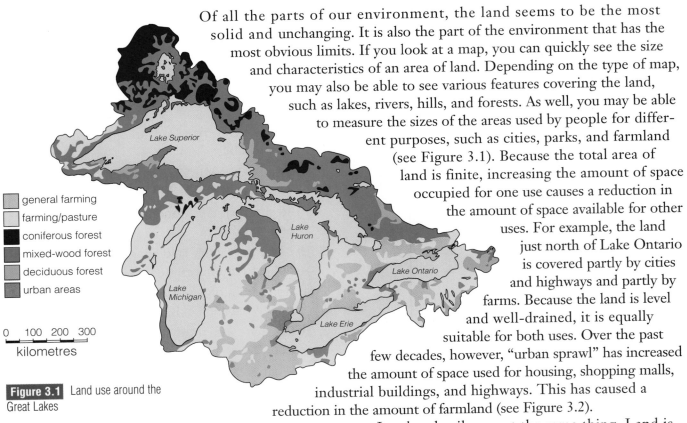

general farming
farming/pasture
coniferous forest
mixed-wood forest
deciduous forest
urban areas

0   100 200 300
kilometres

Figure 3.1 Land use around the Great Lakes

Figure 3.2 Many cities are built on good farmland. Their highways and buildings are spread over soil that could be used to grow food.

Land and soil are not the same thing. Land is the part of the world that is not covered by oceans. **Soil** is the layer of material that covers the land and supports the growth of plants. Seeds germinate in soil. Plants anchor their roots in soil and obtain water and nutrients from it. The depth and characteristics of soil affect the growth and productivity of the plants. This, in turn, affects the lives of all the organisms that live above the ground.

Soil is a mixture of particles of weathered rock and decomposing plant and animal matter. It includes spaces that hold air and water. The characteristics and depth of soil vary from one area to another. These characteristics depend partly on the kind of underlying rock but mainly on the climate and vegetation in the area. Grassland soil and forest soil are the two major types of soil that have been used for farmland. Figure 3.3 shows the soil profiles (horizontal layers of different composition, called horizons A, B, and C) of three major types of soil found in North America.

Grassland soil occurs naturally in areas with lower rainfall. The surface soil, or topsoil, is deep and supports most of the root growth.

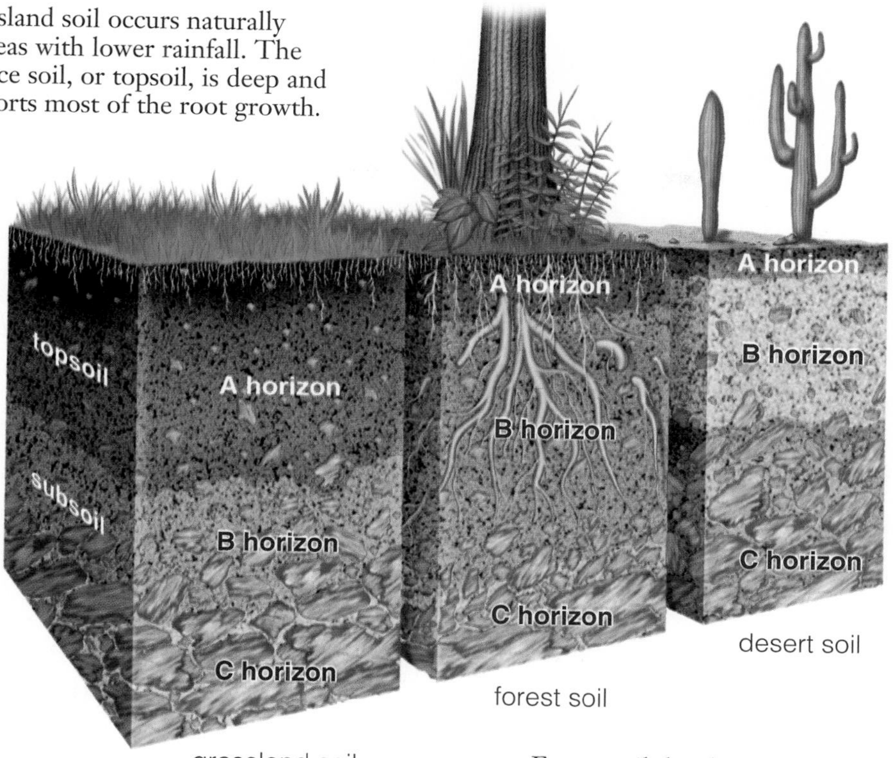

topsoil

subsoil

A horizon

B horizon

C horizon

grassland soil

A horizon

B horizon

C horizon

forest soil

A horizon

B horizon

C horizon

desert soil

Deserts have limited plant growth due to low levels of precipitation. As a result, there is little decomposing plant matter in the soil and a very thin layer of topsoil, or none at all.

Forest soil develops in areas with more precipitation. The precipitation carries materials deeper beneath the surface of the soil, into the subsoil. In forests, the layer of topsoil is not as thick as in grassland soil.

Figure 3.3 Soil profiles of grassland, forest, and desert ecosytems

Beneath the surface of the soil, countless tiny organisms live in a sunless world of tunnels and caves (see Figure 3.4). These organisms range from earthworms and beetles to ants and microscopic bacteria. In Chapters 1 and 2, you learned that some soil organisms break down animal wastes and dead plants into nutrients. Other soil organisms (bacteria) play an essential part in nutrient cycles, such as the nitrogen cycle. Some soil organisms feed on plant roots, and others are predators. The plants interact with the animals and micro-organisms to form a biological **community.** They form a network of food chains within the soil. The animal burrows and the tunnels made by the plant roots mix and rearrange the soil particles. They also open up spaces in the soil for air and water to move through. In the following investigation, you will study the composition of several different types of soil. You will also examine the effect of soil pH on plant growth.

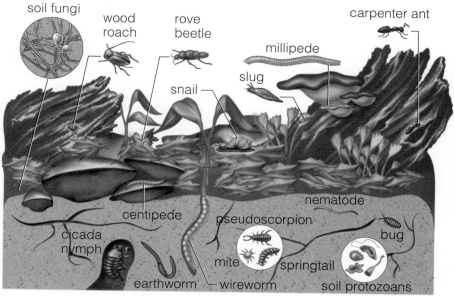

soil fungi
wood roach
rove beetle
carpenter ant
millipede
slug
snail
centipede
nematode
pseudoscorpion
bug
cicada nymph
mite
springtail
earthworm
wireworm
soil protozoans

Figure 3.4 A community of soil organisms

Investigating Soil

What makes one soil different from another? How do the characteristics of soil affect plant growth? In Part 1 of this investigation, you will analyze certain characteristics of soil and interpret how they formed. In Part 2, you will design an experiment to measure the effect of soil pH on the germination and growth of plants.

Part 1
Characteristics of Soil

Problem
What are some of the physical and chemical properties of soil?

Safety Precautions

- You will be using sulfuric acid which is very corrosive. Wear safety equipment at all times.
- Be careful when working with an open flame.
- Follow your teacher's instructions to dispose of materials.
- Rinse any spill with plenty of water. Immediately inform your teacher about any spills.

Apparatus
4 Petri dishes
small spoons
   for sampling
hand lens
microscope
microscope
   slides
pH chart
50 mL
   graduated
   cylinder

stirring rods
balance
crucible
crucible holder
support stand
support ring
Bunsen burner
set of sorting
   sieves

Materials
4 different soil samples
3 sheets of paper
distilled water
universal pH indicator

Procedure

1. Make a data table like the one below, and give your table a title.

2. Work in a group of four. Place two teaspoons of the first soil sample in each Petri dish. Each student in your group will study one of four soil properties (see steps 3 to 6) in this soil sample.

3. Particle size: Using the sieves, sort the sample into particles of different sizes. Use the sheets of paper to capture the soil particles. Record whether the variation in particle size is low, medium, or high. (For example, if all the particles are of similar size, record the particle size variation as "low.")

Soil sample	Variation in particle size	Colour	Percent organic content	pH
deciduous forest				
coniferous forest				
meadow				
bog				

④ Colour: Determine the colour of the soil. Use the hand lens or the microscope to examine the soil more closely. Are all the soil particles the same colour?

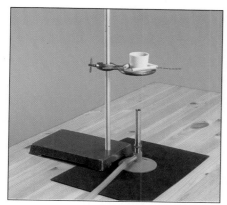

⑤ Organic matter: Soil is partly mineral (rock) matter and partly organic (decomposed animal and plant) matter. Follow the steps below to determine the percent dry weight of organic matter in the soil.

(a) Using the balance, measure 10 g of your sample of soil.

(b) Place the measured amount of soil in a crucible. Heat the crucible above a Bunsen burner until all the organic matter has burned. **CAUTION:** Always be careful when using an open flame and hot objects.

(c) Allow the soil to cool, then determine its mass.

(d) Calculate the difference in mass and the percent weight of organic matter.

⑥ pH: Add 10 to 20 mL of distilled water to the soil sample. Stir well. Place one end of a pH paper into the wet mixture. Find the colour in the pH chart, and record the pH value in your table.

⑦ Dispose of the samples as directed by your teacher. Rinse out the Petri dishes, and dry them thoroughly.

⑧ Repeat steps 2 to 7 for the remaining samples. Study a different property for each sample. For example, if you studied particle size for the first sample, you could study colour for the second sample, organic matter for the third sample, and pH for the fourth sample.

⑨ Wash your hands after completing this investigation.

Analyze

1. Is there a relationship between the colour of the soil and the amount of organic matter? If so, describe this relationship.

2. What rock type might produce soils with a neutral or high pH? Hint: What stone is used to neutralize an acidified lake?

Conclude and Apply

3. Soil texture is determined by the size of the soil particles. How might soil texture affect the growth of plants? Which soil texture would produce the greatest plant growth? Explain your answer.

4. Explain how the organic content of a soil might affect plant growth.

Extend Your Skills

5. **Design Your Own** Design an experiment to measure the permeability of soils to water. Sketch your apparatus, and describe your procedure. With your teacher's approval, carry out the experiment. Why might the permeability of soil be important for plant growth?

CONTINUED ▶

Part 2
Soils and Plant Growth

Problem
How does the pH of soil affect the germination and growth of plants?

Apparatus
flats, small pots, or plastic cups
100 mL graduated cylinder
ruler
pH chart

Materials
radish or bean seedlings
labels
potting soil
water
universal pH indicator
dilute sulfuric acid

Procedure

1. Make a hypothesis about the effect of soil pH on plant growth.

2. Using the materials listed, design an experiment to test your hypothesis. Record your procedure, including the data you will collect.

3. What will be your independent variable(s)? What will be your dependent variable(s)? What will be your control variable(s)?

4. Review the design of your experiment with your teacher, and then carry out the experiment. **CAUTION:** Wear safety equipment when handling acid solutions.

5. Plot your results on a graph.

Analyze

1. Did your results support your hypothesis? Explain your answer.

2. At which pH level did the seedlings grow best?

3. Suggest why the seedlings did not grow as well in soils with other pH levels.

Conclude and Apply

4. Based on your results, how might acid precipitation affect the productivity of farmlands or forests?

Extend Your Knowledge

5. The effects of acid precipitation on soil pH vary with the type of underlying bedrock. Carry out research to identify which major types of rock are able to neutralize acidic conditions. Which types of rock are not able to neutralize acid conditions? On a map, identify the locations of the Canadian Shield and the Appalachians. What type of rock is most common in these areas of Canada? From your findings, would you expect soil in these areas to experience more damage or less damage from acid precipitation?

Disturbing Soil

Like all parts of the environment, soil changes over time. Think of some ways in which soil might increase or decrease in depth. How might it become more suitable or less suitable for plant growth? Such changes in soil occur through both natural processes and human activities, as shown in Figures 3.5A and 3.5B.

INTERNET CONNECT

www.school.mcgrawhill.ca/resources/

To find out more about soils and their classifications in different regions of Canada, go to the web site above. Go to **Science Resources**, then to **SCIENCEPOWER 10** to know where to go next. Which type of soil is dominant (most common) in the area where you live? What factors produce this type of soil? How does the soil and climate of your area determine the natural vegetation? Prepare a poster of your findings. Use illustrations to show which plants are common in your area.

Figure 3.5A Dead leaves, and sediments washed away by flooding rivers are deposited down stream. Deposits build up the thickness of soil and add nutrients and organic matter to soil, improving its fertility.

Figure 3.5B Erosion by wind or water carries soil away from an area.

Soil type, climate, and vegetation are the three most important factors that determine where populations of people can live. Regions with poor soils, which cannot be used for growing crops or grazing livestock, have the lowest densities of human population. Regions with fertile soils have the highest densities. Table 3.1 shows the percentage of land used for crops and pasture (grassland where livestock graze) in different regions of the world. Which region has the lowest percentage of land used for agriculture? In this region, where do you think most of the farmland is located?

From Table 3.1, you can see that 11 percent of Earth's land surface is used for growing crops. Could this amount be increased? In Europe and North America, there is very little land with suitable soil and climate that is not already farmed. In other parts of the world, attempts to convert grasslands and forests into farmland often fail due to unsuitable soil or climate. For example, as you learned in Chapter 1, the logging of tropical forests exposes the thin soils to rapid erosion from heavy rainfall.

Table 3.1 Percentage of Land Suitable for Agriculture

Region	Percentage of cropland	Percentage of pasture	Total farmland
Canada	4.9	3.0	7.9
U.S.A.	19.6	25.0	44.6
North America	13.0	16.8	29.8
Europe	29.9	17.1	47.0
Asia	15.2	25.9	41.1
South America	6.0	28.3	34.3
Africa	6.3	28.8	35.1
World	11.0	26.0	37.0

Figure 3.6 More grazing mammals live on savanna grasslands than anywhere else in the world.

Natural grasslands in drier parts of the tropics, such as the savannas of East Africa, support large herds of grazing animals (see Figure 3.6). Could these native animals be replaced with livestock? When cattle, goats, and other farm animals are introduced to tropical grasslands from other parts of the world, they often suffer from diseases to which the native wildlife is resistant. Domesticated animals have a higher demand for drinking water. In large herds, they overgraze the grasses and trample the soil. As a result, the tropical grasslands are slowly converted to dusty deserts and the productivity of the land is reduced.

The most important resource of farms, forests, and prairies across Canada is the soil. If the soil is washed or blown from the land, or damaged by toxic chemicals, we lose areas that might otherwise produce food or other crops. In the next section, you will learn how different ecosystems change over time, beginning with an area that has no soil or plants. Why do you think some areas develop into forests while others become grasslands?

Pause& Reflect

Not all land is suitable for cultivation or grazing. Food production, however, is only one of the uses for which land is important to people. What other values of the land can you think of? How does the land benefit other organisms?

Check Your Understanding

1. What are the two main ingredients of soil?

2. Name three characteristics of soil.

3. Name three organisms that live in soil. Describe the importance of each in its soil ecosystem.

4. **Apply** Write a "recipe" for producing a high-quality potting soil for growing young plants. Include the proportions of each ingredient.

5. **Thinking Critically** Name two plants that commonly grow in each of the following ecosystems. How is each plant adapted to the conditions of the soil and climate?

    (a) grassland

    (b) forest

    (c) desert

6. **Thinking Critically** How can soil erosion in one area add to the productivity of farmland in another area?

3.2 Change and Succession

Most of the ecosystems in Canada today did not exist before about 10 000 years ago. For a long period just before this time, most of Canada was covered with glaciers. When the glaciers melted, the landscape consisted mainly of bare rock and gravel covered by millions of lakes and ponds. How did the forests, prairies, and other ecosystems we see today get here? They developed by a process called **succession**, in which one ecosystem is gradually replaced by another over time. Succession is a process of change that you can see for yourself, since it is constantly occurring.

Word CONNECT

The word "succession" is very closely connected with the word "success." Write four sentences, each containing one of the following related words: succession, success, successful, succeeds. Define a common meaning for the word "succession," which is different from the biological meaning used in this chapter.

Figure 3.7 A journey to the Canadian Arctic is like a journey back in time. Much of the rest of Canada looked like this after the last ice age ended, about 10 000 years ago.

Primary Succession

The best way to understand succession is to analyze an example. Imagine an area of bare rock and gravel — perhaps the remains of a forest after the last ice age, or an area that was covered by lava from a volcanic eruption, or a modern building site where bulldozers have stripped away all the soil. The first organisms to grow on bare rock are lichens, carried there by wind or on the feet of birds (see Figure 3.8). Organisms that can live in such inhospitable places, without soil or shelter, are called **pioneer organisms**. They slowly start to transform the environment and create conditions that are suitable for other organisms. In the next activity, you will examine the structure and diversity of different species of lichens.

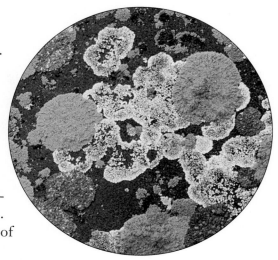

Figure 3.8 Lichens are able to live in conditions where few plants can survive, such as in the Far North and on rocky mountain slopes.

Looking at Lichens

Lichens are an association between two kinds of organisms: algae and fungi. The algae are green and carry out photosynthesis. The fungi retain moisture and attach to the surface of the rock. How many forms of lichen can you identify?

What You Need

lichen collection or field guide

hand lens

pencil

paper

What to Do

1. Work with a partner. Examine the variety of lichens in the collection or field guide. Use the hand lens to help you see the minute structures.

2. Describe the variety of shapes and forms of growth. For instance, is the growth scale-like or hair-like? What other forms of growth can you identify?

3. Where do the different kinds of lichens grow? Is there a relationship between the form of growth and the location of growth?

4. Make diagrams of four different kinds of lichen.

5. If you handled lichens, wash your hands.

What Did You Discover?

1. What features did all the different kinds of lichens share?

2. Explain why you think lichens are well-adapted as pioneer species.

Extensions

3. How can lichens be used to monitor the health of ecosystems?

Skill
P O W E R

For tips on how to make scientific drawings, turn to page 609.

B The lichens are joined by tiny plants, such as mosses. These plants can grow in very thin soil. Insects and other small animals gather around the clumps of vegetation to find shelter and food, forming the first ecological communities.

A Lichens first become established on bare rock. They produce acidic compounds that slowly start to break down the rock. The acidic compounds release nutrients from the rock, which are absorbed by the lichens. Decaying matter from dead lichens begins the process of soil formation.

C The organisms help to break down the rock substrate. Soil begins to form in cracks in the rock where moisture collects. Eroded particles of rock are mixed with decomposing plant and animal materials. Larger plants, such as ferns, begin to take root in these cracks and accelerate the changes.

Figure 3.9 Stages of primary succession

Figure 3.9 shows the process of succession from lichens to shrubs and trees. Read the captions to learn how bare rock can be transformed into a forest ecosystem.

The details and rate of successional changes depend on the climate and other conditions of the physical environment. Do these changes ever stop? If left undisturbed, an ecosystem will eventually develop into a **climax community.** This is a community of organisms that has a maximum level of productivity. In other words, the plants in the community are producing a maximum amount of biomass for the environmental conditions of the area. The type of climax community in an ecosystem depends on a combination of climate and soil. For example, deserts form climax communities in dry areas. Grasslands are climax communities where there is more precipitation, but not enough to support tree growth. Forests are climax communities in wetter areas of Earth (see Figure 3.10). The sequence of changes that begins with a bare landscape and ends with a climax community is known as **primary succession.**

Figure 3.10 A climax forest on Vancouver Island, British Columbia

As the decomposing materials build up, the soil is able to hold more water. The environment is now suitable for a wider range of organisms. Grasses, wildflowers, and other plants begin to take over. These plants attract bees, butterflies, and other insects, that come to feed on the flowers and leaves. A larger community of soil organisms also becomes established.

E Gradually the composition of the community changes as one species replaces another. The new plants and animals crowd out the original pioneer species, which cannot survive in shadier, damper conditions. As the new organisms continue building the soil, they alter their environment and, in turn, are replaced by taller shrubs and trees.

Secondary Succession

All communities are subject to disturbances — some major and some minor. A severe storm may blow down trees, a grass fire may sweep across the Prairies, or a beaver dam may block a stream and flood a woodland, killing the trees. After each disturbance, we can observe how the environment responds. Succession eventually restores a climax community, but this kind of succession is called **secondary succession.** It does not have to start from bare rock, because communities can rebuild from the remains of the previous ecosystem and from the surrounding, undamaged communities.

A climax community that is formed by secondary succession resembles the climax community that existed before the disturbance. It usually, however, has a slightly different combination of species. In northern ecosystems, secondary succession transforms shallow beaver ponds back into dry land. This process is shown in Figure 3.11. In your notebook, make a quick sketch of each stage of succession. Describe what is happening during each stage.

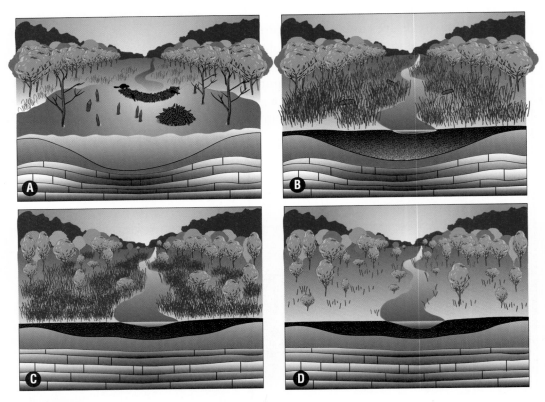

Figure 3.11 Secondary succession: beaver pond to dry land

Forest fires are a common cause of secondary succession in Canada. Each year, hundreds of hectares of fire spread through forests, sending thick clouds of black smoke high into the sky. Trees groan and crack as they disappear into the inferno (see Figure 3.12). The fire passes on, leaving behind the charred remains of tree trunks jutting from a blanket of smoking grey ashes that covers the scorched soil. These silent ruins are all that is left of what had been a thriving community of plants and animals.

A forest fire is a dramatic reminder of how a disturbance can quickly change the environment. By studying what happens after a fire, we can learn how the environment responds to a major, sudden change.

Natural events — such as lightning strikes following hot, dry weather — can start forest fires. Many are caused by people, however. In the activity on page 86, you will look for relationships between human activities and the incidence of forest fires.

Immediately after a forest fire, it is difficult or impossible for many organisms to continue living in the area. Those that need the shade and shelter of large trees cannot easily survive there. The open, sunny area that is left by the fire, however, creates conditions that are suitable for a different community of organisms. The seeds of wildflowers, such as fireweed, are dispersed by the wind and settle on areas of ground cleared by the flames. Ashes from the burned wood add nutrients to the soil, and plants that are adapted to these conditions germinate quickly. Soon there is a flower meadow in the burned area. This meadow attracts insects, mice, and birds, and their predators (see Figure 3.13).

Figure 3.12 Forest fires play an important role in secondary succession.

DidYouKnow?

Blueberry farmers in Nova Scotia regularly burn the vegetation in their fields. They do this to maintain the correct pH level in the soil for growing their crops.

Figure 3.13 Wildflowers and other small plants can grow in a sunny, open patch of forest after a fire has killed the trees.

As the meadow community thrives, the plants shade the surface of the ground and trap moisture. Larger shrubs and bushes grow. Trees begin to reappear. Some trees, such as the jack pine, are adapted to fires. They produce special cones, near their tops, that are stimulated to open and release seeds when exposed to the heat of a fire (see Figure 3.14). Secondary succession occurs more quickly than primary succession. Ten years after a fire, the forest has begun to grow back, and forest animals have returned.

Figure 3.14 Seeds from this charred cone of a jack pine will be among the first to germinate after a forest fire.

Fire!

How many forest fires occur naturally? How many are a result of human activities? Use your detective skills to interpret data and answer these questions.

What to Do

1. The map below shows the frequency of forest fires in bush, grassland, and forest each year in eastern Canada. Study it carefully. Can you interpret the pattern? What additional data do you need to link the frequency of fires with human activities? Where will you find these data? Hint: Other maps of the same area will show a variety of other data.

2. When you think you know the additional data that you need, find the data and make your comparisons.

What Did You Discover?

1. Describe the relationship between the incidence of fires and any other patterns that you discovered during your research.

2. From your comparison, do you think human activities play a large part, a small part, or no part in the occurrence of forest fires each year in eastern Canada? Explain your conclusion.

3. **Thinking Critically** Why do you think the incidence of fires around the city of Sudbury, in northern Ontario, is greater than the incidence of fires around the city of Toronto?

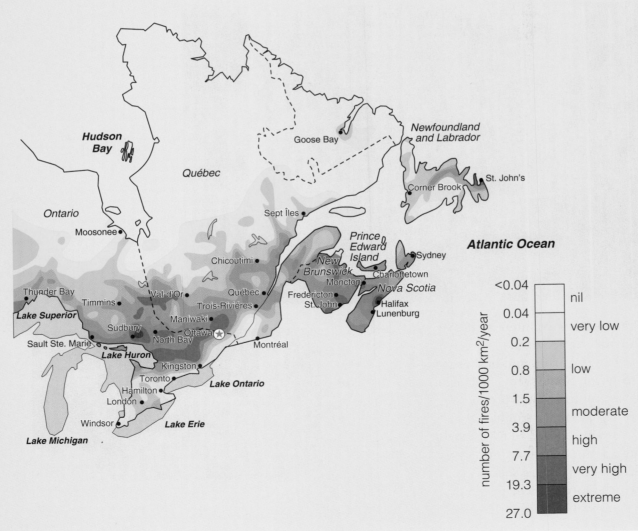

Think again about your school playing field and the biological community that it has replaced. To maintain your playing field, it must be mowed, fertilized, and watered. What would happen if these activities were stopped? Think about cities and farmland. These human-made systems can only be maintained by using energy and materials to prevent the return of unwanted organisms. What happens when a field is abandoned or a city lot is left vacant for a year or two? The process of succession is always at work to establish a community of organisms that is typical of the climate and soil in an area (see Figures 3.15A and 3.15B).

Figure 3.15A Shrubs and trees grow back in areas that were disturbed by humans.

Tools of Science

To lower the risk of *wildfires* (large, destructive, forest fires), forest managers sometimes carry out *prescribed burns.* These are small fires that are deliberately set under strict conditions within fire barriers, such as rivers or cleared areas. They help to prevent the buildup of dry wood and underbrush that could create more severe fires later. Prescribed burns also maintain biodiversity by producing open patches within a forest. In these patches, sunlight can reach the forest floor, allowing the seeds of sun-loving species of plants to germinate. As well, the seedlings of large, slow-growing trees can become established here.

Figure 3.15B Vegetation has covered these Mayan ruins. Do you think the town or city where you live now might one day be replaced by a forest?

The Impact of Change

Somewhere in your community is an area where the vegetation has been disturbed by natural events or human activities. It may be a plot of land cleared for building, an area of shrubs or trees killed by pests, a logged woodlot, or a gravel pit. By studying one of these areas, you can get a "snapshot" of a community of organisms in the process of change. How are the plants and animals that live there adapted to the existing conditions? How might they help to change these conditions? In this investigation, you will study the process of succession along a country road.

Problem

What are the characteristics of a community in the process of succession?

Safety Precaution
- Conduct this investigation only under the supervision of your teacher.
- Remain 2 m back from the edge of the road at all times.

Apparatus
field guide   hand lens
tape measure   camera (optional)

Materials
notebook   pencil

Procedure

1. Work in a small group. Under your teacher's supervision, you will be studying succession along a 5 m wide transect that is perpendicular to the edge of the road. The biological community in this transect is undergoing secondary succession as a result of disturbance caused by the road. **Note:** Minimize your disturbance of organisms and habitats in your study area. Do not damage or remove any plants.

2. Sketch a scale map of your study area. Note the general distribution of vegetation, bare ground, and other significant features.

3. Is there a greater abundance of plants on your transect near the edge of the road or farther from the road, or is there no obvious pattern? Where is the greatest diversity of plants?

4. Using a field guide, identify five common plants that are growing along your transect.

5. On a sketch of the study area, indicate the approximate locations where each plant is growing.

6. List three characteristics that you would expect to find in pioneer plant species. For example, would they be tall or short? How would they reproduce? Use your list to determine which plants in your study area are pioneer species.

7. Observe and record the characteristics of the soil in the area.

8. Wash your hands after completing this investigation.

Analyze

1. How does the plant community in your study area differ from a climax community?

2. What characteristics help a plant species grow in a disturbed area? Explain.

3. How might the plants you observed affect the characteristics of the soil over time?

Succession and Energy Flow

How does succession affect energy flow in an ecosystem? Imagine that you are managing a forest in order to harvest the trees there. The forest has just been logged, and new trees are starting to grow back. When should you harvest these trees to obtain the greatest yield of timber? Figure 3.16 shows how much energy from the Sun is converted into biomass by trees in a forest ecosystem. (You learned about this process in Chapter 1.) How would you interpret the graph?

You know that energy from the Sun is captured by the growing trees for photosynthesis. Some of this energy is used to produce new tree tissue (gain in biomass), and some is used to carry out the life functions of the trees (breakdown of energy-rich carbohydrates during cellular respiration). At what stage in a tree's life is most energy used to build biomass? At what stage is most energy used to carry out life functions? At what age would you harvest a tree to take greatest advantage of the productivity of the ecosystem? Why is it more efficient to harvest a tree that is 100 years old than a tree that is 150 years old?

INTERNET CONNECT

www.school.mcgrawhill.ca/resources/

Where in Canada have human activities produced the greatest changes in the environment? Where have they produced the least changes? How do these changes affect biodiversity? Go to the web site above. Go to **Science Resources**, then to **SCIENCEPOWER 10** to know where to go next. Study the map that shows the extent to which ecological regions throughout Canada have been changed by human activities. Find areas in your province with a high human impact and a low human impact. What human activities are responsible for causing the changes?

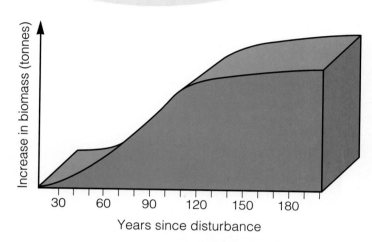

Figure 3.16 Tree productivity in a forest undergoing secondary succession

Irreversible Change

Although succession can change disturbed ecosystems back to more complex biological communities, frequent and severe disturbances can produce irreversible changes. The risk is especially great if species of organisms are exterminated or if soil is lost or poisoned over a wide area. How might the loss of species make it difficult for a community to recover? How might soil erosion make it difficult for trees to grow back? A severe disturbance can produce areas of land that may remain unproductive for hundreds or even thousands of years (see Figure 3.17).

Figure 3.17 In the Badlands of Alberta, soil erosion makes it difficult for plants to become established.

Figure 3.18A This photograph shows an area that has been surface mined. There was no effort to reclaim the land.

Figure 3.18B Proper reclamation has restored the vegetation in this abandoned mine site in New Brunswick.

Sometimes heavily disturbed areas can be made productive once again. For example, consider an abandoned mine site, where the land has been cleared of all topsoil and vegetation (see Figure 3.18A). The remaining rock debris often contains toxic metals, such as copper, mercury, and zinc. Across Canada, there are thousands of abandoned mine sites. Some cause serious environmental problems, while others simply limit the ways in which the land can be re-used. If left to itself, the abandoned mine site might remain bare of plant life for many years.

How can such an area be **remediated,** or restored, to become suitable for wildlife, forestry, or recreation? First toxic materials must be removed, neutralized, or covered with layers of rock. For instance, strong acids may be used to wash out the contaminants. Then calcium carbonate may be applied to counteract soil acidity. Fertilizers may also be added to the soil to help increase plant growth. Landscaping to create hills and valleys can provide suitable drainage for precipitation. Finally the area is covered with topsoil and planted with grasses and shrubs. In time, succession transforms the restored area, as shown in Figure 3.18B. Remediation projects such as this are costly, however. It is usually more effective and less expensive to reduce damage to the land in the first place. How do you think mining operations can reduce their impact on the environment?

There is a cost-effective alternative to cleaning up toxic compounds from the soil. It involves the use of plants, and it is called **phytoremediation.** Some plants, such as mustard, radish, and sunflower, accumulate toxic metals in their tissues (see Figure 3.19). These plants can be planted, grown, and then harvested to remove the toxic metals from the soil.

Figure 3.19 Plants can absorb metals, such as copper(Cu), through their roots and store it in their tissues.

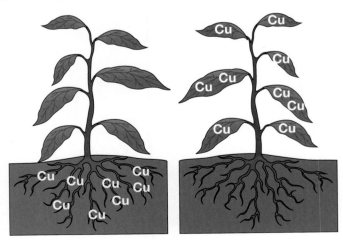

Scientists are using genetic engineering to try to increase the ability of plants to purify the soil. Genes from bacteria, which are able to live in highly toxic conditions, are being added to the DNA of the yellow poplar tree. Laboratory studies show that the genetically modified trees are ten times more resistant to mercury than unmodified trees. The trees can also break down the mercury to a less toxic form. Although phytoremediation is a useful way of decontaminating soil, it does take several years to complete.

Researchers are discovering that bacteria are particularly useful for cleaning up chemical pollution. The reason is that different species of bacteria are able to break down a huge variety of molecules to use as a source of energy. This includes molecules of chemicals that would be toxic to other forms of life, such as pesticides, PCBs, detergents, oil, creosote, and dynamite.

Scientists discover suitable bacteria by looking for species that survive in polluted areas. They can then use genetic engineering techniques to improve the microbes' pollution-fighting qualities or to transfer the genes that are responsible into other species, such as plants that grow on polluted soil.

Carry out your own research to learn how genetic engineering is being used for bioremediation. What advantages do genetic engineering techniques have over older methods of cleaning up polluted areas? What disadvantages do they have?

Check Your Understanding

1. Explain the difference between primary succession and secondary succession.

2. Give one example of a natural event and one example of a human activity which are followed by secondary succession.

3. In your own words, define "pioneer organisms"?

4. In your own words, define a "climax community"?

5. What evidence would show that a shallow lake once existed in an area that is now a forest?

6. **Apply** Imagine an area that has been damaged by pollution and soil erosion. Describe some ways in which people might help this area become suitable for a wildlife community.

7. **Thinking Critically** In the past, forest managers attempted to extinguish all forest fires as quickly as possible. Why might this policy cause long-term problems in a forest ecosystem?

3.3 Understanding Land Use

Figure 3.20 In many northern areas, sphagnum moss forms thick mats that float on the surface of the water. These floating mats support the growth of other plants.

Over large areas of northern Canada, the cold, wet climate produces bogs: waterlogged ground covered with a thick, spongy layer of sphagnum moss and other vegetation (see Figure 3.20). Under the surface layer of living plants, dead vegetation decomposes slowly. It does not mix into the rocky material below it to produce soil. Instead, it forms a material called *peat*, which builds up at an average rate of 6 to 7 cm per century. Canada has about one quarter of the world's total peat-land. This includes areas where the layer of peat is at least 40 cm thick. Where do you think most of the remainder of the world's peatland is found?

For settlers and developers, bogs and other **wetlands** (mixtures of land, water, and plants) were generally regarded as wastelands. They were not usable for building or farming, and they provided habitats in which mosquitoes could breed. People and farm animals had a difficult time trying to cross bogs because they got "bogged down." Seen as having no value, an estimated 20 million hectares of wetlands in Canada were drained, starting in the early nineteenth century. The land was used for farms, towns, and industrial developments. In the southern part of the Prairies and in southern Ontario, over 70 percent of the wetlands have been converted to other land uses.

The Value of Bogs

How might draining bogs affect the environment? Bogs act like sponges, holding tremendous quantities of water and releasing it slowly over time. This helps to prevent flooding and erosion. Bogs also help to improve water quality by trapping suspended particles and some dissolved substances. When bogs are drained, the volume and timing of water flowing through nearby waterways and ground water are affected. The changes in water flow, in turn, affect the growth of plants in the waterways and the animals that depend on them.

Off the **Wall** About 2000 years ago, several people were buried in a bog in Denmark. When scientists found them in the late twentieth century, the bodies of these people were so well preserved that their skin, hair, and finger-prints were still intact. The lack of oxygen and acidic conditions in the bog prevented decomposers from breaking down the bodies.

Sponges of the Land 🧪

The peat in a bog acts like a sponge to hold water. What is the maximum amount of water that peat can hold? In this activity, you will devise a method to determine the answer to this question.

What You Need

peat   balance
beaker or graduated cylinder   water

What to Do

1. Using the listed materials and any other materials that you think are necessary, devise a method to measure the maximum amount of water that a known quantity of peat can hold. Carry out your procedure.

2. Determine the saturation point of the peat.

3. Present your results as a ratio.

4. Wash your hands after completing this activity.

What Did You Discover?

1. How much water can peat hold?

2. Peat is often added to soil. Why do you think this is done? What naturally occurring components of the soil does peat increase?

Extensions

3. How much water can be absorbed by 1 ha of bog with a peat layer 1 m thick? Devise a method that you could use to answer this question. What information would you need? What problems could you encounter?

4. Think of some other uses of peat that take advantage of its water-holding ability.

Bogs are important not only in the water cycle but also for a resource they provide — peat. Dried peat is sold for use in gardens and nurseries to improve soil. When mixed with heavy clay soil, it loosens the texture to let air and water move through more easily. When mixed with sandy soil, peat helps the soil retain water and nutrients. As well, peat is added to soil to lower its pH so that acid-loving species of plants, such as heather, can grow.

Peat harvesting has occurred in every province at one time or another. The majority of Canadian peat is exported to the United States and Japan, with sales totalling over $100 million annually. To prepare a site for peat harvesting, drainage ditches are dug to channel excess water from the bog. After the peat has dried out, it is removed, compressed, and packaged into bales.

A harvested bog can be restored to a wetland by blocking the drainage ditches and allowing the land to flood, forming ponds or lakes for waterfowl. Peat takes hundreds of years to form, however, and the new wetland is not the same as the original one. Over time, wetland vegetation will return to the area.

Figure 3.21 Adding peat to soil improves the fertility of the soil.

Figure 3.22 Holland Marsh is a former wetland area in southern Ontario. It is now used for market gardening.

Figure 3.23 The pitcher plant is the provincial flower for the Province of Newfoundland and Labrador. Insects that are attracted to the plant slip down the smooth lip of the flower into a liquid at the base. There they drown and are digested.

Word CONNECT

Some people believe that the *preservation* of certain natural areas is not possible. They argue that *conservation* of these areas is a more realistic approach. In the glossary, look up the terms "preservation" and "conservation." Now that you know what these terms mean, which side of the argument do you agree with? Explain your answer.

A harvested bog can also be converted to another use. For example, former peatlands in parts of southern Ontario, Québec, Newfoundland, and New Brunswick are now used for pasture and the production of such vegetables as carrots, cabbages, and onions (see Figure 3.22). Agricultural use, however, is restricted to more southerly parts of Canada where the climate is suitable. In many European countries, drained peatlands are converted to forests.

Protecting Wetlands

When bogs disappear, plants and animals that live in bog habitats, such as mosses and frogs, also disappear. This reduces the biodiversity of the area. Many bog plants are specially adapted to the conditions of bogs and cannot grow easily in other ecosystems. For example, plants that grow in bogs must be able to survive without the rich supply of nutrients found in soils. Some, such as pitcher plants, butterworts, and sundews, do this by trapping and digesting small insects. Enzymes in the plants break down the insects' tissues, which are a source of nitrogen and other nutrients.

Organisms that live in bogs all year round are not the only ones that are affected. In the summer, ducks and geese breed in wetlands. Other insect-eating birds feed on the clouds of insects that are found there. In the winter, these birds fly south. The loss of bogs in Canada therefore affects populations of animals far beyond the bogs and even beyond Canada (see Figure 3.24). In the next activity, you will research ways in which people are trying to protect areas of ecological importance.

Natural areas are not only important for maintaining biodiversity, they are also important for cultural and scientific reasons. Many wilderness areas are sacred to Aboriginal people, whose cultures show a deep appreciation for Earth as a whole. People who visit wilderness areas can experience nature first-hand. They can learn more about their natural surroundings or simply relax in the great outdoors. How are natural areas important to you?

Figure 3.24 The endangered whooping crane breeds in the wetlands of northern Alberta and winters in the southern United States. There are fewer than 400 whooping cranes in the world.

Protecting Canada's Ecosystems

Much of Canada's wilderness has been greatly reduced. Many people are concerned that our natural areas are being destroyed by human activities, including farming, urban sprawl, mining, and forestry. In this activity, you will research the ways in which people are trying to protect ecosystems in Canada.

What to Do

1. Work in a small group. At your local library and/or on the Internet, research one of the following questions:
   - How are Canada's Aboriginal people involved in protecting natural areas?
   - What are the goals of Canada's National Parks system? Have these goals been met? What challenges remain?
   - What function does the Canadian Wildlife Service provide in protecting natural areas?
   - What non-governmental organizations (NGOs) in Canada are involved in protecting natural areas? Choose one organization and outline its main concerns.
   - How many different areas of protected land and water are there in Canada? Choose a province or region of Canada to investigate this question. Make a map to show the protected areas. What types of ecosystems are these areas meant to protect?

   - How are federal and provincial governments involved in protecting natural areas?
   - What are some plants and animals that are at risk? What is the status of these organisms? What threats do they face? What is being done to protect them, and who is involved?

2. Share your findings with the class in the form of a presentation. Use visual aids, and include a question-and-answer period.

What Did You Discover?

1. How are the different sectors of society — corporations, consumers, NGOs, and governments — involved in the protection of natural areas?

2. Have current approaches to protecting natural areas been successful? What problems have been encountered? How were they resolved? What challenges remain?

3. What recommendations would you provide to organizations involved in protecting natural areas? Be specific.

Extensions

4. What job opportunities might be created through sustaining our biological resources?

5. What is the Canadian Wilderness Charter? Who was involved in formulating it?

Scientists gain much information by studying natural areas. Recall, from Chapter 2, that human activity has disrupted the nutrient cycles, thus affecting our air, water and soil. Scientists collect data about the quality of our air and water, and plant productivity, to learn about the health of our ecosystems. For example, scientists are studying the protected soils in Riding Mountain National Park, Manitoba (see Figure 3.25) to learn more about the rates of erosion in the surrounding agricultural areas. This has helped to establish criteria for measuring the erosion of these farmlands.

Figure 3.25 Scientific research in protected areas, such as Riding Mountain National Park, help us monitor the health of our ecosystems.

Modelling an Environmental Impact Assessment (EIA)

Think About It

The ways in which people use land can have far-reaching effects. How much land should be used for farming, for forests, for urban development and industry, and for wildlife habitats? Your decisions on land use should be based on ecological factors as well as social and economic factors.

Most of the provincial governments in Canada have procedures that try to balance the conflicting demands over land use. For example, before a major building project (such as a new highway, gas pipeline, shopping mall, or factory) can begin, the government requires an *Environmental Impact Assessment (EIA)*. A team of investigators examines the issues and assesses the possible impact of the development on the natural environment. The team also considers any positive effects, such as creating jobs or providing money for the local community. Based on the EIA, the government may decide to approve the proposed development, to turn it down, or to allow it to go ahead with modifications to protect the environment. In this activity, you will integrate the skills and knowledge you have learned so far to simulate the process of an EIA.

Arial view of a construction site

What to Do

1 Identify a local project that involves a conflict over land use. Perhaps there is a proposal to expand a landfill site or to build on agricultural land. Maybe a highway is being extended or a hotel is being built on the edge of a lake. If there is no suitable local project, find a project in another part of your province.

2 As a class, agree on four roles to discuss the project and identify its impact on the environment and on different groups in society. Two roles will favour the project, and two will oppose it.

3 Form four groups, so that each group can represent one role. You do not have to agree with the point of view of your group's role, but you must present it fairly. Create a profile of your group's role.

Gathering Information

4 Use your local library and/or the Internet to research the project. To help you focus, consider the objectives of your group. Develop a list of questions related to your group's role: for example,
- What is the cost of the project?
- What will be its impact on wildlife habitats or soil?
- How will the project affect people in the local community?
- What are the health concerns?
- What are the short-term and long-term consequences of the project?

5 When you have gathered information that answers your questions, decide how you will use this information to develop a land-use proposal that furthers your role's objectives.

Developing a Proposal

6 Develop a proposal that presents your group's point of view on the project. You may present the proposal using any resources available. For example, you may present your proposal in a video, a skit, a series of charts, or a model.

7 Present your group's proposal to the class. Allow for a brief question-and-answer period at the end. As each group makes its presentation, other groups should take notes for later discussion.

8 You may want to revise your proposal after having heard all the other groups make their presentations.

Debate and Decision

9 Have a class debate to evaluate the arguments for and against the land-development project. During the course of the debate, record any new information that you learn about the impact of the project. Be courteous to all the other students, since you are participating in a joint decision-making process.

10 As a class, draft a final Environmental Impact Assessment. Base your recommendations on what you have learned through your research and your development of the four proposals. The EIA report may approve the development or recommend that it be abandoned or modified.

Analyze

1. Describe some advantages and disadvantages of the EIA process you simulated in this investigation.

2. Were there critical questions or issues that were not covered in this process? If so, what were they?

3. Do you think that facts, presentation skills, or some other factor is most effective in determining the outcome of decisions over land use? Give reasons for your answer.

4. Give an example of how your studies of ecosystems helped you either present a point of view or make your decision on the EIA.

Conclude and Apply

5. "The Environmental Impact Assessment process can both solve and create problems." Based on your model of an EIA, provide examples to support this statement.

Extend Your Skills

6. Now that you have some experience in organizing an EIA, prepare a graphic organizer, such as a flow chart or concept map, to show the stages involved in the EIA process.

Skill
POWER

For tips on how to prepare a concept map, turn to page 578.

Check Your Understanding

1. In which two climatic conditions are bogs formed?

2. What plant is the main component of peat?

3. Contrast common attitudes to bogs in the past and the present.

4. Why are insect-trapping plants common in bogs?

5. When are Environmental Impact Assessments required by governments?

6. **Apply** Bogs were considered wastelands until their environmental values were more widely understood. What other area might be considered wasteland, and what ecological values might it have?

Now that you have completed this chapter, try to do the following. If you cannot, go back to the sections indicated.

Describe several different characteristics of soil. (3.1)

Explain why soil differs from one area to another. (3.1)

Relate different soil types to different climatic conditions. (3.1)

Explain why a forest ecosystem in the Tropics has greater biodiversity than a forest ecosystem in Canada. (3.1)

List some soil organisms, and describe their roles in the soil ecosystem. (3.1)

Outline a typical sequence of changes that occur during the process of succession, starting with bare rock and ending with a forest. (3.2)

Define the term "climax community." (3.2)

Describe an example of secondary succession. (3.2)

Define "remediation" as it relates to land use, and give an example. (3.2)

Explain the importance of lichens in the process of succession. (3.2)

Describe how a disturbed area of land can be remediated. (3.2)

Explain why a forest fire is less damaging than soil erosion. (3.2)

Outline the process that is used to produce an Environmental Impact Assessment. (3.3)

List some of the ecological values of a wetland. (3.3)

Describe how peat is formed. (3.3)

Discuss the advantages and disadvantages of using a bog for peat harvesting versus conserving the bog as wildlife habitat. (3.3)

Summarize this chapter by doing one of the following. Use a graphic organizer (such as a concept map), produce a poster, or write the summary to include the key chapter concepts. Here are a few ideas to use as a guide:

• How do the characteristics of soil affect the plants growing in it?

• Why do different parts of Canada have different types of soil?

• How might a wetland community become transformed into a forest community over time?

• Why does the community of plants and animals in a field or a vacant building lot change if the field or lot is abandoned?

• How is a forest community in the Tropics different from a forest community in Canada?

• How do some human activities reduce the productivity of land?

• What reasons could you give to oppose or support the building of a shopping mall on an area of productive farming land?

• What is the value of protecting wetlands?

Reviewing Key Terms

If you need to review, the section numbers show you where these terms were introduced.

1. In your notebook, use the terms in column B to complete the sentences in column A.

A

- ▓▓▓▓▓▓▓ transforms a bare landscape into a forest.
- The plants, animals, and micro-organisms that live together in an area form a ▓▓▓▓▓▓▓ .
- ▓▓▓▓▓▓▓ involves the use of plants to remove toxins from the soil.
- ▓▓▓▓▓▓▓ are the first to live in an inhospitable landscape.
- After a forest fire, ▓▓▓▓▓▓▓ restores the forest ecosystem.
- People can ▓▓▓▓▓▓▓ a site by removing toxic materials there.
- A ▓▓▓▓▓▓▓ has the maximum level of plant productivity for its given environmental conditions.
- ▓▓▓▓▓▓▓ are mixtures of land, water, and plants.

B

- soil (3.1)
- community (3.1)
- succession (3.2)
- primary succession (3.2)
- secondary succession (3.2)
- pioneer organisms (3.2)
- climax community (3.2)
- remediate (3.2)
- phytoremediation (3.2)
- wetlands (3.3)

Understanding Key Concepts

Section numbers are provided if you need to review.

2. Name three of the characteristics of soil. (3.1)

3. How do the organisms that live in soil affect the characteristics of soil? (3.1)

4. Why might the soil in one area of Canada differ from the soil in another area? (3.1)

5. What process would alter the community of organisms in a school playing field if the field were not maintained? Describe what would happen. (3.2)

6. Why do ecosystems change naturally over time? (3.2)

7. How are primary and secondary succession similar? How are they different? (3.2)

8. Where would you expect to find a pioneer species? Why? (3.2)

9. Give an example of how human activities can affect the process of succession. (3.3)

Developing Skills

10. Examine the following illustration. Describe what is happening at each stage indicated by the letters.

11. A developer wants to build a new shopping mall at the edge of a town, on a piece of land that is now a wetland. How would you organize an Environmental Impact Assessment to recommend whether this project should proceed? Make lists of the different groups involved and the questions that you would ask in order to make your recommendation.

12. Make a field guide for a particular group of plants in your neighbourhood. Work on your own or in a small group. Focus your guide to answer a specific question, such as

   • Which pioneer species grow near the school?
   • Are there any medicinal plants in the neighbourhood?
   • What native trees are present?

   First identify and classify the plants in your chosen group. Sketch or photograph the plants, and organize them in your guide. Include a map to show where people might find them growing.

Problem Solving/Applying

13. List the characteristics that you would expect to find in soil taken from

   (a) a farmer's field

   (b) a desert

   (c) a supply of commercial potting soil

   (d) a wetland

14. Why are decomposers important in the process of primary succession?

15. Your school is applying for a grant from a local community foundation to naturalize half of the playing field. Prepare a "case for support", which outlines the environmental and social implications of the project. Also consider the costs involved, and prepare a budget to do the work.

16. Some parks have signs that read "Keep off the grass." Explain what might happen to a grassy area that is heavily used by people.

Critical Thinking

17. An area of forest is logged, and the exposed soil is washed away by heavy rains. A similar area of forest is destroyed by a forest fire. Explain which of these two disturbances is likely to have a longer effect.

18. How can draining a wetland in Canada affect the population of insect-eating birds in Central America?

19. In some parts of Canada, a grassland prairie is a climax community. In other parts of Canada, a forest is a climax community. Discuss what factors might produce different climax communities in different areas.

Pause& Reflect

1. Go back to the beginning of the chapter, on page 72, and check your original answers to the Opening Ideas questions. How has your thinking changed? How would you answer those questions now that you have investigated the topics in this chapter?

2. How can a climax community be stable and changing at the same time?

4 Planet Home

Opening Ideas...

- How much land is necessary to support the needs of one Canadian?
- Should Canadian wilderness parks be open to unlimited numbers of visitors?
- Why does a litre of oil cost more than a litre of water?

Science Log

In your Science Log, write the heading "Ecology and Economy." Look up the meanings of "ecology" and "economy" in a dictionary, and write them down. With your class, discuss ideas about how our economy depends on supplies of natural resources. Then write your thoughts about the Opening Ideas questions.

How would you study the ecology of a group of people? Suppose that you want to record the behaviour of a family of Canadians as they go about their daily business. You follow them in the morning as they leave their home and note how far they move. You observe them in a shopping mall and record what food they eat and what other resources in their environment they use. How are they affected by the weather? What features of the environment threaten their survival?

If you try to do this, you will soon discover that it is not the same as studying the ecology of, say, a family of deer in a forest, for instance. Deer can only eat food growing in the place where they live. Canadians, however, might eat bananas harvested in the tropics or fish caught in the ocean off South America. Deer cannot escape the weather by sheltering inside a heated home or flying south in an airplane.

Do the relationships that apply to other species apply to humans? Are the limits of food, space, disease, predators, climate, and competition, which control animal populations, relevant to us? Some people think that we will always be able to use technology to change the environment so that it meets our needs. We can increase our food production, live in high densities in cities, and restrict or eliminate diseases, predators, and pests. Does this mean that there are no limits on the human population? In this chapter, you will explore links between our society and technology and our use of resources. Can ecosystems around the world sustain our demands? Will we always be able to develop new supplies of resources if old supplies run out?

Where Does It Come From?

Have you ever stopped to think that everything you buy and use is related to the land? How much land was used to produce your food, or your home, or the materials that your clothes are made from? How much land is used to dispose of the waste that you produce every day?

Key Concepts

In this chapter, you will discover

- what happens when there is growing demand for a limited resource
- how managing the environment is different from managing a warehouse
- how technology affects our relationship with the environment
- how economics affects our relationship with the environment

Key Skills

In this chapter, you will

- use a model to simulate a wildlife management project
- graph deer population data and interpret the results
- convert population size and use of resources into equivalent areas of land
- research and analyze how new technologies increase our use of resources
- produce an information brochure about food biotechnology

Key Terms

- tragedy of the commons
- commons
- ecological footprint
- paradigm
- economics

Starting Point ACTIVITY

What to Do

1. As a class, make a list of products that you use every day, such as a telephone, a tube of toothpaste, and a bed.

2. In a small group, select one product from the class list for analysis. Obtain an illustration or a sample of your product.

3. Make a table like the one below. Give your table a title. Write the name of your product in the first column. In the second column, list all the materials that are used to make the product. Include the package materials.

Product	Materials used	Resources used	Related activities

4. Find out how each material in your product is produced. What natural resources are used? What activities are needed to convert each natural resource into the material: for example, logging or mining? Use your findings to complete the table.

5. Construct a chain concept map that begins with one natural resource and ends with your product. Show the different steps and the types of land use involved.

What Did You Discover?

1. Think about the materials that were used to make your product.
   (a) Which materials are non-renewable?
   (b) Which materials can be recycled?

2. How many different types of land use were involved to make your product?

3. Choose one resource that was used to make your group's product, and imagine that it no longer exists. Would people still be able to make the product? Explain.

4.1 Managing Resources

Figure 4.1 How many cows do you think this pasture can sustain?

Suppose that you have just inherited 10 ha of good pasture. You think that you might like to keep some cows on it and sell their milk to make money. How many cows will give you the most profit? If you keep 10 cows, each cow will have 1 ha of pasture on which to graze. If you keep 50 cows, you will get five times more milk, but each cow will have only 0.2 ha of pasture. You do not want to spend money on extra food. What questions must you ask before you can calculate the optimum number of cows that could graze on your land for an indefinite period?

Suppose that the pasture you inherited is not for your use alone. It is to be shared with nine other people as common property. All ten of you have equal rights to use the land for grazing, but nobody can fence off a 1 ha portion for his or her exclusive use. How do you think this might affect the way that the pasture is managed and the number of cows that you might decide to graze on it? Complete the following activity to find out.

Science Inquiry ACTIVITY

The Common Good

What problems occur when a population shares a limited resource? This activity is a simulation model that will help you analyze the problems of sustainability.

What You Need
bingo chips or similar items (100 per group)
watch or clock

What to Do

1. Work in a group of ten. Arrange yourselves in a circle.

2. Place 100 chips in the centre of the circle.

3. You will "harvest" chips from your group's supply for short periods of time (between 30 s and 2 min). Your teacher will signal the start and end of each harvest. Your goal is to obtain maximum points *for your group.*
   Points are obtained as follows:
   • Each student obtains one point for each 10 chips she or he harvests.
   • At the end of each harvest, the supply of chips that remains in the centre of each group will be doubled (to a maximum of 100 chips).
   • The group with the largest supply of chips left in the centre after each harvest will obtain one point for each student in the group.

4. Carry out the first harvest as directed by your teacher.

5. Calculate the total points obtained by each group.

6. Discuss reasons why different groups obtained different numbers of points.

7. Repeat the harvest three more times.

What Did You Discover?

1. What strategies of harvesting led to the greatest decline in a group's resources (the chips)?

2. What strategy of harvesting led to the highest number of points obtained by a group?

3. Is the strategy that provides maximum points to individuals the same as the strategy that provides maximum points to groups? Explain.

4. **Apply** Suggest some resources that the chips in this model might represent.

Skill
P O W E R

For tips on using models in science, turn to page 606.

Tragedy of the Commons

The model that you explored in the previous activity is an example of a situation called the **tragedy of the commons.** The **commons** is any resource that is shared by a group of people. For example, the air we breathe and the water we drink are commons. Grazing land, forests, lakes, and oceans are also commons. Everybody has the right to freely use the resources of the commons, as either a supply of materials or a place to put wastes. Why do you think this relationship with the environment leads to tragedy?

In Britain before 1700 B.C.E., most people lived in villages that had a common pasture on which all the villagers could graze their horses, cattle, and sheep (see Figure 4.2). This system can work if the population is small, the area of the commons is large, and nobody is rich or greedy. It often fails to work, however, because of the way that the gains and costs of the commons are calculated.

Figure 4.2 Unfenced common land in Great Britain could be used by anyone to graze animals.

Each household gains from putting animals on the commons. The more animals that a household grazes, the more it gains and the richer it becomes. Without proper management, however, the commons can become overgrazed. This causes the quantity and quality of the grass to decline and the food supply for the animals to be reduced. Although the gains of free grazing benefit individual households, the costs of overgrazing are shared among all households. As a result, the system actually encourages people to put as many animals onto the commons as they can afford. The tragedy is that the commons are used in an unsustainable way, leading to a shrinking resource for everyone.

In Britain, many commons were ruined by overuse as villages and wealth grew. To solve this problem, large common lands were divided into smaller areas, each owned by one household. There was now no advantage to exploiting the land. The system of private ownership encouraged people to maintain their land for the long-term benefit of their children and future generations. This system was not without problems, however. What new problems do you think were created? In the following investigation, you will examine various factors that are involved in managing a population in a modern commons.

Balancing Populations and the Environment

Provincial parks are modern examples of commons. The resources of a park are shared by human visitors and by all the organisms that live in the park. One goal of a park manager is to maintain the resources of the park for the benefit of all its users over many years. An increase in demand for resources by any species affects all the other users.

In this investigation, you will play the role of a park manager. Your job is to help maintain the deer population at or near the carrying capacity for the park. (Recall the definition of "carrying capacity," given on page 19.)

Problem

What factors might cause a population to be out of balance with the carrying capacity of the environment?

Safety Precautions

You will be using a sharp pencil to make holes through poster paper.

Apparatus

bag of 100 checkers or similar
 objects (50 black and 50 red)
calculator
pencils
eraser
ruler

Materials

2 sheets of white poster paper
 (32 cm × 32 cm each)
32 squares of green adhesive
 notepaper (4 cm × 4 cm each)
graph paper

Procedure

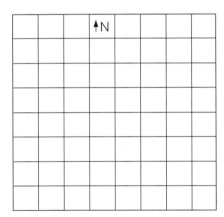

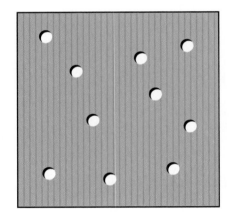

1 Work in a group of four. On one sheet of poster paper, draw a grid of eight squares by eight squares. Each square should be 4 cm × 4 cm. This grid represents a provincial park. Indicate which direction is north, and give your park a name.

2 Prepare a hunting screen from the second sheet of poster paper. Using a sharp pencil, make ten holes at random in the paper. **CAUTION:** Push the pencil though the poster paper carefully to make the holes.

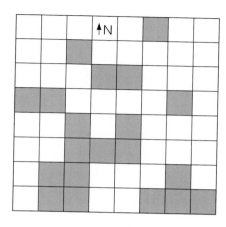

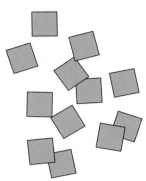

3 The 32 adhesive green squares of paper represent land with sufficient vegetation for deer to browse. Stick all the squares onto your park, within the squares created by the grid lines. Think about how the pattern of squares you create might affect the deer. The 32 uncovered (white) squares represent land that is overgrazed or otherwise unsuitable for deer.

4 The black checkers are male deer (bucks), and the red checkers are female deer (does). To begin, stock your park with 32 deer randomly chosen from the bag. Place one deer on each green square. This population size (32) represents the carrying capacity of the park.

5 You will manage your deer population for five years. At the start of each year, you will establish a wildlife management policy. (For example, you may restrict hunting or supply extra food in the winter.) During the rest of the year, the following four factors will affect the number of deer:
- mating season (see rules of the game)
- a seasonal impact, either human or natural: for example, a forest fire or flood, disease, deep snow, or poaching
- hunting season (see "Rules of the Game")
- immigration and emigration (see "Rules of the Game")

RULES OF THE GAME

Mating Season

Any doe that has sufficient nutrition (she must be on a green square) and has a buck in an adjacent square, mates to produce one fawn. The fawn (a new checker chosen at random from the bag) is placed under the doe checker. At the end of each year, the fawns must move from their mother's care into a vacant adjacent square. If suitable land (a green square) is unavailable, they must move to overgrazed land (a white square). If there is no vacant adjacent square, they die and are removed from the board.

Rules for mating season: Doe A can mate. Doe B cannot mate (no adjacent buck). Doe C cannot mate (on white square).

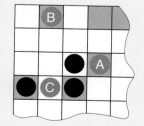

Hunting Season

Place the hunting screen on top of your park. Any deer that can be seen through the holes is shot by hunters and removed from the park — unless your management policy affects the hunting rules for the year. Each year, exchange hunting screens with a different group.

Immigration and Emigration

Any deer on a perimeter white square (overgrazed land) either moves to an empty adjacent green square or leaves the park (emigration). Any unoccupied good land (a green square) on the perimeter of the park is filled by new deer entering the park (immigration). Choose new deer at random from the bag.

Rules for migration: Doe A moves to adjacent green square. Buck B leaves park (no adjacent vacant green square). Doe C enters park (vacant green square on perimeter).

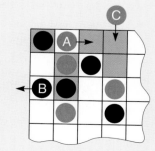

CONTINUED ▶

6 As a class, create a list of events for each of the five years, using all the factors in the order presented in step 5. All the groups will follow the same list, but it may produce different results in different parks.

7 Make a data table, as shown here. After each event, record the number of deer in your data table. At the end of the game, make line graphs of your data.

8 Present your results to the class.

Deer Population Study Data

Time	Factor	Number of deer		
		Females	**Males**	**Total**
start				
year 1	mating season			
	seasonal impact			
	hunting season			
	migration			
year 2	mating season			
	seasonal impact			
	hunting season			
	migration			

Analyze

1. Was there a trend in the deer population in your park? In other words, did the population increase, decrease, or remain at about the same number during the five years?

2. If you experienced a consistent increase or decrease in deer numbers, explain the main reason for this change. How could you achieve a more stable population?

3. Did different parks experience different results? If so, suggest the main cause of the differences.

Conclude and Apply

4. Local conservation groups want to reintroduce wolves to your park. As park manager, explain why you would agree or disagree with the proposal. List various effects that a population of wolves might produce in your park.

5. A major goal of provincial parks is to conserve natural ecosystems. Give an example of how a particular land use next to a park might affect this goal.

6. How are the factors that determine the size of a deer population in a park similar to the factors that determine the human population of Canada? How are they different?

7. Over the past two centuries, the numbers and distribution of deer in parts of North America have varied greatly as a result of human activities. How would each of the following activities affect deer numbers?
   - removing forests
   - regenerating forests
   - removing wolves
   - restricting hunting

Extend Your Knowledge

8. In this investigation, you examined some of the factors that affect a deer population. Suggest other factors that could affect a real population of deer in a real forest.

Skill
P O W E R
For tips on how to make a line graph, turn to page 602.

Can People Manage Nature?

So far in this unit, you have learned about the following ecological processes:

- Energy from the Sun is captured by plants and transferred from species to species through food webs.
- Materials, such as carbon and nitrogen, are continually recycled from the abiotic part of the environment to organisms, and back again.
- Populations of organisms continually interact with one another and their environment.
- Ecosystems change over time in response to changes in the environment.

When you think about these processes, what images come to mind? All of these processes involve movement and change. They involve connections between parts. They create images of ecosystems that are dynamic and interconnected, as shown in Figure 4.3.

Figure 4.3 Natural ecosystems are based on dynamic relationships in which everything is connected to everything else.

Our ability to manage ecosystems in a sustainable way depends, in part, on the images of nature that we have. Until recently, most people ignored or overlooked the connections between the different parts of the environment. How do you think our understanding of nature has been affected by the culture in which we live?

In western culture, a traditional view is that Earth's resources are for human use — much like the products in a warehouse, as shown in Figure 4.4. How is this view misleading? How is managing a warehouse different from managing an ecosystem?

Figure 4.4 Traditional western culture views organisms as goods in a warehouse, with no connections to other organisms and their environment.

We can take products from a warehouse and move them from one shelf to another. If we leave the warehouse and return later, we will find everything the same as we left it. In contrast, an ecosystem is continually changing, independent of human actions. For example, follow the events in Figure 4.5 to see what might happen if white-tailed deer in a park were protected from hunting.

A Lack of hunting results in greater survival of deer. The deer population increases.

B Deer feed on the growing tips and leaves of seedlings. This damages or kills the young trees. If the young trees are unable to survive to maturity, the forest may be unable to regenerate itself.

C Deer prefer some species of trees — such as the sugar maple, hemlock, and white ash — over others. Their feeding preferences can lead to changes in plant populations and loss of species diversity over time.

D Deer feed on low-growing vegetation. As a result, they may remove much of the ground cover and shrubs. Other species of wildlife, such the indigo bunting, depend on these layers of vegetation for food and shelter. Numbers of songbirds have declined in some areas where the deer population is high.

E As deer compete for food and space in the forest, some move onto neighbouring land. There they damage agricultural crops, gardens, and landscape plants.

F Deer carry ticks that transmit Lyme disease. An increase in the deer population spreads this disease to other organisms, including people.

G Deer that leave the forest create a traffic hazard. In Canada, deer are involved in many thousands of collisions with vehicles each year.

Figure 4.5 Some effects of a growing deer population.

Deer play an important role in the food chain and the cycling of nutrients in the forest ecosystem. However, deer can have a negative impact on other organisms when their numbers exceed the carrying capacity of the environment.

Understanding the processes in an ecosystem is only one step in managing nature. We must also change the way in which our culture views the relationships between people, other species, and the environment.

Figure 4.6 Aboriginal peoples have an extensive knowledge of the plants and animals in their environment.

INTERNET CONNECT

www.school.mcgrawhill.ca/resources/

The field of environmental education among Aboriginal people is known as Traditional Ecological Knowledge (TEK). Aboriginal people have their own views of the environment, which are different from the views of western culture. To learn more about TEK, go to the web site above. Go to **Science Resources**, then to **SCIENCEPOWER 10** to know where to go next. What is TEK? What is being done to encourage and broaden TEK? How is TEK being used to manage resources? Prepare a brief report based on your research.

Check Your Understanding

1. What is a commons?

2. Briefly describe what is meant by the tragedy of the commons.

3. Give examples to show how an increasing population of herbivores in a forest might affect

    (a) forest vegetation

    (b) another species of forest animal

    (c) an ecosystem that is adjacent to the forest

4. **Apply** In a wilderness park, Canadians can experience unspoiled natural ecosystems. Give two specific examples to show how too many visitors to a wilderness park might prevent this from happening.

5. **Thinking Critically** A good model behaves much like the real thing. Why is managing a warehouse not a good model for managing an ecosystem? Give a detailed explanation of your answer.

Word CONNECT

A *metaphor* is a figure of speech that compares one thing with another in order to illustrate a meaning. Metaphors are used by both scientists and artists. The tragedy of the commons is a metaphor that compares a village commons with Earth's land, atmosphere, and oceans. In this section, a warehouse was used as a metaphor to illustrate how people try to manage the environment. Create your own metaphor to illustrate your understanding of people's relationships with the natural environment.

4.2 Ecological Footprints

Figure 4.7 People could not live in cities unless there were areas of land elsewhere on which to produce the food and materials they need every day.

Try the following thought experiment: Imagine that your city is suddenly covered with a huge transparent dome, so that it is like the Biosphere II project described on page 38. Nothing can get in or out of the dome except sunlight. What would happen to the people in the city? Think about all the things that people need (including all the things that they must get rid of) to survive. Can these needs be met by the environment within the dome?

You probably realized that the city would cease to function and its inhabitants would perish within a few days. The environment of a city cannot support the population of humans that live there. One reason is that a city is a place where large quantities of resources are consumed but few resources are produced. For example, nearly all the food that the citizens need to survive must be transported to the city from somewhere else. Most of the waste materials that are produced by the citizens are transported out of the city. In other words, the geographic location of a city population is not the same as its ecological location (the places where the population obtains its needs). For instance, compare a city population with a population of deer. The deer population is limited to the carrying capacity of the forest where the deer live. The human population of the city, however, is sustained by other ecosystems in other parts of the world.

Figure 4.8 Our technology increases our ability to extract resources from the environment and increases the amount of waste that we put back into the environment.

We are able to use resources that originate far from where we live because we have technology. In effect, all our tools and toys are extensions of our bodies. Cars and bicycles extend our legs, buildings and clothes extend our skin, telephones and televisions extend our ears and voices, books and computers extend our brains, construction machinery extends our hands, and so on. Like our bodies, our technology requires a supply of materials and energy from the environment. Our technology also produces wastes that must be disposed of in the land, water, or air.

Our use of technology is the most important way in which humans differ from other species. If you think of technology as extensions of our bodies, then humans are like very large animals with very large demands for resources. Our biological needs plus our technological needs produce a combined human-technology impact on the world (see Figure 4.9).

Recall that carrying capacity is defined as the largest population of a species that an environment can support over the long term. Does this definition apply to humans? If the factors that limit other species do not apply to humans, how can we think about the carrying capacity of Earth for the human population? One solution to this problem was developed during the 1990s by a Canadian scientist working at the University of British Columbia. Dr. William Rees and his students proposed that population size should be combined with resource consumption and waste production, then converted into equivalent units of productive land and water area. He used the metaphor of an **ecological footprint** to describe his idea. It is summarized in the following equation.

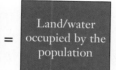

$$\text{Ecological footprint of a population} = \text{Land/water occupied by the population} + \text{Land/water used to produce resources for the population} + \text{Land/water used to dispose of wastes for the population}$$

Figure 4.9 One Canadian, plus all the technology that he or she uses, has a huge impact on Earth. A Canadian's impact is more like the impact of Godzilla than the impact of a gorilla.

This equation reminds us that we depend on land and water ecosystems for our survival. Because most of us now live in towns and cities, it is easy for us to be unaware of our demands on the environment. Most of the resources that we use come from outside our communities, and even from outside our country. To study the impact of the people in your community on the environment, you need to study the entire planet, including the oceans and atmosphere.

As an example, Dr. Rees' group calculated the ecological footprint of the city of Vancouver, British Columbia, not including its suburds (see Figure 4.10). The city boundary encloses an area of 11 400 ha (114 km²), with a population (1991) of about 472 000 people. Table 4.1 shows the land and water demand by each person in the city.

Table 4.1 Area of Land and Water Needed by Vancouverites.

Individual demand	Area of land/water needed per person (ha)
farmland to produce meat protein	2.1
forests to produce wood and paper	1.5
space to live	0.2
forests to absorb CO_2 from the burning of fossil fuels	2.3
oceans to produce seafood	1.0

Figure 4.10 How large do you think the ecological footprint of Vancouver, British Columbia, is?

Adding the five values in the table, the ecological footprint of a typical Vancouverite is about 7 ha. The total footprint for the city is over 3 300 000 ha of land! This means that the city population uses an area of land and water that is about 290 times larger than the area of the city in order to maintain its present level of consumption. In the next investigation, you will analyze a model of growth in consumption.

Alternatives to Growth

People who live in developed countries, such as Canada, consume more resources and produce more wastes per person than people living in developing countries. One goal of international development is to raise the material standards of developing countries. Achieving this goal requires an increase in the production and consumption of materials and energy. Is continual growth in material consumption possible in a world with finite (limited) resources? Can the quality of life be maintained or improved without growth? You can examine these questions by analyzing a model of growth.

What to Do

Carefully read the scenario below, and then answer the questions that follow.

The Ever-Growing Library

The number of books and journals in a university library has been doubling every 15 years since the 1960s. The library is running out of room to add more books. Some publications have been transferred onto microfilm or computer to save space. This new technology has not reduced the size of the collection, however, but only made it possible to add even more publications. Publishers produce new volumes with new information every year. The librarians realize that their library cannot grow forever. On the other hand, they cannot stop buying new books nor throw out all the old books. Students at the university need to keep up to date, but they also need access to important materials from the past. What should the librarians do?

Analyze

1. Given a choice, would you prefer a library that had only books published before 2000, only books published after 2000, or a mixture of books from both periods? Explain your reasons.

2. What criteria would you use to select new books to add to the library?

3. What criteria would you use to discard old books from the library?

4. Do you think that a new technology, in the future, will make it possible to increase a library collection forever? Explain why or why not.

5. To keep the size of the library collection in the scenario constant but updated, you must discard one old book for every new book you acquire. How will you determine the rate at which new books are acquired?

6. Does the quality of a library depend on the number of publications it has? Explain.

Conclude and Apply

7. Does the model of the library suggest that it is possible to maintain or improve the quality of people's lives without a continual growth in consumption? Explain.

8. What other types of resources might the books represent?

The concept of the ecological footprint helps us to see the "big picture" — the relationships between people and resources. As a measure of overall resource consumption, it indicates if everybody can consume resources at current levels without endangering the planet's capacity to support life.

From an analysis of 52 countries, researchers found only 10 countries in which the average citizen used fewer resources than were available on a world-wide per capita basis. This means the ecological footprint of these countries were the same size as, or smaller than, the land areas of the countries themselves. The ecological footprints of the other 42 countries were larger than the land areas of the countries themselves. These figures show that present rates of growth in population and consumption worldwide are not sustainable. At some point, we must reduce consumption, population, or both.

What would be the ecological footprint of the global population if all the 6 billion people in the world lived at current Canadian levels of consumption? Use a value of 7 ha of land per person. Draw a scale diagram to compare the size of this footprint with the total land area of Earth (13 billion hectares) and the total area of ecologically productive cropland, pasture, and forest (8.8 billion hectares). During your lifetime, the global population will double to 12 billion people if present rates of growth are maintained. How many hectares of productive land will be available to each person, assuming no further decline in the area of productive land?

INTERNET CONNECT

www.school.mcgrawhill.ca/resources/

The *human population clock* gives the total global human population size. It is constantly updated. To visit this clock on the Internet, go to the web site above. Go to **Science Resources**, then to **SCIENCEPOWER 10** to know where to go next. Decide on a specific time period to analyze. Record the population changes over ten consecutive intervals during the time period. Make a graph, or use another method, to illustrate the rate of change of the population for the time period. On the same graph, illustrate changes in the ecological footprint of the world population relative to the total land area of Earth. Use an average ecological footprint of 1 ha per person.

Check Your Understanding

1. Explain what is meant by the following statement: The geographic locations of human populations are no longer the same as their ecological locations.

2. Describe two ways in which the tools of technology are extensions of our bodies.

3. In your own words, the term "ecological footprint."

4. Explain why the size of a deer population is limited by the carrying capacity of the particular area where the deer live while the size of a human population is not.

5. **Apply** Prepare a poster illustrating the following idea: a higher-than-average level of resource consumption by the human population in one part of Earth must be balanced by a lower-than-average level of resource consumption by the population in another part of Earth.

6. **Thinking Critically** Is the average ecological footprint of a Canadian larger or smaller than the global average of 1 ha per person, or is it about the same? Explain your answer.

4.3 Sustainable Future

Pause&
Reflect

In your notebook, write an example of a paradigm from the past that seems strange to us today. Why did people of the past believe this paradigm? What happened to cause us to think differently?

A **paradigm** is a way of looking at the world that is shared by most people in a community. Paradigms may change as a result of scientific discoveries, observations, and new understandings. In the first half of the twentieth century, for example, most people believed that the continents on Earth have always been fixed in one place. There was a shift in the paradigm as more evidence led to the theory of plate tectonics. By the end of the twentieth century, most people believed that the continents move very slowly over the surface of Earth.

Can you think of any other recent paradigm shifts? Are we living in the middle of a paradigm shift today, related to the way we think about the environment? A hundred years ago, most people believed that Earth had unlimited resources and that the human impact on Earth was insignificant. Today we can see for ourselves the harmful effects that humans have on the environment. As a result, government and business policies have changed to reflect the new paradigm. For example, there are now controls on such things as waste disposal, pollution, and overfishing (see Figure 4.11).

Is the new focus on protecting the environment enough to avoid more problems? Has it produced a way of life that is sustainable for the future? The debate has not ended. Some people are optimistic that new technologies and economic growth will help to improve conditions for people and the environment around the world. Others, including many scientists, argue that another new paradigm is needed. One issue in the debate is how to measure the value of the environment in economic terms.

Figure 4.11 Sights such as this are less common in Canada than they once were. People have realized the harm, to both health and the environment, caused by the unrestricted dumping of pollutants into our air, land, and water.

Economy and Ecology

Economics is the study of how wealth is created and distributed. Like scientists, economists (people who study economics) use theories and models. Economic theories affect the ways that people in society think about the environment. For example, how would you calculate the economic value of a resource such as fish or trees? To do this, economists consider factors such as the quantity of the resource, the cost of obtaining it, and the amount of demand from consumers. The price in dollars (or other currency) per unit can change as any of these factors change.

Figure 4.12 What is the value of a tree? What is the value of a forest?

Suppose that a tree contains a certain quantity of wood with a market value of X dollars. What is the economic value of a forest that contains 1000 trees of the same size? The traditional economic model estimates the value of the forest as 1000X dollars, based on only the quantity of wood it contains. Natural resources, however, are more than goods. As well as supplying wood, a forest also provides services. For example, forests absorb carbon dioxide, filter water, help to prevent soil erosion, and maintain biodiversity. These services usually depend on maintaining the whole forest. If a forest is cut down, these services are lost. Most economic models ignore the value of environmental services. They consider the value of the environment to be only in the materials it contains.

STRETCH Your Mind

What other services are provided by ecosystems, or parts of ecosystems? Make a list of these services. How would you estimate their value to the economy?

Oil and Water

How much is oil worth in our economy? How much is drinking water worth? Is the most expensive of these liquids the most important in our lives? Is it the most important in ecosystems?

What to Do

Conduct research at your local library and/or on the Internet to determine the following:

(a) the average price of 1 L of motor oil and 1 L of drinking water in your community

(b) the estimated volumes of global reserves of fresh water and oil

What Did You Discover?

1. List the most common uses of each liquid.

2. Which liquid was more expensive?

3. Which liquid is non-renewable?

4. Which liquid is essential to life?

5. Which liquid is more important to modern technology?

6. Which liquid is more abundant?

Science Inquiry ACTIVITY

7. Make up a table with two columns. Name one column "Motor oil" and the other column "Water." At the top of each column, write the price per litre of each liquid. Below the price, list the characteristics of each liquid. Include your answers to the previous questions and any other factors that you consider important. Give your table a title.

8. Could you find or develop a substitute for (a) motor oil and (b) water if it were not available?

9. Based on your table, do you think the prices of these two liquids accurately reflect each value below?
   (a) their value relative to one another (for example, is the most common the least expensive?)
   (b) their value to human survival
   (c) their value in natural ecosystems

10. How would your life be affected if (a) motor oil and (b) water cost three times as much to buy?

Extensions

11. Carry out research to find the prices of oil and water in a country in Europe. Are the prices in Europe more, less, or about the same as the prices in Canada? Suggest reasons for any differences.

12. As a class, debate the following proposal: Water and oil are both goods. Canada should be able to sell its fresh water to other countries to earn money and create jobs. Is Canada's fresh water a resource to be conserved or a commodity to be sold?

Pause&
Reflect

Make a list of everyday items you use that were not invented 100 years ago. Could you live without any of these items? How has technology improved everyday life? What problems has it created?

New Technology

Photographs of cities a hundred years ago show busy streets full of vehicles pulled by horses (see Figure 4.13). Today this method of transportation seems old-fashioned and inefficient. A hundred years from now, will people look at photographs of our streets and wonder about the old-fashioned and inefficient gas-powered vehicles that we use?

Figure 4.13 Halifax at the beginning of the twentieth century

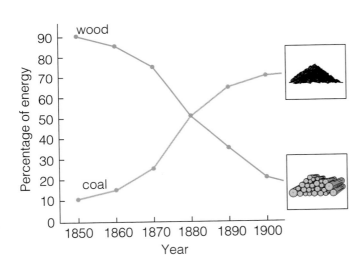

Figure 4.14 Changes in the amount of energy provided by wood and coal in the United States during the nineteenth century

Some economists argue that today's problem of resource depletion can be solved by developing new technologies and new ways of using resources. As in the past, we can invent new methods of transportation, construction, communication, food production, and medical treatment. We can substitute one type of material or one source of energy for another (see Figure 4.14). Biotechnology is an example of a new technology. For example, genetic engineering helps us produce new types of food and combat diseases and pests, by altering or adding genes in animals and plants. Such possibilities, say some economists, will allow us to sustain our levels of population growth and our consumption of resources. In the next investigation, you will explore how biotechnology is being used to produce new types of food.

Using Biotechnology to Produce Food

A growing human population increases the demand for food. Biotechnology is being used to produce food in new ways. What benefits does biotechnology have for society and the environment? What problems might it create? Is the use of genetically altered foods a sustainable method of food production? In this investigation, you will design an information brochure that considers some of these questions.

The salmon at the bottom of the photograph was genetically modified. It contains a gene that allowed it to grow up to six times faster than the two unmodified fish shown above.

Challenge

Design an illustrated information brochure about the biotechnology of food.

Materials

paper, coloured pencils, and markers

Design Criteria

A. Your brochure must feature an application of biotechnology that is used in food production by the Canadian agriculture or fishing industry.

B. Your brochure must be no longer than three pages, yet it should clearly explain the application and the related issues.

C. Your brochure should answer the following questions:
   - How is the application of biotechnology used, and how does it work?
   - How was the research funded?

- How did the scientific community assess its risks and benefits?
- What are the benefits and risks of the application to the following?
  (a) farmers   **(c)** the environment
  (b) consumers   **(d)** the economy

D. Your group will have one class period to design your brochure, as well as additional time to complete it.

E. You may use your local library, the Internet, and/or local government and industry to research your topic.

Plan and Construct

1 Decide on the role of each member of your group. Some of you can research the topic, while others can work on the presentation.

2 Determine who will be your audience. In other words, to whom do you want to distribute the brochure?

3 What types of illustrations will you include?

4 Be prepared to show an outline of your plan to your teacher for approval.

Evaluate

1. Do you think the application you studied will help to produce more food more efficiently and with less risk to the environment and consumers? Explain your answer.

2. Do you think using the application is sustainable? Explain your answer.

3. Could this application increase the carrying capacity of Earth for people? Explain your answer.

4. Was your brochure similar to another group's brochure? If not, in what ways was it unique?

5. How was a group approach useful for working on your design? How could you improve your group work?

Technology and Sustainability

Suppose that a new method of building a house uses only half of the materials that were needed before to build a house. Suppose that a new form of transport uses only half of the fuel that was needed before to carry the same number of people the same distance. If used properly, these new technologies would double our ability to produce housing and transportation from the same quantity of resources. Would this new technology therefore reduce our consumption of resources?

Think about the resources that you consume. Why do you consume them? Our economic system encourages consumption as a good activity and as an indication of our "quality of life." Thus consumption is not linked to our needs as much as to our wants. Although a new technology may reduce our consumption of one resource, we generally use the savings to increase our consumption of another resource.

Figure 4.15 Modern commercial fisheries harvest over 100 million tonnes of fish from the oceans every year.

In many cases, improved technology leads directly to an increase in consumption. For example, electronic fish-finding devices and larger, faster fishing ships have greatly increased the harvest from the sea. Larger harvests of fish feed more people, yet the productivity of marine ecosystems has not increased. When more fish are harvested than can be replaced by natural reproduction, fish populations decline. Eventually the populations are unable to sustain themselves. The result of overfishing is the disappearance of the resource.

Effects of Trade

It would be impossible to live as we do without trade. How many goods in your local store are produced or grown in Canada? How many are imported from somewhere else? We cannot produce or grow certain items, such as tropical fruits, in Canada. Other items may be grown or made in Canada, but are cheaper to import. This is because of differences in currency and in costs of labour, materials, and energy in different parts of the world.

By importing goods, we displace part of our environmental impact to the regions from which we import them. Although importing allows us to increase our own consumption of resources, the total quantity of resources in the world is limited. A gain in resources by one region must be balanced against an equal loss of resources by another region.

Figure 4.16 The large variety of imported goods that are available in developed countries, such as Canada, gives the impression of unlimited abundance.

Outside Link ACTIVITY

The "Global Village"

The well-known Canadian writer Marshall McLuhan (1911–1980) believed that our dependence on electronic forms of communication, such as satellites and the Internet, would eventually lead to a new world culture. In his book *The Gutenberg Galaxy,* published in 1962, he wrote: "The new electronic interdependence recreates the world in the image of a global village." How do you think the world is like a village?

What to Do

1. Explain briefly why the metaphor of a global village is appropriate when talking about ecosystems.

2. In what way are the terms "global village" and "commons" related?

3. How is world trade in resources, such as lumber and other goods, like a nutrient cycle? How is it not?

Extensions

4. What is the World Trade Organization?

5. Why do some people protest world trade meetings, such as the one in Seattle, Washington, in 1999? Do they all protest for the same reasons?

Pause&
Reflect

Ecologist Eugene Odum wrote: " The landscape is not just a supply depot, but it is also the *oikos* — the home — in which we must live."

What did he mean by this statement? In your own words, explain the value of nature to which Odum was referring.

At the start of this chapter, a family of humans was contrasted with a family of deer. Unlike deer, people have technology. In many ways, however, people are similar to deer and other organisms. Like every living thing, people need food, water, and shelter. In most parts of the world today, including Canada, people do not obtain all these essential needs from their local resources. They depend on technology and trade for their supplies. How would you be affected if trade in food items were stopped by world events, such as drought or political unrest? How would you be affected if supplies of fuel for heating and transportation became much more expensive? What might happen if regions that had depleted or polluted their local supplies of water demanded water from other regions with ample supplies?

Trade and technology have made people in all parts of the world dependent on one another. Each community obtains resources from different regions of the world and, in turn, sends local goods and resources to other regions. Because of this, our "home" is not simply the place where we live but the entire planet. As you use resources from day to day, recall the relationships that link you to the rest of the world. By understanding these relationships, you can make choices that will help to sustain the resources and ecosystems on which we all depend.

Check Your Understanding

1. Define the term "paradigm," and give an example.

2. Give one example of environmental
   (a) goods
   (b) services

3. Explain why some economists believe that carrying capacity is generally increased by
   (a) technology
   (b) trade

4. Explain why ecologists believe that carrying capacity is generally reduced by
   (a) technology
   (b) trade

5. **Apply** Suppose that you have $100 to spend. Give an example of a purchase that you think might benefit the environment and an example of a purchase that might promote an unsustainable environment. Explain each choice.

6. **Thinking Critically** Explain why it is much easier for our economic paradigm to be applied to environmental goods than to environmental services.

Now that you have completed this chapter, try to do the following. If you cannot, go back to the sections indicated.

Explain what is meant by the tragedy of the commons. (4.1)

Give an example to show why a change in the population size of one species often results in a change in the population size of another species. (4.1)

Critically analyze the concept of managing nature. (4.1)

Explain why the population of a city is not sustained by resources within the area of the city. (4.2)

Define the term "ecological footprint." (4.2)

Describe key ways in which a human population is similar to and different from populations of other species. (4.2)

Compare a system in a state of continual growth with a system in a state of change without growth. (4.2)

Give an example of an economic paradigm applied to natural ecosystems. (4.3)

Explain how technology affects the sustainability of ecosystems. (4.3)

Explain how international trade affects the sustainability of ecosystems. (4.3)

Prepare Your Own Summary

Summarize this chapter by doing one of the following. Use a graphic organizer (such as a concept map), produce a poster, or write the summary to include the key chapter concepts. Here are a few ideas to use as a guide:

- Explain how the metaphor of the commons applies to Earth's atmosphere and oceans.
- Describe two ways in which technology affects natural resources.
- Compare the paradigms of economy and ecology as they relate to the sustainability of ecosystems.
- Illustrate the meaning of the concept "ecological footprint."

4 Review

Reviewing Key Terms

If you need to review, the section numbers show you where these terms were introduced.

1. What is a commons? (4.1)

2. Compare the term "ecological footprint" with the term "carrying capacity." (4.2)

3. Give an example of
   (a) a past paradigm that is no longer used
   (b) a recent paradigm that has been developed as a result of scientific understanding. (4.3)

4. Distinguish between the meanings of the terms "ecology" and "economy." (4.3)

Understanding Key Concepts

Section numbers are provided if you need to review.

5. Explain why atmospheric pollution can be considered an example of the tragedy of the commons. (4.1)

6. Using a specific example, describe the consequences of an increasing demand for a finite resource. (4.1)

7. Describe some methods that could be used to manage a population of herbivores in a provincial park. (4.1)

8. Explain why managing the stock of merchandise in a store is not a good model for managing wildlife populations in a provincial park. (4.1)

9. List five of the resources that are used by a city but produced elsewhere. (4.2)

10. Why is the concept of the ecological footprint an improvement over the concept of carrying capacity for human populations? (4.2)

11. List some of the ways in which the products of technology may be compared with body parts. (4.2)

12. Dr. Rees, the Canadian scientist who developed the concept of the ecological footprint, has said that modern cities are the human equivalent of cattle feedlots. What do you think he means by this comparison? (4.2)

13. List three examples of environmental goods and three examples of environmental services. (4.3)

14. Explain what is meant by sustainability, as it applies to our use of resources. (4.3)

15. Give an example of a technology that could increase Earth's carrying capacity for the human population. (4.3)

16. Give an example of a natural resource that has a manufactured substitute, developed by technology: for example, a substitute for leather is vinyl. Then give a resource that does not have a manufactured substitute. Do you think scientists may be able to use technology to develop a substitute for your second example at some time in the future? Explain why or why not. (4.3)

Developing Skills

17. Examine the chain concept map that you created in the Starting Point Activity on page 103. Make another concept map that links to one of the steps. For example, transportation requires the construction of roads and railways, the manufacturing of trucks and trains, and the extraction and refining of fuel.

18. Easter Island, in the Pacific Ocean, may be used as a model of what can occur when a society uses its technology to harvest finite resources in an unsustainable way. Research the history of the human inhabitants of this island. Prepare a presentation that illustrates the relationships among their beliefs, their environment, and the sustainability of the island's ecosystems. You may present your findings as a talk, video, display, model, dramatic sketch, or other form.

19. The graph below shows the possible increase in the global human population and energy consumption if current trends continue. Interpret the graph. In your interpretation, use the terms "economics," "ecological footprint," and "sustainability." **Note:** One terawatt of energy is equal to burning five billion barrels of oil.

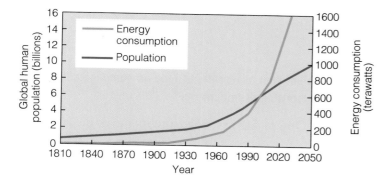

Problem Solving/Applying

20. Earlier in this chapter, the ecological footprint of Vancouver was calculated using five demands: the farmland to produce meat protein, forests to produce wood and paper, space to live, forests to absorb CO_2 from the burning of fossil fuels, and oceans to produce seafood. What other demands could you add? Choose one of your suggestions, and describe the data you would require to estimate the size of the area of land needed per person.

21. Why might an efficient technology decrease Earth's carrying capacity in the long term?

22. Many companies today have a "green" plan. This is an environmental statement that outlines the company's policy on how to minimize its impact on the environment. Imagine that you are an environmental consultant. Choose a company (real or imaginary), and design a green plan for it. Outline how you would reduce the size of the company's ecological footprint. Outline how your plan would include a sustainable solution.

Critical Thinking

23. Our economic system assumes that common natural resources (such as water, air, trees, and fish) are free of cost and inexhaustible. Why did this paradigm develop? How has this paradigm influenced the ways in which these resources have been managed?

24. One economist has said that the resources we use in our economy are infinite because we can always find or develop a substitute for any material or source of energy that runs out. Explain why you agree or disagree with this idea.

25. List five examples of renewable resources. List five examples of non-renewable resources. Which type of resource is more important to the economy? Which type is more important to human survival? For which type of resource is technology less likely to develop substitutes?

Pause& ――Reflect

1. Go back to the beginning of the chapter, on page 102, and check your original answers to the Opening Ideas questions. How has your thinking changed? How would you answer those questions now that you have investigated the topics in this chapter?

2. The Canadian lifestyle is sustained by other areas of the world. How might your daily activities affect someone living in another country?

Ask an Expert

As more and more land in Canada is used for human activities, we can see the increasing impact of such development on the well-being of local wildlife and also on humans. Bernadette Tenning is a biologist who specializes in assessing the negative effects that new development can have on the environment, and helping people take steps to safeguard against them.

Q How long have you been assessing the effects of new development?

A I've been doing environmental assessment since 1998. That's when I graduated from university. Because of my First Nations descent, I've always been interested in biology and concerned about the environment. So after I had my children, I went back to university as a mature student to study human geography and biology.

Q What sort of assessment do you do?

A I do a few different types. For example, I did an assessment for a timber company that was applying for a licence to operate in a northern community. They wanted me to assess the situation and show, in their application, that they had considered environmental factors and were taking precautions to protect the ecosystem from damage.

Q What did your assessment show?

A I explained that the company proposed harvesting the trees in winter when the ground was frozen and less vulnerable to soil erosion. (Soil erosion would decrease plant growth and negatively impact all the animals that depend on those plants.) The company also planned to avoid areas where the layer of topsoil was very thin to begin with, areas in which there lived animals or plants that were particularly susceptible to damage, and areas that are traditional First Nations hunting grounds.

Q Are all of your assessments done for companies that are proposing developments?

A No. One of the first assessments I ever did was for a First Nations lobby group concerned about a hog-processing plant proposed for their area. They wanted someone to assess the existing water quality and predict what sort of environmental impact the proposed plant would have.

Q So you were looking strictly at the water?

A I was looking at the water as an indicator of environmental impact, but I had to consider the ecosystem of the whole area. Everything in an area is affected by the quality of the water.

In this case, the quality of the water was already poor. The hog processor reported high levels of fecal coliforms, bacteria called *E. coli*, in

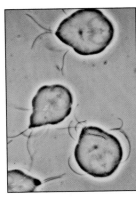

Giardia lamblia is a protozoan that is found in fresh water systems. It can cause severe intestinal illness.

the water. Hog waste leads to high levels of bacteria. The processor believed, however, that additional waste from the hogs would not increase the amount of *E. coli* in the water beyond the level that was acceptable by government standards. I was concerned that the water had not been tested for parasitic protozoans, such as *Giardia* or *Cryptosporidium*. Compared with *E. coli*, these protozoans can infect other organisms at much lower levels.

Disease could spread to local wildlife. Then deer or mice could potentially spread sickness to domestic livestock and humans.

Q If the hog plant had not yet been built, why was the quality of the water already so poor?

A There was a lot of existing development, such as construction and agriculture, in the area. When development takes place and waste materials are not disposed of properly, the natural balance of the ecosystem can be thrown out of whack. My biggest concern was that waste from the hogs could add to the imbalance if it were not disposed of properly. This might result in a positive feedback loop — something every biologist fears.

Q What is a positive feedback loop?

A It's a situation in which a chain of events changes an ecosystem in a way that cannot be reversed. For example, in the proposed hog plant situation, hog waste released into the water would add large amounts of ammonia and other nitrogen-based substances. The nitrogen is involved in what we call "nutrient loading" and causes an increase in algae growth. When the algae build up, they cause an increase in biological oxygen demand. That means there are more organisms in need of oxygen in the water than there were before. Fish populations begin to die from lack of oxygen, which affects birds, otters, bears — anything that depends on the fish for food.

Q And you can't return the populations of fish and their predators to the way they once were, right?

A Not easily, because the biodiversity is greatly reduced. Plus it doesn't end there. The algae begin to take over the water source. Gradually, the solid growth of algae can fill in the lake or river until it becomes a marsh and eventually dries up completely.

Fortunately the public is becoming more knowledgeable about these issues and more vocal in their demands for good-quality water. If enough people ask the right questions, more developers will become environmentally responsible.

EXPLORING Further

Water Quality

One water organism that is common in many water sources in Canada is *Microcystis*. Take a look, under a microscope, at a sample of water from a stream, river, or lake in your area. Can you see any organisms that look like these ones?

People who assess water quality often count the number of these organisms in their samples. How many can you count in your sample? Where do these organisms come from? Why are they a health risk? What population levels of these organisms are considered safe in our water systems? Conduct research to answer the questions. Present your findings in a brief information pamphlet.

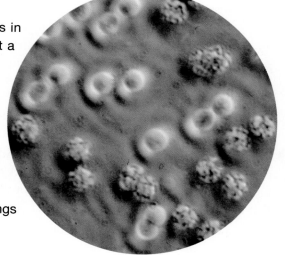

Clearcutting Versus Selective Cutting of Forests

Think About It

Clearcutting is a harvesting practice that removes all the trees and other vegetation from an area of forest. Small crews of workers operate heavy machinery to cut and load the trees onto trucks. In only a couple of hours, workers can clear-cut a forest the size of a football field. About 90 percent of the trees that are harvested in Canada are clear-cut.

In contrast, selective cutting of forests involves the removal of individual trees or small groups of trees from an area. The forest is managed in order to harvest a certain age and/or species of tree. Only about 30 percent of the trees are removed from an area.

Do you think forestry practices should involve clearcutting? Are there better alternatives? Should different forestry practices be used in different situations? How might different tree harvesting practices, affect the environment, economy, and people that depend on this industry for jobs?

Clearcutting removes all the trees in an area of forest.

Resolution

"Be it resolved that clearcutting is the best method for harvesting trees in Canada."

What to Do

1. Read the "Points For" and "Points Against" on this page. What other points could you make in favour of and against the resolution?

2. Two teams, made up of two students each, will debate the resolution. One team will speak in favour of the resolution, and the other team will speak against it. **Note:** If you are on one of the teams, you must try your best to convince the audience of the side that your team is defending — no matter which side you actually support.

3. Two other students will be assigned to work with each team. These students will gather the background information needed to make a strong case for the side that the team is defending.

4. The rest of the class will judge the debate. In preparation for the debate, students should do their own research in order to understand the economics and ecology behind the issues. Take a vote to determine the class' initial stand on the resolution.

5. Your teacher will provide you with the proper *Debating Procedures* to follow.

Points For

- Many Canadian jobs depend on the forest industry.
- Clearcutting produces the most timber for the least amount of money.
- Clear-cut areas are soon replanted with new trees.

Points Against

- Forests maintain biodiversity and provide revenue for the recreation and tourism industries.
- Clearcutting removes nutrients in the trees from the ecosystem.
- Clearcutting exposes forest soil to the weather, causing erosion and landslides.

Analyze

1. For the audience:
   (a) Based on a class vote, which team won the debate?
   (b) What made this team more convincing, its research or its presentation? Explain.
   (c) Did your viewpoint change as a result of the debate? If so, explain why. If not, did the opposing team raise any points that you had not considered? Explain.

2. For the debaters:
   (a) How well did your team work together?
   (b) Which of your opponents' points were hardest to refute?

Lights, Camera, Action!

Many large corporations provide commercial time on television for public service announcements. A multinational corporation has provided you with 2 min of time during a major television event. You must inform the general public about critical environmental issues related to the sustainability of ecosystems.

Challenge

In a small group, design and produce a television commercial about a major environmental impact that humans have had on the planet. You goal is to bring about necessary change through heightened awareness.

Possible Materials

art supplies
video camera
computer
recording equipment
poster board

Design Criteria

A. Prepare a unique television commercial.

B. Your commercial must be clear, concise, and no longer than 2 min.

C. Your commercial must be scientifically accurate.

D. You should strive to make your commercial both informative and interesting for members of the general public.

E. You may use music, animation, live action, or any other form of media for your commercial.

Plan and Construct

1 Your teacher will divide the class into groups. In your group, choose one major topic for your commercial.

2 Analyze any television commercials that you find to be especially effective.

3 Brainstorm the various techniques that can be used to inform and persuade the public.

4 Make a work plan, and assign the various tasks to the members of your group. Show your plan to your teacher.

5 When your teacher approves your plan, gather the appropriate materials and create your commercial.

6 Videotape your commercial so that you can present it to the class.

Evaluate

1. Evaluate the other groups' commercials. How effective were they? How might they appeal to different sectors of the public?

2. Which commercial was most effective? Why?

3. After seeing the commercials produced by your classmates, what changes would you make to your own commercial? Give reasons for your changes.

4. Describe the changes that you would make to your commercial if it were going to be shown during

   (a) a sporting event

   (b) a concert

   (c) an awards program

   (d) a newscast

5. Do you think a 2 min commercial could change attitudes on environmental issues? Explain.

6. How did the planning process help you think about what you have learned in this unit?

Now that you have completed Chapters 1, 2, 3, and 4, you can assess how much you have learned about the sustainability of ecosystems by answering the following questions. Before you begin, you may find it useful to return to each Chapter at a Glance and each Chapter Review.

True/False

In your notebook, indicate whether each statement is true or false. Correct each false statement.

1. Plants add carbon dioxide to the environment through the process of cellular respiration.

2. Organisms require nitrogen to make proteins.

3. Decomposers are an essential part of all nutrient cycles.

4. Green plants occupy the second trophic level in food chains.

5. The biomass of herbivores in an ecosystem is generally greater than the biomass of plants.

6. The process of biomagnification tends to increase the concentration of chemical pollutants in organisms at the bottom of a food chain.

7. The depth of soil in an area can be decreased by erosion, but it can never be increased.

8. The process of succession can convert a pond into a meadow.

Completion

In your notebook, complete each statement with the correct term or phrase.

9. The buildup of nitrogen in lakes produces _____.

10. The process of _____ uses oxygen and produces carbon dioxide.

11. The process of photosynthesis combines water with _____ gas to produce carbohydrates.

12. _____ bacteria convert nitrates into nitrogen gas.

13. Nitrogen-containing gases dissolve in water vapour in the atmosphere to produce _____.

14. Primary consumers are animals that eat _____.

15. There is a loss of _____ at each trophic level.

16. _____ is the total dry mass of an organism.

17. The largest population of a species that an environment can support over the long term is called the _____ of the environment for this species.

18. Competition among members of the same species is called _____ competition.

19. Resources that can be freely used by all members of a population are called _____.

20. A way of looking at the world that is shared by most people in a community is called a _____.

Matching

21. In your notebook, copy the descriptions in column A. Beside each description, write the term from column B that best fits the description. A term may be used once, more than once, or not at all.

A

- process used by green plants to make carbohydrates
- role of green plants in an ecosystem
- role of animals in an ecosystem
- network of links that channel energy and materials through the organisms in an ecosystem
- continual movement of elements between the living and non-living parts of the environment
- process by which pollutants become more concentrated as they move along a food chain
- total area of land that is required to support a human population at a given level of resource consumption
- feeding relationships between organisms at different trophic levels

B

- consumers
- cellular respiration
- producers
- photosynthesis
- food web
- trophic level
- pyramid of numbers
- nutrient cycle
- carrying capacity
- biological magnification
- succession
- ecological footprint

Multiple Choice

In your notebook, write the letter of the best answer for each of the following questions.

22. Which process removes carbon dioxide from the air?

(a) respiration
(b) photosynthesis
(c) acid precipitation
(d) eutrophication

23. Which process removes nitrogen from the air?

(a) nitrogen fixation
(b) denitrification
(c) photosynthesis
(d) nitrification

24. The amount of usable energy that is used for growth and reproduction of organisms at each link in a food chain is about

(a) 10 percent   (c) 50 percent
(b) 30 percent   (d) 90 percent

25. A snake is an example of a

(a) producer
(b) primary consumer
(c) secondary consumer
(d) decomposer

26. Which of the following is not a result of a change in the nitrogen cycle?

(a) eutrophication
(b) acid precipitation
(c) global warming
(d) increased crop production

27. Which of the following cannot be inverted?

(a) pyramid of numbers
(b) pyramid of biomass
(c) pyramid of energy flow

28. The process of succession leads to a(n)

(a) ecological footprint
(b) climax community
(c) pioneer organism
(d) pyramid of biomass

Short Answer

In your notebook, write a sentence or a short paragraph to answer each of the following questions.

29. Explain why a nutrient cycle on Earth is called a closed system.

30. Write an equation that summarizes the process of photosynthesis.

31. Do the materials that make up a tree come mainly from the soil, water, or air? Explain your answer.

32. How does the combustion of fossil fuels affect the carbon cycle?

33. Why might an organic farmer add animal manure to a field?

34. Describe one way in which human activities have an impact on the nitrogen cycle.

35. Why do food webs require a continual input of energy from the Sun?

36. Why does plant productivity vary from one part of the world to another?

37. Describe two factors that affect the carrying capacity of an area.

38. In your notebook, make a sketch of the illustration below. Label each trophic level, and name the types of organisms in each trophic level. Briefly describe what the illustration shows.

39. Describe one way in which an agricultural ecosystem and a natural ecosystem differ.

40. Define the term "soil." How do grassland soils and forest soils differ in Canada?

41. During a walk in a forest, you discover evidence that there was once a small mining town in part of the forest. Name and describe the process by which the abandoned town was replaced by trees and shrubs.

42. Describe what is meant by the tragedy of the commons, using a specific example.

43. List three ways in which you depend on areas of land outside the area where you actually live.

44. Sketch an equation to summarize what is meant by the term "ecological footprint."

45. Give an example of a way in which technology affects sustainability.

46. How might international trade affect the sustainability of an ecosystem in an exporting country?

47. Why are lichens important in the process of primary succession?

48. Define "carrying capacity." List three factors that limit population size.

49. How can a change in the population size of one organism affect a food web?

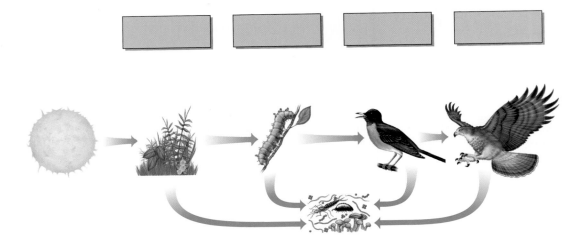

Problem Solving

50. The grain harvest on a farm varies from year to year. The farmer notices that the number of owls around the farm increases during the spring following a large harvest. Suggest an explanation that links the size of the grain harvest to the size of the owl population.

51. Suppose that you want to increase the rate of growth of plants in a greenhouse. Explain how you could do this by changing the air in the greenhouse. Suggest one other method of increasing plant growth.

52. Describe problems that a gardener might experience with soil that contained a large proportion of

(a) clay

(b) sand

How could the gardener reduce the problems with each type of soil?

53. Describe some problems that can occur when people try to manage nature, such as a population of deer. Suggest some solutions for these problems.

Critical Thinking

54. To control populations of insects that eat crops, some farmers use insect predators instead of chemical sprays. Explain the advantages of using predators for pest control.

55. Organisms need chemical elements and energy to survive. Explain why elements, such as carbon and nitrogen, are recycled within ecosystems, while energy is not.

56. Some economists suggest that the tragedy of the commons can be eliminated by a system of private ownership of natural resources. Suggest some problems that might result from such a system.

57. "The surest way to improve your environment is to become rich." Give reasons why you agree or disagree with this statement.

Applications

58. How could you use your knowledge of the nitrogen cycle to develop a sewage treatment plant?

59. Your local community is looking for ideas to promote sustainable development. Describe an activity that is sustainable in your area. Contrast it with a non-sustainable activity to show how it uses resources more efficiently.

60. In the early twentieth century, a marsh was drained to make 50 ha of land for agriculture. Develop a proposal to restore the marsh. What environmental issues should you address in your proposal? What economic and social issues should you consider, as well?

Chemistry in Action

Day after day, you and millions of other people like you, climb into a motor vehicle. The driver turns the key, the engine roars, and you're off. How much thought do you give to the chemical — gasoline — that powers the vehicle? If you are in heavy traffic, such as you see in the photograph, you might be thinking about the exhaust. It can be suffocating. Unless you have been in an accident recently, you probably do not give much thought to the danger of riding in an automobile. On the other hand, you might assume that the air bag will protect you. Did you know that a chemical reaction creates the gas that inflates the air bag? Do not feel too confident, however. If the gasoline escapes from the tank and ignites during an accident, an air bag cannot save you.

In the scene described above, you saw some of the risks of gasoline-powered vehicles. Did you realize that, every day, you are making decisions about risks and benefits of riding in a vehicle? You have to be willing to take the risk of an accident happening in order to receive the benefit of convenient travel. For most people, the benefits of gasoline-powered transportation far exceed the risks.

These are only a few of the hundreds of chemicals and chemical reactions about which you make decisions on almost a daily basis. What scientific knowledge can help you make informed decisions about the chemicals you use? What properties of chemicals affect the way that you should handle them? How does our reliance on chemical products and the industries that make them, affect the environment? Explore this unit to answer these and other questions about our chemical world.

Unit Contents

Patterns and

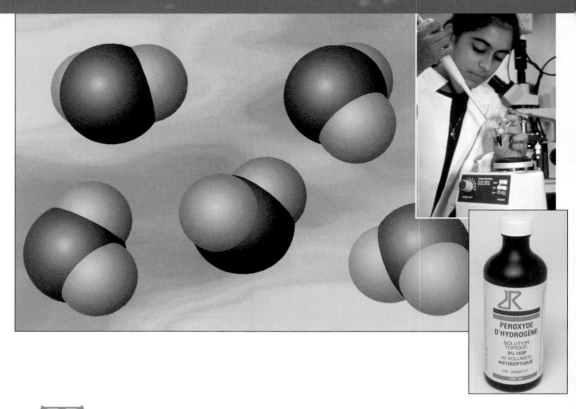

Opening Ideas...

- What properties can help you distinguish a metal from a non-metal?

- How can the periodic table help you predict ways that elements combine to form compounds?

- How can you use the periodic table to infer the names and formulas of compounds?

Science Log

In your Science Log, develop a flow chart or concept map to review what you already know about matter: its classification, composition, and properties. Consider the Opening Ideas questions, and add your own ideas to your flow chart or concept map.

Skill
P O W E R

For tips on how to use a science log, turn to page 580.

There are millions of chemical substances, and we manufacture thousands of new ones regularly. People who work with chemicals must know their properties in order to use them safely and predict how they could interact when they are combined. Looking up the properties of a substance in a database is not always practical, however, and memorizing so much data would be impossible. Instead, scientists have discovered patterns to make inferences and predictions about the properties of substances and their interactions.

To communicate about chemicals, scientists (and people in many other professions) use a special system. This system assigns unique names and chemical formulas to elements and compounds so that they can be recognized instantly anywhere in the world. This system is also used in the symbolic "short-hand" of chemical equations. A **chemical equation** summarizes what happens to substances during a chemical reaction.

In this chapter, you will revisit a powerful organizational tool, the periodic table. You will use it to make predictions about the properties of elements and simple compounds, and to help you write chemical formulas. As well, you will learn how to combine chemical formulas to write chemical equations, as professional chemists do.

Compounds

Groups and Trends

When you do a jigsaw puzzle, you examine the pieces and look for patterns to help you arrange them into groups that fit together. Usually, you have a complete picture of the finished puzzle as a

Key Concepts

In this chapter, you will discover

- why the periodic table can help you predict the properties and bonding of simple compounds
- how to write names and formulas of simple compounds
- how to summarize a chemical reaction using words and symbols

Key Skills

In this chapter, you will

- safely perform laboratory tests to make inferences about substances
- investigate the law of conservation of mass
- represent chemical reactions using a variety of models

Key Terms

- chemical equation
- periodic table
- periods
- groups
- shells
- valence electrons
- valence shell
- ion
- cation
- anion
- electron dot diagram
- ionic compounds
- ionic bond
- covalent bond
- molecule
- molecular compounds

- diatomic molecule
- electrolyte
- binary compound
- classical system
- Stock system
- polyatomic ions
- reactants
- products
- law of conservation of mass
- Dalton's atomic theory
- word equation
- skeleton equation
- balanced chemical equation
- coefficient

Starting Point  ACTIVITY

guide. What if you didn't have that picture, and what if some of the pieces were missing? This is the dilemma chemists faced in the 1800s as they tried to sort the known individual elements into meaningful groups. Why was the task of organizing the elements so challenging?

How can these objects be arranged into different piles with similar properties?

What You Need

bag with a variety of joining devices

What to Do

1. With your partner, examine the objects in the bag. Think about the kinds of materials they might join. Sort them into different piles using this characteristic.

2. Next, sort each "joining pile" into smaller groups. Items in each of the smaller groups should have something in common, and be different from the items in another group.

3. Now sort the smaller groups from step 2 based on a property that changes from item to item. Continue sorting until each item has a unique position on your desk.

4. Devise a summary table to record the way you have sorted the fastening devices. Compare your summary table with others in the class.

What Did You Discover?

1. How many "joining piles" did your class make? How were they similar and different?

2. Did you include space or spaces for missing items in your summary table? If so, describe the characteristics of the missing item or items. If not, how could your summary table accommodate newly "discovered" items?

5.1 Looking for Patterns in Chemical Reactivity

$$2H_2 + O_2 \rightarrow 2H_2O$$

Figure 5.1 What does this equation represent?

The equation above summarizes a chemical reaction that results in a substance vital to the life of all living things, including you. Do you recognize any parts of this equation? For example, you probably know that H_2O is the chemical formula for one of Earth's most common compounds, water. You may be wondering, however, what the arrow in the equation means. Why do the H and O symbols to the left of the arrow have small subscript "2"s? Why are there large "2"s in front of H_2 and H_2O? By the time you complete the chapter, you will not only understand the meaning and format of this equation, but you will also be able to summarize chemical reactions yourself.

Right now, though, you can use this equation in a different way — to help you review major chemistry ideas you have explored in the past. For example, you know that scientists use letters to symbolize chemical elements. In this equation, the letter H is the symbol for hydrogen, the most abundant element in the universe. The letter O is the symbol for oxygen, which your cells need to release energy from the food you eat.

Hydrogen and oxygen have several physical properties in common. They are tasteless, colourless, and odourless gases (under standard conditions of temperature and pressure). They have different melting points and boiling points, however. In what other ways are their physical properties different?

Atoms of hydrogen and oxygen differ in the number of subatomic particles they have (see Figure 5.2). This difference in atomic structure affects their chemical properties. Hydrogen, for example, is so flammable that it can ignite explosively if exposed to a spark in the presence of oxygen. Although oxygen itself does not burn, it is necessary to support the combustion (burning) of other substances and materials, such as hydrogen, wood, and fossil fuels.

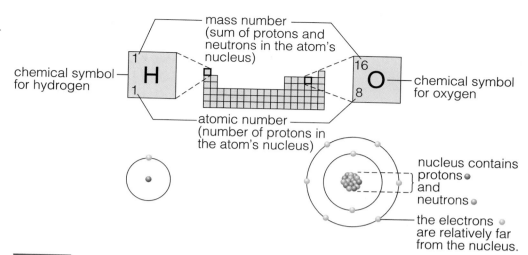

Figure 5.2 This diagram shows the position of hydrogen and oxygen in the Periodic Table of the Elements (see Appendix C). It also shows other information about these two elements. In the Bohr-Rutherford model, atoms are made up of three main subatomic particles: protons, neutrons, and electrons. The nucleus of an atom is made up of positively charged protons and neutral neutrons. Negatively charged electrons orbit the nucleus.

Element or Compound?

A pure substance is either a compound or an element. Elements can be grouped as metals or non-metals. How can you distinguish among a metal, a non-metal, and a compound?

CAUTION

- Review the safety rules on pages xxi–xxiii, and Skill Power 10: Safety Symbols.
- Dilute hydrochloric acid is very corrosive. Rinse any spills immediately with plenty of running water, and tell your teacher.

What You Need

6 unknown solids, labelled A–F
conductivity tester
dilute hydrochloric acid
Bunsen burner
wooden splints
emery cloth or sandpaper
6 small test tubes
scoopula
test tube rack

What to Do

1. Design a table to record the physical properties of each solid. Include electrical

Science Inquiry

conductivity, brittleness, and the appearance of a freshly scraped surface. (Your teacher can help you review how to test electrical conductivity.)

2. *Some* metals react (undergo a chemical change) with hydrochloric acid to generate hydrogen gas. Most non-metals do not react with hydrochloric acid. Some compounds react by generating carbon dioxide gas. Add a pea-sized sample of each solid to a labelled test tube. Add 5 mL of dilute hydrochloric acid. If you observe evidence of a gas being produced, test it with a burning splint. (See page 195 to review chemical tests for gases.) Wash your hands.

What Did You Discover?

1. Summarize the physical properties of metals and non-metals.

2. For each unknown (A-F), state whether there was a chemical change? Explain.

3. Classify each of the unknown solids as an element (metal or non-metal) or a compound. Give reasons for your decisions.

Patterns and Trends in the Periodic Table

When atoms of hydrogen and oxygen bond (chemically join) together, they form molecules of a different substance, the compound water. Water's physical and chemical properties are different from those of the two original elements. What if you had never heard of hydrogen, oxygen, or even water? As long as you understood some basic facts about the organization of the periodic table, you could predict that hydrogen and oxygen should combine to form a new compound with the formula H_2O. The periodic table could also help you predict some properties of this new compound.

The **periodic table** arranges elements into **periods** (horizontal rows) and **groups** (vertical columns) according to their atomic numbers. Figure 5.3 outlines several patterns that result from this arrangement. The most obvious of these is the separation — marked by the dark "staircase" line — of the elements into metals and non-metals. Elements that border this line tend to have some metallic properties as well as some non-metallic properties. These elements are called metalloids. Table 5.1 summarizes what you may recall about the physical properties of the three kinds of elements.

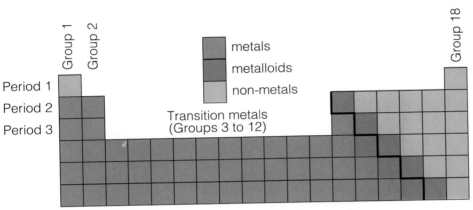

Figure 5.3 Patterns and trends in the periods and groups of the periodic table

Table 5.1 Properties of Metals, Non-Metals, and Metalloids

	State	Appearance	Conductivity	Malleability and ductility
Metals	• solids at room temperature, except for mercury (a liquid)	• shiny lustre	• good conductors of heat and electricity	• malleable • ductile
Non-metals	• some gases at room temperature • some solids • one liquid (bromine)	• not very shiny	• poor conductors of heat and electricity	• brittle • not ductile
Metalloids	• solids at room temperature	• can be shiny or dull	• may conduct electricity • poor conductors of heat	• brittle • not ductile

Visible differences in physical properties make it easy to distinguish metals from non-metals. The periodic table represents patterns related to the chemical properties of substances. These patterns describe how substances behave during a chemical change. For example, the periodic table can help you answer questions such as:

• Why do elements in the same group have similar chemical properties?
• What is it about metals and non-metals that allows you to predict the kinds of compounds they are likely to form?

The answer to both of these questions comes from the negatively charged subatomic particles that surround the nucleus of an atom — the electrons.

Electrons move rapidly around the nucleus in regions called **shells**. The atoms of different elements have different numbers of shells. Each shell can accommodate a certain number of electrons but no more. For example, the first shell can hold a maximum of two electrons. The second shell holds a maximum of eight electrons. Examine Figure 5.4, and refer to it as you read the next few paragraphs.

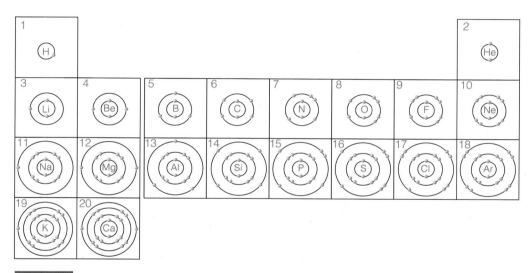

Figure 5.4 Electron shells for the first 20 elements in the periodic table

Pause&
Reflect

You may recall that the Group 18 elements, the noble gases, are very unlikely to take part in chemical reactions. Why might that be? Record your ideas, and your reasons for them, in your Science Log. You can assess your ideas when you investigate this question in section 5.2.

Notice that the two elements in Period 1 have a single electron shell. Recall that the first shell can hold up to two electrons. Helium, the second element in Period 1, has a full complement of two electrons in its shell. Hydrogen, the first element, has only one electron.

Turn your attention to Period 2, which has two electron shells. The first shell — the shell that is closest to the nucleus — is full. The second shell contains different numbers of electrons. You can see that lithium has one electron in its second shell. As you move from one element to the next across Period 2, one more electron is added to the second shell of each atom. The second shell can contain a maximum of eight electrons. Since neon's second shell has this maximum, the second period must end with neon.

Elements in Period 3 have a third electron shell. What do you notice about the number of electrons in the first two shells of Period 3 elements? What about the number of electrons in the third shell?

Up to now, you have focussed on recognizing a pattern in the periods of the periodic table. Have you recognized a pattern in the groups, as well? Scan the number of outer-shell electrons in atoms of the same group. What do you notice?

Predicting Chemical Reactivity

Electron shell diagrams are useful because they show the number of electrons in the shells of atoms. Knowing this is the key to understanding the organization of the periodic table and the chemical properties of the elements. Elements in the same group have similar chemical properties because they have the same number of electrons in their outer shell. For example, lithium and all the elements in Group 1 (the alkali family) have one electron in their outer shell. All the elements in Group 17 (the halogen family) have seven electrons in their outer shell.

Knowing the number of outer shell electrons helps you to predict the formation of compounds, name the compounds, and write their chemical formulas. A chemical bond forms between two atoms when electrons in the outer shell of each atom form a stable arrangement together. The outer shell is called the **valence shell.** The electrons that occupy it are called **valence electrons**.

The chemical properties of elements are related to the energy changes that take place when their atoms lose, gain, or share electrons to obtain a filled valence shell. Metals are elements that tend to lose their valence electrons relatively easily, and this accounts for many of their physical and chemical properties. Consider the alkali metals in Group 1. All the alkali metals are electrically neutral (that is, they have equal numbers of protons and electrons), and they have a single valence shell electron. If this electron is removed, a particle with a single positive charge is formed, as you can see in Figure 5.5. Look closely at the electron shell diagram of the charged sodium particle. What other element in the periodic table has the same electron shell configuration?

Positively Charged: Cations

Any atom or group of atoms that carries an electrical charge is called an **ion.** When a neutral atom gives up an electron, the positively charged ion that results is called a **cation** (pronounced "cat-eye-on").

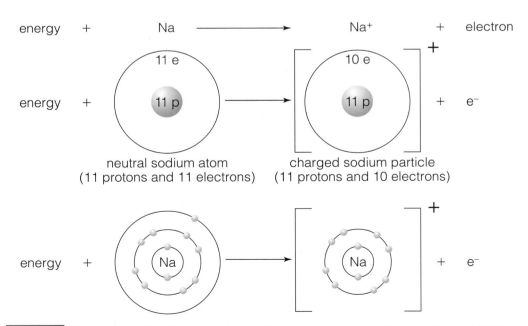

Figure 5.5 These diagrams show three ways to represent what happens when a sodium atom loses an electron. A neutral sodium atom has 11 protons in its nucleus and 11 electrons, including 1 valence electron. Adding energy to a neutral sodium atom removes the valence electron, leaving a positively charged sodium ion and a free electron.

Removing an electron from an alkali metal atom requires relatively little energy. Thus all the alkali metals form cations easily and are chemically very reactive. This reactivity generally increases as you move down the elements in the alkali metal group. Thus potassium is more reactive than sodium; rubidium is more reactive than potassium. This trend in increasing chemical reactivity occurs because of differences in the distance between the valence shell and the nucleus. Potassium's single valence electron is farther from its positive nucleus than of sodium's. Rubidium's valence electron is farther away from the positive rubidium nucleus than potassium's. The farther the valence electron is from its positive nucleus, the more easily it is removed and, therefore, the more reactive the atom is.

To obtain a valence shell like that of a noble gas, the Group 1 elements must give up one electron. What about the Group 2 elements, the alkaline earth metals? These elements have two electrons in their valence shell. Group 2 elements must give up two electrons to obtain a noble gas valence shell arrangement. Calcium, for example, forms a cation with a charge of 2+, written symbolically as Ca^{2+}. Alkaline earth metals are quite reactive. They are generally less reactive than their Group 1 neighbours, however. Infer a reason why.

Negatively Charged: Anions

You have observed evidence to suggest a pattern involving Group 1 and Group 2 elements. The pattern is based on the number of valence shell electrons these elements must give up to obtain an electron arrangement like that of a noble gas. To obtain this structure, neutral atoms of Group 1 and 2 give up electrons to become positively charged ions — cations.

Ions can be negatively charged, as well. Since non-metals have greater numbers of valence shell electrons, they must *gain* electrons to fill their valence shells. For example, all the Group 17 elements, the halogens, must gain one electron to obtain a noble gas electron arrangement. When this happens, halogen atoms become negatively charged particles called **anions** (pronounced "an-eye-ons"). Figure 5.6 summarizes how a chlorine atom becomes a chloride anion.

Halogens gain an electron easily and release a great deal of energy in the process. They are very reactive elements. The reactivity trend you observed for the alkali metals is reversed for the halogens. Chemical reactivity generally decreases as you move down the group. Fluorine's valence shell, for example, is closer to its atom's positive nucleus than chlorine's valence shell. As a result, fluorine attracts the extra electron more strongly than chlorine does. Therefore fluorine should react more energetically than chlorine — which it does. Similarly, chlorine's chemical reactivity is greater than the reactivity of the halogens below it.

Pause& Reflect

How many valence electrons do atoms of aluminum have? Is aluminum more or less chemically reactive than magnesium, its Group 2 neighbour in the periodic table? Record your ideas in your Science Log. Share and discuss your reasoning with a partner. Then add a statement in your Science Log, explaining why you do or do not have confidence in your answer. If you are not confident, what could you do to gain confidence?

Figure 5.6 A neutral chlorine atom has 17 protons in its nucleus and 17 electrons, including 7 valence electrons. Adding an electron results in a negatively charged chlorine ion (anion) and a release of energy.

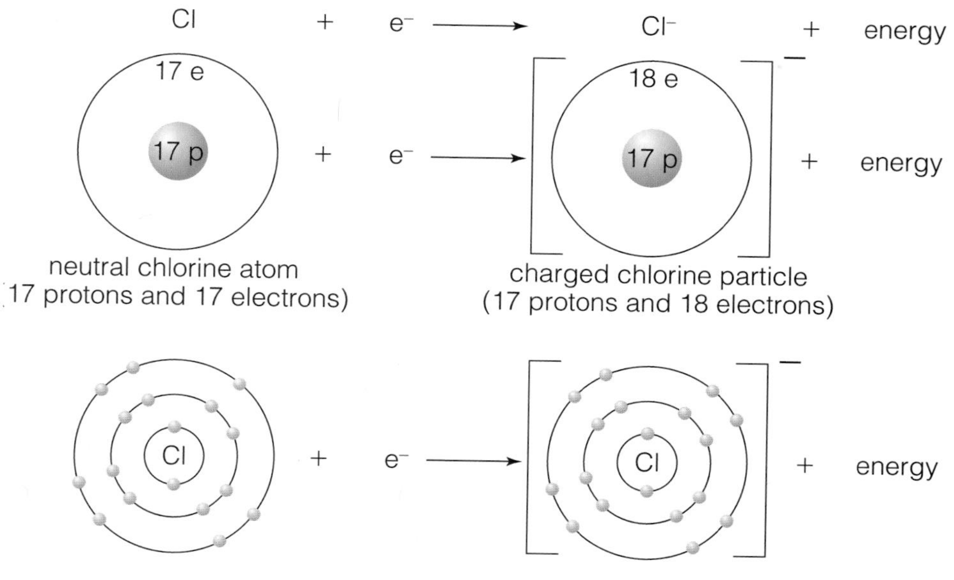

$$Cl + e^- \longrightarrow Cl^- + energy$$

neutral chlorine atom
(17 protons and 17 electrons)

charged chlorine particle
(17 protons and 18 electrons)

The elements in Group 16 must gain two electrons to fill their valence shells. Because the second electron is added to an already negative anion, and because like charges repel, energy is required to form anions with the charge 2−. Consequently Group 16 elements are generally less reactive than their halogen neighbours.

Using Electron Dot Diagrams to Represent Valences

In any group, all the elements have atoms with the same number of valence electrons. You can use a simple model, called an **electron dot diagram** or Lewis diagram, to represent an atom and its valence electrons. An electron dot diagram uses the symbol of the element to replace the nucleus and inner shell electrons. The electrons in the valence shell are shown as dots placed around the symbol (see Figure 5.7). Electron dot diagrams are a valuable tool for describing, predicting, and explaining compound formation. In the next activity, you will practise drawing them.

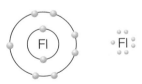

Figure 5.7 How do these two representations of lithium and fluorine compare?

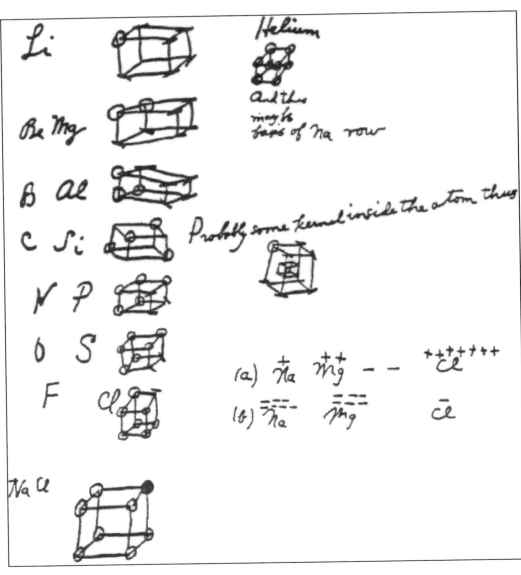

Figure 5.8 The American chemist Gilbert Lewis (1875–1946) invented electron dot diagrams (also called Lewis symbols, in his honour) to help him understand and predict the bonding that occurs between atoms. This reproduction from his notes, made in 1902, records his early thinking about what bonding is and how to represent it.

A *mnemonic device* (memory aid) can help you remember something. The word "mnemonic" is pronounced "nemonic" (the m is silent). It comes from the name of the Greek goddess of memory, Mnemosyne, pronounced "ne-MAH-suh-nee." Here is a mnemonic device to help you remember the difference between cations and anions.

Ca⊞ions are posi⊞ive.
Anions are negative.

Mnemonic devices are only valuable if they work. If this one does not help you, try coming up with your own.

Drawing Electron Dot Diagrams

How do you draw an electron dot diagram? Imagine a square around the symbol for an element. You can place a dot (representing an electron) on any side of the imaginary square. When an element has more than four valence electrons, you arrange the dots in twos. For example, nitrogen has five electrons in its valence shell, so the fifth dot is paired with one of the other four dots. While there is no rule for where you place your first dot, and subsequent dots, you may find it easiest to start at the top (the "12 o'clock" position) and add dots clockwise.

Science Inquiry **ACTIVITY**

What to Do

1. Copy the table below into your notebook. Then draw the missing electron dot diagrams. Refer to a periodic table as necessary.

2. Notice that helium is shown with its electrons paired. This contradicts what you just read about adding dots in a clockwise direction. Offer a reason to support representing helium as shown in the table.

3. Draw electron dot diagrams for the following elements: selenium (Se), bromine (Br), strontium (Sr), radon (Rn), and Francium (Fr). Explain how you decided on the number and placement of the dots.

H							He
Li	Be	B	C	N	O	F	Ne
Na	Mg	Al	Si	P	S	Cl	Ar
K	Ca						

Check Your Understanding

1. Find rubidium (Rb) in the periodic table, and answer the following questions.
   (a) How many electrons are in an atom of rubidium?
   (b) How many electron shells does a rubidium atom have?
   (c) How many electrons are in the valence shell of a rubidium atom?
   (d) Write the symbol for the ion that you would expect rubidium to form.

2. (a) Why is the number of electrons in the valence shell of an atom important?
   (b) How is the number of valence electrons in the atom of an element related to the position of the element in the periodic table?

Bromine, another halogen

3. How do you think the reaction of bromine (shown in the photograph) with sodium would compare with the reaction of chlorine with sodium? Give reasons for your answer.

4. Distinguish between an anion and a cation. Give two different examples of each.

5. What is the total charge on each of the following ions? (You may find a periodic table useful. See page 570.)
   (a) one fluorine anion   (c) two nitrogen anions
   (b) one sulfur anion

6. **Apply** Examine these electron dot diagrams of three hypothetical elements.

   (a) Which elements are non-metals? How do you know?
   (b) Predict which element will not combine with oxygen. Give reasons to explain your answer.

7. **Thinking Critically** An unknown element forms ions with a 2− charge.
   (a) Classify this element as a metal or a non-metal.
   (b) Suppose that you were given a pure sample of this element. What chemical tests would you perform to support your answer to part (a)?
   (c) Where is the periodic table would you expect to find this element? Why?

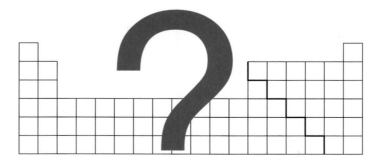

5.2 Forming Compounds

The noble gases of Group 18 are very unlikely to take part in chemical reactions. Their valence shells are completely filled with electrons. The link between chemical stability and a full valence shell is the clue to understanding how atoms of the other elements combine.

When two atoms collide, valence electrons on each atom interact. A chemical bond forms between the atoms if their valence electrons make a new arrangement that has less energy than their previous arrangement. For many atoms, the lowest energy arrangement of valence electrons is the same as the arrangement for the noble gas to which they are closest in the periodic table.

An atom may acquire a valence shell like that of its closest noble gas in one of three ways:

- *An atom may give up electrons.* Atoms have an equal number of positive protons and negative electrons. When an atom gives up one or more electrons, it forms an ion with a positive charge: a cation.
- *An atom may gain electrons.* When an atom gains one or more electrons, it forms an ion with a negative charge: an anion.
- *An atom may share electrons.* Two atoms might share one pair of electrons, two pairs, or three pairs. The bonds that are formed when atoms share electrons are called, as you might expect, single bonds, double bonds, and triple bonds.

Substances that are composed of cations and anions are called **ionic compounds.** The attraction between the oppositely charged ions is called an **ionic bond.** A metal cation has the same number of electrons as an atom of the closest noble gas with a lower atomic number. For example, neon is the closest noble gas in the periodic table to sodium, magnesium, and aluminum. The cations Na^+, Mg^{2+}, and Al^{3+} all have the same number of electrons as atoms of neon.

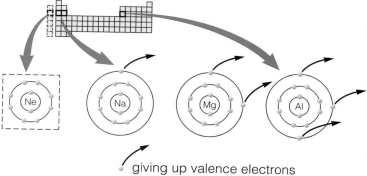

giving up valence electrons

Atoms that share a pair of electrons are joined by a **covalent bond.** A neutral particle that is composed of atoms joined together by covalent bonds is called a **molecule.** Substances that are composed of molecules are called **molecular compounds.** Most molecular compounds are composed of atoms of two or more non-metallic elements. As you know, the atoms of these elements gain electrons to obtain the same number of electrons as the closest noble gas with a larger atomic number.

Non-metals may acquire the stability of a noble gas valence shell arrangement in one of two ways. You have already seen that they may form anions and then interact with metals to form ionic compounds. Alternatively, they may form molecules or molecular compounds by sharing electrons in a covalent bond.

For example, oxygen and fluorine form anions, O^{2-} and F^-, with the same number of electrons as neon. A fluorine atom can share a pair of electrons with another fluorine atom to form a fluorine molecule, F_2. In chemistry, the prefix "di" means "two". Thus a **diatomic molecule,** such as fluorine, is a molecule that contains two atoms. In the following investigation, you will use electron dot diagrams to explore the formation of ionic and covalent bonds.

Ions of calcium and magnesium dissolved in your water supply can become a problem. Electric kettles need to be "descaled" from time to time to get rid of magnesium and calcium compounds left behind by the evaporating water.

DidYouKnow?

Seven elements exist as diatomic molecules in the gaseous state. These elements are hydrogen, oxygen, nitrogen, and the halogens fluorine, chlorine, bromine, and iodine.

Ionic or Covalent: Track Those Electrons

Think About It

Atoms give up, gain, or share electrons to acquire a stable valence-shell arrangement: that is, to obtain the same number of electrons as the atoms of a noble gas. The compounds that are formed must contain the same number of electrons that were present in the atoms before a reaction took place. Using small rings to represent electrons can help you keep track of them.

What You Need

bag containing small rings, such as washers or coloured hole-punch reinforcers
sheets of blank paper
notebook

Part 1
Modelling Ionic Bonds

What to Do

1. Place a blank sheet of paper in landscape orientation. Write the symbols for helium, neon, and argon in a column along the left edge. Repeat this column along the right edge. Use the rings to depict their valence electrons, as shown in the photograph.

2. Hydrogen reacts with the alkali metals to form ionic compounds. In the empty space between your two noble gas columns, use rings to model the electron dot diagrams for lithium and hydrogen. Then move one ring to model the formation of a lithium cation and a hydrogen anion. Use the diagrams on the next page to check your modelling. Notice the square brackets around the electron dot diagram of each ion, as well as the charge shown as a superscript outside the brackets. Copy these diagrams into your notebook, so that you have a summary of the formation of this ionic compound, lithium hydride.

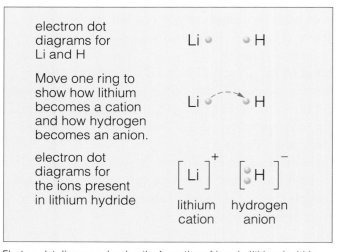

Electron dot diagrams showing the formation of ions in lithium hydride

3. Now model atoms of sodium and fluorine. Decide how atoms of sodium and fluorine become stable ions when they form the ionic compound sodium fluoride. (This compound is added to toothpaste.) In your notebook, record the electron transfer and ions formed, using the format for electron dot diagrams in step 2.

4 Some ionic compounds form when two or more electrons are transferred between atoms. The number of electrons given up by the atoms that form cations must always equal the number of electrons gained by the atoms that form anions. Calcium oxide is an ionic compound that is used to make cement. (Its common name is lime, and its formula is CaO.) Model the ions that are present in this compound, and record the electron dot diagrams in your notebook.

5 Using electron dot diagrams can help you determine the formula of an ionic compound. Ionic compounds always contain cations and anions in simple whole number ratios, such as 1:1, 1:2, and so on. Model atoms of magnesium and chlorine. Decide how stable ions can be formed when these atoms react. Use the diagrams below to check your modelling. Then record the electron dot diagrams in your notebook. What is the formula of magnesium chloride?

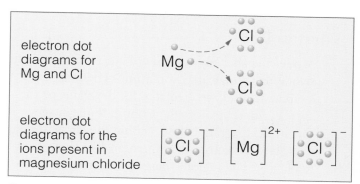

Electron dot diagrams showing the formation of ions in magnesium chloride

6 Repeat step 5 for atoms of aluminum and oxygen. Model the formation of stable ions, draw electron dot diagrams, and write the formula of the resulting ionic compound, aluminum oxide.

CONTINUED ▶

Tools of
Science

Most ionic substances are soluble in water. Barium sulfate is an exception. This is important because barium is a toxic element. Barium sulfate has another property, however, that physicians and surgeons find useful: it absorbs X-rays. When they suspect that a patient has a digestive disorder, such as an ulcer or cancer, they may prescribe a barium sulfate "cocktail" for the patient to drink. Soft tissues and organs are transparent to X-rays, so they do not show up on radiographs (X-ray photographs). Since barium sulfate absorbs X-rays, it makes organs visible as white regions on radiographs, as it passes through the digestive system. Outlines of ulcers or tumours, if present, also become visible. Because barium sulfate is insoluble, it passes through the patient without any threat of poisoning.

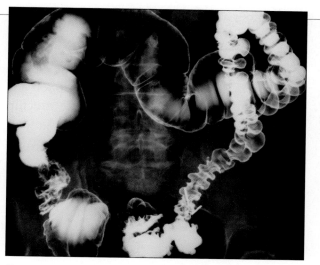

Chemistry often plays a key role in medical testing and diagnosis. What other examples, can you think of?

Part 2

Modelling Covalent Bonds

What to Do

1 Model the sharing of a pair of electrons between two hydrogen atoms. Sometimes chemists draw a circle around the electron dot diagrams of the atoms joined by a covalent bond. You can see this in the diagram below. Within the circle, there must be an electron arrangement like that of a noble gas. The region where circles around different atoms overlap represents a covalent bond. Copy this diagram into your notebook.

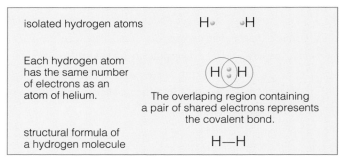

The bonding in a hydrogen molecule

2 Sharing electrons always increases the number of electrons in the valence shell of an atom. Sometimes all the electrons of an atom are not shared, however. Any electrons that are not involved in bonding are shown as pairs. Copy the following diagrams, which show the bonding in water molecules. Then model the bonding process and final result. Notice that the structural formula of a molecular compound replaces the shared electrons with a solid line.

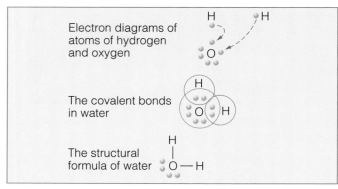

The bonding in a water molecule

3 Methane is one of the gases found in natural gas. It is a molecular compound with the formula CH_4. Model the bonding in methane. Then draw electron dot diagrams and show the structural formula of methane.

4 Atoms can share more than one pair of electrons in a covalent bond. When two pairs of electrons are shared, a double bond is formed between the atoms. This is what happens in oxygen, one of the diatomic molecules. Model the bonding in O_2, and draw diagrams.

5 Nitrogen molecules are also diatomic. Model the bonding, and draw diagrams. How many bonds are formed when two nitrogen atoms join?

6 Carbon monoxide, CO, and carbon dioxide, CO_2, both contain covalent bonds. Make models and draw diagrams to show the bonding in these two molecules.

Analyze

1. How is the valence shell of hydrogen in hydrogen compounds different from the valence shell of other atoms when they form bonds? How is it the same?

2. How is the bonding in calcium oxide different from the bonding in carbon monoxide and carbon dioxide?

3. For each question below, state and justify your opinions.
   (a) Can a covalent bond form between a metal atom and a non-metal atom?
   (b) Can two non-metal atoms exchange an electron to form ions?

4. How many covalent bonds join the atoms in N_2? Why do you think nitrogen gas is generally unreactive?

Conclude and Apply

5. Make up a rule to describe the number of valence electrons in an atom that has formed a stable ion. **Note:** Think carefully about hydrogen. Can you include it in your rule?

Bonding and the Properties of Ionic Compounds

Nearly all ionic compounds involve bonds between metal cations and non-metal anions. The cations and anions form a regular, repeating pattern. A compound with a characteristic, crystalline shape is formed. The attraction between the oppositely charged ions is strong. It extends from one ion to the next throughout the crystal. Consequently ionic compounds have several characteristic physical properties.

- Ionic compounds tend to have relatively high melting points because a large amount of energy is needed to break the strong forces of attraction in ionic bonds.
- Ionic compounds conduct electricity when they are molten or when they are dissolved in water. This is because melting or dissolving allows the ions to move freely. Thus they can carry an electric charge.
- Ionic compounds in the solid state are not electrical conductors; the ions are not able to move.

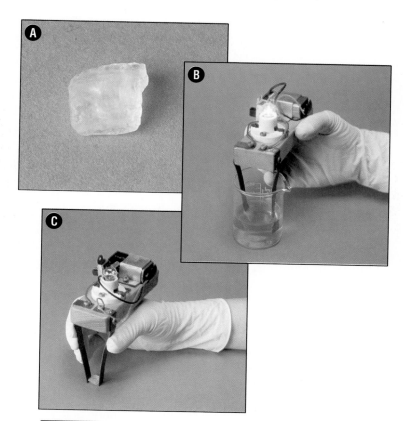

Figure 5.9 Like most ionic compounds, sodium chloride (A) has a relatively high melting point (801°C). It conducts electricity in solution (B) and does not conduct electricity in its solid state (C).

Bonding and the Properties of Molecular Compounds

Molecular compounds are formed when atoms of non-metals are joined by covalent bonds. Although the bonds between atoms within a molecule are strong, the forces of attraction between the molecules is weak. As a result, molecular compounds have the following characteristic properties:

- Molecular compounds have relatively low melting points because little energy is needed to break the forces of attraction between molecules.
- Molecular compounds tend not to conduct electricity when they are in the solid or liquid state, or when they are dissolved in water, because they do not contain ions.

An **electrolyte** is a substance that dissolves in water to produce a solution that conducts electricity. Ionic substances tend to be electrolytes. Molecular substances tend to be non-electrolytes. Testing aqueous (water) solutions for conductivity can help you decide whether a substance is composed of molecules or ions.

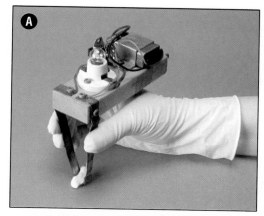

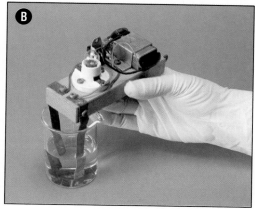

Figure 5.10 Like most molecular compounds, glucose has a relatively low melting point (146°C). It does not conduct electricity in solid form (A) or in an aqueous solution (B).

Molecules or Ions?

The forces of attraction between the particles in a compound affect the physical properties of the compound. Weak forces of attraction hold together the molecules in a molecular compound. Strong forces of attraction hold together the oppositely charged ions in an ionic compound. Thus molecular compounds and ionic compounds have different physical properties.

Problem

Which compounds in this investigation are composed of molecules and which are composed of ions?

Safety Precautions

Materials

9 labels
distilled water
solid honey
Epsom salts
lauric acid
washing soda

Apparatus

magnifying lens	Bunsen burner
5 beakers (100 mL)	test tube rack
scoopula	4 test tubes
stirring rod	test tube holder
conductivity tester	

Procedure

1 Make a table like the one below to record your observations. Give your table a title.

2 Examine a small sample of each substance using a magnifying lens. Record its appearance. Note, in particular, if the edges of the sample have a characteristic shape.

Substance	Appearance	Odour	Hardness	Solubility in water	Conductivity in aqueous solution	Relative melting point	Ionic or covalent?
honey							
Epsom salts							
lauric acid*							
washing soda							

*comes from coconut fat, and is used to make soap and cosmetics

3 **CAUTION:** Use the proper technique to carefully smell each compound. If you detect an odour, try to describe it in your table.

4 **CAUTION:** You must wear protective gloves for this step. Test the hardness of each substance by rubbing a small sample between your thumb and forefinger. Use words such as "soft," "waxy," and "brittle" to record your observations. Wash your hands thoroughly when you have completed this step, and follow your teacher's instructions for cleaning the gloves.

5 Label each beaker with the name of one of the test substances. Pour 50 mL of distilled water into each beaker. Label one beaker "control."

6 Predict whether the control will conduct electricity or not. Then test your prediction and record your results.

7 Use the scoopula to add a peanut-sized quantity of honey to the appropriate beaker. Stir with a stirring rod, and note whether the substance dissolves completely.

8 Test the solution for conductivity, and record your results.

9 Repeat steps 7 and 8 for each of the other substances.

10 Label each test tube with the name of one of the test substances. Use the scoopula to add a peanut-sized quantity of honey to the appropriate test tube.

11 **CAUTION:** Using the tongs, gently heat the test tube over a Bunsen burner flame. If the substance melts, record the relative melting point as "low." If the substance does not melt, record the relative melting point as "high."

12 Repeat steps 10 and 11 for each of the other substances.

13 After the test tubes have cooled, clean them and put them away. Wash your hands.

Analyze

1. Which substances have edges with a characteristic shape? What does this suggest about the arrangement of their particles?

2. Which substances have no odour, or are hard and brittle? What do these properties suggest about the strength of the forces of attraction?

3. Classify the test substances as electrolytes and non-electrolytes.

Conclude and Apply

4. Which of the compounds in this investigation are made of ions, and which are made of molecules? Share your conclusions with others in the class, and discuss any conclusions about which you disagree.

Pause& Reflect

In steps 5 to 9, you used a control. In steps 10 to 12, you did not. Explain why a control was necessary in the first case but not in the second.

Check Your Understanding

1. Think of two cations and two anions that have the same number of electrons as an atom of argon. Use chemical symbols to represent these cations and anions.

2. Draw electron dot diagrams to show how bonding occurs between atoms of
   (a) magnesium and oxygen
   (b) nitrogen and hydrogen

3. Which of the following substances are probably electrolytes? Why?
   (a) KBr
   (b) $AlCl_3$
   (c) C_3H_8 (propane, a gas used in barbecue tanks)
   (d) CS_2
   (e) CaF_2

4. **Thinking Critically** Modern light bulbs, such as the one shown here, are filled with the noble gas argon. The earliest light bulbs, 100 years ago, were simply filled with air. Do you think these early bulbs would have lasted a long time before burning out? Why or why not? Why do you think argon is now used instead?

5. **Apply** Which types of elements combine to form molecular compounds? Give one example. Then describe two properties that could distinguish a molecular compound from an ionic compound.

6. **Thinking Critically** Could a lithium atom and a hydrogen atom share a pair of electrons to form a covalent bond? Explain your answer.

7. **Thinking Critically** Examine the data in the table below. In your notebook, identify each substance as an ionic or a molecular compound, and give reasons to justify your choice. Suggest at least one test you could do, and the results you would expect, to provide additional evidence to support your choice.

Substance	Appearance	Odour	Hardness	Solubility in water	Conductivity in aqueous solution	Relative melting point	Ionic or covalent?
moth balls	white solid	distinctive odour	soft	insoluble	non-conductor	low	
sodium thiosulfate (photographer's "hypo")	white solid	none	brittle	very soluble	conductor	low	
antifreeze	colourless liquid	"sweet" odour	liquid	very soluble	non-conductor	low	
potassium permanganate	deep purple crystals	none	brittle	very soluble	conductor	high	
benzoic acid	white solid	distinctive odour	soft	slightly soluble	poor conductor	low	

5.3 Chemical Names and Formulas

Who decides how compounds should be named? The International Union of Pure and Applied Chemistry (IUPAC) is a global organization of scientists that is responsible for setting standards in chemistry. Committees of the IUPAC make recommendations on how compounds should be named.

IUPAC assigns each compound a unique name to distinguish it from other chemicals. When you are given the name of a chemical, you need to be able to write its formula, because you need to use chemical formulas to write chemical equations. You will learn how to write chemical equations in section 5.4, and you will use this skill throughout the rest of the unit. To prepare yourself, complete the next investigation. You will use your knowledge of chemical bonding to write the names and formulas of compounds that contain two different atoms or ions. Compounds that contain two different elements are called **binary compounds.**

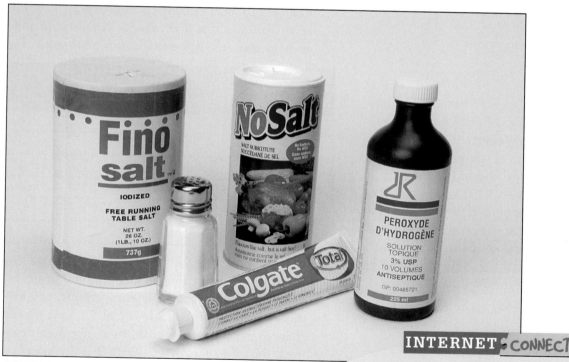

Figure 5.11 Binary compounds are ingredients in many consumer products.

INTERNET CONNECT

www.school.mcgrawhill.ca/resources/

The IUPAC web site provides an enormous amount of facts, figures, and phenomena. Much of the information on this web site is aimed at professional scientists and engineers. Even so, a casual "surf" can help you gain an appreciation for the role that chemistry — its theories and its applications — plays in your daily life. Explore the IUPAC web site, and write an e-mail message to a friend to summarize the kinds of information you can find there. Start your investigation of worldwide chemistry by going to the web site above. Go to Science Resources, then to SCIENCEPOWER 10 to know where to go next.

Writing Names and Formulas of Binary Ionic Compounds

Think About It

Bonding involves either a transfer or a sharing of electrons to form ions or atoms that have the same number of electrons as a noble gas. You can use the periodic table to predict the number of electrons that are transferred or shared. Then you can use this information to determine the number of atoms that must be present in the chemical formula.

Apparatus

periodic table (see page 570)
notebook

What to Do

1 If you are given the chemical formula of a compound, count the number of different element symbols that are in the formula. The formula of a binary compound has two different symbols. For example, NaCl, $MgCl_2$, and H_2O are all binary compounds, but KOH is not. If you are given the name of a compound, look at the end of the name. If the name ends with the suffix "ide," the compound is usually (but not always) binary. In your notebook, copy the following list and identify the binary compounds.

(a) HCl   (d) hydrogen sulfide

(b) SO_3 (e) copper sulfate

(c) $MgCO_3$

2 How do you decide whether the name or formula refers to an ionic compound or a molecular compound? Examine the name or formula, and identify the types of elements that the compound contains. To help you with this, answer these two questions.

(a) Which types of elements combine to form ionic compounds?

(b) Which types of elements combine to form molecular compounds?

3 Now copy the following list, and identify each name or formula as belonging to an ionic or a molecular compound.

(a) sodium sulfide   (d) zinc oxide

(b) PCl_3 (e) MgI_2

(c) nitrogen dioxide

4 Simple anions are named according to the element that forms the anion, with the ending changed to "ide." Copy the table below, and fill in the blanks. The first row has been completed to help you. (Do not write in this textbook.)

Element		Anion	
Name	Symbol	Name	Symbol
fluorine	F	fluoride	F^-
		chloride	
		bromide	
		oxide	
		sulfide	
		nitride	

5 Multiple atoms or ions in a compound are specified with a subscript. For example, the formula for calcium chloride is $CaCl_2$. This means that for each 1 calcium ion, there are 2 chloride ions. (Notice that the subscript 1 is not used for calcium.) Overall, ionic compounds must have a net charge of zero. The total positive charge on the cations must be balanced by the total negative charge on the anions. The 2+ charge on a calcium ion is balanced by the negative charges on two chloride ions. (Do you see why? If not, solve this equation and then continue at the top of the next page.
$+ 2 + 2 \times (-1) = ?$)

Copy the formulas below, and identify those that are correct. Correct any that are wrong, and write the names of all the compounds. **Note:** If you are unsure, try steps 6 and 7 first and then come back to this step.)

(a) LiO   (c) K_2S (e) KN_3

(b) MgO   (d) $AlBr_3$

6 One way to make sure that a formula you write has balanced charges is to use the "cross-over" method. Write the formulas of the ions beside each other. Then cross over the magnitude (amount or size) of the charge on the cation so that it becomes the subscript for the anion. Cross over the magnitude of the charge on the anion to get the cation subscript. Copy the following examples in your notebook.

These cross-over diagrams show how to write the formulas for magnesium chloride and calcium oxide.

A   Determining the formula of magnesium chloride

Mg^{2+} Cl^- You determine the subscripts by "crossing over" the magnitude of the charges. Remember that you do not write the number 1.

$MgCl_2$ magnesium chloride

B   Determining the formula of calcium oxide

Ca^{2+} O^{2-}

Ca_2O_2

Because a formula shows the ratio of ions, you write the simplest ratio. For calcium oxide, the simplest ratio of ions is 1:1.

CaO   calcium oxide

7 Use the cross-over method to write the formula of each of the following.

(a) beryllium fluoride   (e) lithium oxide

(b) sodium nitride   (f) magnesium nitride

(c) calcium sulfide   (g) gallium sulfide

(d) aluminum chloride   (h) barium bromide

8 Nearly all the transition metals (the elements in Groups 3 to 12 in the periodic table) are able to form more than one cation. For example, iron can form the cations Fe^{2+} and Fe^{3+}. Given the formula of an ionic compound, you can use the reverse of the cross-over method to determine the charge on the cation. Copy the following example, and explain it to a partner so that you will remember how it works.

Determining the charge on a cation

A   Formula: $FeCl_3$

Use the reverse of the cross-over method.   **Fe Cl₃**   Remember that you do not write the number 1.

Add the charge signs to each ion. Fe^{3+} Cl^-

The charge on the chloride anion is correct. (Use your understanding of valence electron patterns in the periodic table to explain why.) Therefore the cation charge must be correct. In $FeCl_3$, the iron cation is Fe^{3+}.

B   Formula: FeO

Use the reverse of the cross-over method   **Fe O**

.Add the charge signs to each ion. Fe^+ O^-

In this case, the anion charge is incorrect. The oxygen anion should be O^{2-}. Therefore double the charges on each ion. Thus the iron cation in FeO is Fe^{2+}.

9 Use the reverse cross-over method to find the charge on the cation in these compounds. Decide if your answers are reasonable before you move on to step 10.

(a) Cu_2S (d) $NiCl_2$

(b) Fe_2O_3 (e) CrN

(c) PbO_2 (f) HgO

CONTINUED ▶

10 There are two ways to name the cation of a transition element (an element with more than one valence). One way, called the **classical system,** is based on the Latin names for metals that form more than one ion. The Latin names for iron, copper, and lead are *ferrum, cuprum,* and *plumbum.* The "um" ending is dropped, and the suffix "ic" is added to indicate the ion with the higher charge. The suffix "ous" indicates the ion with the lower charge. Copy and complete the table below by adding the missing names. The first line is given to help you. Do not write in this textbook.

Element	Latin name	Ion with lower charge		Ion with larger charge	
iron	ferrum	ferrous	Fe^{2+}	ferric	Fe^{3+}
	cuprum		Cu^+		Cu^{2+}
	plumbum		Pb^{2+}		Pb^{4+}

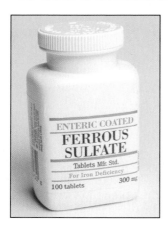

The classical system for naming compounds is still commonly used.

11 The second, more current way to distinguish between cations was invented by German chemist, Alfred Stock. In the **Stock system,** you use the English name of the element, rather than the Latin name. The charge on the cation is written, in parentheses, as a Roman numeral after the name of the metal. Copy and complete the following table by adding the missing Stock system names. The first line is given to help you. Do not write in this textbook.

Classical System versus Stock System

Formula	Classical system	Stock system
$FeCl_3$	ferric chloride	iron(III) chloride
FeO	ferrous oxide	
Cu_2S	cuprous sulfide	
PbO_2	plumbic oxide	

12 The Stock system is used for metals that have more than one type of cation. Thus you do not need to write sodium(I), for example, because sodium forms only a single ion: Na^+. When an ionic compound is named using the Stock system, the name tells you the cation charge to use in the cross over method. Copy the following example.

> Writing a chemical formula given the Stock system name of a compound
>
> In iron(II) sulfide, the iron cation must be Fe^{2+}, and the sulfur anion is S^{2-}.
>
> Use the cross-over method.
>
> $$Fe^{2+} \quad S^{2-}$$
>
> Since Fe_2S_2 is not the simplest ratio,
>
> the formula of iron(II) sulfide is FeS.

13 Write the chemical formula for each of the following compounds.

(a) copper(I) oxide   **(d)** nickel(III) fluoride

(b) lead(IV) bromide   **(e)** manganese(IV) sulfide

(c) iron(III) sulfide

Analyze

Compare the Stock system to the classical system. Which do you think works better, and why? Why might you still need to understand the other system?

Names and Formulas for Polyatomic Ions

Many ionic compounds are not binary because one or both ions contain atoms of more than one element. These **polyatomic ions** consist of two or more different non-metal atoms, which are joined by covalent bonds. For example, the hydroxide ion, OH^-, is a polyatomic ion. It is formed when one covalent bond in a water molecule is broken. Think about the formula of water as H-O-H, and imagine forming hydroxide ions by removing H^+.

There is only one common polyatomic cation: the ammonium ion, NH_4^+. In comparison, there are many polyatomic anions. Table 5.2 gives the names and formulas of the more common ones.

Except for the hydroxide ion, the names of the anions in Table 5.2 end in "-ate" instead of "-ide" (the ending that is used when an anion is formed from one atom). Otherwise, the procedure for naming ionic compounds that contain polyatomic ions is the same as the procedure for naming binary ionic compounds. Writing formulas is also the same, except that you have to add parentheses when the formula requires more than one polyatomic ion. For example, iron(III) hydroxide, which has the chemical formula $Fe(OH)_3$, must have three hydroxide ions for every Fe^{3+} in order to have a net charge of zero. Figure 5.12 gives examples for writing names and formuals for polyatomic oinic compounds.

As you know, must ionic compounds are soluble in water. Is this still true if one of the ions is polyatomic? You will find out in the next investigation.

Table 5.2 Common Polyatomic Ions

Name	Chemical formula
ammonium ion	NH_4^+
hydroxide ion	OH^-
carbonate	CO_3^{2-}
nitrate	NO_3^-
sulfate	SO_4^{2-}
hydrogen carbonate	HCO_3^-
hydrogen sulfate	HSO_4^-
phosphate	PO_4^{3-}

Figure 5.12 Writing formulas and names for polyatomic ionic compounds

What is the formula of ammonium sulfide?
Write the formula of each ion:

$$NH_4^+ \quad S^{2-}$$

Use the cross-over method to find the subscript needed for each ion:

$$NH_4^+ \quad S^{2-}$$

Use parentheses to indicate the two ammonium ions present
The formula of ammonium sulfide is $(NH_4)_2S$

What is the name of $CuCO_3$?
Use the reverse cross-over method to find the charges on each ion.
The formula shows only one carbonate ion:

$$Cu \quad CO_3$$

Add signs for each ion, and check to make sure the ions are correct:

$$Cu^+ \quad CO_3^-$$

The copper ion could be correct, but the carbonate ion charge is wrong
When the charge on the carbonate ion is doubled to make it correct, the charge on the copper ion must also be doubled. The ions present in $CuCO_3$ must be Cu^{2+} and CO_3^{2-}
The name of $CuCO_3$ is copper(II) carbonate, or cupric carbonate

Discovering Insoluble Ionic Compounds

Many ionic compounds dissolve in water, but some do not. Chemists can sometimes identify unknown ionic compounds by performing reactions that combine ions in aqueous solutions. These reactions occasionally produce an insoluble solid, called a precipitate. You will learn more about reactions that produce a precipitate in the next chapter. In this investigation, you will observe the formation of a precipitate and identify the ions that have combined.

Problem

When two aqueous solutions react to form a precipitate, how can you identify which ions are present in the precipitate?

Safety Precautions

Apparatus

test tube rack
6 test tubes

Materials

6 labels
sodium nitrate solution
calcium chloride solution
sodium sulfate solution

Calcium chloride is a more expensive, but less corrosive, alternative to road salt for icy streets and pavement.

Procedure

1 Label three test tubes with the names of the solutions to be tested. For your interest, the photographs provide some information about the compounds you are using in this investigation.

2 Pour 10 mL of each solution into the test tube with the appropriate label.

Sodium nitrate is used to make explosives.

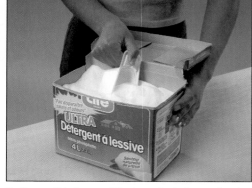

Sodium sulfate is one of the ingredients in powdered washing detergents.

3 Carefully pour about half the sodium sulfate solution into another test tube. To this test tube, add about half the calcium chloride solution. Record your observations. Make up a label to identify this test tube.

4 Pour about half the sodium nitrate solution into another test tube, and add the remaining calcium chloride solution. Record your observations, and make a label to identify the test tube.

5 Pour the remaining sodium nitrate solution and sodium sulfate solution into the last empty test tube. Record your observations, and make a label to identify the test tube.

6 Dispose of the solutions as your teacher directs. Wash your hands thoroughly.

Analyze

1. In step 3, you mixed solutions of sodium sulfate and calcium chloride. Write down the names and formulas of the ions in the sodium sulfate solution. Then do the same for the calcium chloride solution.

2. The cations and anions in each solution combined to form two new compounds. For example, the calcium ion combined with the sulfate ion to form calcium sulfate, which has the formula $CaSO_4$. (When dried, calcium sulfate is used in plaster of Paris to make casts.) What is the name and formula of the other compound that formed in the reaction in step 3?

3. If a precipitate forms, one or both new compounds may be insoluble. If no precipitate forms, you know that both new substances must be soluble. Identify the new substances that formed in the step 3 reaction as either possibly insoluble or definitely soluble.

4. In the next reaction, in step 4, you mixed solutions of sodium nitrate and calcium chloride. Write the names and formulas of the ions present. Then write the names and formulas of the two new compounds that formed. Refer to your observations of the reaction, and identify the two new compounds as possibly insoluble or definitely soluble.

Conclude and Apply

5. Based on your analysis, write the name and formula of the insoluble compound — the precipitate — that formed in the reactions.

6. When you mixed solutions of sodium nitrate and sodium sulfate in step 5, did new compounds form? Explain your answer.

Extend Your Knowledge

7. From your teacher, obtain another set of three solutions of ionic compounds. Two of the ions in these solutions combine to form a precipitate. Design a set of tests to identify the precipitate, and perform them. **CAUTION:** One of these solutions, silver nitrate solution, can stain your skin. Handle it very carefully.

Names and Formulas for Binary Molecular Compounds

Binary molecular compounds consist of covalent bonds between atoms of two different non-metals. Three simple rules will help you write the names and formulas of these compounds.

Table 5.3 Prefixes for Binary Molecular Compounds

Prefix	Number it represents
mono	1
di	2
tri	3
tetra	4
penta	5
hexa	6

The prefix "mono" is only used for the second element. When the second element is oxygen, the "o" is dropped. Thus the second part of the name is monoxide, not monooxide.

1. The name of a binary molecular compound ends in "ide," just like the name of a binary ionic compound.

2. The name and the formula usually begin with the element that is more to the left on the periodic table.

3. In the name, use a prefix to specify the number of atoms of each element that are present in a molecule. Some prefixes, and the numbers they represent, are shown in Table 5.3. Prefixes for larger numbers exist, but binary compounds that have more than six atoms of an element are rare.

Nitrogen combines with oxygen to form a number of oxides. Notice how the prefixes allow each different compound to have a unique name.

STRETCH Your Mind

Compounds with poly-atomic ions contain both ionic and covalent bonds. For example, sodium sulfate, Na_2SO_4, is classified as an ionic substance because it is made up of different ions. Sodium sulfate dissolves in water, and the solution conducts electricity. Because the sulfate ion, SO_4^{2-}, is made up of non-metal atoms, however, the bonding between sulfur and oxygen atoms is covalent.

Table 5.4 Naming the Oxides of Nitrogen

Formula	Systematic name	Common name	Comments
NO	nitrogen monoxide	nitric oxide	• helps to maintain blood pressure • pollutant from vehicle exhaust
N_2O	dinitrogen monoxide	nitrous oxide	• also known as laughing gas • used as the propellant gas in cans of whipped cream
NO_2	nitrogen dioxide	none	• brown gas • used to manufacture nitric acid
N_2O_3	dinitrogen trioxide	none	• deep blue liquid
N_2O_4	dinitrogen tetroxide	none	• used in rocket fuels
N_2O_5	dinitrogen pentoxide	none	• dissolves in water to form nitric acid

Figure 5.13 Car exhaust is a mixture of gases that includes carbon monoxide and carbon dioxide. The rules for naming binary molecular compounds can help you understand the names and formulas of these two gases. For carbon monoxide, CO, carbon is to the left of oxygen in the periodic table, so it comes first in both the name and formula. The "di" prefix of carbon dioxide, CO_2, you now know.

Chemical Bingo

This activity is similar to the game of Bingo. Your playing card will have the formulas of ions and binary molecular compounds, like the sample below. As the names of ions or compounds are randomly drawn and announced, you will check them off on your card.

Na^+ ✓	Cl^-	HSO_4^-	PCl_5
Cu^{2+}	Br^- ✓	NO_3^-	SO_2
Be^{2+}	S^{2-}	OH^- ✓	SF_6
Ca^{2+}	N^{3-} ✓	CO_3^{2-}	N_2O_3

Sample Chemical Bingo card after five names have been called

What You Need

Chemical Bingo card
pencil

What to Do

1. Decide what is required to win the game: a line in any direction or a full card.

2. Your teacher or a volunteer will randomly draw a piece of paper with the name of an ion or a compound on it. Check off the formula on your card if you have it. Listen carefully. If the name is "cuprous," would you check Cu^{2+} on the sample card?

3. Call "bingo" when you think that you have a line or a full card, and wait for your matches to be checked. If someone else calls "bingo," wait until the matches are checked. If the bingo is not correct, the game can continue.

Sample Play

1. After "cuprous," suppose that "phosphorus trichloride" is called. This is a covalent compound with the formula PCl_3. Since the sample card has only PCl_5, phosphorus pentachloride, there is no match.

2. Suppose that the following names are called: bromide, ammonium, and hydroxide. What is the name of the compound you need for a straight-line bingo on the sample card?

Communicating Information about Chemical Safety

Mistakes in chemistry can be dangerous. A Bayer chemical plant in Germany manufactures a chemical used to kill parasites. One of the reactions involved in making this chemical uses potassium carbonate. On June 8, 1999, however, potassium hydroxide was added by mistake. When the reactants were heated, a violent reaction took place, causing an explosion and a fire. Although no one was seriously injured, 91 people, including workers and nearby residents, required hospital treatment. Damage to the chemical plant was estimated at over $100 million.

Figure 5.14 The aftermath of a chemical explosion at a Bayer plant in Germany.

INTERNET CONNECT

www.school.mcgrawhill.ca/resources/

To find out more about the Workplace Hazardous Materials Information System (WHMIS) and Material Safety Data Sheets (MSDS), go to the web site above. Go to **Science Resources**, then to **SCIENCEPOWER 10** to know where to go next. Write a short report, or design your own web site, to explain the purpose and history of WHMIS legislation and the information required on a Material Safety Data Sheet.

Using the correct compound in a reaction is very important. Chemists and chemical-product handlers must read and understand the labels of the chemicals they use. As well, they must know which chemicals require special handling and disposal procedures. The management of hazardous materials is legislated by WHMIS, the Workplace Hazardous Materials Information System. WHMIS legislation is designed to ensure that workers are informed about, and prepared to handle, the hazards they may encounter. There are three ways that WHMIS informs workers about the chemicals they may use:

1. Controlled products must have informative labels, in both English and French, on their containers.

2. Each controlled product must have a Material Safety Data Sheet (MSDS).

3. Workers who handle chemicals must complete an education program provided through their employer.

MATERIAL SAFETY DATA SHEET

PRODUCT NAME: CHLORINE

1. Chemical Product and Company identification

ABC Gases,
Ddvision of
The ABC Group, Inc.
313 Oxygen Road
North Bay, Ontario

TELEPHONE NUMBER: (705)555 5555
24-HOUR EMERGENCY TELEPHONE NUMBER: (705) 444-4444

EMERGENCY RESPONSE PLAN NO: 20101

PRODUCT NAME: CHLORINE
CHEMICAL NAME: Chlorine
COMMON NAMES/SYNONYMS: Bertholite, Molecular Chlorine
TDG (Canada) CLASSIFICATION: 2.3 (5.1)
WHMIS CLASSIFICATION: A, DIA, D2A, D2B, E, C

PREPARED BY: ABC GASES (705)555-5555
PREPERATION DATE: 3/1/00
REVIEW DATES: 3/7/01

2. Composition, Information on Ingredients

Figure 5.15 An MSDS includes important information about a chemical, including physical properties (such as melting point, boiling point, and odour) and chemical hazards. Instructions are given for the handling, storage, and disposal of the chemical, as well as the procedure to follow in case of an accident.

INGREDIENT	% VOLUME	PEL-OSHA[1]	TLV-ACGIH[2]	LD_{50} or LC_{50} Route/Species
Chlorine FORMULA: CL2 CAS: 7782-50-5 RTECS #: FO2100000	100.0	1 ppm Ceiling	0.5 ppm TWA 1 ppm STEL	LC_{50} 293 ppm/1H (rat)

[1] As stated in 29 CFR 1910, Subpart Z (revised July 1, 1993)
[2] As stated in the ACGIH 1994-95 Threshold Limit Values for Chemical Substances and Physical Agents

3. Hazards Identification

EMERGENCY OVERVIEW
Corrosive and irritating to the eyes, skin and mucous membranes. Inhalation may result in chemical pneumonitis and pulmonary edema. Nonflammable Oxidizer, may explode or accelerate combustion if contacting reducing agents.

Understanding an MSDS

Certain information must be included on a Material Safety Data Sheet, but there is no set format. In this activity, you will search the Internet to find information about a chemical from its MSDS.

What to Do

1. Design your own form to record the following MSDS information:
   - chemical name
   - chemical formula
   - physical properties (appearance, odour, melting point, and boiling point)
   - chemical stability and reactivity
   - potential health effects
   - handling and storage
   - disposal

2. If you have not already done so, use the InternetConnect on page 164 to learn about the Workplace Hazardous Materials Information System and Material Safety Data Sheets. Bookmark at least one site that has MSDS information.

3. Your teacher will give you the formula of a chemical. Write the formula on your form, as well as the name of the chemical.

4. Most MSDS searches are by chemical name. A search for a particular name often turns up several possibilities, however, depending on how the chemical is sold. For example, sodium hydroxide is sold in solid form as pellets, at different levels of purity, and in various solutions. Look up your chemical in pure, solid form.

5. As you proceed, keep a list of any words that are unfamiliar to you.

6. Record the appropriate information about your chemical on your form. Here are some things to keep in mind:
   - Note any unusual information, such as the chemical decomposing before it boils.
   - For chemical stability and reactivity, note any dangerous decomposition products. List any warnings about contact with other chemicals.
   - List any potential health hazards, such as exposure to the skin or eyes. Is the chemical poisonous?
   - Is special handling or storage required, other than a cool, dry, ventilated area?
   - What procedures should be followed if there is an accidental leak or spill?

What Did You Discover?

1. What dangers and precautions are involved for someone working with the chemical you researched?

2. WHMIS legislation requires that workers take an education program to understand the information on an MSDS. Based on what you have learned about chemicals and chemical reactions so far, what additional information would you expect to learn from an education program? Use your list of unfamiliar words to help you answer this question.

Extensions

3. Use suitable resources to find the meanings of the unfamiliar words you listed.

4. To comply with WHMIS legislation, chemical manufacturers must provide detailed information about the chemical ingredients in their products. In some cases, manufacturers might argue that this forces them to disclose information that a competitor could use to make its own version of the same products, thus jeopardizing their sales. Can manufacturers be exempted from providing information? Research this question, and share your findings in the form of a brief report.

Check Your Understanding

1. In your notebook, identify each of the following compounds as ionic or molecular. Place an asterisk beside those that are binary.

   (a) P_2O_5 (d) CH_4

   (b) $CaSO_4$ (e) Na_2CO_3

   (c) KNO_3

2. Name the following compounds.

   (a) $MgBr_2$ (d) $PbSO_4$

   (b) K_2SO_4 (e) PH_3

   (c) CCl_4

3. Some compounds have non-systematic names that are often used. For example, the non-systematic name for phosphorus trihydride is phosphine. Write the systematic name for each of the following.

   (a) water, H_2O (d) potash, K_2CO_3

   (b) ammonia, NH_3 (e) methane, CH_4

   (c) lye, $NaOH$

4. Write the chemical formula for each of the following.

   (a) ammonium bromide   (d) ferrous nitrate

   (b) lead(II) carbonate   (e) strontium iodide

   (c) barium sulfate

5. What does the abbreviation WHMIS stand for? A Material Safety Data Sheet is one part of WHMIS legislation. What are the other two parts?

6. **Apply** Many of the chemical products in your home are mixtures that contain an ionic compound as their active ingredient. Copy the table at the right, and look for the products in the table around your home. **CAUTION:** Remember what you learned in the MSDS activity. Handle all chemical products safely.

   (a) Examine the label on each product you find to determine its active ingredient. Record the active ingredient and its formula in the table.

   (b) Make a list of the substances that are most often found in cleaners. What do you know, or what can you find out, about these substances to account for their use?

   (c) Which substance is the most common ingredient in the antacids you examined? What do you know, or what can you find out, about this substance to account for its use?

Common Chemical Products in the Home

Product	Name	Formula
baking soda	sodium bicarbonate or sodium hydrogen carbonate	$NaHCO_3$
solid Drano™		
Liquid Plumber™		
liquid bleach		
Comet™		
Epsom salts		
Rolaids™		
Tums™		
milk of magnesia		
fluoride toothpaste		
dishwasher detergent		

5.4 Chemical Equations and Chemical Reactions

At the start of section 5.1, you saw an equation that summarized the formation of water:

$$2H_2 + O_2 \rightarrow 2H_2O$$

You read that by the end of the chapter, you would understand what it means and why it is written this way. Now, with your understanding of periodic patterns and your ability to name and write formulas for a variety of compounds, you are ready to explore chemical equations.

You and chemists around the world are able to write chemical equations because of the work done by two scientists just before and just after the turn of the nineteenth century: the French chemist Antoine Lavoisier and the English philosopher and teacher John Dalton. Two of their important contributions to chemistry are given below.

Figure 5.16 During the late eighteenth century, Antoine Lavoisier conducted numerous experiments that involved chemical reactions. His belief in the need to make accurate measurements resulted in precise values for the masses of the substances in his experiments. Based on numerous observations of the same results, Lavoisier wrote his version of the law of conservation of mass: in every chemical reaction, there is an equal quantity of matter before and after the reaction.

Lavoisier's law of conservation of mass	Dalton's atomic theory
During a chemical reaction, the total mass of the reacting substances, the **reactants**, is always equal to the total mass of the resulting substances, the **products**.	• All matter is made up of small particles called atoms. • Atoms cannot be created, destroyed, or divided into smaller particles. • All atoms of the same element are identical in mass and size, but they are different in mass and size from the atoms of other elements. • Compounds are formed when atoms of different elements combine in fixed (definite) proportions.

The law of conservation of mass is still accepted by chemists today. Dalton's atomic theory was a major breakthrough in its time, even though some of the details are no longer accepted by modern science. From your grade 9 science studies, try to recall the changes made to Dalton's ideas by more recent scientists.

Figure 5.17 John Dalton's interest in meteorology, and his experiments with the gases that make up air, led him to redevelop a 2000-year-old idea about the fundamental nature of matter. Dalton's great gift to science was his ability to recognize patterns in experimental results — his own and those of others — and to interpret these results in new ways.

Comparing the Masses of Reactants and Products

Dalton explained chemical reactions as the rearrangement of bonds between the atoms of elements. He argued that mass must be conserved during chemical reactions because atoms cannot be created or destroyed. Notice how Lavoisier's law of conservation of mass forms an integral part of Dalton's argument.

Problem

How can you collect experimental data to test the law of conservation of mass?

Safety Precautions

- Always report spills of any chemicals to your teacher.
- Rinse any spills with plenty of water.
- Wash your hands thoroughly at the end of this investigation.

Apparatus

balance
Erlenmeyer flask
stopper
small test tube
tongs

Materials

copper(II) sulfate solution
sodium hydroxide solution

Procedure

1. Pour 20 mL of sodium hydroxide solution into the Erlenmeyer flask.

2. Pour copper(II) sulfate solution into the small test tube until the test tube is about half full.

3. Tilt the Erlenmeyer flask to one side, and carefully place the test tube inside. Do not let the solutions mix. Seal the flask with the stopper.

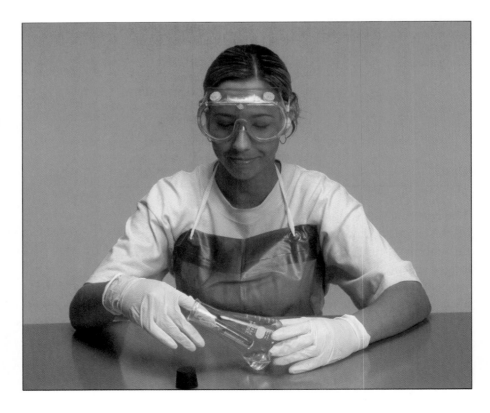

④ Determine the mass of the flask and its contents. In your notebook, record your measurement, as well as the appearance of both solutions.

⑤ Tip the flask to allow the solutions to mix.

⑥ Predict the mass of the flask and its contents. Verify your prediction. Describe the appearance of the contents.

⑦ Use tongs to carefully remove the small test tube. Then pour the contents of the flask into a container provided by your teacher. Wash your hands thoroughly.

Analyze

1. When the solutions were mixed, did a chemical change occur? What is your evidence?

2. How did the mass of the reactants and glassware before the reaction compare with the mass after the reaction? Check your classmates' values to see how they compare with yours.

3. If you noted a change in mass, offer an explanation to account for it.

Conclude and Apply

4. Do your results support the law of conservation of mass? If not, what sources of error might have affected your observations and measurements?

5. The products of the reaction are copper(II) hydroxide and sodium sulfate. Write a word equation and a balanced chemical equation to describe the reaction.

Extend Your Knowledge

6. Suppose that you performed a reaction in a flask without a stopper. If the products included a gas, predict whether the mass of the products and glassware would be greater than or less than the mass of the reactants and glassware. Use the law of conservation of mass and your results from this investigation to support your answer.

7. Ari performed an experiment to check the law of conservation of mass using the reaction of an Alka-Seltzer® tablet with water in a beaker. The following masses were recorded.

Mass of beaker and water: 47.26 g

Mass of Alka-Seltzer® tablet: 3.205 g

Mass after reaction: 47.96 g

(a) Do these results suggest that the law of conservation of mass does not apply to this reaction? Explain.

(b) Assume that the balance was working properly, and Ari recorded the masses correctly. Describe at least two reasons why the mass of the reactants is not equal to the mass of the products.

(c) Based on your answer to part (b), how could Ari modify the experimental procedure to obtain results that are more consistent with the law of conservation of mass?

Writing Chemical Equations

Throughout this chapter, you have used chemical symbols, such as H and O, to represent elements. You have also used chemical formulas, such as H_2O, to represent compounds.

Since you can use symbols and formulas as a shorthand to represent elements and compounds, you would probably expect that there is a shorthand for representing chemical reactions: for example, a shorthand to express the statement "Hydrogen gas reacts with oxygen gas to form liquid water." There is. It is called a chemical equation.

The simplest form of a chemical equation is a **word equation:** for example,

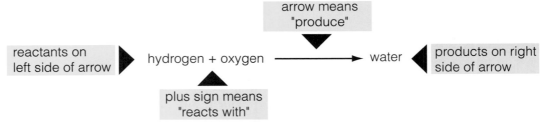

reactants on left side of arrow

arrow means "produce"

hydrogen + oxygen → water

products on right side of arrow

plus sign means "reacts with"

Word equations are fine in casual conversation, but they provide limited information about a chemical reaction. They do not tell anything about the chemical composition of the reactants and products; nor do they give the numbers of elements, molecules, and compounds that are involved. To develop an equation that supplies more meaningful information, you start by replacing words with chemical symbols and formulas:

$$H_2 + O_2 \rightarrow H_2O$$

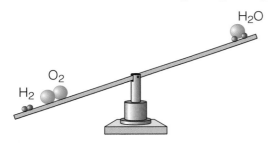

This "bare-bones" representation of a word equation is called a **skeleton equation.** A skeleton equation summarizes a chemical reaction in symbolic form. It is not a complete or accurate equation, however, because it may violate the law of conservation of mass and Dalton's atomic theory. Use Figure 5.18 to help you understand why.

Lavoisier's law and Dalton's theory demand that reactants and products always have the same number of atoms. (Otherwise, atoms would not be conserved.) This is why chemists insist on writing **balanced chemical equations.** You must always check a skeleton equation to see if it is balanced. For example, in the skeleton equation above, you can see that the number of hydrogen atoms is balanced. There are 2 hydrogen atoms on each side. The oxygen atoms are not balanced, however. There are 2 oxygen atoms on the left, and there is only 1 on the right. So the skeleton equation is unbalanced. To make it balanced, you add (where necessary) numbers called **coefficients** before the formulas of the compounds. Examine the modified chemical equation below. The coefficient 2 in front of the formula for water means that there are two molecules of water:

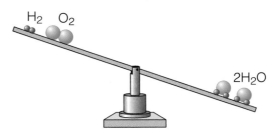

$$H_2 + O_2 \rightarrow 2H_2O$$

Figure 5.19 Why is the scale still unbalanced?

Does adding this coefficient balance the equation? No. Count the number of hydrogen atoms on both sides, and you will see why. There are 2 hydrogen atoms on the left, but 2 molecules of water would contain 4 atoms of hydrogen. To finally balance this chemical equation, you need to add one more coefficient:

$$2H_2 + O_2 \rightarrow 2H_2O$$

Sometimes you need to know the state of the chemicals that are involved in a chemical reaction. You can easily add this information to a chemical equation by inserting an abbreviation in parentheses after each chemical formula. The following abbreviations are commonly used. **Note:** The state of the substance may depend on its temperature in the reaction.

Figure 5.20 Why is the scale finally balanced?

Table 5.5 Abbreviations for States of Reactants and Products

State	Abbreviation	Examples (at room temperature)
solid	(s)	iron: Fe(s) salt: NaCl(s) limestone: $CaCO_3$(s)
liquid	(ℓ)	water: H_2O(ℓ) octane (found in gasoline): C_8H_{18}(ℓ)
gas	(g)	helium: He(g) nitrogen: N_2(g) ozone: O_3(g)
aqueous solution	(aq)	salt solution (brine): NaCl(aq) ammonia solution (found in glass cleaner): NH_3(aq)

Including the information about state, the final balanced equation for water, representing reactants and product at room temperature, is

$$2H_2(g) + O_2(g) \rightarrow 2H_2O(ℓ)$$

Notice that you do not include a coefficient 1.

Writing Balanced Chemical Equations

Balancing a chemical equation requires patience, practice, and perseverance. One set of steps or rules will not apply to all the equations you are asked to write. The guidelines and examples that follow will help, however.

• Write the skeleton equation. Be sure you have the right formulas for all the compounds (the "terms" in the equation).

• Look for an element or a polyatomic ion that appears just once on each side of the equation. Balance these two terms.

• Pick another element that appears once on each side. Choose coefficients to balance this element as well. Remember that the terms you balanced in the previous step have to remain balanced. Repeat for any other elements that appear once on each side.

- Check for any term you have not yet looked at. Adjust the coefficient of the term so that the numbers of the elements appearing in that term are balanced across the whole equation. Remember to clear any fraction coefficients by multiplying through.
- Check the equation. A good technique is to make a table of the atoms of each element on each side of the equation.

Examples of Balancing Chemical Equations

Example 1

Word Equation

sodium + water → sodium hydroxide + hydrogen gas

Remember: Hydrogen gas is diatomic.

Skeleton Equation

$Na(s) + H_2O(\ell) \rightarrow NaOH(aq) + H_2(g)$

What to Look For

On the left and right sides of the equation, there is a compound with one oxygen atom. The coefficients for these compounds must therefore be the same. The oxygen and sodium atoms are already balanced. You need to balance the hydrogen atoms by using the coefficient $\frac{1}{2}$ for the hydrogen molecule.

$Na(s) + H_2O(\ell) \rightarrow NaOH(aq) + \frac{1}{2}H_2(g)$

The equation seems to be balanced, so remove the fraction by multiplying each coefficient by 2.

$2Na(s) + 2H_2O(\ell) \rightarrow 2NaOH(aq) + H_2(g)$

Check It

Your final step should always be checking the total number of atoms or ions on each side of the equation. Make a chart to list the reactants and products, and record the number of atoms and ions to see if they match.

Reactants	Products
2 Na atoms	2 Na atoms
2 O atoms	2 O atoms
4 H atoms	4 H atoms

The equation is properly balanced.

Example 2

Word Equation
copper + silver nitrate → copper(II) nitrate + silver

Skeleton Equation
$Cu(s) + AgNO_3(aq) \rightarrow Cu(NO_3)_2(aq) + Ag(s)$

What to Look For
On the left and right sides, there are compounds that contain nitrate ions, NO_3^-. Balance these ions as a unit first.

$Cu(s) + 2AgNO_3(aq) \rightarrow Cu(NO_3)_2(aq) + Ag(s)$

Then balance the silver.

$Cu(s) + 2AgNO_3(aq) \rightarrow Cu(NO_3)_2(aq) + 2Ag(s)$

The copper is balanced.

Check It

Reactants	Products
1 Cu atom	1 Cu atom
2 Ag atoms	2 Ag atoms
2 NO_3^- ions	2 NO_3^- ions

The equation is properly balanced.

Example 3

Word Equation
calcium nitrate + sodium hydroxide → calcium hydroxide + sodium nitrate

Skeleton Equation
$Ca(NO_3)_2(aq) + NaOH(aq) \rightarrow Ca(OH)_2(s) + NaNO_3(aq)$

What to Look For
First balance the nitrate ions and the hydroxide ions.

$Ca(NO_3)_2(aq) + 2NaOH(aq) \rightarrow Ca(OH)_2(s) + 2NaNO_3(aq)$

The equation appears to be balanced.

Check It

Reactants	Products
1 Ca atom	1 Ca atom
2 NO_3^- ions	2 NO_3^- ions
2 Na atoms	2 Na atoms
2 OH^- ions	2 OH^- ions

The equation is properly balanced.

You will have many opportunities to practise writing and balancing chemical equations throughout the rest of this unit. The Check Your Understanding questions below will allow you to "get your feet wet." The Chapter Review includes a few more.

Check Your Understanding

1. Explain the principle or reasoning behind balancing chemical equations.

2. Use a graphic organizer, such as a Venn diagram, to show the relationship among the following: word equation, skeleton equation, and balanced chemical equation.

Skill
P O W E R

To review types of graphic organizers, turn to page 578.

3. Each of the following chemical equations is balanced, but it is incorrect in some other way. State what is wrong and then write the equation correctly.

   (a) $H_2O \rightarrow H_2 + \frac{1}{2} O_2$

   (b) $NH_3 \rightarrow N + 3H$

   (c) $2C + 2O_2 \rightarrow 2CO_2$

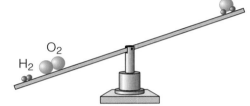

4. **Apply** Given the following word and skeleton equations, write the balanced chemical equations.

   (a) sulfur dioxide + oxygen $\rightarrow$ sulfur trioxide

   $SO_2(g) \quad + \quad O_2(g) \rightarrow \quad SO_3(g)$

   (b) methane + oxygen $\rightarrow$ carbon dioxide + water

   $CH_4(g) + O_2(g) \rightarrow \quad CO_2(g) \quad + H_2O(g)$

   (c) aluminum chloride + potassium $\rightarrow$ potassium chloride + aluminum

   $AlCl_3 \quad + \quad K \quad \rightarrow \quad KCl \quad + \quad Al$

   (d) ammonia gas + oxygen $\rightarrow$ nitrogen + water

   $NH_3(g) \quad + \quad O_2(g) \rightarrow \quad N_2(g) \quad + H_2O(\ell)$

   (e) copper(II) oxide $\rightarrow$ copper + oxygen gas

   $CuO(s) \quad \rightarrow \quad Cu(s) + \quad O_2(g)$

5. **Apply** When you light a campfire, you are burning carbon compounds in the wood. What are two products that are produced in these reactions?

6. **Thinking Critically** Suppose that you measure the mass of a chemical in an open container, and then heat it for a few minutes over a Bunsen burner flame. After the container and contents have cooled, you find that the mass is larger than before. If you accept the law of conservation of mass, how can you explain your observation?

Now that you have completed this chapter, try to do the following. If you cannot, go back to the sections indicated.

Describe how the elements are organized on the periodic table. (5.1)

Draw an electron shell diagram for any of the first 20 elements, and show the corresponding electron dot diagram. (5.1)

Explain why an alkali metal in Group 1 is more reactive than its alkaline earth neighbour in Group 2. (5.1)

State which type of element tends to form cations and which type tends to form anions. Give one example of each. (5.1)

Describe the special relationship between the valence shell of the noble gases and the formation of chemical bonds. (5.2)

Distinguish between an ionic compound and a molecular compound. Give an example of each. (5.2)

Name two atoms that would combine to form an ionic bond. Describe (using words, diagrams, or both) the transfer of electrons between atoms to form ions. (5.2)

Name two atoms that would combine to form a covalent bond. Describe (using words, diagrams, or both) the sharing of electrons between the atoms. (5.2)

Use electron dot diagrams to explain the formation of ionic and covalent compounds. (5.2)

Outline an experimental procedure to determine whether a substance is made up of ions or molecules. (5.2)

Explain how to identify a compound as an electrolyte or a non-electrolyte, given its name or chemical formula. (5.2)

Define the term "binary compound." Give the name and formula of a binary ionic compound and a binary covalent compound. (5.3)

Name at least three examples of compounds of transition elements, using both the classical system and the Stock system. (5.3)

Write the chemical formula of a compound containing a transition metal, and indicate the charge on the metal cation. (5.3)

Write the name and formula of two polyatomic ions. (5.3)

Outline the main features of WHMIS legislation. Recognize and summarize key safety information from an MSDS. (5.3)

State the law of conservation of mass. Explain how it is related to writing balanced chemical equations. (5.4)

Outline how to balance a chemical equation. (5.4)

Prepare Your Own Summary

Summarize this chapter by doing one of the following. Use a graphic organizer (such as a concept map), produce a poster, or write the summary to include the key chapter concepts. Here are a few ideas to use as a guide:

• Explain how the periodic table can be used to predict the formation of ions.
• Explain the reactivity of the alkali metals and the halogens.
• Give examples of ionic and covalent compounds. Explain their physical properties based on the strength of attraction between particles.

• Explain how the periodic table can be used to predict the formula of a binary compound.
• Describe how the Stock system is used to name a compound or write its chemical formula.
• Show how Lavoisier and Dalton are linked to writing balanced chemical equations.
• Describe how to check that a chemical equation is balanced.

Reviewing Key Terms

If you need to review, the section numbers show you where these terms were introduced.

1. What do the atoms of elements in the same period have in common? What do the atoms of elements in the same family have in common? (5.1).

2. What are electron dot diagrams? How are they useful? (5.1)

3. Describe two ways that a chemical bond can form between two atoms. Give an example of each type of chemical bond. (5.2)

4. Which type of chemical bond must be present in an electrolyte? Explain how you know. (5.2)

5. When must you use the Stock system to name a compound? Explain with an example. (5.3)

Understanding Key Concepts

Section numbers are provided if you need to review.

6. Explain how the electrons in atoms of aluminum are related the position of aluminum in the periodic table. (5.1)

7. Distinguish between different types of ions. Give three examples of each type of ion. (5.1)

8. Why are ionic solids non-conductors of electricity, but good conductors when melted? (5.1)

9. Use a periodic table to answer the following questions. (5.1)
   (a) How many valence electrons does calcium have?
   (b) What would you expect the valence of phosphorus to be? Why?

10. Draw electron dot diagrams for the following covalent molecules. (5.2)
   (a) phosphine, PH_3
   (b) carbon tetrachloride, CCl_4
   (c) sulfur dichloride, SCl_2
   (d) nitrogen dioxide, NO_2

11. Each of the following statements is incorrect. Identify the mistake, and re-write the statement correctly in your notebook. (5.3)
   (a) When chromium gives up 6 electrons, it forms Cr^{6-} ions.
   (b) Cobalt(II) anions are written Co^{2+}.
   (c) Titanium forms two ions, Ti (3) and Ti (4).

12. When an ionic compound is named or its formula is written, which ion is placed first, the anion or the cation? (5.3)

13. Copy this table into your notebook, and complete it using the line for $Ca(NO_3)_2$ to help you. Do not write in this textbook. (5.4)

Coefficient and formula	Cation(s)	Anion(s)
$Ca(NO_3)_2$	1 Ca^{2+}	2 NO_3^-
$2Na_2SO_4$		
$3Mg(OH)_2$		
$Ca_3(PO_4)_2$		

14. Name the elements present, and the number of atoms of each element, in each of the following compounds. (5.4)
   (a) chloromethane, CH_3Cl
   (b) ammonium nitrate, NH_4NO_3
   (c) glucose, $C_6H_{12}O_6$
   (d) sodium sulfate, Na_2SO_4
   (e) calcium phosphate, $Ca_3(PO_4)_2$

15. Can a skeleton equation be balanced? Explain with an example. (5.4)

Developing Skills

16. In your notebook, name each of the following using the Stock system.
   (a) MgI_2 (d) Cu_3P_2
   (b) Hg_2Cl_2 (e) $FeBr_2$
   (c) CaO (f) K_2O

17. Determine whether each of the following equations is balanced.
    (a) $P + 5Cl_2 \rightarrow PCl_5$
    (b) $H_2SO_4 + FeS \rightarrow FeSO_4 + H_2S$
    (c) $HBr + Fe(OH)_3 \rightarrow FeBr_3 + 3H_2O$
    (d) $Zn + 2HCl \rightarrow ZnCl_2 + 2H_2$
    (e) $P_4 + 5O_2 \rightarrow P_4O_{10}$
    (f) $C_2H_5OH + O_2 \rightarrow 2CO_2 + H_2O$
    (g) $2Fe + O_2 \rightarrow Fe_2O_3$

18. Write these skeleton equations in your notebook. Balance each equation.
    (a) $HCl + Na_2CO_3 \rightarrow NaCl + H_2O + CO_2$
    (b) $C_3H_8 + O_2 \rightarrow CO_2 + H_2O$
    (c) $HF + K_2CO_3 \rightarrow KF + H_2O + CO_2$
    (d) $CO_2 + H_2O \rightarrow C_6H_{12}O_6 + O_2$
    (e) $Al(OH)_3 + HCl \rightarrow AlCl_3 + H_2O$

19. The rusting of iron produces a compound with the formula $Fe_2O_3 \cdot 3H_2O$. This is an iron compound combined with three water molecules.
    (a) Name the elements present, as well as the number of atoms of each element in rust.
    (b) The skeleton equation for the reaction is
    $$Fe + O_2 + H_2O \rightarrow Fe_2O_3 \cdot 3H_2O$$
    Write the balanced chemical equation for the rusting of iron.

Problem Solving/Applying

20. State the total charge on
    (a) one calcium cation
    (b) one sodium cation
    (c) two magnesium cations
    (d) two aluminum cations

21. Element Q is a metal with two valence electons, and element X is a non-metal with five valence electrons. They combine to form an ionic compound. What is its formula?

22. Oxygen usually has 6 valence electrons. How many valence electrons does the other element have in each of the following?
    (a) Na_2O (c) P_2O_5
    (b) AgO (d) SnO_2

23. Draw electron dot diagrams for each of the following compounds.
    (a) carbon disulfide, CS_2 (c) ozone, O_3
    (b) silane, SiH_4

Critical Thinking

24. How is the number of electrons in the valence shell of a metal atom different from the number of electrons in the valence shell of a non-metal atom?

25. Which of the following formulas are impossible? Give reasons for your answers.
    (a) $NaBr_2$ (c) BaS_2
    (b) OF_2 (d) NF_3

26. Why does magnesium increase in mass and wood decrease in mass when each burns in air?

Pause&
──Reflect

1. Go back to page 136, and check your original answers to the Opening Ideas questions. How has your thinking changed? How would you answer those questions now?

2. Can an ionic substance be a non-electrolyte? Explain.

3. Food additives are carefully tested and controlled. If you drink a cup of coffee, however, you will consume over 1000 different chemicals, and only about a quarter are known to be safe. Should coffee be banned until all the chemicals it contains have been fully tested? Discuss.

Opening
Ideas...

- What energy changes take place during chemical reactions?

- What patterns can you use to classify chemical reactions?

- How can you predict whether two chemicals will react or not?

Science
Log

Consider the questions above. Reflect on the chemical reactions that you have observed in class. Also reflect on the chemical reactions that you experience each day. What patterns could help you classify them? Record your answers in your Science Log. As you study this chapter, check your answers and explain why your ideas have or have not changed.

Moment by moment, chemical reactions occur in laboratories, in industrial plants, and, of course, in the natural world. You and other living things benefit from these reactions. The photographs on this page provide a mere glimpse at the multitude of chemical reactions that connect your life with chemical substances and their interactions.

In Chapter 5, you looked for patterns to help you recognize,

name, and describe chemical substances and reactions. Your pattern-seeking will continue here as you model and observe a wide variety of chemical reactions and the energy changes that accompany them. Your experiences will enable you to identify several types of chemical reactions. As well, you will have opportunities to practise your formula-writing and equation-writing skills.

Chemical Reactions

Energy Changes

How can you recognize if a physical or chemical change involves energy?

What You Need

dilute hydrochloric acid
sodium hydroxide pellets
ammonium nitrate

test tube rack
stopper
3 labels

Key Concepts

In this chapter, you will discover

- how energy plays a role in chemical reactions
- how similarities and differences between reactions can help you distinguish several main types of reactions
- how to predict the products of certain chemical reactions
- which combinations of ion-containing solutions will react
- which reactions involve organic chemicals called hydrocarbons

Key Skills

In this chapter, you will

- perform chemical reactions using appropriate safety and disposal procedures
- identify reactions that generate heat energy
- classify chemical reactions
- practise balancing chemical equations

Key Terms

- exothermic
- endothermic
- law of conservation of energy
- synthesis reaction
- decomposition reaction
- single displacement reaction
- activity series
- double displacement reaction
- neutralization
- organic chemistry
- hydrocarbon
- complete combustion
- incomplete combustion

Starting Point  ACTIVITY

water
3 medium-sized test tubes

thermometer
scoopula

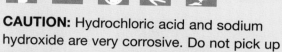

CAUTION: Hydrochloric acid and sodium hydroxide are very corrosive. Do not pick up sodium hydroxide pellets with your fingers.

What to Do

1. Label one test tube "control," put it in the rack, and add 10 mL of water. Measure and record the temperature. Dry the thermometer.

2. Label a second test tube "HCl + NaOH." Pour 10 mL of hydrochloric acid, HCl(aq), into this test tube. Measure the temperature. Use your scoopula to add two sodium hydroxide pellets, NaOH(s). Gently shake the test tube. Feel the test tube and compare it with the control. Measure and record the temperature when you cannot see the pellets any longer. Rinse and dry the thermometer.

3. Label the third test tube "NH_4NO_3." Use your scoopula to add ammonium nitrate, NH_4NO_3(s), until it is at about the same depth as the liquids in the other two test tubes. Add 1 or 2 mL of water, place the stopper in the test tube, and shake to dissolve the solid. If necessary, add a bit more water to dissolve it completely. Feel the test tube, and compare it with the control. Measure and record the temperature of the solution.

4. Return the test tubes to your teacher for safe disposal.

What Did You Discover?

1. Write a sentence that compares the energy changes you observed in steps 2 and 3.

2. Classify each change as physical or chemical. If you are unsure, describe experiments that could help you decide.

6.1 Energy Changes and Chemical Reactions

Figure 6.1 Which of these changes involve a release of energy? Which involve an absorption of energy? What other examples of each type of reaction can you suggest?

Word ● **CONNECT**

"Exo" and "endo" come from Greek words meaning "out of" and "into" respectively. "Therm" comes from a Greek word that means "heat." What words can you think of that have "exo," "endo," and "therm" in them?

All chemical reactions involve the release or the absorption of energy. Often, thermal energy is involved. Energy may also be released or absorbed in other forms, however, such as light, electricity, and sound. Physical changes of matter also involve energy being released or absorbed.

You can classify chemical and physical changes on the basis of whether they release or absorb energy. Energy-releasing reactions are **exothermic**. An explosion is an example of an exothermic reaction, as is the burning of fuel, and the rusting of iron.

Some reactions require the addition of energy to cause a chemical change. For example, when you cook food the energy you add, usually thermal energy, is absorbed by the reactants. Energy-absorbing reactions are **endothermic**. Electrolysis, the process of separating a compound into its component elements, is an example of an endothermic reaction. In this case, electrical energy is the form of energy that is absorbed.

Changes of state may also be exothermic or endothermic. For example, the vaporization of water is endothermic. Thus wet skin is cooled when the water vaporizes in a breeze. The thermal energy that is required for the state change is absorbed from the skin, causing it to feel cooler. The reverse physical change, condensation, is exothermic. This is why a burn that is caused by steam is dangerous and painful. Not only is the steam itself hot, but also, energy is released as the hot steam condenses.

The Halifax Explosion

Canada has the unwelcome distinction of being home to the largest, most violent, human-made exothermic chemical reaction in history. The Halifax explosion on December 6, 1917, claimed the lives of nearly 2000 people and injured about 9000 others. In this activity, you will do research to uncover the cause.

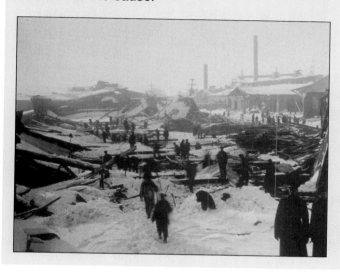

Outside Link **ACTIVITY**

What to Do

1. Use print and electronic resources to investigate the cause, the chemistry, and the consequences of the Halifax explosion.

2. Organize and present your findings using one or several media, such as a mural, television or radio script, web site, or special newspaper edition that chronicles the events.

What Did You Discover?

1. What reactants were involved in this disaster? How did they come to be chemically combined?

2. Why did the explosion occur? Could it have been prevented? How?

3. What were the economic and social costs?

4. What was done to cope with the immediate and long-term effects of the disaster?

Chemical Reactions and the Law of Conservation of Energy

All endothermic reactions require a continuous input of energy. For example, if you remove pancake batter from its supply of heat, the batter stops cooking. Although exothermic reactions require some form of energy for the reaction to start, the reactions continue and generate heat energy on their own. No additional supply of energy is needed. For example, a tree may ignite from the electrical energy of a lightning strike, or the heat energy of a carelessly tossed match, or the radiant energy of the Sun focussed through a magnifying lens. The chemical reaction continues until the supply of either wood or oxygen is exhausted.

One of the cornerstones of science is the **law of conservation of energy**. It states that energy can be converted from one form to another, but the total quantity of energy is constant. At first, this may seem puzzling when you think of chemical reactions. For example, burning wood generates heat energy, so you might conclude that energy has not been conserved. This conclusion, however, is inaccurate. It overlooks the fact that chemical energy is present in the bonds of the reactants and the products. The term "total quantity of energy" *does* take this energy into account.

Energy is always required to break chemical bonds. As well, energy is always released when new bonds form. The difference between the energy that is absorbed in breaking bonds in reactants and the energy that is released in forming bonds in products determines whether a reaction is exothermic or endothermic.

The law of conservation of energy reminds us that the energy released during an exothermic reaction must equal the decrease in the chemical energy of the reactants. The product chemicals of an exothermic reaction always have less energy in their bonds than the reactant chemicals had. The sum of all the energy changes is zero, however. In other words, the total quantity of energy is unchanged.

Classifying Chemical Reactions by Type

One way that scientists classify chemical reactions is based on energy — whether they are exothermic or endothermic. Since most chemical reactions are exo-thermic, and since there are so many types of chemical reactions, this simple classification system is quite limited. In the following investigation, you will model different chemical reactions and look for patterns that can help you classify them in a more useful way.

Pause& Reflect

Cold packs contain ammonium nitrate and water in two separate compartments. When the barrier between the compartments is broken, the ammonium nitrate dissolves. This absorbs thermal energy. Heat packs, on the other hand, release energy when the liquid inside the pack solidifies. Which of these processes is endothermic, and which is exothermic? Are they examples of physical or chemical change? What is your evidence?

Modelling Chemical Reactions

Chemical reactions occur when some of the bonds between the atoms in the reacting compounds break and form new bonds between the atoms in the products. The number of atoms of each element in the reaction must be the same. You can classify many simple chemical reactions by paying close attention to the products and the reactants involved.

Problem

How can you model and classify chemical reactions?

Apparatus

paper clips that are different sizes and colours

Procedure

① Working in groups, use paper clips to represent atoms and model chemical reactions. To identify your paper clip atoms, make up symbols based on rules like those that are used to represent elements. For example, you could give a large paper clip the symbol L, a regular-sized paper clip the symbol R, and a regular-sized green paper clip the symbol Rg.

② Use your paper clips to model the reaction between iron and sulfur. Copy the following word equation into your notebook:

iron + sulfur → iron(II) sulfide

③ Use the formula-writing skills you learned in Chapter 5 to write the formula for iron(II) sulfide. If you are not sure of the formula, ask another group or your teacher for help.

④ Under the word equation, write the skeleton equation for the reaction.

⑤ Choose one type of paper clip to represent iron atoms, and another type to represent sulfur atoms. Make a paper clip model of iron(II) sulfide.

⑥ Next make a paper clip model of the reaction. Check that you have the same number of paper clips for iron atoms on both sides of the equation, and the same number for sulfur atoms.

⑦ Check the skeleton equation, and balance it if necessary.

⑧ Finally, draw diagrams in your notebook to represent the reaction. Use shaded or coloured circles to represent atoms. Check that you have the same number of atoms on both sides of the reaction.

CONTINUED ▶

9 Divide the following reactions among all the groups in your class. Then repeat steps 2 to 8 for your assigned reactions:

(a) calcium + oxygen gas → calcium oxide

(b) calcium oxide + carbon dioxide
　　　　　　　　→ calcium carbonate

(c) copper(II) oxide → copper + oxygen gas

(d) water → hydrogen gas + oxygen gas

(e) sodium hydrogen carbonate →
　　sodium carbonate + carbon dioxide + water

(f) potassium + water →
　　　　potassium hydroxide + hydrogen gas

(g) zinc + tin(II) chloride → zinc chloride + tin

(h) copper + silver nitrate →
　　　　　　　　copper(II) nitrate + silver

(i) potassium iodide + lead(II) nitrate →
　　　　　potassium nitrate + lead(II) iodide

(j) sodium chloride + silver nitrate →
　　　　　sodium nitrate + silver chloride

(k) barium chloride + potassium sulfate →
　　　　barium sulfate + potassium chloride

10 Share your diagrams with other groups so that everyone has a complete record of the reactions from this investigation.

Analyze

1. You used two methods for modelling chemical reactions: one with paper clips and another with diagrams. Which method better helped you understand how the law of conservation of mass applies during a chemical change? Which method helped you think about the different states of matter in chemical reactions?

2. Think about the models you made and the diagrams you drew for the following groups of reactions in step 9:
- (a) and (b)
- (c), (d), and (e)
- (f), (g), and (h)
- (i), (j), and (k)

For each reaction, compare the products with the reactants. What do the reactions in each group have in common?

Conclude and Apply

3. Develop a classification system for the chemical reactions you observed in this investigation.

Extend Your Knowledge

4. In what ways are paper clips like atoms? In what ways are they different? Develop another model that you could have used for this investigation. Explain why it does, or does not, work better than the paper clip or diagram models you used.

Check Your Understanding

1. Distinguish between an exothermic reaction and an endothermic reaction, using examples to explain your answers fully. In the laboratory, which type of reaction is more likely to be dangerous? Why?

2. In your own words, state the law of conservation of energy, and explain its application to chemical reactions.

3. An iron ore found in Canada is called hematite, Fe_2O_3. In the smelting process to obtain iron, carbon reacts with hematite at high temperatures. The skeleton equation is

   $$Fe_2O_3(s) + C(s) \rightarrow Fe(\ell) + CO(g)$$

   Balance the equation, and place the energy term on the correct side. (Note that at this high temperature, the iron is in the liquid state.)

4. **Apply** Identify each of the following changes as exothermic or endothermic:
   (a) Ice melts.
   (b) A match burns after it is rubbed on a rough surface.
   (c) Adding concentrated sulfuric acid to water raises the temperature of the solution.
   (d) Heating a frying pan that contains a raw egg starts a chemical reaction. When the source of heat energy is removed, the reaction stops.
   (e) A mixture of hydrogen gas and chlorine gas will explode if it is exposed to ultraviolet light.

5. **Apply** Identify each of the following reactions as exothermic or endothermic, and balance the skeleton equation.

   (a) thermal energy $+ N_2(g) + O_2(g) \rightarrow NO_2(g)$
   (b) $Na(s) + Cl_2(g) \rightarrow NaCl(s) +$ thermal energy
   (c) thermal energy $+ C(s) + H_2(g) + O_2(g) \rightarrow CH_3CH_2OH(\ell)$
   (d) $N_2H_4(g) + O_2(g) \rightarrow N_2(g) + H_2O(\ell) +$ thermal energy

6. **Thinking Critically** A moving object has mechanical energy. Describe an example where chemical energy is transformed into mechanical energy.

7. **Thinking Critically** The following reaction can be used in cells that provide energy for watches or hearing aids:

   $$HgO(s) + Zn(s) \rightarrow ZnO(s) + Hg(\ell) +$$ electrical energy

   (a) What energy transformation takes place during the reaction?
   (b) Why should cells and batteries that use this reaction be recycled or sent to a hazardous waste facility?

DidYouKnow?

Many cooks use sodium hydrogen carbonate (commonly called sodium bicarbonate or baking soda) to put out small fires. When heated, sodium hydrogen carbonate forms carbon dioxide gas, which does not support combustion. The solid residue of sodium carbonate helps to smother the fire.

6.2 Synthesis and Decomposition Reactions

Chemists classify reactions to make it easier to predict the products of reactions and recognize new reactions. In general, there are four main types of chemical reactions. In this section, you will learn about two of them: synthesis reactions and decomposition reactions. In section 6.3, you will investigate single-replacement reactions and double-replacement reactions. Some chemists consider combustion to be a fifth type of chemical reaction. Section 6.4 looks at combustion and the special compounds that usually take part in this type of reaction.

Synthesis Reactions

In a **synthesis reaction**, two or more reactants combine to produce a new product. This general equation represents a synthesis reaction:

$$X + Y \rightarrow XY$$

Often the reactants in synthesis reactions are elements. Below is an example that you know fairly well. The photos and captions provide several other examples.

$$2H_2(g) + O_2(g) \rightarrow 2H_2O(\ell) + \text{thermal energy}$$

Figure 6.3 Nitrogen is essential to all living things because it is a component of proteins, genetic material, and chlorophyll in green plants. There is plenty of nitrogen in the atmosphere. Nitrogen is, however, fairly unreactive, and few organisms can use it in its elemental form. Farmers often supply nitrogen to their crops by applying fertilizers as shown in the photograph. These fertilizers contain nitrogen compounds such as ammonia, which plants can use easily. The following exothermic synthesis reaction is used to produce ammonia.

$$N_2(g) + 3H_2(g) \rightarrow 2NH_3(g) + \text{thermal energy}$$

Energy released by the synthesis reaction between liquid hydrogen and liquid oxygen propels the space shuttle into orbit.

Figure 6.4 Atmospheric pollution problems often begin with simple synthesis reactions. For example, nitrogen reacts with oxygen at high temperatures to form colourless nitric oxide, NO(g), according to the equation below:

thermal energy $+ N_2(g) + O_2(g) \rightarrow 2NO(g)$

This synthesis reaction is endothermic. Gasoline and diesel engines provide the high temperatures that are required for the reaction. Unfortunately it is followed immediately by another synthesis reaction that produces nitrogen dioxide, a reactive brown gas:

$2NO(g) + O_2(g) \rightarrow 2NO_2(g)$

Further reactions can take place, producing the polluting, brown haze that you can see (and smell!) over most large cities in the summer.

Decomposition Reactions

In a **decomposition reaction,** a compound breaks down into two or more simpler compounds or elements. The general equation is

$$XY \rightarrow X + Y$$

If you compare this general equation with the one for synthesis reactions, you will see that you can think of decomposition reactions as the opposite of synthesis reactions. The photo captions on the next two pages show several examples of decomposition reactions.

A nitrogen molecule contains covalent bonds. In Chapter 5, you learned that a covalent bond consists of a pair of shared electrons. You also learned that atoms form stable compounds when their outer shells are filled with electrons. Use a periodic table to help you determine how many electrons are in the outer shell of a nitrogen atom. How many electrons must each nitrogen atom share to form nitrogen molecules? How many covalent bonds join the atoms in N_2? Why do you think nitrogen gas is generally unreactive?

Pause& —Reflect

In your Science Log summarize your ideas about synthesis and decomposition reactions write down any questions you may have. As you continue to study, search for information that will answer your questions.

Figure 6.6 The decomposition of water only takes place at very high temperatures — thousands of degrees Celsius. Yet green plants produce oxygen gas daily as a product of photosynthesis reactions. These reactions occur inside their leaves, where temperatures are a fraction of those that scientists require in a laboratory to perform the same feat!

Figure 6.7 A common decomposition reaction occurs when soda pop "goes flat." The fizz in soda pop comes from dissolving carbon dioxide gas in water. This synthesis reaction produces an aqueous solution of carbonic acid:

$$CO_2(g) + H_2O(\ell) \rightarrow H_2CO_3(aq)$$

When you open a can or bottle of pop, the pressure of gas above the drink is reduced. You see excess carbon dioxide leaving the solution as bubbles. Over time, especially if the drink is heated, the carbonic acid decomposes according to this equation:

$$H_2CO_3(aq) \rightarrow CO_2(g) + H_2O(\ell)$$

On the morning of April 16, 1947, the French ship *S.S. Grandcamp* was docked in the harbour of Texas City, Texas. It was being loaded with 900 t of ammonium nitrate, bound for Europe to be used for fertilizer. A fire began, and a little over an hour later the fire's heat activated a decomposition reaction that resulted in a violent explosion. A nearby ship, also loaded with ammonium nitrate, exploded 16 h later. The disaster took the lives of nearly 600 people, injured about 3500, and caused millions of dollars of damage.

Figure 6.8 Ammonia is used to manufacture ammonium nitrate, NH_4NO_3. This chemical has applications as a fertilizer and as an explosive. The decomposition of ammonium nitrate produces water vapour and dinitrogen oxide, a combustible gas:

thermal energy $+ NH_4NO_3(s) \rightarrow 2H_2O(g) + N_2O(g)$

Figure 6.9 Good cookies are the result of good chemistry. Most cookie recipes call for baking soda, which is the common name for sodium hydrogen carbonate (or sodium bicarbonate), $NaHCO_3$. In the oven, a decomposition reaction occurs. The carbon dioxide gas that is produced makes the cookies "rise":

thermal energy $+ 2NaHCO_3(s) \rightarrow Na_2CO_3(s) + CO_2(g) + H_2O(g)$

Check Your Understanding

1. Suppose that you have a supply of nuts and bolts. Describe how you could use them to model a synthesis reaction and a decomposition reaction.

2. Ammonium hydrogen carbonate, NH_4HCO_3, is one of the ingredients used to bake some brands of snacking crackers. During baking, this compound decomposes to form ammonia gas, water vapour, and carbon dioxide gas. Write the word equation and a balanced chemical equation for the decomposition of ammonium hydrogen carbonate.

3. Write a balanced chemical equation for each of the following word equations. State whether the reaction is a synthesis or decomposition reaction, and identify each as exothermic or endothermic.

   (a) sodium + bromine gas $\rightarrow$ sodium bromide + thermal energy

   (b) thermal energy + lead(II) oxide $\rightarrow$ lead + oxygen gas

   (c) thermal energy + sodium nitride $\rightarrow$ sodium + nitrogen gas

   (d) tin + chlorine gas $\rightarrow$ tin(IV) chloride + thermal energy

4. **Apply** Balance the following skeleton equations if necessary. Identify each reaction as a synthesis or a decomposition reaction.

   (a) $CaO(s) + H_2O(\ell) \rightarrow Ca(OH)_2(aq)$ ◀ **$Ca(OH)_2(aq)$ is called limewater**

   (b) $NiCO_3(s) \rightarrow NiO(s) + CO_2(g)$

   (c) $Mg(ClO_3)_2(s) \rightarrow MgCl_2(s) + O_2(g)$

   (d) $N_2O_5(s) + H_2O(\ell) \rightarrow HNO_3(aq)$ ◀ **$HNO_3(aq)$ is nitric acid**

   (e) $Ag_2CO_3(s) \rightarrow Ag_2O(s) + CO_2(g) + O_2(g)$

5. **Thinking Critically** Ammonium perchlorate, NH_4ClO_4, is a white crystalline solid at room temperature. It is commonly used as a solid propellant in missiles.

   (a) Balance the skeleton equation and identify the type of reaction.

   $NH_4ClO_4(s) \rightarrow N_2(g) + Cl_2(g) + O_2(g) + H_2O(g)$

   (b) Suggest two reasons why ammonium perchlorate is used to propel missiles.

   (c) Suggest a reason for showing water as a gaseous product.

6.3 Single Displacement and Double Displacement Reactions

Figure 6.10 A chemical reaction occurs when copper wire combines with silver nitrate solution.

Figure 6.11 You know that table salt, sodium chloride, is an ionic solid formed when sodium metal combines with chlorine gas. This is not the only way to form sodium chloride, however. Aqueous solutions of two dangerous, corrosive compounds, hydrochloric acid and sodium hydroxide, combine to form water and chemically safe sodium chloride.

Figures 6.10 and 6.11 show an example of each of the two types of chemical reactions you will investigate in this section. In Chapter 5 you had some hands-on experience with the type of reaction shown in Figure 6.11. See if you can identify where.

Single Displacement Reactions

In a **single displacement reaction**, one element takes the place of (*displaces*) another element in a compound. There are two general forms of equations for a single displacement reaction:

$$A + BX \rightarrow AX + B$$

or

$$AX + Y \rightarrow AY + X$$

You may recall that some metals react with water to produce hydrogen gas, while other metals are unreactive. All the alkali metals are able to displace hydrogen from water in exothermic reactions such as the following:

$$2Na(s) + 2H_2O(\ell) \rightarrow 2NaOH(aq) + H_2(g) + \text{thermal energy}$$

DidYouKnow?

The single displacement reaction between sodium and water is quite spectacular.

You may be able to picture the displacement better if you think of water as hydrogen hydroxide, H-OH. When hydrogen hydroxide combines with sodium, a sodium atom takes the place of the hydrogen atom to form sodium hydroxide, NaOH. The displaced hydrogen atoms combine to form hydrogen gas.

Metals that are not reactive enough to displace hydrogen from water may be able to displace hydrogen from an acid. For example, magnesium does not react with water at room temperature, but it generates hydrogen gas with hydrochloric acid, $HCl(aq)$:

$$Mg(s) + 2HCl(aq) \rightarrow MgCl_2(aq) + H_2(g)$$

Valuable silver can be recovered from a solution that contains silver ions by using copper in the single displacement reaction you saw in Figure 6.10:

$$2AgNO_3(aq) + Cu(s) \rightarrow Cu(NO_3)_2(aq) + 2Ag(s)$$

Metals differ in their reactivity. This is an important consideration in refining them from their mineral sources. For example, gold is quite unreactive. It is found in nature uncombined with other elements. Sodium, on the other hand, is very reactive, so it is always found combined with other elements. Chemists use their understanding of single displacement reactions to determine the relative reactivity of metals. Their observations are recorded as a list of metals in order of their chemical reactivity. This list is called the **activity series** of metals.

Develop Your Own Activity Series

In this investigation, you will perform a number of single displacement reactions to make an activity series for some metals. In the activity series, any metal will displace the ions of a metal that comes after it. The displaced ions precipitate (separate in the form of a solid) from solution. For example, copper is above silver in the activity series, so copper displaces silver ions and silver precipitates:

$$Cu(s) + 2AgNO_3(aq) \rightarrow Cu(NO_3)_2(aq) + 2Ag(s)$$

Can silver precipitate copper from solution? Because silver is lower in the activity series (less reactive) than copper, the answer is no.

$$Ag(s) + Cu(NO_3)_2 \rightarrow \text{no reaction (NR)}$$

You can develop your own activity series. Just carefully observe how particular metals displace other metal cations from solutions.

Problem

What observations can help you compare the reactivity of different metals?

Safety Precautions

The chemicals used are toxic and irritative. Handle them carefully, and rinse well if you get any on your skin or clothes.

Apparatus

six-well plate, or 5 small test tubes and a test tube rack
5 labels

Procedure

❶ Make a table like the one at the right. Give your table a title. What do the shaded areas in the table indicate?

❷ Label the wells (or test tubes) with symbols for the metal cations in solution: Ca^{2+}, Cu^{2+}, Fe^{3+}, Mg^{2+}, Sn^{4+}, Zn^{2+}.

Materials

dropper bottles containing aqueous solutions of the following:
calcium nitrate, $Ca(NO_3)_2(aq)$
copper(II) nitrate, $Cu(NO_3)_2(aq)$
iron(II) nitrate, $Fe(NO_3)_2(aq)$
magnesium nitrate, $Mg(NO_3)_2(aq)$

tin(IV) chloride, $SnCl_4(aq)$
zinc nitrate, $Zn(NO_3)_2(aq)$
5 small pieces of each of the following: calcium, copper, iron (in the form of iron wool), magnesium, tin, zinc

Metal ion / Metal	Ca^{2+}	Cu^{2+}	Fe^{3+}	Mg^{2+}	Sn^{4+}	Zn^{2+}
Ca	■					
Cu		■				
Fe			■			
Mg				■		
Sn					■	
Zn						■

3 Half-fill each well or test tube with the solution that matches each label.

4 Add a small piece of calcium metal to each test tube (except the one containing Ca^{2+}). Observe for evidence of a chemical reaction, and record your observations. If there is no evidence of a chemical reaction, write "NR" for "no reaction."

5 Empty the solutions into a container supplied by your teacher. Thoroughly rinse the well plate or test tubes. It is not necessary to dry them.

6 Repeat steps 3 to 5, adding fresh solution and a small piece of copper to each test tube (except the one with Cu^{2+}).

7 Repeat steps 3 to 5 for the remaining metals.

8 When you have finished the investigation, wash your hands thoroughly.

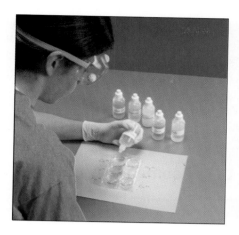 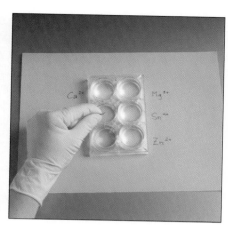

Analyze

1. Compare your observations with those of your classmates. Discuss the similarities and differences. For each entry in the table, try to agree on whether or not a displacement reaction took place.

2. Identify the most active metal in your table. On what basis did you select this metal?

3. Identify the next most active metal, and continue the process for all the metals in your table. The least active metal is the one that did not displace any of the metals you tested.

Conclude and Apply

4. Summarize your results by listing the six metals you tested. Go from most reactive (at the top of your list) to least reactive (at the bottom).

5. In the complete activity series, lead is below tin but above copper. Suppose that you wanted to remove lead ions from a solution to make it less poisonous. Would you add a strip of tin or copper to the solution? Explain your answer.

Extend Your Skills

6. What tests would you perform to add aluminum to your activity series? What apparatus and materials would you need? Briefly outline the procedure, including all safety precautions. With your teacher's approval, perform the tests.

During the Second World War, lithium hydride helped to save lives. If an airplane crashed at sea, the pilot used the reaction between lithium hydride and seawater to generate hydrogen to fill a lifebelt and lifeboat. Write the balanced chemical equation for the reaction.

Off the Wall

Children and pets often swallow coins, but usually these pass through the digestive system harmlessly. Sometimes, however, problems occur because of the chemical reactivity of the metals that are used to make the coins. Older pennies were made from copper, which does not react with stomach acid. Because the cost of copper has risen over the years, a cheaper metal, zinc, is often substituted today. Pennies minted in the United States after 1982 and in Canada from 1995 have a thin copper plating over a zinc core. If the surface of a new penny is scratched, zinc will react with hydrochloric acid in the stomach and the irritation can form an ulcer. Canadian quarters and dimes are made from nickel, and five-cent coins are now made from an alloy of nickel and copper. These coins do not react with stomach acid.

Double Displacement Reactions

In a **double displacement reaction,** the cations of two different compounds exchange places, forming two new compounds. The general form of the equation is

WX + YZ → WZ + YX

You can tell that a double displacement reaction has occurred if either a precipitate or water forms as one of the products. For example, aqueous solutions of barium hydroxide and sodium sulfate are both clear and colourless. When the solutions are mixed, a white precipitate of barium sulfate forms and sodium hydroxide remains dissolved in a clear colourless solution:

barium hydroxide + sodium sulfate → barium sulfate + sodium hydroxide

$$Ba(OH)_2(aq) \ + \ Na_2SO_4(aq) \ \rightarrow \ BaSO_4(s) \ + \ 2NaOH(aq)$$

Acids and bases are chemical compounds. (You will learn more about them in Chapter 7.) Like all pure substances, acids and bases have their own distinctive properties. When they react together, however, they both lose their properties. The reaction between an acid and a base is a special kind of double displacement reaction called **neutralization**. For example, sodium hydroxide is a chemical that is found in drain cleaner, while hydrochloric acid is sold (under the name "muriatic acid") to clean bricks and stone. As you saw at the beginning of this section, the reaction between these two dangerous substances produces a harmless aqueous solution of sodium chloride:

$$NaOH(aq) + HCl(aq) \rightarrow NaCl(aq) + H_2O(\ell)$$

Acids react with carbonates (for example, sodium carbonate) to produce carbon dioxide gas. This is a double displacement reaction that is followed by the decomposition of carbonic acid, H_2CO_3. For example, examine the equations for the reaction between sodium carbonate and hydrochloric acid:

$$Na_2CO_3(aq) + 2HCl(aq) \rightarrow 2NaCl(aq) + H_2CO_3(aq)$$
$$H_2CO_3(aq) \rightarrow H_2O(\ell) + CO_2(g)$$

Much like equations in mathematics, chemical equations can be added together. Terms (chemicals) that appear on both sides of the equation, such as those shaded above, can be removed. Thus the final equation for the reaction between sodium carbonate and hydrochloric acid is

$$Na_2CO_3(aq) + 2HCl(aq) \rightarrow 2NaCl(aq) + H_2O(\ell) + CO_2(g)$$

Looking Back at Chemical Reactions

You have observed and considered examples of the four main types of chemical reactions: synthesis, decomposition, single displacement, and double displacement. In Investigation 6-C, you will apply your understanding to a variety of chemical reactions. Then, in Investigation 6-D, you will analyze and interpret the chemical reactions that take place during an important industrial process.

Tools of Science

One sign that a chemical reaction has occurred is the formation of a gas. Since gases such as hydrogen, oxygen, and carbon dioxide are clear and colourless, chemists have developed standard tests to identify them. **CAUTION:** Hydrogen gas is highly combustible. Oxygen gas, while not combustible itself, supports the combustion of other substances and materials. Chemical tests like those outlined here must always be performed with the same attitude toward safety that you would use whenever you handle and work with chemicals. Your teacher will provide you with detailed instructions if you are asked to perform any of these tests yourself.

Standard Chemical Test for Hydrogen A burning wooden splint is lowered into a jar that contains an unknown gas. Positive Result: If the gas is hydrogen, you will hear an explosive "pop" sound, and the flame will be extinguished. Negative Result: If the gas is carbon dioxide, the flame will be extinguished (no "pop"). If the gas is oxygen, it will burn more brightly.

Standard Chemical Test for Oxygen A glowing wooden splint is lowered into a jar that contains an unknown gas. Positive Result: If the gas is oxygen, the splint will ignite. Negative Result: If the gas is not oxygen, the splint will not ignite and may stop glowing completely.

Standard Chemical Test for Carbon Dioxide Limewater, an aqueous solution of calcium hydroxide, is added to a jar that contains the unknown gas. (Alternatively, the unknown gas is bubbled into a test tube or beaker that contains limewater.) Positive Result: If the gas is carbon dioxide, the limewater will become milky. Negative Result: If the gas is not carbon dioxide, no change in the limewater occurs.

Putting It Together: Classifying Chemical Reactions

Practice makes perfect. In this investigation you will combine all of the knowledge you have gained. You will perform experiments and identify reactants and products. Then, you will balance chemical equations and classify the reactions you observe.

Problem

How can you show your understanding of the four types of chemical reactions?

Safety Precautions

- Handle all chemicals with care. They may be toxic, irritative, or corrosive.
- Hydrogen peroxide is an irritant.
- Hydrochloric acid, sulfuric acid, and sodium hydroxide are caustic. Rinse any spills immediately with plenty of water, and inform your teacher.
- Copper(II) chloride is a poison. Silver nitrate and potassium permanganate will stain skin and clothing.
- Manganese dioxide, copper nitrate, nickel nitrate, and ammonium nitrate are toxic.
- Phenolphthalein is flammable.
- Use the proper technique for smelling chemicals.
- Wash your hands thoroughly at the end of each part of this investigation.

Part 1

Note: Your teacher will demonstrate this reaction.

Apparatus

Bunsen burner
heat-resistant pad
crucible tongs

Materials

2 cm strip of magnesium ribbon, Mg(s)

Procedure

1. Make a table like the one below, and give it a title. Use a whole page turned sideways. Use your table for all parts of the investigation. After each part, fill in the table.

2. Your teacher will hold the magnesium ribbon in the flame. **CAUTION:** Burning magnesium produces an intense white flame. Do not look directly at the flame.

3. In your table, describe the magnesium and the way it burns. Is the reaction exothermic or endothermic? In this reaction, two different binary products are formed because magnesium reacts with oxygen and with nitrogen. Include thermal energy on the correct side of the chemical equation.

Part 2

Apparatus

test tube and a test tube rack

Materials

dilute hydrochloric acid, HCl(aq)
mossy zinc, Zn(s)
wooden splint

Procedure

1. Place about 3 mL of hydrochloric acid in the test tube. Add a small piece of mossy zinc to the acid solution. Test for any gas with a burning splint.

2. Dispose of the materials as directed by your teacher.

Part	Reactants	Description of the reactions, reactants, and products	Type of reaction	Word equation	Balanced chemical equation

Part 3

Apparatus

drip catcher (aluminum dish or a piece of cardboard)
small beaker (50 mL or 100 mL)
large beaker (500 mL or 1 L)
Erlenmeyer flask

Materials

candle
3 strips of cobalt chloride paper
limewater

Procedure

1 Before investigating the combustion of candle wax, you need to know the test for identifying the presence of water. Take two strips of cobalt chloride paper. Moisten one of the strips with water and compare its appearance with that of the dry strip. In your notebook, summarize the test for identifying water.

2 Place the drip catcher under the candle. Light the candle and place a large beaker over it.

3 When the flame goes out, examine the inside of the beaker. Test any moisture with a strip of cobalt chloride paper.

4 Add 25 mL of limewater to a small beaker. Describe its appearance.

5 Repeat step 2, but use the Erlenmeyer flask over the burning candle.

6 When the flame goes out, quickly turn the flask upright and add the limewater. Swirl the solution. Note any change in the appearance of the limewater.

7 Waxes are a group of pure substances with varying numbers of carbon and hydrogen atoms. Use the formula $C_{20}H_{42}$ to represent wax, and try to balance the combustion equation. Is the reaction exothermic or endothermic?

Part 4

Apparatus

2 test tubes and a test tube rack
scoopula

Materials

hydrogen peroxide, H_2O_2(aq)
manganese dioxide, MnO_2(s)
wooden splint

Procedure

1 Place about 2 mL of hydrogen peroxide solution in the test tube. Use the end of the scoopula to add a small amount of manganese dioxide, about the size of a grain of rice, to the test tube.

2 Test the escaping gas with a glowing splint and record the result. A second product of the reaction is water.

3 When the reaction has finished, carefully pour off the liquid from the solid in the test tube. Add another 2 cm depth of hydrogen peroxide solution to the test tube from step 3. Do *not* add more manganese dioxide.

4 Record your observations and the result of any test you performed.

5 Dispose of the materials as directed by your teacher.

Part 5

Apparatus

test tube and a test tube rack

Materials

copper(II) chloride
$CuCl_2$(aq)
2 cm strip of magnesium ribbon, Mg(s)

Procedure

1 Place about 2 mL of copper(II) chloride solution in the test tube.

2 Add a small strip of magnesium ribbon to the solution. After a few minutes, record any changes you observe.

3 Dispose of the materials as directed by your teacher.

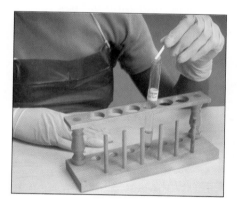

CONTINUED ▶

Part 6

Apparatus

2 test tubes and a test tube rack
50 mL beaker
medicine dropper
2 labels

Materials

dilute sulfuric acid, H_2SO_4
dilute sodium hydroxide, NaOH(aq)
dropper bottle containing
  phenolphthalein

Procedure

1. Phenolphthalein is a chemical that changes colour in solutions of acids and bases. Before investigating the reaction between an acid and a base, you need to know what colour phenolphthalein is in each solution. Label one test tube "acid" and another "base."

2. Pour about 2 mL of sodium hydroxide into the test tube marked "base." Add two drops of phenolphthalein and record the colour.

3. Repeat the test using sulfuric acid.

4. Use the test tube from step 3. With the medicine dropper, carefully add sodium hydroxide, one or two drops at a time, until you just see a colour change. If you add too much base, the colour change will be too intense.

5. Dispose of the materials as directed by your teacher.

Part 7

Apparatus

2 test tubes and a test tube rack
evaporating dish
2 labels

Materials

dilute solutions of:
ammonium nitrate, NH_4NO_3(aq)
sodium hydroxide, NaOH(aq)

Procedure

1. Pour about 2 mL of ammonium nitrate solution into a labelled test tube. Pour the same quantity of sodium hydroxide solution into another labelled test tube. Record your observations of both solutions.

2. Mix the solutions in an evaporating dish. Use the proper method for smelling chemicals to observe for evidence of any chemical change. See if you can identify the gas that is produced. The other products of this reaction are water and an aqueous solution of sodium nitrate, $NaNO_3$(aq).

3. Dispose of the materials as directed by your teacher.

Part 8

Apparatus

2 test tubes and a test tube rack

Materials

silver nitrate solution, $AgNO_3$(aq)
sodium chloride solution, NaCl(aq)

Procedure

1. Pour about 2 mL of silver nitrate solution into a labelled test tube. Pour the same quantity of sodium chloride solution into another labelled test tube. Record your observations of both solutions.

2. Pour the contents of one test tube into the other. Note any change.

3. Dispose of the materials as directed by your teacher.

Word CONNECT

A chemical indicator, such as phenolphthalein, distinguishes between two possibilities, acid and base. A crossing light tells you whether or not it is safe to cross the road. Make a list of other examples of indicators.

Part 9

Apparatus

2 beakers (50 mL)
2 labels

Materials

solution of copper(II) nitrate,
  $Cu(NO_3)_2(aq)$
solution of nickel(II) nitrate,
  $Ni(NO_3)_2$ (aq)
strip of copper, Cu(s)
strip of nickel, Ni(s)

Procedure

① Prepare two labelled beakers.
Pour about 20 mL of
copper(II) nitrate into one
and the same quantity of
nickel(II) nitrate into the
other. Record your observations of these solutions.

② Add a strip of nickel to the
copper(II) nitrate solution.
Part of the strip should be
above the solution so you can
compare it with the part
below. After a few minutes,
record your observations.

③ Add a strip of copper to the
nickel(II) nitrate solution. As
before, part of the strip
should be above the solution.
After a few minutes, record
your observations.

④ Return the strips of metal to
your teacher. Dispose of the
liquids as directed.

Part 10

Apparatus

test tube and a test tube rack

Materials

dilute hydrochloric acid, HCl(aq)
marble chip

Procedure

① Place about 3 mL of
hydrochloric acid in a test
tube. Obtain a marble chip,
which is calcium carbonate,
$CaCO_3$(s). Record your observations of these substances.

② Add the marble chip to the
acid, and record what happens. Perform any further
tests that may help you
understand the reaction.

③ Dispose of the materials as
directed by your teacher.

Analyze

1. Compare the data in your completed table with those of your
classmates. Discuss and resolve any discrepancies or disagree-
ments.

2. A catalyst is a substance that speeds up the rate of reaction but is
unchanged at the end of the reaction. (You will explore catalysts
in greater depth in Chapter 8.) In which reaction do you think a
catalyst was used? What evidence supports your claim?

3. Which reactions generated gases as products? Summarize the
tests for oxygen, hydrogen, and carbon dioxide. What is the
name of the gas that smells like household glass cleaner?

Conclude and Apply

4. Which reaction(s) were you unsure about? Why? How did you
resolve your uncertainty?

5. Which metal is higher on the activity series, copper or nickel?
Summarize your reasoning.

6. In many experiments, aqueous solutions are made using nitrates.
What property do you think nitrates have that makes them suitable for making aqueous solutions?

Analyzing an Industrial Process

Think About It

Magnesium and its compounds have numerous applications in the world around you. If you have ever flown in a jet airplane, driven in a car, used a flash bulb to take a picture, or enjoyed a fireworks display, magnesium has touched your life. Magnesium touches your life in another vital way, as well. It is a nutrient that your body's cells need to release energy from food and perform other life functions. Compounds such as magnesium oxide are also used to make fertilizers and insulation for pipes, refine sugar, and treat waste water.

What to Do

The diagram shows how magnesium is obtained commercially from seawater, using a technique called the Dow process. The raw materials are seawater, seashells, and hydrochloric acid. Examine the diagram, and the numbered steps, to identify the physical and chemical changes involved.

1 Seashells are mostly calcium carbonate, $CaCO_3$. They are heated to produce calcium oxide and carbon dioxide.

(a) Write the word equation and the balanced chemical equation.

(b) Identify the type of chemical reaction.

2 The calcium oxide is added to seawater, and a number of changes occur. First calcium oxide reacts with water to form calcium hydroxide.

(a) Write the word equation and the balanced chemical equation.

(b) Identify the type of chemical reaction.

Next the calcium hydroxide reacts with magnesium ions, $Mg^{2+}(aq)$, in the seawater to produce magnesium hydroxide and calcium ions.

(c) Write the word equation and the balanced chemical equation.

(d) Identify the type of chemical reaction.

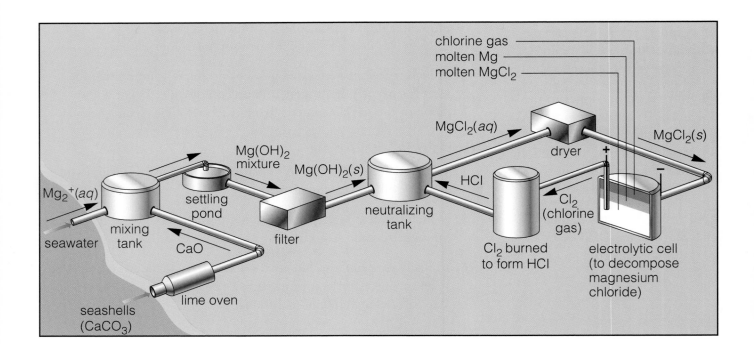

3 Magnesium hydroxide is insoluble. It is pumped as a suspension through filters. How does a filter separate $Mg(OH)_2(s)$ from water?

4 In the next step, the magnesium hydroxide reacts with hydrochloric acid to produce an aqueous solution of magnesium chloride and water.

(a) Write the word equation and the balanced chemical equation.

(b) Identify the type of chemical reaction.

5 Water is evaporated from the magnesium chloride solution. The resulting solid is melted at 700°C and decomposed by passing electric current through it.

(a) What is the name of the physical change that occurs first in the magnesium chloride?

(b) Name the process in which an electric current is used to decompose a compound.

(c) Write the balanced chemical equation for this step.

6 One of the products in step 5 is chlorine gas. This can be burned with natural gas, which is mostly methane, $CH_4(g)$, and oxygen to provide the hydrochloric acid needed for step 4. Balance the skeleton equation for this reaction.

$$CH_4(g) + O_2(g) + Cl_2(g) \rightarrow HCl(g) + CO(g)$$

Extend Your Knowledge

When the space shuttle *Challenger* exploded in 1986, scientists recovered the data recorder from the ocean several weeks after the accident. They were not able to analyze the tape at first because magnesium from the recorder case had reacted with the water. The tapes were coated with insoluble magnesium hydroxide, $Mg(OH)_2(s)$, which had to be removed.

1. Write a balanced chemical equation for the reaction between water and magnesium to form magnesium hydroxide, and identify the type of reaction.

2. Scientists removed the magnesium hydroxide by reacting it carefully with nitric acid, $HNO_3(aq)$. The skeleton equation is

$$Mg(OH)_2(s) + HNO_3(aq) \rightarrow Mg(NO_3)_2(aq) + H_2O(\ell)$$

Balance the equation, and identify the type of reaction.

3. Why was magnesium hydroxide converted to magnesium nitrate?

Check Your Understanding

1. Distinguish between a single displacement reaction and a double displacement reaction.

2. Part of the activity series of metals is shown below. The most active metal is at the top.

   potassium
   aluminum
   nickel
   mercury

   For each of the following, predict whether or not a reaction will occur and balance the equation. If you predict that a reaction will not occur, write "NR." If you predict that it will occur, write the complete equation, and balance it. (Do not write in this textbook.)

   (a) $Al(s) + KNO_3(aq) \rightarrow$
   (b) $Al(s) + NiCl_2(aq) \rightarrow$
   (c) $Ni(s) + Hg(NO_3)_2(aq) \rightarrow$

3. **Apply** Balance the following skeleton equations, if necessary. Identify each as a single displacement reaction or a double displacement reaction. Underline the formula of any product that is a precipitate.

   (a) $Zn(s) + H_2SO_4(aq) \rightarrow ZnSO_4(aq) + H_2(g)$
   (b) $Al(s) + CuSO_4(aq) \rightarrow Al_2(SO_4)_3(aq) + Cu(s)$
   (c) $Na_2S(aq) + HBr(aq) \rightarrow NaBr(aq) + H_2S(g)$
   (d) $HNO_3(aq) + Mg(OH)_2(ess) \rightarrow Mg(NO_3)_2(aq) + H_2O(\ell)$

4. **Apply** Balance the following skeleton equations, if necessary. Identify each as a single displacement reaction or a double displacement reaction. Write names for as many of the chemicals as possible.

   (a) $Pb(NO_3)_2(aq) + KI(aq) \rightarrow PbI_2(s) + KNO_3(aq)$
   (b) $Ca(OH)_2(aq) + HCl(aq) \rightarrow CaCl_2(aq) + H_2O(\ell)$
   (c) $MgCO_3(s) + HBr(aq) \rightarrow MgBr_2(aq) + CO_2(g) + H_2O(\ell)$
   (d) $Sn(s) + AgNO_3(aq) \rightarrow Sn(NO_3)_4(aq) + Ag(s)$

5. **Thinking Critically** Metals that are very high on the activity series, such as sodium and calcium, cannot be precipitated from aqueous solution. Explain why.

Pause& Reflect

Now that you have studied the four types of reactions, think back to Investigation 6-C. In your own words, summarize what you did, and what your results were.

6.4 Reactions Involving Carbon Compounds

The study of carbon-containing compounds and their properties is called **organic chemistry.** A few carbon-containing compounds (such as carbon dioxide, carbon monoxide, and ionic carbonates) are not considered organic. This still leaves millions of different compounds, however. In fact, organic compounds far outnumber inorganic compounds.

A **hydrocarbon** is an organic compound that contains only carbon and hydrogen atoms. The chief sources for the hydrocarbons we use are crude oil and natural gas. About 95 percent of these hydrocarbons are burned as fuels. The combustion reactions are exothermic. The resulting thermal energy warms our homes, businesses, and schools, and provides energy for transportation.

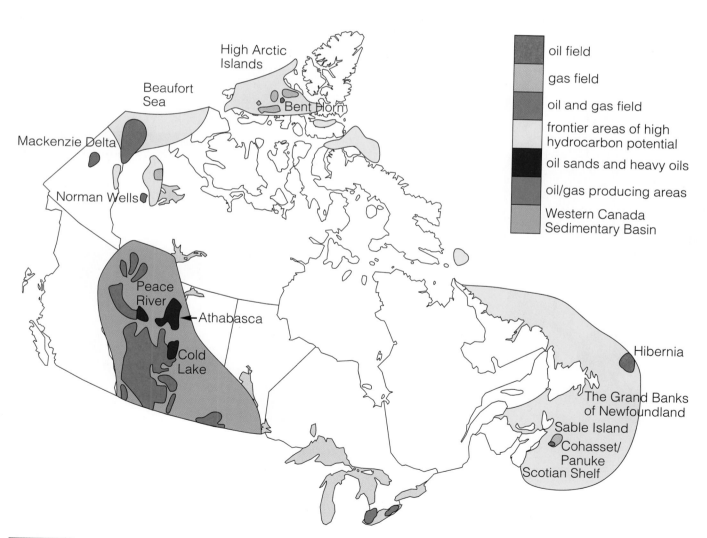

Figure 6.12 Canada's oil and gas resources

When hydrocarbons such as those in Figure 6.13 are burned in a plentiful supply of oxygen, **complete combustion** occurs. This reaction produces carbon dioxide and water vapour, and, of course, generates energy.

hydrocarbon + oxygen gas (good supply) → carbon dioxide + water

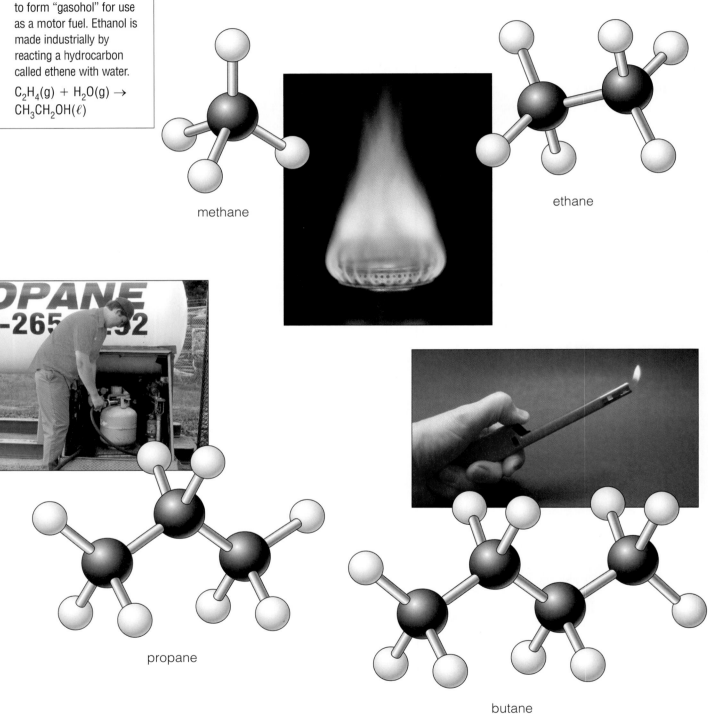

methane

ethane

propane

butane

Figure 6.13 These fairly simple hydrocarbon fuels are gases at room temperature and pressure. Propane and butane are easily liquefied under pressure, however.

When hydrocarbons are burned in a poor supply of oxygen, **incomplete combustion** results. This reaction is still exothermic, but it does not generate as much heat energy as complete combustion. The products of incomplete combustion are carbon dioxide and water, as before, but also carbon (soot) and carbon monoxide. Carbon monoxide is a colourless, odourless, highly toxic gas. Your blood cells contain a chemical, called hemoglobin, that combines with oxygen in your lungs. The oxygen is later released to other cells in your body. Carbon monoxide bonds about 200 times more strongly than oxygen to hemoglobin. Cells, like all living things, require oxygen to survive and carry out life processes. If less hemoglobin is available to carry oxygen, cells die. You must make sure that there is a plentiful supply of oxygen when you burn carbon or any hydrocarbon fuel.

Figure 6.14 The simplest hydrocarbon is methane, $CH_4(g)$, which is present in natural gas. If you have a gas furnace at home, the following reaction keeps you warm during the winter:

$$CH_4(g) + 2O_2(g) \rightarrow CO_2(g) + 2H_2O(g) + \text{heat energy}$$

Gasoline is a homogeneous mixture of hydrocarbons. What is another name for a homogeneous mixture? A key compound in gasoline is octane, C_8H_{18}. Can you see from the formula why it has this name? Try to balance the equation for the complete combustion of octane.

Ethene, C_2H_4, contains two carbon atoms like ethane, C_2H_6. Whereas two carbon atoms in ethane are joined by a single bond, CH_3–CH_3, the two carbons in ethene are joined by a double bond $CH_2=CH_2$. Ethene can be used to make many familiar products that belong to a class of chemicals called polymers. A polymer is a giant molecule that is made by joining many simpler molecules. For example, ethene can be polymerized into polyethene (usually called polyethylene). In this reaction the double bond breaks and links to other similar molecules:

$$n CH_2=CH_2 \rightarrow -(-CH_2\text{-}CH_2\text{-})_n-$$

In this equation, n represents a large number, usually several thousand. This reaction is similar to a huge synthesis reaction. Polyethene is tough and flexible, making it suitable for manufacturing plastic garbage bags, bottles, pipes, and many other products. Other polymers are made in reactions that begin with ethene. Examples include polyvinyl chloride (PVC), polypropylene, and Teflon™.

Suppose that a polyethene chain contains 50 000 ethene molecules. How many carbon atoms and how many hydrogen atoms would be present in the chain?

Figure 6.15 These, and many other familiar materials, are made from polymers based on ethene.

Check Your Understanding

1. What is organic chemistry? Give four examples of organic compounds.

2. How are the products of the complete combustion of a hydrocarbon different from those of incomplete combustion? How would observing the flame of a burning hydrocarbon help you determine whether the combustion is complete or incomplete?

3. **(a)** Why do people often think propane and butane are liquids at room temperature and pressure? How could you convince them otherwise?

   (b) At atmospheric pressure, a hydrocarbon called hexane has a boiling point of 69°C. In which state would you expect to find hexane at room temperature?

4. **Apply** Identify one example of a synthesis reaction in this section.

5. **Apply** Do the photographs below show complete or incomplete combustion? On what evidence are you basing your answer?

Pause& Reflect

You may have been familiar with the term "combustion" before reading this section. In your Science Log summarize what you now know about combustion. Write down any questions you have about combustion, and look for information that will answer your questions.

6. **Thinking Critically** Suppose that an ice storm brings down electrical lines over a wide area. You are told that there will be no electricity for three or four days. It is bitterly cold outside and, unfortunately, your home is electrically heated. Someone in your family suggests placing towels around doors and windows to keep out drafts, and bringing in the barbecue as a source of heat. How would you convince your family that the last action would be very dangerous?

Now that you have completed this chapter, try to do the following. If you cannot, go back to the sections indicated.

Describe how to distinguish experimentally between an exothermic reaction and an endothermic reaction. (6.1)

Write a sentence defining the law of conservation of energy. Describe how the law applies to both exothermic and endothermic chemical reactions. (6.1)

Describe the energy change required to break a chemical bond and the energy change that takes place when a new bond is formed. (6.1)

Identify where you would place the term "thermal energy" in an equation for a reaction that is either exothermic or endothermic. (6.1)

Write the balanced chemical equation for a specific example of a synthesis reaction. (6.2)

Write the balanced chemical equation for a specific example of a decomposition reaction. (6.2)

Write the balanced chemical equation for a specific example of a single displacement reaction. (6.3)

Write a set of procedures that could be used to compare experimentally the chemical reactivity of aluminum, copper, and magnesium. (6.3)

Describe how an activity list of metals can help you predict whether one metal will cause a displacement reaction with another metal. (6.3)

Write the balanced chemical equation for a specific example of a double displacement reaction. (6.3)

Write the balanced chemical equation for a specific example of a neutralization reaction. (6.3)

For each of the reaction types studied, give one example of a chemical reaction that is important in industry or in the home. (6.2, 6.3)

Write a sentence outlining the compounds studied in organic chemistry. (6.4)

Define the term "hydrocarbon." Give examples of at least two different hydrocarbons in common use. (6.4)

List the products of burning a hydrocarbon by complete combustion and by incomplete combustion. (6.4)

Prepare Your Own Summary

Summarize this chapter by doing one of the following. Use a graphic organizer (such as a concept map), produce a poster, or write the summary to include the key chapter concepts. Here are a few ideas to use as a guide:

- Use the law of conservation of energy to describe energy transformations in chemical reactions.
- Describe how the making and breaking of chemical bonds can result in a source of chemical energy.

- Classify chemical reactions into four types. How are the reactants and products different in each type?
- Describe what an activity list of metals is. How might it be used? How can the order of metals be experimentally determined?
- Make a list of some important organic compounds and their uses.

Reviewing Key Terms

If you need to review, the section numbers show you where these terms were introduced.

1. Distinguish between an exothermic change and an endothermic change. Give one example of each. (6.1)

2. How could the activity series help you purify a metal from a solution of one of its compounds? (6.3)

3. Which types of chemical compounds are involved in a neutralization reaction? (6.3)

4. Represent four different terms in a chemical equation using the letters A, B, C, and D. Using some or all of these letters, write four equations to illustrate each of the different types of reaction (6.2, 6.3)

5. In what circumstances can incomplete combustion occur, and why can it be dangerous? (6.4)

Understanding Key Concepts

Section numbers are provided if you need to review.

6. Write a balanced chemical equation for each of the following word equations. Use the description of energy change to write the term "thermal energy" on the correct side of the equation. (6.1)

   (a) Solid sulfur combines with oxygen gas to form sulfur dioxide gas. The reaction is exothermic.

   (b) Solid sulfur combines with oxygen gas exothermically to form sulfur trioxide gas.

   (c) The thermal decomposition of sulfur trioxide gas produces sulfur dioxide gas and oxygen gas.

   (d) The decomposition of carbon dioxide gas into solid carbon and oxygen gas is endothermic.

7. Distinguish a synthesis reaction from a decomposition reaction. Give one example of each. (6.2)

8. Write the balanced chemical equation for the displacement of aluminum in aluminum chloride by magnesium.

9. Gold is usually found as small, uncombined pieces of metal. One way to extract gold is to dissolve it in a cyanide solution (a hazardous procedure!). The gold can be precipitated from the cyanide solution by adding a metal such as zinc:

   $$2Au(CN)_2(aq) + Zn(s) \longrightarrow 2Au(s) + Zn(CN)_4(aq)$$

   What type of reaction is this, and which metal is more active? (6.3)

10. Describe an experiment you could perform to show that magnesium is above copper in the activity series. (6.3)

11. Which of the following compounds are hydrocarbons? Explain your reasoning. (6.4)

    (a) C_3H_8 (d) H_2CO_3

    (b) $C_6H_{12}O_6$ (e) CH_3OH

    (c) $CH_2{=}CH_2$ (f) C_6H_6

12. Methane, CH_4, is the most important hydrocarbon in natural gas. (6.4)

    (a) Write the balanced chemical equation for the complete combustion of methane.

    (b) Write the balanced chemical equation for the incomplete combustion of methane. Assume that the only product that contains carbon atoms is carbon monoxide.

Developing Skills

13. Balance each of the following skeleton equations, write the word equation, and classify the reaction. Also add the states, where necessary.

    (a) $Sn + AgNO_3 \rightarrow Sn(NO_3)_2 + Ag$

    (b) $Al + O_2 \rightarrow Al_2O_3$

    (c) $NaCl(aq) + Pb(NO_3)_2(aq) \rightarrow$
       $NaNO_3(aq) + PbCl_2(s)$

    (d) $CaCO_3 + HCl \rightarrow CaCl_2 + H_2O + CO_2$

    (e) $MgI_2(aq) + Br_2(g) \rightarrow MgBr_2(aq) + I_2(s)$

    (f) $(NH_4)_2S(aq) + Pb(NO_3)_2(aq) \rightarrow$
       $PbS(s) + NH_4NO_3(aq)$

14. Titanium dioxide, TiO_2, scatters light very well. It is used as a pigment in white paints, a whitener for paper, and a filler in white plastics. Mineral sources of titanium dioxide (called "rutile") must be purified because the impurities are coloured. The rutile is heated at a high temperature with carbon and chlorine to form $TiCl_4$. The skeleton equation is

$$TiO_2(s) + C(s) + Cl_2(g) \rightarrow TiCl_4(g) + CO_2(g) + CO(g)$$

(a) Suggest a chemical name for $TiCl_4$

(b) Balance the skeleton equation.

(c) $TiCl_4$ is easily separated from the other products because it condenses to a liquid at room temperature. It is then heated to a high temperature to produce a fine powder of titanium dioxide. The skeleton equation is

$$TiCl_4(g) + O_2(g) \longrightarrow TiO_2(s) + Cl_2(g)$$

Balance the equation, and identify the type of reaction.

15. Alloys of titanium with iron are used in airplanes and racing bicycles because of their strength and relatively low density. Titanium can be obtained by reacting $TiCl_4$ at a high temperature with magnesium. The skeleton equation is

$$TiCl_4(g) + Mg(l) \rightarrow Ti(s) + MgCl_2(l)$$

(a) What is an alloy?

(b) Balance the equation, and identify the type of reaction.

(c) At the temperature of the reaction, which metal has the higher melting point? Explain.

16. Most manufacturers identify the plastic from which an object is made with a symbol. You can identify one form of polyethene commonly used for containers by looking for the numeral "2" inside a triangular symbol. Identify containers used for cleaning products and food in your home made using this form of polyethene.

17. Draw the outline of a barrel of oil. Divide your outline, to scale, to show what proportion is used as fuel, and what proportion is used to make other chemicals.

18. On a cold day, you may see a liquid dripping from the tailpipe of a newly started car. What is the liquid? Explain how you know. What test could you perform to be sure?

Critical Thinking

19. Copper and silver tend to tarnish. The surface of copper becomes green over time, and silver turns black. Which type of chemical reaction do you think is illustrated by these examples? Briefly explain your answer.

20. In a double displacement reaction, why must one of the products be insoluble?

21. Copper is widely used for water pipes. Suggest reasons for using copper rather than another metal, such as lead, zinc, or iron.

Pause& Reflect

1. Go back to your original answers to the Opening Ideas questions on page 178. How has your thinking changed? How would you answer those questions now that you have investigated the topics in this chapter?

2. We usually write reactants on the left of a chemical equation and products on the right. Some reactions are described as "reversible." What do you think happens in a reversible reaction?

3. The following reaction is exothermic:

$$CO(g) + 2H_2(g) \rightarrow CH_3OH(g)$$

Note: CH_3OH is the alcohol methanol.

(a) Carbon monoxide and hydrogen are both dangerous chemicals. State one danger associated with each.

(b) If methanol is decomposed into carbon monoxide and hydrogen, would the reaction be exothermic or endothermic? Explain.

(c) Methanol can be used as a fuel. Write the balanced chemical equation for the complete combustion of methanol.

7 Acids and Bases

Some of the most spectacular products of the chemistry of acids are found in limestone caves such as the one you see here. Natural acids literally carved out these caves.

The first stage in "cave building" is the formation of layers of limestone. Over a period of millions of years, the shells of dead sea creatures form a calcium carbonate, or limestone, sea bed. Movements deep inside Earth lift the limestone layer above sea level. Eventually the original sea bed becomes a limestone layer deep below the surface of the land. Later, as rain falls through the atmosphere, carbon dioxide in the air dissolves in the rainwater. The carbon dioxide and water react to form carbonic acid. The acidic water seeps through the soil down to the limestone. Very slowly, the acid dissolves the calcium carbonate and washes it away. At

times, underground streams may speed the process. When large caverns have formed, a reversal of the carving process may occur. Small drops of calcium carbonate dissolved in carbonic acid cling to the top of the cave. Some of the carbonic acid changes back into carbon dioxide and water. As the carbon dioxide escapes into the air, the calcium carbonate stays on the roof of the cave and eventually forms stalactites.

From giant limestone structures to delicate flower petals, acids are at work. The flowers you see here are hydrangeas. Instead of acting over millions of years, acids determine the colour of these flowers in a period of days or weeks. Acidic soil causes the flowers to develop the blue colour. In basic soil, the plants produce pink flowers. You might say that acids colour your world.

How Do Acids React with Shells?

Limestone, marble, and chalk are building materials formed from the shells of ancient ocean organisms. These materials are all natural forms of calcium carbonate, $CaCO_3$. If acids react with shells, they will also react with these building materials.

Key Concepts

In this chapter, you will discover

- why acids and bases have different chemical properties, and how we use our understanding of those properties
- what kinds of compounds form acids in solution
- how the pH scale measures a wide variation in acidic and basic solutions
- how certain acids and bases react together to keep the water in a swimming pool safe

Key Skills

In this chapter, you will

- design and perform experiments safely to identify a solution as acidic or basic
- estimate and determine the pH of a solution
- compare the reactions of different elements that burn in air with the same reactions in oxygen, and investigate the acid/base nature of the compounds formed
- investigate the effect of reacting an acid with a base

Key Terms

- acid
- base
- indicator
- oxide
- pH scale
- pH meter
- universal indicator paper
- concentration
- percent ionization
- strong acids
- weak acids
- strong bases
- weak bases
- salt

Starting Point   ACTIVITY

What You Need

2 beakers
white vinegar (acetic acid)
masking tape or grease pencil

2 marble chips
tap water
2 raw eggs, in their shells

What to Do

1. Label one beaker "water." Place two marble chips inside. Carefully pour water into the beaker to cover the marble chips completely.

2. Repeat step 1 with vinegar. Observe both beakers for evidence of a chemical change. Leave the beakers overnight.

3. Over a sink, carefully pour off the liquid from the "water" beaker. Leave the marble chips inside. Carefully pour the liquid in the "vinegar" beaker over them. Is there a chemical change? Compare with your observations from step 2.

4. Rinse the marble chips with water, and return them to your teacher. The liquids in this activity can go down the sink. Wash your hands thoroughly.

5. Repeat steps 1 and 2 using raw eggs. (Your teacher may demonstrate this step.)

What Did You Discover?

1. What evidence showed that vinegar reacts with marble chips and eggshells?

2. If vinegar reacts with calcium carbonate, is the product of the reaction soluble or not soluble? How can you tell? Why would this be important for marble buildings and monuments?

3. Compare the reactions in steps 2 and 3. In which reaction was the vinegar more reactive? Explain your observations.

7.1 Common Acids and Bases

Do your muscles ever feel sore after a heavy workout? If so, you can blame a buildup of lactic acid in your muscles. Lactic acid is a by-product of cell metabolism when too little oxygen is available. Lactic acid is also produced by bacteria in milk — this is why milk turns sour. Acids occur naturally in many fruits. Insects such as millipedes, scorpions, and ants use acids to deter predators. A physician may use a solution of boric acid to rinse out your eyes, but a drop or two of many other acids would blind you. Some acids add a tangy, sour flavour to foods and drinks, while others are deadly.

Bases are bitter-tasting compounds with a slippery feel. Most soaps and drain and window cleaners are bases. Quinine is a base which is responsible for the bitter flavour of tonic water and it occurs naturally in the bark of the cinchona tree. Quinine is also used as a drug to treat malaria. Many other drugs are bases, too. For example, lidocaine, a local anaesthetic used by dentists, is a base. Like acids, some bases are harmless while others are very dangerous.

Figure 7.1 Sore muscles and sour milk are caused by the same acid.

Figure 7.2 Some common bases around your home

Word Connect

The word "acid" comes from the Latin *acidus*, meaning "sour." Think of the taste of fruits such as lemons or limes. These fruits contain citric acid. Vinegar, a common household product, contains acetic acid. What do you mean if you say that someone has an "acid tongue" or a "sour personality?"

Chemists sometimes use the term "alkali" for a base that is soluble in water. The solution is said to be "alkaline." These words show the Arabic origins of chemistry. The earliest source of bases was the ash obtained by burning plants. Thus the Arabic word *alkali* means "ashes of a plant." What clue does the word "alkali" give you about the kinds of elements that you might find in a basic compound?

Acids, Bases, Ions, and Indicators

Most acids and bases dissolve in water. In 1884 the Swedish chemist Svante Arrhenius defined an **acid** as a substance that produces hydrogen ions in solution, $H^+(aq)$. For example, hydrochloric acid, $HCl(aq)$, is an ionic compound that dissolves in water, splitting into $H^+(aq)$ ions and $Cl^-(aq)$ ions. The resulting solution is an electrolyte.

Arrhenius also defined a **base** as a substance that produces hydroxide ions in solution, $OH^-(aq)$. An example of a base is sodium hydroxide, $NaOH(aq)$. You have worked with this ionic compound in Chapters 5 and 6. Sodium hydroxide forms OH^- ions in solution.

Figure 7.3 Svante Arrhenius (1859–1927)

Figure 7.4 Litmus is a compound that is extracted from lichens, a plant-like member of the fungi kingdom. Litmus paper is made by dipping paper in litmus solution.

Most solutions of acids or bases are clear and colourless. Therefore they cannot be distinguished from ordinary water by appearance alone. The simplest way to distinguish them from water is to use an indicator. An **indicator** is a chemical that changes colour as the concentration of $H^+(aq)$ or $OH^-(aq)$ changes. Two of the most common indicators are phenolphthalein and litmus. In Investigation 7-A, you will design an experiment to discover the properties of these indicators, then use them to test for acids and bases.

Since the early twentieth century, chemists have refined Arrhenius' theory and definitions. Chemists now describe the hydrogen ion, $H^+(aq)$, as being bonded to a water molecule to form the hydronium ion, $H_3O^+(aq)$. Even so, we can still use Arrhenius' theory, with $H^+(aq)$ as a shorthand for $H_3O^+(aq)$, to understand the properties of acids and bases. Why do you think this shorthand can be used without causing mistakes?

The Oxides of Elements

Oxides of many elements react with water to form an acid or a base. An **oxide** is a compound that consists of an element combined with only oxygen. For example, CO (carbon monoxide), CO_2 (carbon dioxide), and Al_2O_3 (aluminum oxide) are oxides. H_2SO_4 and HNO_3 are not. (Why not? What kind of ions are SO_4^{2-} and NO_3^-?)

You can compare the chemical properties of different kinds of elements by testing their oxides. In Investigation 7-B, you will study these properties and discover pattern.

Acid or Base?

An indicator's colour tells you whether a substance is acidic or basic. Thus indicators help you determine whether substances are acids or bases.

Problem

Which common substances are acids, and which are bases? How can indicators help you identify common substances as acids or bases?

Safety Precautions

- Hydrochloric acid and sodium hydroxide are caustic. Glass cleaner and bleach are strong irritants.
- Phenolphthalein is flammable.

Apparatus

spot plate and 12-well plate
labels
stirring rod
glass plate

Materials

phenolphthalein solution in dropper bottle
red litmus paper
blue litmus paper

Known Solutions

dilute hydrochloric acid, HCl(aq)
dilute sodium hydroxide solution, NaOH(aq)
distilled water

Solutions to Test

grapefruit juice
club soda
household glass cleaner
vinegar
household bleach
milk
shampoo

Procedure

1. You have a range of chemicals to identify as acids, bases, or neutral (neither acidic nor basic). To do this, you have three indicator substances: red litmus paper, blue litmus paper, and phenolphthalein solution. Use a stirring rod and a glass plate to test the chemicals with litmus paper. Test with phenolphthalein by adding one or two drops to a sample of each chemical.

2. Predict which chemicals belong in which categories. Design a procedure to test each chemical. Begin by investigating the behaviour of the indicators with a known acid, base, and neutral substance. Be careful to keep the chemicals separate at each step of your procedure, and to make sure that you know which chemical is which. Plan how you will record your observations.

3. Ask your teacher to approve your procedure. Then carry it out. Wash your hands when finished.

Analyze

1. How did your results compare with other groups' results? Discuss any differences.

Conclude and Apply

2. Can you say which of the solutions you identified as an acid was the most or least acidic? Why or why not? Why is it important to be able to identify a very acidic or a very basic solution?

The Oxides of Metals and Non-Metals

Oxygen is the most reactive gas in the atmosphere. Combustion reactions of oxygen with wood, paper, natural gas, and many other substances are common. Many elements combine with oxygen, and the oxides that are formed can be tested with acid/base indicators.

Problem

How does a combustion reaction in air compare with a combustion reaction in pure oxygen? Do certain kinds of elements form acidic or basic oxides? Form hypotheses based on each of these questions.

Part 1
All About Oxides

Safety Precautions

- Take extra care with safety procedures. The reactions in this investigation are potentially hazardous. Your teacher may choose to demonstrate all or some of them.
- Do not look directly at the brilliant light that is produced by burning magnesium.
- Phenolphthalein is flammable, so keep it well away from flames.

Apparatus

oxygen cylinder and tubing
gas bottle
water trough
glass cover plate
heat-resistant pad
Bunsen burner
combustion spoon
stirring rod
500 mL beaker
test tube
test tube rack
fume hood

Materials

sulfur (small lump)
carbon (small lump)
magnesium (2 cm strip)
iron (ball of steel wool, about 1 cm in diameter)
phenolphthalein indicator
red and blue litmus paper

Procedure

1 Make a table like the one below. Give your table a title.

Element	Metal or non-metal?	Combustion observations		Indicator tests on the oxide solution	
		In air	In oxygen	Phenolphthalein	Litmus paper
sulfur					
carbon					
magnesium					
iron					

CONTINUED ▶

2 Put about 1 cm of water in the gas bottle. Then fill the bottle with oxygen gas. Cover the opening of the bottle with a glass cover plate to prevent too much oxygen from escaping. Your teacher will use a cylinder of oxygen, rubber tubing, and a water trough to make oxygen available. **Note:** If you wish, you can add 1 cm of water after you have filled the bottle with oxygen gas. Quickly slide back the glass cover plate and add the water.

3 **CAUTION:** The burning of sulfur is shown in photographs because the product of the reaction, sulfur dioxide (SO_2), is a poisonous gas with a choking odour. If a fume hood is available, your teacher will demonstrate this reaction. Otherwise, observe the photographs carefully.

Your teacher will:
- place a Bunsen burner on a heat-resistant pad
- add water to a 500 mL beaker until half full
- place a small piece of sulfur in the bowl of a combustion spoon
- heat until the sulfur melts and begins to burn

Record your observations for combustion in air.

4 Your teacher will slide back the glass cover plate from the opening of the gas bottle, just enough to insert the combustion spoon. Notice that the bowl of the spoon is not allowed to touch the gas bottle because the heat will break the glass. Record your observations for combustion in oxygen.

5 When the combustion reaction has stopped, your teacher will remove the combustion spoon and put the bowl of the spoon into the beaker of water. The glass cover plate is placed over the gas bottle to help prevent gaseous products from escaping.

6 Swirl the water in the gas bottle to dissolve the gaseous reaction products. Pour the solution into a clean, dry test tube. Use the stirring rod, glass cover plate, and litmus paper to test the solution. Then add a drop of phenolphthalein to the solution. Record your observations.

7 Your teacher will wash the solutions down the sink with plenty of water, dispose of the used litmus paper, and dry the combustion spoon by gently heating it in the Bunsen burner flame and then letting it cool.

8 Repeat steps 3 to 7 using carbon, magnesium, and iron. You can perform these combustion reactions yourself, with proper safety precautions. **CAUTION:** Do not look at the magnesium as it burns.

Part 2

A Mystery Oxide

Safety Precautions

- Rinse any spills of sodium hydroxide or hydrochloric acid using plenty of water. Inform your teacher of any spills.

Apparatus

3 test tubes and a test tube rack
stoppers
scoopula

Materials

aluminum oxide, Al_2O_3
50 mL distilled water
50 mL dilute sodium hydroxide
50 mL dilute hydrochloric acid

Procedure

❶ Using the scoopula, place a rice-grain-sized sample of aluminum oxide in each of the three test tubes.

❷ Add distilled water to the first test tube until it is about half full. Place a stopper in the test tube, and gently shake it. Note any indication of a chemical reaction or the powder dissolving.

❸ Repeat step 2 using sodium hydroxide instead of water, and then using hydrochloric acid.

❹ Dispose of the materials as directed by your teacher. Wash your hands thoroughly.

Analyze

1. How did the combustion reactions in oxygen compare with the combustion reactions in air?

2. Infer which oxides produced acidic solutions and which produced basic solutions. Which reactions were you unsure about? Compare your inferences with those of another group.

3. Is aluminum oxide soluble or insoluble in distilled water? Was there any evidence of aluminum oxide reacting with sodium hydroxide or hydrochloric acid? Explain.

Conclude and Apply

4. **(a)** Approximately what percentage of air is oxygen?

   (b) Which contains the greater *quantity* of oxygen, your lab or a newly filled gas bottle? Which contains the greater *concentration* of oxygen?

   (c) Explain the difference between combustion reactions in air and combustion reactions in a gas bottle containing oxygen. Does this difference support your hypothesis?

5. Write a conclusion about the reactions of non-metal oxides with water. Then write a conclusion about the reactions of metal oxides with water. Was your hypothesis confirmed?

6. Would you classify aluminum oxide as acidic, basic, both, or neither? State your reasons.

Extend Your Knowledge

7. Look at a periodic table of elements. Where is aluminum located, compared with other metals and the non-metals? Does the position of aluminum help to explain the properties of aluminum oxide? Explain your answer.

8. Which of the following elements would you expect to form acidic oxides, and which would you expect to form basic oxides? Why?

   (a) sodium   **(b)** nitrogen   **(c)** chlorine   **(d)** calcium

DidYou**Know**?

Sulfur dioxide gas is very soluble in water. At room temperature and pressure, 1 L of water will dissolve 40 L of sulfur dioxide gas.

Velcro™ may not seem like a very dangerous substance. It is resilient and non-toxic, and it does not burn in air. In pure oxygen, however, Velcro™ burns explosively. NASA's Apollo program, which took the first humans to the Moon, was nearly cancelled before the first launch because of a terrible and unexpected accident. The *Apollo 1* capsule, with three astronauts locked inside, caught fire during a routine pre-launch test early in 1967. The fire was caused by faulty wiring, but it was the combination of a high-pressure, pure oxygen atmosphere and a lot of Velcro™ (to hold items securely in weightless conditions) that proved lethal. The fire was so violent that all three men were dead within 15 s.

The *Apollo 1* capsule, destroyed by a pure oxygen combustion

Pause& Reflect

Summarize what you have learned in this section about acids and bases. What kinds of oxides form acids in aqueous solutions? Which oxides form bases? What types of natural or everyday substances fall into one or other of these categories?

Check Your Understanding

1. In your own words, summarize Arrhenius' theory about acids and bases.

2. Balance each of the following skeleton equations. Identify the substance on the left of the equation as an acid or a base.

   (a) $H_2CO_3(aq) \rightarrow H^+(aq) + CO_3^{2-}(aq)$

   (b) $Ca(OH)_2(aq) \rightarrow Ca^{2+}(aq) + OH^-(aq)$

   (c) $NH_3(g) + H_2O(\ell) \rightarrow NH_4^+(aq) + OH^-(aq)$

   (d) $KOH(aq) \rightarrow K^+(aq) + OH^-(aq)$

   (e) $H_2SO_4(aq) \rightarrow H^+(aq) + SO_4^{2-}(aq)$

3. What is an indicator? Describe what you would expect to see if one or two drops of phenolphthalein were added to solutions that were

   (a) neutral

   (b) basic

   (c) acidic

4. **Apply** Chris observes that a drop of an unknown solution on red litmus paper causes no colour change. Chris correctly concludes the solution is either neutral or acidic, but cannot be sure which. Explain. What further test(s) could Chris perform to identify whether the solution is, in fact, neutral or acidic?

7.2 pH: A Powerful Scale

You have seen that litmus is red in acid solutions and blue in basic solutions. If you have two acidic solutions, however, litmus paper will not tell you which is more acidic. Yet this information can be a matter of life or death. A delicate balance between acids and bases is vital for organisms to survive. For example, whether fish are in an aquarium, a stream, or a large lake, the concentration of $H^+(aq)$ determines which species will live and which (if not all) will die. Like water, blood is an acid-base solution, and its balance is critical for us to remain in good health.

Neutral water contains $H^+(aq)$ and $OH^-(aq)$ ions, because a tiny number of water molecules ionize:

$$H_2O(\ell) \leftrightarrow H^+(aq) + OH^-(aq)$$

This equation is balanced with one $H^+(aq)$ and one $OH^-(aq)$. Therefore neutral water must contain equal numbers of these ions. The double arrow in a chemical equation shows that the reaction is reversible. In other words, products can also combine to form reactants.

When an acid dissolves in water, it produces $H^+(aq)$ ions. As a result, there are more $H^+(aq)$ ions than $OH^-(aq)$ ions in the solution. The concentration of $H^+(aq)$ ions determines whether an acid solution is safe or dangerous. On the other hand, $OH^-(aq)$ ions outnumber $H^+(aq)$ ions in basic solutions. Very basic solutions have a high concentration of $OH^-(aq)$, and they are just as dangerous as very acidic solutions. To help describe the concentration of $H^+(aq)$, which can vary greatly in different solutions, scientists use the **pH scale.** pH is a measure of the acidity of a solution. (Notice that the "p" in "pH" is always lower case, even at the beginning of a sentence.)

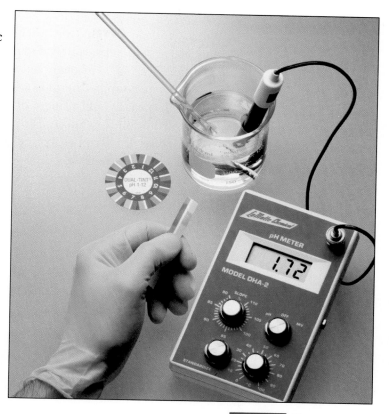

Figure 7.5 There are several ways to determine the pH of a substance. A pH meter and pH paper are two ways shown here.

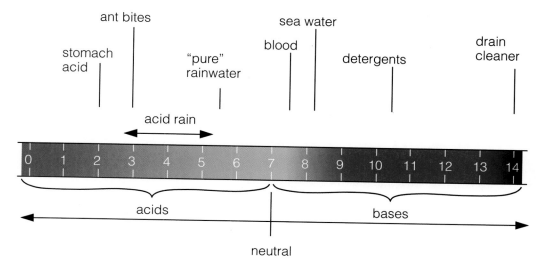

Figure 7.6 This diagram shows the pH of some common substances. How much more acidic is stomach acid than sea water?

Word CONNECT

In Danish, the "p" of pH stands for *portenz,* meaning "strength." In German, the word for "power" is *potenz.* Both of these words come from the Latin *potens.* Which words in English are related to the Latin word *potens*?

The pH scale has a useful range of values, between 0 and 14. A solution with pH 7 is neutral. Below pH 7, a solution is acidic. Above 7, it is basic. The scale was suggested in 1909 by a Danish biochemist, Søren Sørenson (1868–1939). The letters "pH" stand for "power of the hydrogen ion." A high pH means that there are many more $OH^-(aq)$ ions than $H^+(aq)$ ions, so the solution is very basic. A low pH means just the opposite: there are many $H^+(aq)$ ions, and the solution is highly acidic.

You can estimate the pH of a solution using pH paper. For more precise results, you can measure pH using a pH meter. A **pH meter** measures an electrical property of the solution and uses this to determine the pH. **Universal indicator paper** (also called "pH paper") contains a number of indicators that turn different colours depending on the pH of the solution. The colour of the pH paper is then matched against a chart that shows the colours at known pH values.

STRETCH Your Mind

The "power" reported as pH is actually a power of ten in scientific notation. Take a maximum-strength acid, with pH 0.0, as a starting point. An acid with pH 1.0 has one tenth, or 10^{-1} times, the concentration of $H^+(aq)$ ions. Vinegar, with pH 3.0, has only one thousandth, or 10^{-3} times, the concentration. How many times lower is the $H^+(aq)$ ion concentration of distilled water?

Power relationships, like the one used for the pH scale, are used when values can cover a wide range. Sound intensity, measured in a unit called the *bel*, is similar. The noise in your school cafeteria at lunchtime might be 8 bel (or 80 decibel, db) — 100 times the sound energy of a typical conversation of 6 bel (60 dB). The shriek of a frightened potbellied pig reaches between 10 and 11 bel (100 to 110 dB). How much louder is this than a typical conversation?

On the Richter scale, a magnitude 4 earthquake is felt as a faint tremor, causing little damage. A magnitude 8 earthquake can destroy large buildings. How much more energy do you think is released in a magnitude 8 earthquake, compared with a magnitude 4 earthquake?

Figure 7.7 How are these phenomena connected?

The pH of Common Acids and Bases

Many common substances are either acidic or basic. In this investigation, you will make your own indicator and use it to find the pH of some common substances.

Problem

What is the pH of a carbonated drink, and other common solutions?

Part 1
The Cabbage Test

Safety Precautions

- Ammonia is corrosive and toxic. Any spills should be cleaned up carefully. Inform your teacher of any spills.

Apparatus

plastic container with a tight lid
universal pH paper
test tubes and a test tube rack
100 mL beaker
glass stirring rod
medicine dropper
pH meter (for teacher use)
kettle (for teacher use)

Materials

2 red cabbage leaves

Solutions to Test (10 mL each)
lemon juice
vinegar
rainwater
distilled water
black coffee
liquid soap or shampoo
milk of magnesia
household ammonia
club soda (leave to last)

Procedure

1 Take two leaves from a red cabbage. Tear them into pieces about the size of a postage stamp. Put the pieces into a plastic container.

2 Ask your teacher to pour about 40 mL of hot water from a kettle into the container. Carefully seal the container, and leave it on your table to cool until it can be handled safely. While the water is cooling, complete step 3.

3 Copy the table below into your notebook. You will need enough space to record your observations for nine solutions. Also make a pH diagram similar to Figure 7.6. You will fill in substances as you determine their pH.

4 When the water in the container has cooled enough for you to hold the container safely, squeeze the container and mash its contents. Keep doing this until the liquid is deep blue or purple.

Solution	Colour of cabbage indicator	Approximate pH range
lemon juice		

CONTINUED ▶

5 Open the container, and carefully pour the liquid into a 100 mL beaker. Discard the cabbage leaves as directed by your teacher, and return the container to your teacher.

6 Pour about 10 mL of lemon juice into a test tube. Use a clean glass stirring rod to transfer a drop of the juice to a piece of universal indicator paper. Compare the colour with the colours in the chart. Estimate the pH of lemon juice, and record it in your table. Write "lemon juice" above the pH on your diagram. Rinse the stirring rod with water, and dry it with a paper towel.

7 Use the medicine dropper to add a few drops of cabbage juice indicator to the lemon juice. Record the colour of the indicator beneath the pH you estimated for the lemon juice.

8 Repeat steps 6 and 7 for each of the other solutions, except the club soda. About 20 mL of cabbage juice indicator should be left for step 9 and Part 2.

9 Pour about 10 mL of club soda into a test tube. Using only your observations of the colours of the cabbage juice indicator, estimate the pH of the club soda. Enter your observations for club soda in your table.

10 Set aside the cabbage juice indicator for Part 2. All other solutions can be rinsed down the sink with plenty of water. Discard indicator paper as directed. Wash your hands.

TEACHER DEMONSTRATION

11 Although pH meters are more accurate than indicator paper, they are relatively expensive and require larger volumes of liquid. For these reasons, your teacher may demonstrate how a pH meter is used to measure the pH of the solutions you tested.

Part 2
Breath Check

In this part of the investigation, you will use your indicator to analyze your breath. Does breath produce an acidic, basic, or neutral solution in water?

Apparatus
clean drinking straw
250 mL beaker
medicine dropper
stirring rod

Materials
cabbage juice indicator from Part 1
100 mL distilled water
5 mL household ammonia
20 mL vinegar

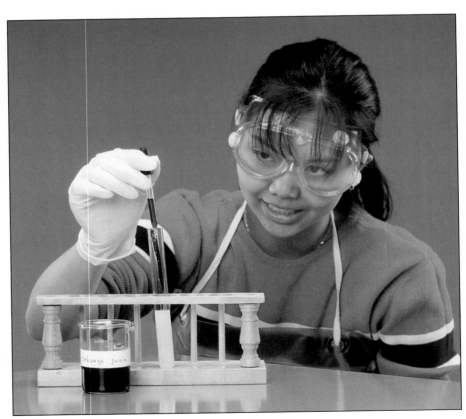

You can make your own indicator to test for acids and bases.

Procedure

1 Pour about 100 mL of distilled water into the 250 mL beaker. Use the medicine dropper to add two drops of household ammonia to the water. Stir the solution. Rinse the medicine dropper with distilled water.

2 Add, drop by drop, just enough of the dilute ammonia solution from step 1 to the cabbage juice indicator to change the colour from deep blue or purple to pale green.

3 Use a clean straw to blow a steady stream of bubbles through the indicator solution. Continue blowing until you see a change. Describe the change in your notebook.

4 Pour a little vinegar into the solution from step 3, until the colour changes. Record the new colour. Pour your solutions down the sink, and rinse with plenty of water. Wash your hands.

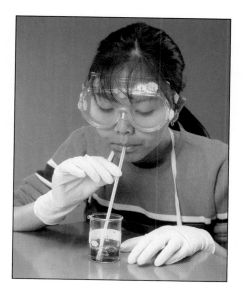

Analyze

1. Which do you think gives more accurate results, universal indicator paper or a pH meter? Why?

2. List the solutions you tested from most acidic to most basic. Compare your list with the lists of other classmates.

3. Which is more acidic, club soda or a cola drink with a pH of about 3.0? Check the labels on containers for both drinks, and find an ingredient that might account for the difference.

4. Did the gas in exhaled breath dissolve in water to produce a solution that is acidic, basic, or neutral? Summarize the evidence that supports your conclusion. Which gas in exhaled breath caused the change?

Since soils in different environments have different natural pH values, the plants that grow there have evolved to suit the pH ranges they must grow and live in. For example, rhododendrons flourish in moist, acidic environments and grow best at a pH of about 5. Many grasses, including wheat and maize, grow in drier environments, where they must tolerate a pH of 7 or 8. (What can you deduce about the "natural" pH of rain water from this?)

Gardeners and farmers can adjust the pH balance to suit the plants and crops they want to grow. Sensitive electronic equipment can measure, not only the pH of the soil, but also how easy it will be to change the pH. Clay soils are harder to "fix" than sandy soils, for example. Lime (calcium carbonate) or dolomitic lime (which also contains magnesium carbonate) can be added to acidic soils, while ferrous sulfate or aluminum sulfate can help correct soil that is too alkaline.

Why do you think these substances can change the pH of a soil? Work out balanced chemical equations for reactions when (a) calcium carbonate is added to soil with excess nitric acid and (b) aluminum sulfate reacts with the water in an alkaline soil. Why are sodium hydroxide and sulfuric acid never used to adjust the pH of soil?

Home-Grown Indicators

There are many natural indicators. In this activity, you will use "clear" tea and purple grape juice to test household chemicals and decide whether they are acidic or basic.

Many common products, such as Rolaids™, are acids or bases.

What You Need

kettle
tea bag
teapot
5 clear glasses or jars
4 plastic bags
rolling pin or hammer
water
20 mL purple grape juice
20 mL vinegar
20 mL household ammonia
20 mL lemon juice
2 Aspirin™ tablets
2 Tums™ or Rolaids™ (tablets)
baking soda

What to Do

1. Make a cup of tea, without milk or sugar. Let the tea cool while you test the grape juice indicator in steps 2 to 5.

2. Pour about 20 mL of grape juice into a clear glass or jar. Add about 80 mL of water to the juice. Use four more containers, and divide the grape juice indicator into five roughly equal portions.

3. Add vinegar to one portion and household ammonia to another. Record the colour of your indicator in acidic and basic solutions. **CAUTION:** Ammonia is a poisonous, caustic liquid and should be handled carefully.

4. Place an Aspirin™ tablet in a plastic bag, and crush it using a rolling pin or hammer. Dissolve the powder in a small quantity of water. Add the Aspirin™ solution to the third container of grape juice indicator. Record the colour change, if any.

5. Repeat step 4 using a Tums™ or Rolaids™ tablet. Rinse all solutions down the sink. Clean and dry the five containers you used.

6. Pour roughly equal volumes of the cool tea into the five glasses or jars. Add lemon juice to one portion, and record the colour of the tea in an acidic solution. Add baking soda to a second portion, and record the colour of the tea in a basic solution.

7. Test the Aspirin™ and Tums™ or Rolaids™ tablets as before, but use tea as an indicator. Rinse all solutions down the sink. Clean and dry the five containers you used.

What Did You Discover?

1. Why were no tests performed on one portion of indicator solution?

2. Classify Aspirin™ and Tums™ or Rolaids™ tablets as acidic or basic.

The following sentence is taken from an article about a talented young tennis player. "The acid test for this promising athlete will be . . . ." How would you complete the sentence?

The phrase "acid test" is now in common use. It comes from chemical tests that use nitric acid to determine the purity of gold alloys. A tiny spot can be tested to determine the amount of gold present, which affects the value of jewellery. If an alloy is less than 9-karat or 10-karat gold, the spot turns green. Alloys up to 18-karat gold can be tested with a mixture of nitric and hydrochloric acids, known as *aqua regia*. When a spot on an alloy is tested with aqua regia, the spot turns pale yellow. How many karats is pure gold? Why might you be happy to buy 12-karat gold, as long as you knew how impure it was?

Check Your Understanding

1. Some common aqueous solutions, with typical pH values, are given below. Classify each solution as acidic, basic, or neutral. Then arrange the solutions in order of increasing acidity.

   (a) human blood, 7.4

   (b) tomatoes, 4.5

   (c) liquid drain cleaner, 14.0

   (d) battery acid, 1.0

   (e) salt dissolved in pure water, 7.0

   (f) sea water, 8.0

2. Which has the greater concentration of H^+(aq), an orange with pH 4 or a solution of baking soda with pH 8? How much greater is the actual concentration of H^+(aq)?

3. Cheese and yogurt are made by the action of certain bacteria on milk. The pH of fresh milk is about 6.5, the pH of cheese is usually about 5.5, and the pH of yogurt is about 4.5.

   (a) Which of these common foods is most acidic?

   (b) How does the taste of these foods support your answer to part (a)?

4. **Apply** To increase your income, you have decided to sell paper indicator strips based on cabbage juice rather than litmus. Describe how you would prepare cabbage indicator paper. How would you make sure that your customers could use your indicator paper to determine the pH of an unknown solution?

5. **Thinking Critically** Are all compounds that contain hydrogen atoms acids? Support your answer with examples.

Pause&
Reflect

Make a table in your Science Log to record the pH of different substances. Each time you learn the pH of a new substance, add it to your table.

7.3 The Properties of Acids and Bases

Measuring the pH of two acid solutions shows how acidic or basic they are. It does not tell you, however, *why* one solution is more acidic than the other.

The more H^+ ions that are present in a given volume of water, the more acidic a solution is and the lower its pH. Two factors determine how many H^+ ions a solution will contain: concentration and ionization. The **concentration** of an acid is the amount of pure acid that is dissolved per litre of water. Not all the acid will ionize, however. Some acids may ionize completely, while in other acids, only a few molecules in a thousand will ionize.

The term **percent ionization** refers to the number of molecules that will ionize for every 100 molecules that dissolve.

Figure 7.8 Sulfuric acid is one of the strongest acids, and also one of the most widely used. Industries all over the world consume millions of tonnes of sulfuric acid each year.

Only a few acids ionize completely in water (100 percent ionization). These are called **strong acids.** Sulfuric acid, H_2SO_4, is a strong acid that is extremely important in many chemical processes. **Weak acids** are acids that only partly ionize in water. For example, in acetic acid, CH_3COOH, only about one in 200 molecules ionizes. (Acetic acid is the acid in vinegar.) A solution of a strong acid is much more acidic than a solution of a weak acid of the same concentration.

A strong acid in a concentrated solution is very hazardous. Concentrated sulfuric acid immediately causes a chemical burn to exposed skin. Very dilute sulfuric acid, however, or a concentrated solution of a very weak acid, is less dangerous.

The terms "strong" and "weak" apply to bases, as well. **Strong bases** ionize completely in water. **Weak bases** have low percent ionization. A concentrated solution of a strong base, such as sodium hydroxide, NaOH, is just as hazardous as a concentrated solution of a strong acid. When handling solutions of acids and bases, you should always be aware of their concentration and strength.

Pause&
Reflect

One way to highlight the difference between a strong acid and a weak acid is to use different arrows in the equations describing ionization. The one way arrow indicates that ionization is essentially complete. The double arrow indicates that the reaction can go both ways. Some ions recombine to form the unionized acid. The equations below also have labels to remind you of approximately how much ionization occurs in solutions of sulfuric and acetic acids.

none   all
$$H_2SO_4(aq) \rightarrow 2H^1(aq) + SO_4(aq)$$

200   1
$$CH_3COOH(aq) \leftrightarrow CH_3COO^-(aq) + H^+(aq)$$

Why are some acids stronger than others? When an acid dissolves in water, at least one hydrogen atom is pulled away from some of the acid molecules to form an $H^+(aq)$ ion. This happens because a water molecule can act like a tiny bar magnet: the oxygen "end" has a slightly negative charge that attracts protons (or H^+ ions). Therefore the difference between a strong acid and a weak acid is the relative attraction of the H atom bond in the acid, compared with its attraction to water molecules. Acid strength is *not* related to the number of hydrogen atoms in the molecules of an acid. For example, carbonic acid forms when carbon dioxide dissolves in water.

$$CO_2(g) + H_2O(\ell) \rightarrow H_2CO_3(aq)$$

Carbonic acid is a weak acid with two H atoms that can ionize.

$$H_2CO_3(aq) \rightarrow H^+(aq) + HCO_3{}^-(aq)$$

$$HCO_3{}^-(aq) \rightarrow H^+(aq) + CO_3{}^{2-}(aq)$$

A molecule of acetic acid contains four H atoms, but only one may ionize.

$$CH_3COOH(aq) \rightarrow H^+(aq) + CH_3COO^-(aq)$$

Carbonic acid and acetic acid are weak acids because few molecules actually ionize. In contrast, hydrochloric acid (HCl) contains only one H atom per molecule, but it has 100 percent ionization. Therefore it is a strong acid.

Tables 7.1 and 7.2 give the names, formulas, and uses of some important acids and bases. Practise using both the names and formulas of compounds. For example, if you need HCl(aq) in the next investigation, ask your teacher for "hydrochloric acid" rather than "H C L."

Table 7.1 Some Important Acids

Name	Formula	Notes
sulfuric acid	H_2SO_4	• strong acid • most widely used industrial chemical • used to clean metals and to manufacture fertilizers and detergents • present in automobile batteries
hydrochloric acid	HCl(aq)	• strong acid • sold in hardware stores as muriatic acid • produced by the reaction of sulfuric acid and brine (sodium chloride solution)
nitric acid	HNO_3	• strong acid • used to manufacture fertilizers, explosives, and dyes
carbonic acid	H_2CO_3	• weak acid • present in rainwater and carbonated drinks

Table 7.2 Some Important Bases

Name	Formula	Notes
sodium hydroxide	NaOH	• strong base • common name is lye • most widely used industrial base • used to manufacture paper, glass, and soap • present in drain cleaners
potassium hydroxide	KOH	• strong base • used to make some liquid soaps
calcium hydroxide	$Ca(OH)_2$	• strong base • used to manufacture paper and cement
magnesium hydroxide	$Mg(OH)_2$	• strong base, but not very soluble • active ingredient in some antacids
ammonia	NH_3	• weak base • used to make fertilizer and cleaning solutions

Pause&Reflect

In your Science Log, make a graphic organizer of your choice that relates these concepts: concentration, percent ionization, strong and weak acids, strong and weak bases, pH.

Chemical Properties of Acids and Bases

A strong, concentrated acid or base is a very hazardous substance. For this reason, it is important for anyone using chemicals to identify strong acids and bases, and to know their chemical properties. In this investigation, you will design and perform experiments to distinguish between acidic and basic solutions of the same concentration but different strengths. You will then use the strong acids and bases to verify some chemical properties.

Problem

Design and perform experiments to distinguish between a strong acid or base and a weak acid or base, and to verify some chemical properties of acids and bases.

Safety Precautions

 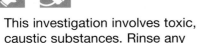

- This investigation involves toxic, caustic substances. Rinse any spills using plenty of water, and inform your teacher.
- If you are using a conductivity tester with two separate electrodes, be extremely careful to keep the electrodes well separated while you perform your tests.
- Follow your teacher's instructions for disposing of the chemicals and cleaning up after each part of the investigation.
- Wash your hands thoroughly after each part of the investigation.

Part 1
Apparatus
labels
test tubes and a test tube rack
stirring rod
glass plate
small beakers
universal indicator paper
conductivity tester

Materials
4 different solutions, labelled A, B, C, and D

What to Do

1. The four labelled solutions are samples of a strong acid, a weak acid, a strong base, and a weak base. All the solutions are the same concentration. Design an experiment to identify each type of solution, by checking pH and conductivity. Include any safety precautions that you think are needed. Have your teacher approve your experiment before you begin.

2. Perform your experiment.

Part 2
Apparatus
masking tape or grease pencil
4 test tubes and a test tube rack
wooden splint

Materials
4 solutions from Part 1
4 small strips of magnesium ribbon, Mg(s)

What to Do

1. Magnesium is a reactive metal that displaces hydrogen gas from strong acids. Design an experiment to confirm your identification of the solutions in Part 1. Include a hypothesis that relates Parts 1 and 2, a procedure for testing hydrogen gas, and any safety precautions. Ask your teacher to approve your experiment before you begin.

2. Carry out your experiment.

Part 3

Apparatus

labels
2 test tubes and a test tube rack

Materials

strong acid and strong base from Part 1

small marble chip (calcium carbonate, $CaCO_3$)

What to Do

1 Strong acids react with carbonates to generate carbon dioxide gas. When an acid and a base react together, each solution loses its properties. Predict what you will observe if you add a marble chip to the solution of a strong acid. Then predict what will happen if you add a strong base to the marble chip while it is reacting with the acid. Design an experiment to test both predictions (include safety precautions). Ask your teacher to approve your experiment before you begin.

2 Perform the experiment, record your observations, and evaluate your predictions.

Part 4

Apparatus

test tube, with rack and holder
Bunsen burner
scoopula
evaporating dish

Materials

strong base from Part 1
ammonium chloride

What to Do

1 Pour about 5 mL of the strong base into a test tube. Add a small amount of ammonium chloride, equal to about half the size of a pea. Heat the solution gently.

2 Smell the solution carefully by using a hand to wave gas toward your nose. If you do not detect a strong characteristic odour, pour the solution into an evaporating dish and try again. Record your observations.

3 Pour the solution down the sink, along with running water. Wash your hands.

Analyze

1. **(a)** What was the independent variable in Parts 1 and 2? How is this variable expressed qualitatively?

   (b) Which variable was controlled?

2. Which solutions were the best electrical conductors? What can you infer about the presence of ions in these solutions?

3. When reactions in liquids generate gases, you can compare the reactions by observing the production of bubbles. Which solution reacted most vigorously with magnesium? Is this what you expected? Which solution(s) reacted least, or not at all?

4. What happened to the rate of production of bubbles, as a strong base was added to the marble chip reacting with the acid? Could the reaction producing carbon dioxide be stopped? Explain.

Conclude and Apply

5. Name a cleaning product that has the same odour as the gas produced in Part 4. What do you think the gas was?

Extend Your Skills

6. Based on your observations, write a word equation and a balanced chemical equation for each of these reactions.
   (a) magnesium with hydrochloric acid
   (b) magnesium with sulfuric acid
   (c) calcium carbonate with hydrochloric acid
   (d) calcium carbonate with sulfuric acid

Acids and Bases: A Summary

Table 7.3 summarizes the general properties of acids and bases that you have observed so far. Copy it into your notebook, or design your own version as a handy reference.

Table 7.3 Properties of Acids and Bases

Property	Acids	Bases
taste **CAUTION:** Never taste chemicals in the lab.	Acids taste sour. Lemons, limes, and vinegar are common examples.	Bases taste bitter.
"feel" **CAUTION:** Never deliberately touch chemicals.	Strong concentrated acids will burn your skin.	Strong concentrated bases will burn your skin. Bases feel slippery.
indicator tests	Acids turn blue litmus red. Phenolphthalein is colourless.	Bases turn red litmus blue. Phenolphthalein is pink.
reaction with metals	Reactive metals (such as Mg, Zn, Fe, and Al) displace hydrogen gas.	Bases react with certain metals (such as Al) to form hydrogen gas.
reaction with carbonates	Carbon dioxide is formed.	No reaction occurs.
reaction with ammonium chloride	No reaction occurs.	Ammonia, NH_3, a gas with a characteristic odour, is produced.
type of oxide reacting with water	Acids form from non-metal oxides.	Bases form from metal oxides.

Check Your Understanding

1. What is ionization? Write a balanced equation showing ionization for
   (a) H_2SO_4
   (b) NaOH
   (c) CaO

2. Distinguish between concentration and strength when describing a solution of either an acid or a base.

3. Write the name and formula of a chemical that is
   (a) a strong acid
   (b) a strong base
   (c) a weak acid
   (d) a weak base

4. **Apply** Describe three chemical tests that would identify a solution as a strong acid. What observations would you expect for each test?

5. **Thinking Critically** One drop of concentrated sulfuric acid will burn a hole through a piece of cloth or a paper towel. (It will do the same to your skin, too!) If you add one drop of the same acid to a large bucket of water, a cloth or towel can be soaked in the solution with no change, other than being wet. Explain the different effects.

7.4 Neutralization Reactions

Word CONNECT

In the past, even as recently as the late nineteenth century, salt was traded and used in much the same way that we use money today. For example, Roman soldiers were given rations of salt called *salarium argentium*. Which word in English is derived from this Roman term? What is the corresponding word in French?

Figure 7.9 This spectacular mineral formation is formed by erosion from natural deposits of salts.

In Chapter 6, you learned that the reaction between an acid and a base is a special kind of double displacement reaction called neutralization. An acid and a base react together to form a new compound, called a salt, and water. The general word equation is

$$Acid + Base \rightarrow Salt + Water$$

A **salt** is an ionic compound that is produced by the reaction of an acid with a base. Because there are many different acids and bases, there are many different salts. The "salt" that we add to our food is mostly one particular salt, sodium chloride. This salt can be made by reacting hydrochloric acid with sodium hydroxide.

$$HCl(aq) + NaOH(aq) \rightarrow NaCl(aq) + H_2O(\ell)$$

Drop-by-Drop Neutralization

When a basic solution is gradually added to an acidic solution, all the base will react at first. Because there is initially more acid than base, some acid will be left over. As more base is added, more and more acid will react until you have added just the right quantity of base to neutralize the acid completely. Adding more base will make the solution basic. In this activity, you will perform neutralization reactions. You will use phenolphthalein indicator to determine when the acid and base completely neutralize each other.

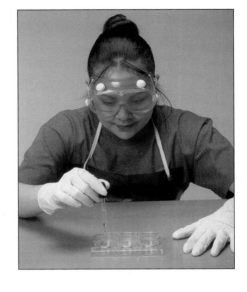

Probem

How can you determine when an acid and a base completely neutralize each other?

Safety Precautions

- This investigation uses caustic, corrosive substances. Clean up any spills carefully, and inform your teacher.
- Phenolphthalein is flammable. Keep it well away from flames.

Part 1
Apparatus

3 beakers (100 mL) or a six-well plate
2 medicine droppers or 1 mL micro-pipettes
toothpick
evaporating dish
conductivity tester
Bunsen burner
ring clamp
wire gauze

Materials

dilute sodium hydroxide, NaOH(aq)
dilute hydrochloric acid, HCl(aq)
(**Note:** These two solutions have the same concentration.)
dropper bottle of phenolphthalein

Procedure

❶ Read steps 2 to 7, and design a data table to record your results. Give your table a title.

❷ Place one drop of phenolphthalein indicator in a small, clean beaker or in one well of the six-well plate. **Tip:** Hold the medicine dropper or micro-pipette vertically to make sure that the volume of the drop is always the same.

❸ Add 10 drops of hydrochloric acid to the container. Stir the solution using a toothpick. Record the appearance of the solution.

❹ Use a second medicine dropper or pipette to add sodium hydroxide solution, drop by drop, and stir. Count the number of drops you need to add until the colour of the indicator just changes, and the colour change lasts for at least 20 s. Record the number of drops added and the appearance of the solution.

❺ Repeat steps 2 to 4 twice more, first using 15 drops of hydrochloric acid and then using 25 drops.

❻ Pour the solution from the last test into a clean, dry evaporating dish. Add a drop or two of acid to change the colour of the indicator. Test the solution with a conductivity tester. Record your observations.

Some people like a wedge of lemon with fish. Others prefer to sprinkle vinegar on their fish and chips. Did you know that both of these are examples of neutralization reactions? Fish contains a compound that is basic, so the acid in lemon juice or vinegar neutralizes the base. It may sound fishy, but it's true!

7 Place the evaporating dish on a ring clamp and wire gauze. Heat it *gently* using a low Bunsen burner flame. **(CAUTION:** The contents may spit as the solution dries. Keep your face away.) Record your observations of the contents of the evaporating dish. Wash the dish when it is cool. Wash your hands.

Part 2

Apparatus

3 beakers (100 mL) or a six-well plate

2 medicine droppers or 1 mL micro-pipettes

toothpick

Materials

dilute sodium hydroxide, NaOH(aq)

dilute sulfuric acid, H_2SO_4(aq)

(Note: These solutions have the same concentration as the solutions you used in Part 1.)

dropper bottle of phenolphthalein

Procedure

1 Repeat steps 1 to 4 of the procedure in Part 1, using 10 drops of sulfuric acid instead of hydrochloric acid.

2 Repeat these steps using 15 drops of sulfuric acid.

3 Rinse the apparatus with water. Wash your hands.

Analyze

1. Compare your results (the number of drops added in the five neutralization reactions) with your classmates' results. Discuss the similarities and differences.

2. Find a simple ratio to compare the number of drops of sodium hydroxide required to neutralize 10 drops of hydrochloric acid with the number of drops required to neutralize 10 drops of sulfuric acid. Why do you think this ratio occurs?

3. Next examine your data for the neutralization of 15 drops of each acid. Is the ratio the same?

Conclude and Apply

4. When hydrochloric acid reacts with sodium hydroxide, a solution of sodium chloride is produced. What experimental evidence supports this conclusion?

5. Suppose that you have samples of hydrochloric acid and sulfuric acid, with the same concentration and volume. Which sample would require more base to be neutralized? How much more base?

6. **(a)** If you were given two vinegar samples with different concentrations, how could you determine which was more concentrated?

   (b) Think about the apparatus you used in this investigation. Would you need any different apparatus to increase the accuracy of your experiment?

Extend Your Knowledge

7. The chemical equation for the neutralization reaction between hydrochloric acid and sodium hydroxide is

   $$HCl(aq) + NaOH(aq) \rightarrow NaCl(aq) + H_2O(\ell)$$

   The *skeleton* equation for the neutralization reaction between sulfuric acid and sodium hydroxide is

   $$H_2SO_4(aq) + NaOH(aq) \rightarrow Na_2SO_4(aq) + H_2O(\ell)$$

   (a) Balance the skeleton equation.

   (b) Compare the two chemical equations. Explain why different volumes of sodium hydroxide are needed to neutralize the same concentrations of sulfuric acid and hydrochloric acid.

Figure 7.10 The right balance of acids and bases helps to keep the water in a swimming pool safe.

In the Swim of Things

When you swim in a swimming pool, you do not worry about getting ill or about algae growing in the pool. For this, you can be grateful to the pool manager, who relies on acids, bases, and neutralization reactions to maintain the water in the pool.

Chlorine compounds kill bacteria and algae. The most effective chlorine compound for this purpose is hypochlorous acid, $HOCl(aq)$. Hypochlorous acid is also used to purify drinking water. Molecules of $HOCl$ are similar to water molecules (think of water as HOH). Thus hypochlorous acid can enter the cells of micro-organisms. Once inside the cells, the acid takes part in a substitution reaction with an important enzyme, and kills the cells.

Bubbling chlorine gas through water produces hypochlorous acid.

$$Cl_2(g) + H_2O(\ell) \rightarrow HOCl(aq) + H^+(aq) + Cl^-(aq)$$

Chlorine gas is corrosive and toxic. These properties led to its use as a chemical weapon in the First World War. Chlorine would be dangerous around a swimming pool, however, so a salt of hypochlorous acid is frequently used instead. Can you write a neutralization reaction between hypochlorous acid and sodium hydroxide to produce sodium hypochlorite, $NaOCl$? If you have a bleach solution at home, check the label. Household bleach is a good disinfectant because it contains a solution of sodium hypochlorite, $NaOCl(aq)$.

Sodium hypochlorite is much safer to handle than chlorine. It reacts with water to produce the hypochlorous acid needed to kill micro-organisms.

$$NaOCl(aq) + H_2O(\ell) \rightarrow HOCl(aq) + Na^+(aq) + OH^-(aq)$$

Hypochlorous acid is a weak acid, which ionizes to form hypochlorite ions, OCl^-.

$$HOCl(aq) \rightarrow H^+(aq) + OCl^-(aq)$$

The charge on the hypochlorite ion prevents it from entering cells, so it is not as effective as $HOCl$ in killing micro-organisms. The relative amounts of $HOCl$ and OCl^- change with pH, but the ideal range is 7.2 to 7.8. This is why the pH of a pool must be tested regularly. If the pH is too low, the water is too acidic and the acid may make your eyes sore. Also, the acid will attack the concrete in pools or the mortar between the tiles, because these materials contain calcium carbonate, $CaCO_3$. To treat acidic water, the pool manager can add sodium carbonate, Na_2CO_3, which reacts with the acid.

$$Na_2CO_3(s) + 2H^+(aq) \rightarrow 2Na^+(aq) + H_2O(\ell) + CO_2(g)$$

If the pH of the water becomes too high, the concentration of hypochlorous acid drops below the one part per million (1 ppm is the same ratio as 1 cent in $10 000, or 1 minute in two years) needed to kill micro-organisms. When this happens, the pool manager can add hydrochloric acid to remove the excess hydroxide ions.

$$HCl(aq) + OH^-(aq) \rightarrow H_2O(\ell) + Cl^-(aq)$$

There is a lot of chemistry going on in a swimming pool!

What Is the pH of Your Rain?

What You Need

plastic container

pH paper or homemade indicator

rainwater (or melted snow)

What to Do

1. Decide which indicator you can use to test the pH of rain or snow.

2. During the next rainfall or snowfall, use the plastic container to collect a sample of the rain or snow. If you collect snow, let it melt.

3. Use your indicator to determine the pH of your sample.

4. Compare your results with your classmates' results.

What Did You Discover?

1. How did the pH value you obtained compare with your classmates' pH values? Account for any large discrepancies.

2. Calculate the average pH of the samples your class obtained. Is this value what you might expect for your area? Why or why not?

Looking Ahead to Acid Rain

All non-metal oxides dissolve in water to form acidic solutions. Club soda has a pH of about 5 because it contains water saturated with carbon dioxide. The carbon dioxide has dissolved to form carbonic acid.

$$CO_2(g) + H_2O(\ell) \rightarrow H_2CO_3(aq)$$

The same process happens naturally with rainwater and the carbon dioxide that is in the atmosphere. Uncontaminated rainwater has a pH of about 5.5. Even distilled water may be slightly acidic if it contains a little dissolved carbon dioxide. Rainwater with a pH that is below about 5.5 is called acid rain because it is more acidic than would be expected naturally. You will learn more about acid rain and its effects on the environment in the next chapter. This will help you prepare for the Unit 2 Project on page 275.

Did You Know?

Oxalic acid is found in many foods, such as cucumbers, carrots, beets, and some berries. There are relatively large amounts of oxalic acid in rhubarb. For some people, oxalic acid is a problem because the oxalate ion combines with calcium ions to form an insoluble salt, calcium oxalate (CaC_2O_4). Gallstones and kidney stones may be the painful result of unwelcome deposits of this salt in the body.

Pause&
Reflect

You have read about many different acids, bases, and salts in this section. In your Science Log make a list of the different formulas you have seen. Beside each formula write the name of the acid, base, or salt. Write some sentences using the names, followed by the formulas, of three of these substances.

Check Your Understanding

1. What is a salt? Write the general word equation for a neutralization reaction that forms a salt.

2. Balance the following skeleton equations for reactions between an acid and a base.

   (a) $H_2CO_3(aq) + KOH(aq) \rightarrow K_2CO_3(s) + H_2O(\ell)$

   (b) $HNO_3(aq) + Ca(OH)_2(aq) \rightarrow Ca(NO_3)_2(aq) + H_2O(\ell)$

   (c) $HCl(aq) + Mg(OH)_2(aq) \rightarrow MgCl_2(aq) + H_2O(\ell)$

   (d) $H_2SO_4(aq) + NaOH(aq) \rightarrow Na_2SO_4(aq) + H_2O(\ell)$

3. It is thought that pain results from a change in the pH of solutions that surround nerves. Many irritating insect bites, for example, are acidic. The fluid inside your cells is also slightly acidic. When a cut or a burn releases this fluid, pain is signalled through your nerve endings. What would you expect to find if you tested the pH of creams and lotions that are used to treat burns and insect bites?

4. **Apply** Baking soda is the common name for sodium hydrogen carbonate, $NaHCO_3$. In the laboratory, baking soda can be used to neutralize an acid spill. One of the reaction products is carbon dioxide gas. Write a balanced chemical equation for the reaction between hydrochloric acid and sodium hydrogen carbonate.

5. **Thinking Critically** Tooth enamel contains a compound with the formula $Ca_{10}(PO_4)_6(OH)_2$. Why can a child's teeth be damaged over time if the child is put to bed with a bottle of milk? (Hint: Which acidic substance might be formed from milk residue in the child's mouth? What happens then?)

Now that you have completed this chapter, try to do the following. If you cannot, go back to the sections indicated.

List some naturally occurring acids and bases, and their uses. (7.1)

Explain Arrhenius' theory of ions in acids and bases. (7.1)

State which kinds of oxides form acidic solutions and which kinds form basic solutions. (7.1)

Make a list of natural indicators and pure chemical indicators. Show how they are used to test acidic and/or basic solutions. (7.1, 7.2)

Explain why the pH scale is useful. (7.2)

Describe an experiment to find the pH of the reaction product of water and your breath. Explain the results you would expect. (7.2)

Distinguish between concentration and percent ionization. (7.3)

List some chemical properties of
(a) strong acids
(b) strong bases (7.3)

List the physical properties of some common acids and bases. (7.3)

Explain the concept of neutralization. (7.4)

Identify the salt that is used in swimming pools, and the important element in the salt. Explain why this element is added in salt form. (7.4)

Define acid rain in terms of its pH. (7.4)

Prepare Your Own Summary

Summarize this chapter by doing one of the following. Use a graphic organizer (such as a concept map), produce a poster, or write the summary to include the key chapter concepts. Here are a few ideas to use as a guide:
- In which natural or domestic situations would you find acids or bases?
- How did Arrhenius explain acids and bases?
- Which factors can affect pH?
- What tests could you perform to identify solutions as acidic or basic, and to measure their pH?
- How do strong acids and bases react with other substances?
- How do acids and bases react with each other?
- Why is salt important?

Reviewing Key Terms

If you need to review, the section numbers show you where these terms were introduced.

1. Use two columns to list some common acids and common bases found in the home. (7.1)

2. According to Arrhenius' theory, what is an acid and what is a base? Give an example of a strong acid and a strong base. (7.1)

3. Compare the relative concentrations of hydroxide and hydronium ions in solutions that are
   (a) acidic
   (b) basic
   (c) neutral (7.2)

4. How does ionization affect the strength of an acid or a base? (7.3)

5. How does the concentration of H^+ ions change as the pH of a solution increases? (7.3)

6. What is neutralized as a result of a neutralization reaction? (7.4)

7. Write the word equation for a neutralization reaction. Then write a balanced chemical equation for a specific example. (7.4)

Understanding Key Concepts

Section numbers are provided if you need to review.

8. List the characteristic properties of acids and bases. (7.1–7.4)

9. Using a periodic table, decide whether each of the following oxides, after reacting with water, is likely to be acidic or basic. (7.1)
   (a) P_4O_{10}
   (b) Na_2O
   (c) Cl_2O
   (d) SrO
   (e) Cr_2O_3

10. What key property do all indicators possess? (7.1)

11. Why should you never add more than a few drops of indicator to a solution you are testing? (7.1)

12. Why does tea change colour when lemon juice is added? (7.2)

13. How would you describe the pH scale to a friend or relative? What two factors might determine whether an acid has a pH of 1.0 or 5.5? (7.2)

14. Is it possible to make two solutions — one using a strong acid and the other using a weak acid — so the pH of both solutions is the same? Explain your answer. (7.3)

15. State some similarities and differences between solutions of the following acids, with the same concentration: sulfuric acid, H_2SO_4; nitric acid, HNO_3; and carbonic acid, H_2CO_3. (7.3)

16. Perchloric acid, $HClO_4$, is a strong acid. Write an equation to show the ionization of this acid. (7.3)

Developing Skills

17. Why do many household cleaning products carry warning labels? Why should you wear gloves when using an oven cleaner?

18. Watch the newspapers for two weeks, and cut out any articles about air, water, or land pollution. What are people doing about these environmental problems? If pollution is a global issue, how can everyone work together to help the environment? What can you do?

19. Research a chemical plant that operates in your province. How many people are employed? What is the plant's economic benefit to the community? What environmental problems result from daily operations? How is the company that owns the plant trying to reduce these environmental problems?

Problem Solving/Applying

20. Several solutions were tested at room temperature, and their pH values are given below.

(A) 10.4   (C) 5.1   (E) 2.8

(B) 7.8   (D) 7.0   (F) 11.2

(a) Identify each solution as acidic, basic, or neutral.

(b) Which solution is most acidic, and which is most basic?

21. State whether each of the following solutions is acidic, basic, or neutral.

(a) a cleaning solution that contains dissolved ammonia

(b) a solution that remains colourless when phenolphthalein is added

(c) a solution that produces carbon dioxide when sodium carbonate is added

(d) a solution that turns blue litmus red

(e) a solution that contains equal concentrations of hydroxide and hydronium ions

22. Iron nails quickly rust when left outside. Galvanized nails are protected with a coating of zinc. What would you expect to see if you placed some iron nails and some galvanized nails in a container of vinegar?

23. Suppose that 5 drops of a sodium hydroxide neutralized 25 drops of a certain hydrochloric acid solution. How many drops of the sodium hydroxide solution would be needed to neutralize 25 drops of a sulfuric acid solution having the same concentration as the hydrochloric acid solution?

24. The scale that builds up on the insides of kettles and coffee makers is made up of calcium carbonate and magnesium carbonate from the water. How can this scale be removed safely?

25. Oxalic acid can be used to remove rust stains. Why should oxalic acid not be used on marble tiles and counters?

Critical Thinking

26. Find the recipe for a sweet and sour sauce. Which ingredients make the sauce sweet, and which ingredients make it sour?

27. A newspaper article claims that acid rain falling in your area has a pH of 4.0, "almost the same as vinegar, which has a pH of 3.0." Write a letter to the editor, explaining why the article is misleading.

Pause& Reflect

1. Go back to the beginning of the chapter, on page 210, and check your original answers to the Opening Ideas questions. How has your thinking changed? How would you answer those questions now that you have investigated the topics in this chapter?

2. Why is it necessary to maintain swimming-pool water within a certain range of pH values?

3. Hard water contains dissolved salts, such as calcium carbonate and magnesium carbonate. If you wash your hair with hard water, your hair tends to look more dull than if you used soft water (water with a lower concentration of dissolved salts). Would rinsing your hair with lemon juice help to return the shine to your hair? Why or why not?

Chemical Reactions

The chemical industry converts our natural resources into substances and products that we use in other industries and our homes. To be cost-effective, it is an advantage for industrial chemical processes to produce large amounts of products quickly. It is the job of chemists and chemical engineers to make sure that this happens.

As the world's population continues to increase, there is a greater stress put on our depleting natural resources. As more products are manufactured, we increase the amount of industrial by-products that must be disposed of safely. As more products get consumed, we increase the amount of waste that is produced. These by-products and wastes are examples of pollution, and they affect our environment. They affect the air we breathe, our fresh-water resources and our oceans, and even the soil in which we grow our food. Although chemistry plays a role in creating pollution, it also gives us ways to clean up our environment, as you will see in this chapter.

and the Environment

Key Concepts

In this chapter, you will discover

- how different factors change the rates of chemical reactions
- how chemicals play a role in our daily lives
- why chemicals are important to the economy of Canada
- how the products and by-products of chemical industries affect our environment

Key Skills

In this chapter, you will

- perform investigations using appropriate safety and disposal procedures
- identify factors that affect rates of chemical reactions
- compare the effectiveness of different antacids
- assess the benefits and risks of our dependence on chemicals

Key Terms

- rate of reaction
- catalysts
- enzymes
- polar molecule
- detergents
- acid precipitation
- scrubber

Starting Point ACTIVITY

A Chemical Clock

Scientists define the rate of a chemical reaction in terms of the time it takes for reactants to be changed into products. In this activity, you will change the rate at which two different substances react so that the reaction occurs in a specific length of time.

What You Need

50 mL solution A

50 mL solution B

25 or 50 mL graduated cylinder

100 mL beaker

hot plate

distilled water

stopwatch or other timing device

What to Do

1. Your teacher will demonstrate what happens when equal amounts of solution A and solution B are mixed together. Observe the reaction carefully.

2. Using the materials provided by your teacher, design and perform an experiment in which solution A and solution B react completely with each other in *exactly* 10 s. Get your teacher's approval first.

3. Dispose of the solutions as your teacher directs. Wash your hands thoroughly.

What Did You Discover?

1. How did you know when solution A had reacted completely with solution B?

2. Describe, in detail, what you did to make the reaction occur in exactly 10 s.

3. What modifications would you make if you wanted the reaction to occur in 5 s, or in 20 s?

8.1 Factors That Affect Chemical Reactions

Figure 8.1 What chemical reactions are taking place in these photographs? Which occur quickly? Which occur slowly? Think of some other examples of chemical reactions.

Some chemical reactions can take hundreds, thousands, or millions of years to complete. Other reactions occur in the blink of an eye. In a chemical reaction, the time it takes for a given amount of product to form, or for given amounts of reactants to react, is called the **rate of reaction.** A *rate* describes how quickly or slowly a change occurs. For example, you use the idea of rate to describe how quickly a car or a bicycle is moving. Speed is a rate because it tells you the distance that something moves during a particular length of time. On most highways, vehicles are allowed to move at a rate of 100 km/h.

To determine the rate of a chemical reaction, you need to be able to measure how quickly the reactants are being used up or how quickly the product is forming. In both cases, you are determining a rate because you are measuring how the amount of a substance is changing over a period of time. For example, the faster that a product forms or reactants are used up, the greater the rate of reaction. In the next investigation, you will examine factors that affect the rate of reaction.

Factors Affecting Chemical Reaction Rate

When two or more substances enter into a chemical reaction, there must be a direct collision between the reactant atoms or molecules. As long as there is sufficient energy, bonds between reactant atoms break and are rearranged to form new products. Think about factors that could make these collisions occur more quickly or more slowly. Write your ideas in your notebook, for later reference.

Safety Precautions

- Hydrochloric acid is a caustic liquid. If it gets on your skin or clothes, rinse the area immediately with plenty of running water and inform your teacher.
- Wash your hands thoroughly at the end of this investigation.

Part 1

Problem

How does the particle size of the reactant affect the reaction rate?

Apparatus

250 mL Erlenmeyer flask
100 mL graduated cylinder
mortar and pestle
balance
stopwatch

Materials

3 effervescent tablets
water

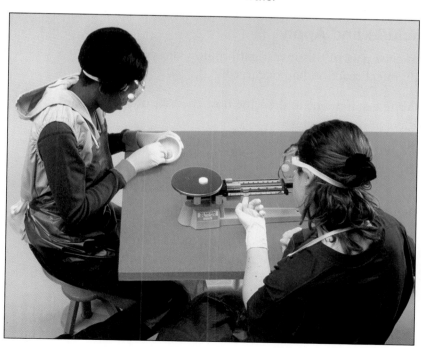

Procedure

❶ Using the apparatus and materials, design an experiment to investigate the relationship between particle size and rate of reaction. Include a hypothesis and an appropriate table to record your observations. How will you make sure that you use exactly the same mass of tablet in your tests?

❷ Get your teacher's approval before carrying out your experiment.

❸ When you are finished, dispose of the materials as directed by your teacher.

CONTINUED ▶

Part 2

Problem

How does the temperature affect the reaction rate?

Apparatus

250 mL Erlenmeyer flask
100 mL graduated cylinder
hot plate
stopwatch

Materials

3 effervescent tablets
water

Procedure

❶ Using the apparatus and materials, design an experiment to investigate the relationship between temperature and rate of reaction. You will need at least three sets of data to investigate this relationship properly. To have greater confidence in your results and interpretations, pool your data with other groups' data. Include a hypothesis and an appropriate table to record your observations.

❷ Get your teacher's approval before carrying out your experiment.

❸ When you are finished, dispose of the materials as directed by your teacher.

Part 3

Problem

How does the concentration of the reactants affect the reaction rate?

Apparatus

2 beakers (250 mL)
graduated cylinder
stopwatch

Materials

4 pieces of magnesium ribbon, Mg(s)
dilute hydrochloric acid, HCl(aq)
water

Procedure

❶ Using the apparatus and materials, design an experiment to investigate the relationship between concentration and rate of reaction. Include a hypothesis and an appropriate table to record your observations.

❷ Get your teacher's approval before carrying out your experiment.

❸ When you are finished, dispose of the materials as directed by your teacher.

Analyze

1. Draw graphs of your results for all three parts. Place time on the horizontal axis and the other variable on the vertical axis for each part. What general trends do you notice?

Conclude and Apply

2. In each part of this investigation, how did you know that a chemical reaction had occurred?

3. Write a statement to describe how the rate of a reaction is affected by changing

   (a) surface area

   (b) temperature

   (c) concentration

   Provide evidence to support each statement.

4. Based on your conclusions, suggest at least one reason why an automobile is more difficult to start in the winter.

Extend Your Knowledge

5. In this investigation, you explored three factors that affect the rate of a chemical reaction. There is a fourth factor, as well. Reflect on what you learned in Chapter 5, and write down your ideas about what this fourth factor might be. How could you test your ideas?

Concentration and Reaction Rate

Concentration refers to the amount of substance in a given volume. In Figure 8.2, the concentration of people in room B is greater than in room A. Thus there is a much greater chance that people in room B will collide with one another.

The situation is similar with chemical reactions. If there is a greater concentration of reactant particles present, there is a greater chance that collisions among them will occur. More collisions means a faster reaction rate. Thus increasing the concentrations of the reactants results in a faster reaction rate. Decreasing the concentrations results in a slower reaction rate.

Here is an example that should be familiar to you. The standard test for identifying oxygen gas involves inserting a glowing wooden splint into a small container of the gas. If the splint bursts into flame, a high concentration of oxygen is present. In air, the splint only glows. It does not burst into flame because the concentration of oxygen in air is only about 20 percent. There are not enough collisions among the oxygen molecules in air and the wooden splint to support a rapid combustion reaction. In a high concentration of oxygen the increased number of collisions between oxygen molecules and the splint cause the flame to burn brightly.

Figure 8.2 The rooms in these two cartoons are the same volume. However, the concentration of people is much greater in room B.

Surface Area and Reaction Rate

Have you ever made a campfire or burned wood in a fireplace? If so, you probably noticed that it is easier to start the fire with kindling than with logs. Using smaller, thinner pieces of wood — kindling — increases the surface area of the wood that is exposed to air. By exposing more wood surface to the oxygen in air, you increase the rate of reaction.

Another substance that reacts with the oxygen in air is iron. A large piece of iron reacts with air slowly over time, producing rust (iron oxide), Fe_2O_3. The powdered iron that is used to make sparklers, on the other hand, dramatically increases the surface area of iron that is exposed to air. As a result, the iron reacts more quickly (the reaction rate increases), producing energy in the form of sparks (light) and heat.

Figure 8.3 In both of these exothermic reactions, iron reacts with the oxygen in air to produce iron oxide. In what ways do the reactions differ?

Temperature and Reaction Rate

Lowering the thermal energy of the reactants decreases the rate of reaction. You know this, from thermal experience, each time you get food out of a refrigerator. Food "keeps" longer when it is kept cool. Put more scientifically, lowering the temperature decreases the rates of the chemical reactions that cause food to spoil.

Figure 8.4 Most food spoils because of the activity of micro-organisms, such as bacteria and yeasts. These organisms release chemicals into the food to break it down. Then they use the resulting nutrient molecules as their own food. Some of the chemicals they release, however, are toxic to other living things, including people.

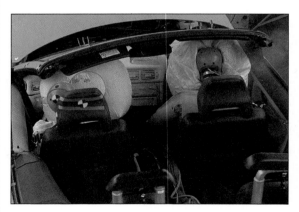

Pause& Reflect

We refrigerate food to reduce the rate of the reactions that spoil it. What other methods do we use to reduce food-spoiling reactions?

Impact! Within 27 ms (milliseconds), a nylon bag inflates. Another 23 ms later, the driver escapes serious injury, perhaps even death.

Air bags are now mandatory features of all new cars and trucks. These devices dramatically illustrate the need for careful, precise control of chemical reactions. Vehicle air bags contain a compound called sodium azide, NaN_3, in the form of pellets. The shape of the pellets allows engineers to determine the precise surface area needed for a reaction to occur within a very specific period of time, measured in milliseconds. If a front-end collision occurs, an electric signal ignites the sodium azide. The compound quickly decomposes, releasing 60 L of nitrogen gas to inflate the bag. The chemical equation for the reaction is

$$2NaN_3(s) \rightarrow 2Na(s) + 3N_2(g)$$

If the sodium that results from the reaction were to come in contact with moisture — for example, from a person's mouth or eyes — caustic sodium hydroxide could form. To prevent this, designers include other compounds in the air bag. These compounds react with the sodium, forming non-toxic salts.

By carefully determining and controlling the surface area, a precise amount of gas is released at a highly specific rate. What would be the consequences if engineers could not control this reaction?

Speeding Up Chemical Reactions

Hydrogen peroxide, H_2O_2, reacts slowly in a decomposition reaction to produce oxygen gas and water. In this activity, you will examine a way to increase the rate of this reaction.

What You Need

100 mL graduated cylinder
2 beakers (250 mL)
6% hydrogen peroxide solution, H_2O_2(aq)
manganese dioxide, MnO_2
food colouring
liquid dishwashing detergent
scoopula
fresh beef liver (ground up or chopped very small)

What to Do

1. Pour 25 mL of hydrogen peroxide solution into one beaker. This is your control. **CAUTION:** 6% hydrogen peroxide solution is corrosive, so wear gloves and goggles at all times.

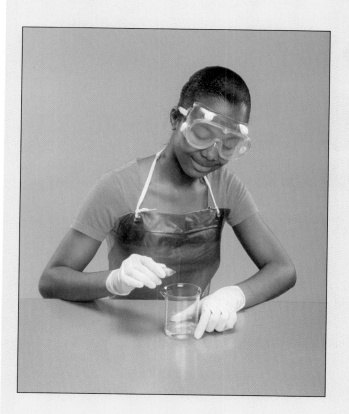

2. Pour 25 mL of hydrogen peroxide solution into a second beaker. Add two drops of food colouring and a small squirt of dishwashing detergent. Observe carefully, and record your observations.

3. Use the scoopula to add a pinch of manganese dioxide. Record what happens.

4. Follow your teacher's instructions to dispose of the contents. Then rinse out the beaker.

5. Repeat step 2. Then use the scoopula to add a small amount of liver. Record your observations. **CAUTION:** Wear gloves when handling the liver.

6. Pour 25 mL of hydrogen peroxide solution into the beaker. Add a few drops of food colouring and a small squirt of dishwashing detergent. Observe carefully.

7. Follow your teacher's instructions to dispose of the contents. Wash your hands thoroughly.

What Did You Discover?

1. How did the contents of your control beaker compare with the contents of the beaker to which you added manganese dioxide?

2. What happened to the manganese dioxide after the reaction finished? Do you think you could re-use it? How could you find out?

3. Based on your observations, would you infer that liver contains chemicals that behave like manganese dioxide? Why or why not?

Using Catalysts to Speed Up Reaction Rate

Energy is required to break bonds in any chemical reaction, whether it is exothermic or endothermic. One way to speed up the rate of a reaction involves lowering the bond-breaking energy. **Catalysts** are substances that speed up the rate of a reaction without being used up in the reaction themselves. These substances lower the amount of energy that is needed to break the bonds. Thus catalysts allow reactions to occur more quickly than the reactions would normally.

All automobiles that have been built in North America since the 1980s have catalyst-containing pollution control devices in their exhaust systems. A catalytic converter is a stainless steel object, shaped like a muffler. Inside it is a ceramic or wire honeycomb-like structure that provides a large surface area for reactions to take place. The surface of the honeycomb is coated with a thin layer of metallic catalysts, such as platinum, rhodium, and palladium.

As exhaust gases pass through the catalytic converter, several reactions occur. Much of the poisonous carbon monoxide, which is produced from the combustion of gasoline, reacts with oxygen and is changed into carbon dioxide. Hydrocarbons (unburned fuel) react with oxygen to produce carbon dioxide and water. Finally, most of the nitrogen oxides are converted into nitrogen gas and oxygen gas.

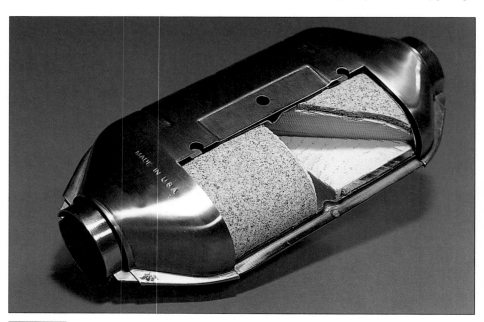

Figure 8.5 While catalytic converters are quite efficient, they work best when the catalysts are warmed up. It takes about 90 s, after a car starts, for the catalysts to be activated. Unfortunately it is during this brief warm-up time that the car produces about 70 percent of all the pollutants that it releases during its driving cycle.

Your body contains thousands of biological catalysts, called **enzymes.** Enzymes are specialized proteins that speed up reactions in living cells. Each enzyme in your body is specialized to perform its own function. For example, saliva contains an enzyme called amylase that breaks down only starch molecules. A large set of enzymes is required for the digestion of carbohydrate, fat, and protein molecules in your diet. Another complex set of enzymes makes new DNA. Still others convert extra nutrients into fat for storage. Like all catalysts, enzymes are not changed or used up by the reactions in which they are involved.

Control a Chemical Reaction

Now that you have examined factors that affect the rates of chemical reactions, you are ready for a design challenge to apply your understanding and experiences.

Challenge

Design a process for making the lid of a film canister pop off in exactly 15 s.

Materials

effervescent tablet
timer
empty 35 mm film canister with lid
water
mortar and pestle

Design Criteria

A. You may use only the materials listed above.
B. You must be able to replicate the process you design at least twice.
C. You must record your final procedure in detail, including safety precautions, so that other groups can test your process. (Get your teacher's approval before trying your ideas.)

Plan and Construct

1. Agree on roles for each group member.

2. Brainstorm and record all the ideas offered by your group members.

3. Discuss these ideas. Keep a record of any comments in favour of or against a particular method or approach.

4. Record appropriate chemical information, such as the names of reactants and products, and word and/or chemical equations.

Evaluate

1. How well were you able to replicate your process? What about other groups? Account for any discrepancies or deviations.

2. What modifications did you have to make to speed up or slow down the rate of your chemical reaction?

3. How would your process be affected if you were asked to make the film canister lid pop off in exactly 20 s, or in exactly 5 s?

Gelling It Together

Gelatin is a protein that is used to make desserts and thicken foods. In this activity, you will investigate the effects of fresh and canned fruits on gelatin's ability to thicken at room temperature.

CAUTION:
- Handle hot water and sharp objects with caution.
- Make sure that the plastic cups are properly cleaned and sterilized before using them.

What You Need

4 sterile plastic cups
masking tape
marker
package of flavoured gelatin
hot water
knife
slice of canned pineapple
2 slices of fresh pineapple
microwave oven or stove element with container of boiling water

What to Do

1. Prepare the gelatin according to the directions on the package.

2. Pour the gelatin solution, while still warm, into four plastic cups to give four approximately equal samples. Number the cups from 1 to 4, using masking tape and a marker.

3. Cut up the slice of canned pineapple into five or six pieces. Place the pieces in cup 2.

4. Cut up one slice of fresh pineapple into five or six pieces. Place the pieces in cup 3.

5. Cut up the other slice of fresh pineapple into five or six pieces. Heat these pieces in a microwave at high power for 1 min, or place them in a container of boiling water on a hot plate for at least 3 min.

6. Place the pieces of cooked pineapple in cup 4.

7. Give the gelatin time to cool. Then observe each cup.

What Did You Discover?

1. What happened to the gelatin in each of the four cups?

2. Why was no pineapple added to the first cup?

3. Think about what you observed in cups 3 and 4. Infer why the fresh pineapple had the effect it did on the gelatin.

Extension

4. Find out how canned pineapple is prepared. What does the processing do to the pineapple?

Check Your Understanding

1. How do chemists define the rate of a reaction?

2. In your own words, describe the effects of the following factors on the rate of a chemical reaction.

   (a) concentration   (c) temperature

   (b) surface area

3. Explain, using an example, what a catalyst is and how it affects the rate of a reaction.

4. What happens to the molecules in food when food is put in a refrigerator?

5. Why does kindling make it easier to start a fire?

6. **Apply** Magnesium reacts with hydrochloric acid to make hydrogen gas, according to the following balanced chemical equation:

   $$Mg(s) + 2HCl(aq) \rightarrow H_2(g) + MgCl_2(aq)$$

   This table gives the mass of magnesium left over after each second of reaction time, over a period of 5 s. Draw a graph of the data. Why does the graph have the shape that you drew?

Time (s)	Mass of Magnesium (g)
0	1.00
1	0.50
2	0.25
3	0.15
4	0.10
5	0.05

7. **Apply** An important step in the commercial production of sulfuric acid is the reaction:

   $$2SO_2(g) + O_2(g) \rightarrow 2SO_3(g)$$

   The reactant gases are passed over many large plates with vanadium oxide on the surfaces. Explain why.

8. **Thinking Critically** What problem do designers of catalytic converters face? Offer at least one design modification that could solve this problem. Explain how you think your solution might affect automobile manufacturers and consumers.

9. **Thinking Critically** Why are important artifacts, such as this preserved body, stored under airtight, temperature-controlled conditions?

8.2 Chemicals for Consumers

Figure 8.6 A look at some chemistry in your everyday life.

There are hundreds of thousands of consumer products that help us fill our stomachs, clean our bodies, remove dirt and stains from our clothes, and do numerous other tasks that are important to our lives. In this section, you will examine the chemistry behind some of the products that you use or hear about every day.

Analyzing Antacids

Chemical reactions change the food you eat into compounds that your body can use for growth, maintenance and repair of cells and tissues, and energy. When you eat a large meal — especially a meal that includes caffeine-containing foods, such as coffee, tea, soft drinks, and chocolate — your stomach secretes more acid to help with these reactions. Stomach acid is hydrochloric acid, which has a pH between 1 and 2. The excess acid can cause what advertisers call "heartburn," or acid indigestion. This is a burning feeling, caused by stomach acid. Heartburn occurs when the acidic stomach contents are pushed into the lower area of the esophagus. The esophagus does not have a protective lining like the stomach does, so you feel a burning sensation in your throat and chest.

Some people are prone to feel the effects of acid indigestion. One way to solve acid indigestion problems is to be more mindful about what you eat. For immediate relief when acid indigestion occurs, however, many people reach for an antacid. As its name implies, an antacid ("anti-acid") is a chemical that opposes acid. Chemically speaking, it is a base that neutralizes excess stomach acid. In Investigation 8-C on page 254, you will measure how effective antacids really are.

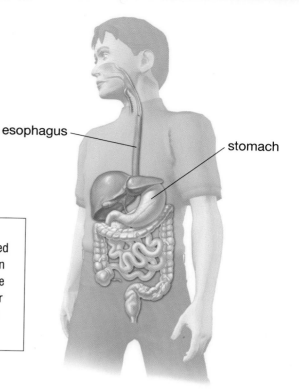

esophagus

stomach

DidYou**Know**?

If you are like most Canadians, one of the acids that you consume regularly is carbonic acid from soft drinks. All soft drinks are made up mostly of carbonated water. This is a solution of carbon dioxide in water, which forms a mild solution of carbonic acid (H_2CO_3). Other ingredients that are found in soft drinks include flavouring materials, preservatives, sodium compounds, sweeteners (natural or artificial), dyes, and caffeine. In addition to these ingredients, some colas have another acid, phosphoric acid, which provides a stronger acid taste.

Keeping Clean with Soap

Our skin contains glands that produce sweat and oils, which are deposited on the surface of the skin. Sweat is salty water — a dilute sodium chloride solution — that helps to maintain constant body temperature through the evaporation process. The oils help to keep the skin soft and flexible. The oils and sweat also trap dirt and grease from our environment. Lastly, they provide a source of food for bacteria and other microscopic organisms. The activity of these micro-organisms is largely responsible for body odour. What sort of chemistry can you use to tackle these sweaty problems?

Figure 8.7 The esophagus connects your mouth with your stomach. If you experience heartburn, you feel it in the lower area of the esophagus. So heartburn has nothing to do with your heart. Why is the name still appropriate?

Across Canada

Born in Montréal, Dr. Mary Fairhurst enjoyed science fairs during high school. After studying chemistry at McGill University, she spent two years teaching in Ghana as a volunteer with CUSO (Canadian University Service Overseas). This was challenging. Her students at St. Peter's School were all boys, all older than Mary, and not used to a female science teacher.

On returning to Canada, Mary did graduate work at the University of Alberta. Today she is Analytical Resource Leader at Dow Chemical Canada in Fort Saskatchewan, Alberta. "The work is never boring," she says. "New challenges come up regularly as we seek to understand all aspects of the ways we make our products." These products include resins used in bicycles; caustic soda used as a neutralizing agent in petroleum refining; and chlorine used to produce chemicals that are, in turn, used to make guitar strings, cosmetics, clothes, computer casings, and more. "Our team provides analytical support for our plants and research programs," Mary explains. "We are usually

trying to find out what components are in a sample and how much of each component is present. To do this, we use a variety of techniques, ranging from simple observations about the properties of a material to highly sophisticated instruments that use spectroscopy (observation of a light spectrum) to identify and quantify individual components."

Dr. Mary Fairhurst

Besides her job, Mary enjoys hiking with her family and encouraging young women in science. She is involved in an organization called WISEST: Women in Scholarship, Engineering, Science, and Technology. What is her advice to students? "Don't limit yourself by dropping subjects that you may need later. Explore areas that you enjoy and keep asking questions."

Testing the Effectiveness of Antacids

Advertisements for antacids often make claims about the antacids' ability to "consume" excess stomach acid. How valid are these claims? In this investigation, you will perform tests to find out.

Problem

Which over-the-counter antacid is most effective in neutralizing acid?

Safety Precautions

- Handle acids and bases carefully. If you get any acid or base on your hands, flush your skin with plenty of water and notify your teacher. Report any spills to your teacher immediately.

Apparatus

250 mL Erlenmeyer flask
stopper
100 mL graduated cylinder
graduated eyedropper (in mL)
balance
mortar and pestle
measuring spoon

Materials

dilute hydrochloric acid, HCl(aq)
dilute sodium hydroxide solution, NaOH(aq)
antacid
methyl orange indicator

Procedure

1 For the antacid that your group tests, prepare a data table like the one here.

2 If you are using a solid antacid, crush the tablet. Measure and record the mass of about half of the crushed tablet. If you are using a liquid or powdered antacid, measure and record the mass of about half of the recommended dosage listed on the container (probably 1 or 2 teaspoons).

3 Put the antacid sample in the Erlenmeyer flask. Add 50 mL of hydrochloric acid, and gently swirl the solution to dissolve the antacid.

Name of antacid:

Mass of antacid (g)	Volume of HCl used (mL)	Volume of NaOH added (mL)	Volume of antacid neutralized by NaOH (mL)	Neutralizing ability of antacid (mL of HCl/g of antacid)

4 Add three drops of methyl orange indicator. The solution should be red. If it is not, add more HCl solution, 5 mL at a time, until the solution turns red. Record the total volume of HCl that you added.

5 Using a graduated eyedropper, add NaOH solution to the flask until the colour of the solution just changes from red to yellow. Record the total volume of NaOH you added.

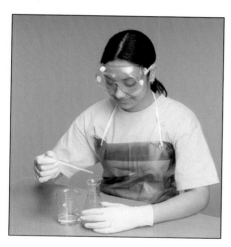

6 Repeat steps 2 and 3 with a second antacid sample, the same mass as the first.

7 Calculate and record the volume of HCl that is neutralized by the antacids. Use this formula.

$$\text{Volume of HCl neutralized by antacid (mL)} = \text{Volume of HCl added (mL)} - \text{Volume of NaOH added (mL)}$$

8 Calculate the neutralizing ability of the antacid by dividing the volume of HCl neutralized (in mL) by the mass of antacid (in g).

9 Calculate the average acid neutralizing ability of the antacid.

10 Compare your results with other groups' results. Design a class data table to record all the results.

11 Flush the neutralized liquids down the sink with plenty of water. Wash your hands.

Analyze

1. What is the active ingredient in the antacid you tested? Write a chemical equation to show how the antacid neutralizes acids.

2. What is the average neutralizing ability of your antacid? How does this compare with the neutralizing ability of the other antacids tested by your class?

Conclude and Apply

3. List the antacids tested by your class from most effective to least effective.

4. Your teacher will provide you with the price of each antacid.
   (a) Calculate the cost of a single dose.
   (b) Which is the least expensive antacid? Is it also the most effective one? Explain, using data to support your answer.

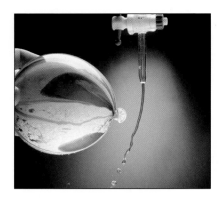

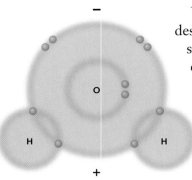

Figure 8.8 This balloon is negatively charged. Why does the stream of water deflect towards it?

Vast numbers of consumer products are designed in response to our desire to look, smell, and be clean. Most of these products exploit certain characteristics of a common substance — water.

As you know, water molecules are formed when hydrogen atoms and oxygen atoms share electrons in a covalent bond. As you can see in Figure 8.8, this sharing of electrons is unequal. The two pairs of electrons in the two bonds between the hydrogen and oxygen are more likely to be found at the oxygen end of the molecule. As a result, the oxygen end has a slightly negative charge and the hydrogen end has a slightly positive charge. A molecule that is bonded like this is referred to as a **polar molecule,** because it has two oppositely charged ends or poles.

Polar substances, such as water, usually dissolve other substances with polar molecules, and also ionic substances, such as salts. (Why do you think this is true?) Water does not dissolve substances with non-polar molecules, such as oils and grease, however. This is why an oil spill forms a "slick" on the surface of the sea. Fortunately, soap has the ability to dissolve oils and grease, because it has a particular structure that enables it to work with both water and grime. Soap belongs to a class of compound called organic salts. A typical soap molecule has an ionic "head" and a non-polar "tail." This means that the tail mixes easily with non-polar substances and materials, such as grease, and the head interacts easily with water. Figure 8.9 shows how this happens.

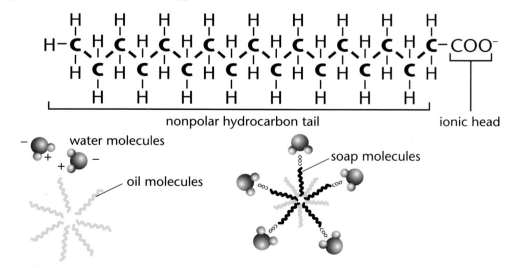

Figure 8.9 Soap enables oils and grease to mix with water so they can be loosened and carried away.

Figure 8.10 Water, by itself, is a poor cleanser.

Soap is formed by reacting a fat (solid or liquid) with a strong base, such as sodium hydroxide or potassium hydroxide. A fat is a compound that is made up of two parts: fatty acids and a substance called glycerol. To make soap, the fatty acids are separated from the glycerol, and sodium or potassium from the base is added to the fatty acid. Another product of this reaction is a compound called glycerol, which is a softening agent that is often added to hand creams. In the next activity, you will make a small sample of your own soap and observe its properties.

Slippery Soap

Many people make their own soap at home. They react plant or animal fat with a strong base such as lye (sodium hydroxide), which can be purchased from the cleaning department of most grocery stores. Although soap has been made like this for centuries, the process is very dangerous. Lye, like all bases, is caustic. It must be handled very carefully when combined with water. Do not attempt to make soap at home. In this activity, you will be making only a very small quantity of soap. Even so, exercise extreme caution and follow all safety precautions. Your teacher may prefer to demonstrate the soap-making process.

CAUTION:
- Avoid inhaling any vapours during this activity.
- Sodium hydroxide is very corrosive. If you get any on your skin or clothing, rinse the area immediately with running water and notify your teacher.

What You Need

1.4 g sodium hydroxide
6.5 mL cold (refrigerated) distilled water
12.5 mL melted lard
5 drops of lemon juice
distilled water
tap water or spring water
25 mL graduated cylinder
100 mL beaker
test tube
stopper
glass or plastic stirring rod
scoopula

What to Do

1. Wearing rubber gloves, place 1.4 g of sodium hydroxide in the beaker. Add 6.5 mL of *cold* water, and stir until the sodium hydroxide is completely dissolved. **CAUTION:** Do not inhale the vapours that may be produced. Note what happens to the cold water.

2. Slowly add 12.5 mL of melted lard to the sodium hydroxide solution. Stir until the mixture thickens. Add the lemon juice, and stir. You have just made lemon-scented soap!

3. Using the scoopula, place a small amount of the soap in a test tube. Add 10 mL of distilled water. Cover the mouth of the test tube with a stopper, and shake the test tube vigorously for several seconds. Record your observations.

4. Repeat step 3 using tap water or spring water. Record your observations.

5. Clean all containers and equipment as directed by your teacher. Wash your hands.

What Did You Discover?

1. What happened to the cold water when you added the sodium hydroxide? What type of reaction is this?

2. Describe the appearance and smell of the soap you made.

3. How did the soap interact with distilled water. How did this compare with how the soap interacted with tap water or spring water?

Extension

4. If there is time, try making soap in your classroom using other lipids such as tallow (rendered beef fat), olive oil, or vegetable shortening. How do the properties of these soaps compare?

DidYou**Know**?

Before people discovered how to make soap, they cleaned themselves as well as they could using water. Since water cannot remove soil and grease, the skin provided a fertile place for bacterial growth. Wealthy people solved the problem of body odour by wearing perfumed wigs and carrying perfumed handkerchiefs to cover their noses when they met others.

How Detergents Differ from Soaps

One of the problems with using soap is that it reacts with the calcium and magnesium ions in hard water to form a solid precipitate, or "soap scum." Since most municipal water supplies are hard water of various concentrations, soap scum forms when you take a bath or a shower. The soap reacts with the magnesium and calcium ions and forms the notorious "bathtub ring." Imagine using soap and hard water to clean your clothing. You would end up with a soap precipitate on your clothing. Luckily **detergents** overcome this precipitation problem.

The ionic head of a detergent molecule is different from that of a soap molecule. Compare the ionic head of the detergent molecule in Figure 8.11 with the head on the soap molecule in Figure 8.9. The detergent molecule does not react with calcium or magnesium ions to form a precipitate. Since detergents are completely soluble in hard water, oily and greasy dirt is removed from clothing without leaving any residue behind. Detergents are not only used to wash clothing. They are also used for dishes and for hair. Can you imagine having soap scum on your hair? Since shampoos are mild detergents, this does not happen.

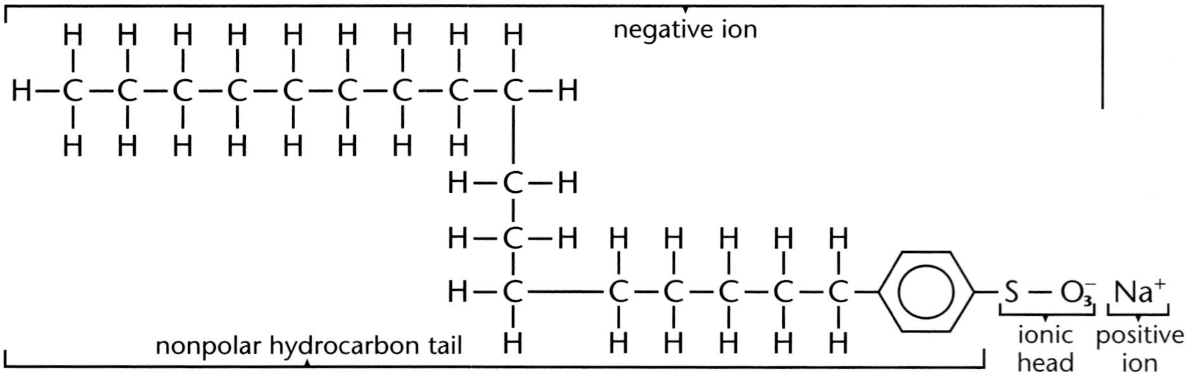

Figure 8.11 The structure of a common detergent molecule

Pause&
Reflect

Which of the cleaning products in your home are soaps, and which are detergents? In your Science Log, write down reasons why you think a soap or a detergent is used in each case.

Household Cleaners

If you did a quick survey of your home, you would probably find all-purpose cleaners, toilet-bowl cleaners, drain cleaners, and a variety of other specialty cleaning products. These products usually contain compounds that are very reactive. Their chemical reactivity is precisely why people use them. It makes cleaning jobs simpler and less strenuous. It also makes these products dangerous, however.

Drain cleaners, for example, often contain strong bases such as sodium hydroxide. Because the base is so corrosive, it easily breaks the bonds that hold the molecules of blockage materials together. These reactions are usually exothermic, so they also generate a lot of thermal energy to help clear drains.

Figure 8.12 Which of these products have you used? Did you read the safety warnings? How do these warnings affect your use of the products?

Check Your Understanding

1. Wayne is experiencing acid indigestion, but he does not have a commercial antacid product. He does, however, have baking soda. Can he use it for the same purpose? Why or why not?

2. Explain what soap is. Briefly describe the process that is involved in making it.

3. Use a Venn diagram to compare the composition and action of a soap and a detergent.

4. Oven cleaners contain sodium hydroxide. Explain why this does or does not surprise you.

5. **Apply** Poor Wayne. First he had acid indigestion, and now he has a clogged drain! In your opinion, could he use baking soda to help "clear up" his second problem? If not, why not? If so, explain how.

6. **Thinking Critically** There are hundreds of drain-cleaning products that consumers can buy. Despite this fact, most plumbers advise against using drain cleaners. Suggest at least two reasons for their advice.

8.3 Chemicals and Our Environment

In the unit opener, you read that everything we do involves risks and benefits. This is especially true of the chemicals that we depend on for the quality of life that we have come to expect. Canadian chemical and related industries employ about 250 000 people, and they generate tens of billions of dollars annually. On a global scale, chemical industries account for 10 percent of *all* world trade. Clearly, chemicals contribute significantly not only to our lives, but also to the health of the Canadian economy.

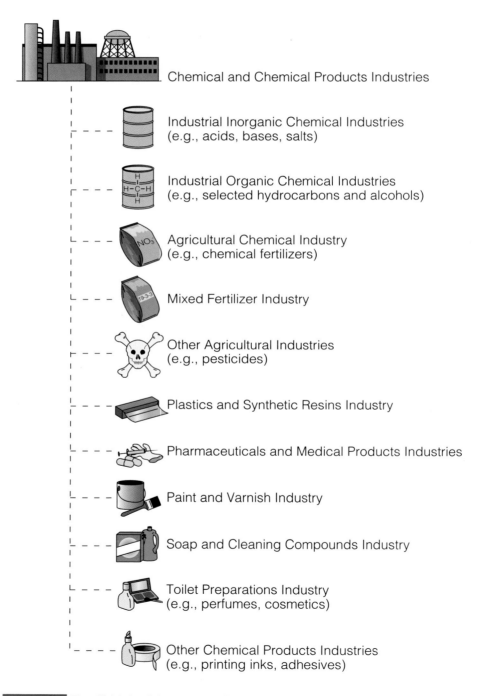

Chemical and Chemical Products Industries

Industrial Inorganic Chemical Industries
(e.g., acids, bases, salts)

Industrial Organic Chemical Industries
(e.g., selected hydrocarbons and alcohols)

Agricultural Chemical Industry
(e.g., chemical fertilizers)

Mixed Fertilizer Industry

Other Agricultural Industries
(e.g., pesticides)

Plastics and Synthetic Resins Industry

Pharmaceuticals and Medical Products Industries

Paint and Varnish Industry

Soap and Cleaning Compounds Industry

Toilet Preparations Industry
(e.g., perfumes, cosmetics)

Other Chemical Products Industries
(e.g., printing inks, adhesives)

Figure 8.13 The official classifying system for Canadian Chemicals and Chemical Products Industries.

Our personal and economic reliance on chemicals and chemical products comes with a cost. The human population is increasing at an alarming rate, from five billion to over six billion in just over a decade. As people in all countries strive for improved standards and conditions of living, chemical industries increase their rates of production. According to United Nations statistics, the worldwide trade in chemicals *doubled* in a mere six years, between 1992 and 1998. Your new understanding of several key chemistry concepts will help you appreciate why this is a concern:

- The raw materials for extracting and producing chemicals and chemical products come from a finite (limited) source of matter. With the exception of interstellar dust and debris from comets and meteors, all the matter on Earth has been here for billions of years. Matter, like energy, cannot be created or destroyed. It can only change form.
- During a chemical reaction, atoms are conserved. Thus, chemical reactions may result in unwanted by-products as well as the products we intend or desire.

It should come as no surprise that pollution is a consequence of human activities. Long ago, before humans learned how to control combustion reactions, the pollution we generated was in a form that natural cycles, such as the water cycle and nitrogen cycle, could easily accommodate. With our increasing numbers, and our increasing technological ingenuity, we have "tipped the scales." We now generate vast volumes and masses of material wastes. We also have invented new chemicals and products, such as plastics, that the chemical processes of natural cycles cannot decompose. In addition, our need for matter and energy results in gaseous by-products of reactions (such as carbon dioxide) that are changing the very nature of our planetary life-support systems.

Fortunately the scientific and technological ingenuity that leads us to invent polluting processes and products also allows us to design new or modified procedures to reduce them. This section focusses on two chemicals that societies around the world depend on: sulfuric acid and nitric acid. You will examine their composition, their industrial applications, and the unwanted products that result from their use. You will also examine several technologies that enable us to minimize their risks. At the end of this unit, you will further consider the risks and benefits of these chemicals.

Math CONNECT

The average Canadian generates an average of 2 kg of unwanted materials per day. The population of Canada is about 30 500 000. Find out the current population of your province. Then calculate the amount of unwanted materials generated per day in your province and in Canada. If 1 kg of trash takes up 0.004 m^3 of space, how tall would a column of the trash produced by your province be, if the column's base had an area of 1 m^2? (The CN Tower in Toronto is 553 m tall. How would the pile of trash compare?)

The Chemistry of Sulfuric Acid and Nitric Acid

Figure 8.14 Piles of sulfur, awaiting processing. More than 90 percent of all the sulfur produced is used to make sulfuric acid.

Sulfuric acid, $H_2SO_4(\ell)$ is a colourless, odourless liquid in its pure form. When concentrated, it is highly corrosive and can cause severe, deep burns to the skin. Despite its hazards, sulfuric acid is the most important industrial chemical in the world. Figure 8.15 can help you appreciate why.

Sulfuric acid is usually produced industrially by the "contact process." In this process, sulfur is burned in the presence of oxygen to produce sulfur dioxide. Then a catalyst is used to change the sulfur dioxide to sulfur trioxide.

$$S(s) + O_2(g) \rightarrow SO_2(g)$$

$$2SO_2(g) + O_2(g) \rightarrow SO_3(g)$$

Finally, the sulfur trioxide is reacted with water to produce sulfuric acid.

$$SO_3(g) + H_2O(\ell) \rightarrow H_2SO_4(\ell)$$

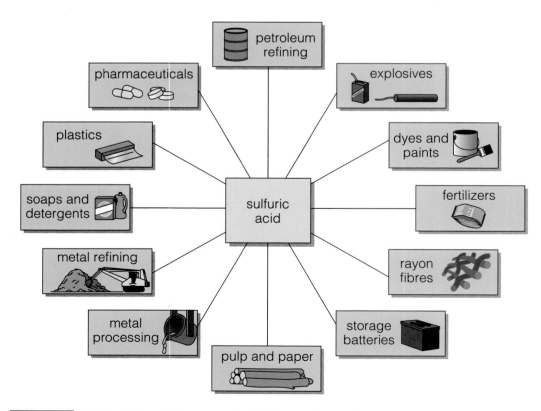

Figure 8.15 Sulfuric acid is used, in some way, in all of these products and processes.

The chemical reactions that produce sulfuric acid are all exothermic. Instead of releasing the wasted heat energy into the environment, the industries usually recycle the heat energy to generate either electricity or steam for use in plant operations.

Nitric acid, HNO_3, is a corrosive acid. In its concentrated form, it gives off choking fumes when it comes in contact with moist air. It is highly reactive when combined with many substances, including alkali metals, ammonia, copper, phosphorus, and numerous bases.

Nitric acid has been known since medieval times, when it was referred to as *aqua fortis*, or strong water. Nitric acid is usually made commercially using a process developed in 1902 by a German chemist, Wilhelm Ostwald. Ostwald's process involves reacting ammonia with air in the presence of a catalyst (platinum) to produce nitrogen dioxide, NO_2. The nitrogen dioxide is then reacted with water to form nitric acid. Today nitric acid is also made commercially by reacting sulfuric acid with sodium nitrate.

Nitroglycerine is a highly unstable, explosive compound. It is derived from the reaction between nitric acid and a substance called glycerol, which comes from fats or hydrocarbons. Nitric acid is also used to produce ammonium nitrate, NH_4NO_3. In Chapter 6, you learned that nitric acid has applications in both the explosives and fertilizer industries. In fact, the largest use of nitric acid is in the production of nitrogen fertilizer.

Researching Other Industrially Important Chemicals

Many of the world's most important chemicals are produced in Canada. These include sulfuric acid and nitric acid, as well as the following:

- ammonia
- urea
- ethylene
- sodium hydroxide (caustic soda)
- chlorine
- ammonium phosphate
- ammonium nitrate
- polyethylene
- benzene
- phosphoric acid

What to Do

1. Select one of these chemicals. Conduct research at your local library and/or on the Internet to answer the following questions.

Outside Link ACTIVITY

(a) What is the source of this chemical?

(b) How is it prepared?

(c) What benefits does it, and its associated applications, provide for society?

(d) What risks does it, its processes, and its associated applications have for the environment?

2. Prepare a written, visual, or multimedia report to communicate your findings.

Computer CONNECT

With your classmates, develop and synthesize the information you have gathered, and design a web site to communicate your findings.

Consequences of Using Sulfuric Acid and Nitric Acid

The different oxides of sulfur (SO_2 and SO_3) and nitrogen (usually NO and NO_2) are sometimes referred to as SO_x and NO_x. When fossil fuels are burned in air, either by industrial plants or automobiles, these gases are by-products. They react with water in the air to form sulfurous, sulfuric, nitrous, and nitric acids.

$$SO_2(g) + H_2O(\ell) \rightarrow H_2SO_3(aq)$$ ◀ **sulfurous acid**

$$SO_3(g) + H_2O(\ell) \rightarrow H_2SO_4(aq)$$ ◀ **sulfuric acid**

$$2NO_2(g) + H_2O(\ell) \rightarrow HNO_2(aq) + HNO_3(aq)$$ ◀ **nitrous acid and nitric acid**

Normal rain, with a pH of 5.5 to 6.2, is already slightly acidic. This is because carbon dioxide, the product of all combustion reactions and respiration, reacts with water vapour. The product is a weak acid called carbonic acid:

$$CO_2(g) + H_2O(\ell) \rightarrow H_2CO_3(aq)$$

Adding sulfurous, sulfuric, nitrous, and nitric acids to the atmosphere increases the acidity of precipitation, such as snow and rain. As a result, the pH of precipitation in most of eastern Canada and the United States is between 4 and 5. This means that the more concentrated **acid precipitation** has about the same pH as tomato juice (4.2). During times of excessive industrial activity, the pH of rain has been as low as 3.0. (For comparison, the pH of soda water is 3.8. The pH of orange juice is 4.0, and the pH of vinegar is about 3.0.)

Acid precipitation has serious consequences for our environment. Because it is so soluble in water, acid precipitation poses a serious threat to bodies of water, especially lakes and ponds. For example, as the pH approaches 6, insects and other aquatic animals begin to die. As the pH approaches 5, many of the plants and plant-like micro-organisms die. This reduces the food source of aquatic animals which, in turn, slowly die off. Below a pH of 5, all the life in a lake or pond is gone and the water appears crystal clear.

These effects reverberate beyond the specific aquatic ecosystem. Birds and mammals that depend on the ecosystem for food must move to other locations or starve to death. As well, because acid precipitation also dissolves metals (such as aluminum, mercury, and copper), these metals may leach into the ground water that feeds rivers and lakes. In high concentrations, these metals are harmful, even deadly, to most organisms, including us.

STRETCH Your Mind

Many countries, and parts of Canada, burn coal — a hydrocarbon — to generate electricity. Coal usually contains about 0.2 to 2 percent sulfur by mass. A large coal-burning electric plant, for example, may consume 1000 t of coal each hour. If the coal contains 1.2 percent sulfur by mass, what mass of sulfur will be converted to sulfur oxides each hour? How much will be produced in a year if the plant consumes coal continuously at the same rate?

Figure 8.16 Many monuments and statues, some thousands of years old, are made of marble and limestone. These substances contain calcium carbonate ($CaCO_3$), which is easily decomposed by sulfuric acid:

$$CaCO_3(s) + H_2SO_4(aq) \rightarrow CaSO_4(s) + H_2O(\ell) + CO_2(g)$$

Calcium sulfate dissolves in water more readily than calcium carbonate. Thus the monuments and statues corrode as the calcium sulfate is washed away.

Figure 8.17 Acid precipitation can leach (dissolve and carry away) soil chemicals. What are some possible consequences?

The Unequal Effects of Acid Precipitation

Acid precipitation falls across Canada. Some areas are affected more than others, however. Levels of acid pollutants in Canada are highest east of Manitoba. Smelters and power plants are concentrated in this area, both north and south of the Canada-U.S. border. Unfortunately, this area is also vulnerable to acid precipitation.

During the last ice age (about 20 000 years ago), glaciers covered much of North America. As they moved, they crushed softer sedimentary rocks, such as limestone and sandstone, and carried the crushed rocks great distances. When the glaciers receded, they left behind the alkaline materials that characterize the soils of much of western Canada. These materials include calcium carbonate, $CaCO_3$. Calcium carbonate accumulated at the bottoms of many lakes in the Canadian west. It reacts with the acids that enter these lakes, keeping the pH close to neutral.

The area east of Manitoba, around the Canadian Shield, lies on ancient igneous and metamorphic rock formations. This area lacks the compounds that naturally neutralize acids. The soils in this area, which makes up nearly half of Canada's land mass, have little ability to neutralize the effects of acid precipitation.

Figure 8.18 In this northern boreal forest, acid precipitation and toxic fumes from a nearby smelting plant have killed many trees.

Using Chemistry to Control Acid Effects

You know from Chapter 7 that limestone (calcium carbonate) reacts with acids in a neutralization reaction. Why not, then, add limestone to acidified lakes?

Adding limestone (a process called "liming") presents problems. Knowing how much limestone to add to a lake, and when to add it, depends on three factors:

- the volume of water in the lake
- the chemical composition and reactivity of its rocks and soil
- the turnover time

Turnover time refers to the time needed for all the water in a lake to be replaced from natural sources. For some lakes, the turnover time may be only a few months.

DidYou**Know**?

You might expect the pH of a lake to change gradually as acid water enters it. This is not what happens, however. As calcium carbonate in the limestone bed of a lake reacts with the acid, the pH remains constant. When all of the limestone has reacted, however, the pH drops suddenly. For example, the pH of Lumsden Lake in the Killarney region of Ontario was 6.8 in 1961. Ten years later, after all the carbonates present had reacted, the pH was 4.4 — an increase in acidity of more than 200 times. Rapid changes in pH are lethal to the ecology of any lake or river.

If the turnover time is short, liming might have to be repeated every third or fourth turnover. Since there are many thousands of lakes that could be treated, liming all of them is unrealistic. Selected lakes have been successfully treated in this way. Treating lakes with lime is not a long-term solution. Lakes are constantly fed acidified water from streams. As well, the volume of water that flows into a lake, and its acidity, are constantly changing. Thus it would be difficult to add the right amount of limestone all the time. The sudden inflow of acid water when snow melts in the spring — a time when fish eggs are most vulnerable — would be especially difficult to treat.

Figure 8.19 Liming is usually done by releasing powdered calcium carbonate from aircraft.

What about adding limestone to the land around affected lakes and rivers? Limestone spread on soil should neutralize acid precipitation as it falls, and should be effective for a number of years. This approach, however, is a massive undertaking, because of the enormous areas involved. As well, results are difficult to predict for many of the same reasons.

Finally, adding limestone does not restore the natural chemical balance of a lake. Liming may kill plants that are sensitive to levels of calcium, such as the bog moss sphagnum. Small insects are also at risk, and this affects food chains. From an ecological point of view, by far the best solution to the effects of acid precipitation is to reduce SO_x and NO_x emissions at their source. (Note: Subscript "x" could be 1, 2, or 3, depending upon the situation.) This is why the Canadian and U.S. governments have co-operated on targets to reduce emissions. They have also introduced legislation to control emissions from industries and motor vehicles.

Using Chemistry to Control Harmful Emissions

After creating environmental problems, such as acid precipitation, through the use of chemistry, scientists and chemical engineers are now applying chemistry to solve these problems.

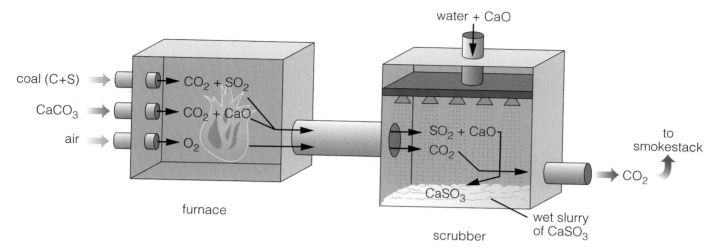

Since 1970, emissions of SO_x and NO_x have been reduced. One of the reasons is the introduction of the catalytic converter as a mandatory feature in most vehicles. Another reason is the installion of **scrubbers** on the smokestacks of many industrial plants that burn coal in their furnaces. Nearly all sources of coal contain sulfur as a contaminant. When the coal burns, the sulfur contaminant burns to sulfue dioxide (SO_2). Scrubbers remove most of the SO_2 by reacting it with calcium oxide or lime (CaO). Figure 8.20 shows an example of a scrubber attached to a coal-burning furnace.

Calcium carbonate ($CaCO_3$) is added to the coal and air as it enters the furnace. While the coal burns in air, it forms CO_2 and SO_2 gases. At the same time, the heat causes the $CaSO_3$ to decompose into CO_2 and CaO. In the furnace, some of the SO_2 reacts with the CaO, forming calcium sulfite ($CaSO_3$). Some of the SO_2 remains unreacted and leaves the furnace with the exhaust gases. The exhaust enters a wet scrubber where a solution of CaO in water is sprayed on the exhaust gases. Most of the remaining SO_2 reacts with the dissolved CaO, again forming $CaSO_3$. The water washes the $CaSO_3$ out of the stream of exhaust gases and forms a wet slurry of $CaSO_3$. The slurry must then be removed and discarded. Scrubbers can remove up to 95 percent of the sulfur dioxide from smokestack emissions.

Another way to reduce harmful emissions is to remove sulfur from fuel. Sulfur, often in the form of hydrogen sulfide, is a natural component of natural gas and other hydrocarbon fuels. Hydrogen sulfide can be eliminated by removing the gas from the fuels and reacting it with oxygen to produce sulfur dioxide:

$$2H_2S(g) + 3O_2(g) \rightarrow 2H_2O(\ell) + SO_2(g)$$

The sulfur dioxide is reacted once again with more hydrogen sulfide, in the presence of a catalyst, to produce water and elemental sulfur:

$$SO_2(g) + 2H_2S(g) \rightarrow 2H_2O(\ell) + 3S(s)$$

This process makes fuels more expensive, both to produce and to purchase. The environmental cost is much less, however.

Figure 8.20 The key to "scrubbing" exhaust gases is the addition of calcium oxide (CaO), which reacts with the sulfur dioxide gas (SO_2) to form calcium sulfite ($CaSO_3$). The calcium sulfite can be washed away with water.

The phosphate ion, PO_4^{3-}, is an essential plant nutrient. Plants cannot absorb phosphate if the soil is too alkaline or too acidic. Scientists have discovered that the roots of certain plants secrete citric acid, which counters alkaline soil. Scientists are studying how to insert the genes that control this process into other plants. If the experiments prove successful, farmers would be able to coax greater crop yields from alkaline soil.

Check Your Understanding

1. **(a)** Design a graphic organizer to summarize the importance of sulfuric acid and nitric acid.

   (b) In what ways are these compounds important in your life?

2. How are sulfuric acid and nitric acid related to acid precipitation? Are there other factors involved in the formation of acid precipitation? Explain.

3. Describe the effects of acid rain on organisms that live in water. How do these effects affect you, directly or indirectly?

4. How do scrubbers remove harmful emissions from industrial smokestacks?

5. **Apply** Examine the data in the graphs below. Compare the sources and amounts of SO_x and NO_x emissions. Explain the differences that you observe.

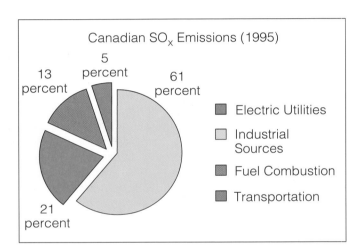

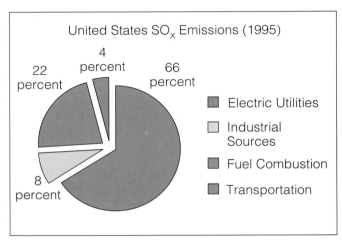

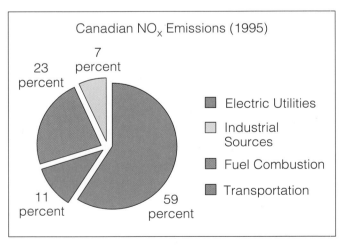

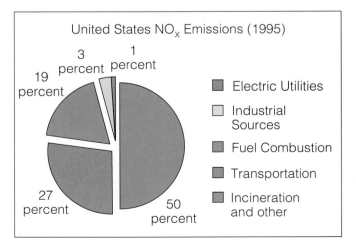

6. **Thinking Critically** Scientists estimate that the amount of carbon dioxide produced by natural sources (such as respiration, forest fires, and plant and animal decay) is about 40 times greater than the amount produced by human activities. If natural sources of carbon dioxide are so much greater, why has there been an increase in the greenhouse effect?

Now that you have completed this chapter, try to do the following. If you cannot, go back to the sections indicated.

Define the term "rate" and give an example involving a chemical reaction. (8.1)

List factors that affect the rate of a chemical reaction. (8.1)

Give at least one specific example of how you can change the rate of a chemical reaction in the home. (8.1)

Use examples to explain how changing each of these factors affects the rate of a chemical reaction. (8.1)
(a) the concentration of a substance
(b) the surface area of a substance
(c) a change in temperature
(d) a catalyst

Describe how enzymes work to change the rate of biological reactions. (8.1)

Explain why water is a polar molecule, and describe how soap works to remove fats and oils from surfaces. (8.2)

Describe the difference between soaps and detergents. (8.2)

Identify common acids and bases used in cleaning products, and explain how they work. (8.2)

Give examples to explain why chemical products are important to Canadians and people in other countries around the world. (8.3)

Outline the steps involved in producing sulfuric acid. (8.3)

Describe the properties and uses of one important industrial compound other than sulfuric acid and nitric acid. (8.3)

Describe the effect of acid rain on land- and water-dwelling organisms. Also explain how and why acid rain damages buildings and statues. (8.3)

Describe the purpose and general function of a scrubber. (8.3)

Prepare Your Own Summary

Summarize this chapter by doing one of the following. Use a graphic organizer (such as a concept map), produce a poster, or write the summary to include the key chapter concepts. Here are a few ideas to use as a guide:
- Explain each of the factors that affect the rate of a chemical reaction in terms of collisions between reactant atoms and molecules.
- Explain the effect of refrigeration on food spoilage.

- Design a brief instruction manual, including appropriate warnings and cautions, for making soap. Provide a simplified MSDS to go with the manual.
- Why were detergents invented?
- What chemicals and chemical processes harm the environment, and how have we used our understanding of chemistry to address this damage?

Reviewing Key Terms

If you need to review, the section numbers show you where these terms were introduced.

1. What is meant by the term "rate of reaction"? How do scientists measure the rate of a chemical reaction? (8.1)

2. What is the difference between a catalyst and an enzyme? (8.1)

3. How is a detergent different from soap? (8.2)

4. Why is acid rain so dangerous to plants and animals living in water? (8.3)

Understanding Key Concepts

Section numbers are provided if you need to review.

5. Explain why a crushed antacid tablet produces carbon dioxide more rapidly than a whole tablet. (8.1)

6. Which of the following reactions occurs more quickly? Explain why. (8.1)

$$2Mg + O_2 \rightarrow 2MgO$$
$$C_6H_{12}O_6 + 6O_2 \rightarrow 6H_2O + 6CO_2$$

7. Explain why water is unable to dissolve oil and grease, and how soap solves this problem. (8.2)

8. Why does chicken cook faster at 200°C than at 175°C? (8.1)

Developing Skills

9. When gases react, the change in concentration of the reactants is measured in terms of pressure. The data below provides information for the reaction between a gas and a powdered solid in terms of time, measured in minutes, and the pressure of the gas, measured in kilopascals (kPa).

Time (min)	Pressure (kPa)
0	400
2	316
4	248
6	196
8	155
10	122

(a) Plot a graph of time *against* pressure for this reaction.

(b) What does the decrease in pressure tell you about the amount of gas?

(c) What will the pressure of the gas be after 12 min?

10. Draw a concept map for the effects of chemical pollution on the environment.

11. One student reacted 0.5 g of an effervescent antacid with water. A second student reacted only 0.3 g of the same antacid. The second student's reaction occurred more quickly than the first student's reaction. Give at least two reasons, with explanations, for this difference.

12. Use a Venn diagram or another graphic organizer to compare properties of sulfuric acid and nitric acid.

Problem Solving/Applying

13. A farmer buys chemical fertilizer by the bag. The manufacturer claims that each bag will cover 100 m² of land surface. If the size of the farm is 5.5 ha, how many bags of fertilizer does the farmer have to buy? **Note:** 1 ha = 100 m × 100 m

14. A scientist measures the rate of a reaction between $NO_2(g)$ and $O_2(g)$ to make nitrogen trioxide gas. She finds that the reaction starts out very quickly and then slows down after approximately 10 s.

(a) Explain the reasons for her observation.

(b) Write a balanced chemical equation for the reaction.

(c) What could she do to make the reaction speed up again?

15. In a train derailment, about one third of a tank of sulfuric acid leaked into a nearby lake. Once the spill had been contained and cleaned up, environmental scientists found that the pH of the lake was normal and had not changed at all. How could this have happened?

Thinking Critically

16. What decisions about chemical products and processes do you make, personally, on a daily basis? What are the benefits and risks associated with your decisions? How can an understanding of chemistry help you better assess the benefits and risks?

17. Give examples of ways we use chemistry to control acid precipitation, and state your opinion, with reasons, on which approach or approaches are best.

18. Our atmosphere includes approximately 78 percent nitrogen, 21 percent oxygen, 0.9 percent argon, and 0.03 percent carbon dioxide. If carbon dioxide makes up such a small proportion of our atmosphere, why is there such a concern about the greenhouse effect?

19. A local chemical industry is accused of emitting a high concentration of sulfur dioxide and particulates into the air. When confronted by local politicians, the company claims that it cannot afford to install pollution control devices and still remain competitive, because of the high cost. If forced to do so, the company will either have to lay off employees or close down the plant.

    (a) What other options might there be for the company?

    (b) Companies often claim that the extra cost of pollution control will make them uncompetitive with companies in other cities or countries. Why does this problem exist? How can it be resolved?

    (c) Would you be willing to pay slightly more for some products so that manufacturers can control their pollution? How well would this change work in practice? Discuss this question with your classmates and family.

    (d) How might atmospheric pollution that has already been released be removed from the air?

20. It is estimated that the Middle East has 57 percent of the world's oil reserves while North America has about 12 percent. The other 31 percent are spread around the rest of the world. The Middle East consumes about 3 percent of its oil. North America consumes 32 percent of the world's oil supply. Discuss the problems that this kind of discrepancy can cause consumers in North America.

Pause& Reflect

1. Go back to the beginning of the chapter, on page 240, and check your original answers to the Opening Ideas questions. How has your thinking changed? How would you answer those questions now that you have investigated the topics in this chapter?

2. As a car ages, why is it not necessary to add more platinum and rhodium to the catalytic converter?

3. In the tropics, one of the most serious diseases, malaria, is caused by the bite of a certain kind of mosquito. Many years ago large areas of the tropics were sprayed with a pesticide called DDT that killed the mosquitoes and saved many lives.

    (a) Research the long-term effects of DDT on human and animal life.

    (b) Was spraying large areas of the tropics the right thing to do? Give reasons for your answer.

Over the past 50 years, countless industrial activities have taken place all over Earth. Unfortunately some of these activities have resulted in the contamination of soil. Researchers like Professor Selma Guigard and her students at the University of Alberta are working to perfect a process that will remove unwanted or even dangerous metals from soil. Thanks to their work, contaminated soil can be made safe and usable once more.

Q I've read about environmental companies using microorganisms to clean soil. Does your research involve anything like that?

A No. Although it's popular for some clean-up jobs, bioremediation is not terribly successful in removing metals. Often the metals are toxic to the organisms that are meant to clean them up. The process we are investigating is a solvent extraction technology. It is a process that has been tried by others in the past, but the result was not very satisfactory.

Q Why not?

A The solvent that was used in the process was usually an organic compound, such as methanol. It successfully cleaned the soil, but it left behind a residue that often made the soil useless for anything but landfill. As well, after the cleaning process, the contaminated solvent had to be disposed of safely.

The blue colour in this soil is due to contamination by toxic metals.

Q Is the method you are researching able to eliminate those problems?

A Yes. We are using a different solvent to clean the soil — carbon dioxide, CO_2. It is environmentally friendly, so there is no problem with disposal or unsafe residues. We're not using CO_2 in its natural state, though. We're using it in its supercritical fluid form. Supercritical CO_2 is the same thing some manufacturers use to remove caffeine from coffee beans.

Q What is supercritical CO_2?

A When we bring CO_2 up to a certain pressure and temperature, it becomes what is called a supercritical fluid. It behaves a little like a liquid and a little like a gas, so it is able to do the job we need it to do. Other researchers have already used CO_2 in its supercritical state to extract unwanted organic compounds from soil. The idea of using it to remove metals was first proposed around 1991. Our lab is one of only a handful in Canada that are pursuing the idea.

Q What does the cleaning process entail?

A A batch of contaminated soil is closed inside a reactor, along with something called a "chelating agent." CO_2 is pumped in, and the pressure and temperature within the reactor are set. The supercritical fluid remains in contact with the soil for several minutes or hours. The length of time depends on the amount of soil and the metal that is being removed. When the CO_2 is removed, depressurized, and brought to normal temperature, it changes from its supercritical fluid state back to a gas. Then the metal deposits just fall out of it. We're left with CO_2, which is recycled. We're also left with a small amount of highly concentrated metal, which we hope we can recycle some day.

A soil-cleaning reactor

Q How exactly does the CO_2 get the metal to leave the soil?

A The metal is usually in the soil in the form of a charged ion. Carbon dioxide is not charged. So the metal won't dissolve in CO_2 on its own. That's why we add the chelating agent. If the right chelate is added, the metal bonds with the chelate more than with whatever it is bonded to in the soil. Once the metal combines with the chelate, the compound has no charge. The compound dissolves in the CO_2 and flows out with it.

Q What sort of metals can you extract using this process?

A We've been using copper as our test metal. Once the process has been perfected, we hope to use it to remove such things as lead, mercury, cadmium, and chromium. One day, far down the road, it may even remove radioactive elements.

Q What stage is your research at right now?

A My students and I are beginning to work on designing a way to pump new batches of soil into the reactor without having to depressurize in between. The depressurizing and repressurizing for each load of soil is one of the most expensive parts of the process right now. For the moment, however, our research is focussed on determining the best chelating agent to use. We hope to do some trials with soil samples in the near future.

EXPLORING Further

Supercritical, Super-Useful

Selma is researching the use of supercritical CO_2 to extract metals from soil. Other scientists are using supercritical CO_2 and other supercritical fluids for many other processes. Use your local library or the Internet to find out more about supercritical fluids and the research that is being carried out with them around the world. As a starting point, go to **www.school.mcgrawhill.ca/resources/.** Go to **Science Resources,** then to **SCIENCEPOWER 10** to know where to go next.

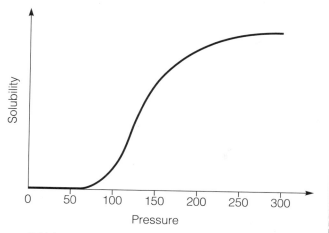

At high pressure, CO_2 becomes a supercritical fluid. Its ability to dissolve other substances increases sharply.

A SIMULATION

Not in My Backyard

Think About It

Ammonia (NH_3) is a colourless, pungent gas at room temperature. Its two most important applications involve one of its compounds, ammonium nitrate. This compound is used to make fertilizers and explosives.

Commercially, ammonia is produced by reacting nitrogen with hydrogen at high temperatures and pressures:

$$N_2(g) + 3H_2(g) \rightarrow 2NH_3(g)$$

The hydrogen for this reaction is purchased from other industries, usually those that use hydrocarbons. Thus ammonia plants are near petrochemical plants.

Suppose that you live in a small, rural community that has grown up around a petrochemical plant. The president of a new chemical company wants to build a chemical plant nearby. This plant will process ammonia to produce fertilizer and precursors for explosives. The president assures the Town Council that the plant will not manufacture the explosives. The company will purchase land near the edge of town, very close to a marsh that is a favourite resting place for migrating ducks.

The company expects to employ up to 150 local residents, mostly for manufacturing jobs. There will also be openings for engineers and chemists. Local farmers expect to benefit from reduced fertilizer costs. Some townspeople, however, are concerned about the consequences for the environment and human health. In particular, they are worried about the effects of fumes, gaseous emissions, and potential spills.

The company president has assured the mayor that the plant will be equipped with pollution-control technologies. As well, every effort will be made to minimize spills and leaks. The proposal includes an action plan, explaining what to do if a spill or leak does occur. This action plan will be delivered to every home.

A town-hall meeting is scheduled for next week. Community members are invited to ask questions and voice their concerns at this meeting.

Plan and Act

1. The following people have submitted requests to make formal presentations at the meeting:
   - an area farmer
   - a member of an environmental advocacy group
   - a chemist who lives in the community
   - a town resident who has a respiratory illness

2. The following company representatives will also speak at the meeting:
   - the president of the company
   - the architect who will design the plant
   - a chemical engineer

3. Briefly outline what you think each person's point of view will be, before the meeting takes place.

4. Your teacher will give your group the role of one of these people. As a group, discuss the issue, gather information, and formulate your point of view. One group member will make the presentation.

5. As a class, your task is to assess the presentations that are made at the meeting and to evaluate the possible risks of the new chemical company. You will then recommend to the mayor (your teacher or another person) whether the application for the new company should be accepted or rejected.

Analyze

1. Compare the presentations on the basis of their scientific soundness, their logic, and their passion.

2. In what ways did your understanding of science and technology assist you in this simulation and in your recommendation?

Acid Precipitation Resource

Acid precipitation, is a problem for all Canadians, but especially for those who live east of Manitoba. More than 300 000 lakes are vulnerable to acidic deposition in this area. The same is true for over half of the forests. To make the situation worse, over 80 percent of all Canadians live in this area.

Current emissions of sulfur dioxide and nitrogen oxides are half of what they were in 1980. Many North American industries have committed themselves to further reductions. Is it too late? What do we know about acid precipitation? What are its effects, both short-term and long-term, on the health of the environment and on wildlife? What are its effects on human health? What is being done now? What more can be done? How can we use our understanding of science and technology to help us?

Challenge

As a class, design an interactive information resource to educate your community about acid precipitation. As part of your resource, prepare an action plan outlining your solutions to at least one associated problem. Invite your audience to comment on the action plan.

Materials

Select a medium (or media) for your information resource. For a three-dimensional display, such as a booth, you will need art supplies and construction materials. For a web site, you will need hardware and software.

Design Criteria

A. As a class, develop criteria for assessing your information resource. You will likely need to develop criteria, such as the following, for different media.
  - three-dimensional display: 3 m high, 6 m wide, easy to set up and take down
  - web site: up to 10 well-designed pages

B. The data must be easy to update on a regular basis.

Plan and Construct

1. This is a long-term project. Brainstorm topics that you will want to research and design experiments for. The following information must be part of your resource. You are free to include additional topics and data.
   - examples of domestic (home-based) and industrial technologies that contribute to acid precipitation
   - descriptions and explanations of the science and technology behind at least three of these examples
   - data about sulfur dioxide and nitrogen oxide emissions that have affected your community over the past three decades
   - data collected by your group over a suitable period of time (for example, testing and monitoring pH levels in selected bodies of water)
   - data for other parts of the province and country, and for other countries, to compare with yours
   - analyses of the data you collect, presented in suitable graphical and/or tabular formats
   - examples of technologies that are currently used to address acid precipitation problems at their source
   - examples of technologies that are currently used to address the effects of acid precipitation
   - proposed or prototype technologies and the likelihood of their full-scale implementation
   - your recommendations for one or more solutions

2. Decide on a medium (or media) for presenting the information you gather, compile, and organize.

3. Develop a plan that allows all group members to find, collect, and organize data, as well as publish it in your chosen medium (or media).

4. Carry out your plan. Be sure that all members of your group understand their responsibilities.

Evaluate

Carry out periodic assessments of your own project and those of other groups. For your final assessment, display or upload your project to the public. Based on the responses you receive modify your project as necessary. Provide reasons for the modifications you make.

Now that you have completed Chapters 5, 6, 7, and 8, you can assess how much you have learned about chemical reactions by answering the following questions. Before you begin, you may find it useful to return to each Chapter at a Glance and each Chapter Review.

True/False

In your notebook, indicate whether each statement is true or false. Correct each false statement.

1. Every element is capable of forming compounds.

2. Metals usually react to form cations.

3. Molecular compounds tend to have higher melting and boiling points than ionic compounds.

4. An equation is balanced when the sums of the coefficients on both sides of the arrow are the same.

5. Weak acids and bases are used to wash clothes.

6. Acid precipitation results mainly from combustion reactions.

Completion

In your notebook, complete each statement with the correct term or phrase.

7. A phosphorus atom has _____ valence electrons.

8. A reaction that absorbs heat energy is described as _____ .

9. An example of an anion with the same number of electrons as Ne is _____ .

10. When a base is dissolved in water, _____ ions are produced.

11. Acid + Base → _____ + _____

12. Organic chemistry is the study of compounds that contain atoms of _____ .

13. Acid precipitation usually has a pH that is less than _____ .

14. Carbon dioxide dissolves in water vapour in the air to form _____ .

Matching

15. In your notebook, copy the descriptions in column A. Beside each description, write the term from column B that best fits the description. A term may be used once, more than once, or not at all.

A	B
• arrangement of elements with similar chemical properties in the periodic table	• acid
• reaction that absorbs energy from its surroundings	• base
• type of ion that is usually formed by metal atoms	• cation
• group of atoms with a net charge; the atoms are joined by covalent bonds	• covalent
• type of bond formed when a pair of electrons is shared	• endothermic
• substance that dissolves in water and forms hydrogen ions	• group
• substance formed when an acid and a base react	• indicator
• chemical that changes colour as the concentration of $H^+(aq)$ or $OH^-(aq)$ changes	• polyatomic ion
	• period
	• salt

Multiple Choice

In your notebook, write the letter of the best answer for each of the following questions.

16. Which of the following is *not* a typical property of an ionic compound?

    (a) Crystals with a well-defined shape form at room temperature.

    (b) Aqueous solutions of ionic compounds are good electrical conductors.

    (c) Ionic solids conduct electricity.

    (d) Ionic solids have relatively high melting points.

    (e) Ionic solids are hard and brittle.

17. When the following equation is correctly balanced, what is the value of x?

    $Al + xH_2SO_4 \rightarrow Al_2(SO_4)_3 + H_2$

    (a) 1   (c) 3   (e) 5

    (b) 2   (d) 4

18. Which of the following equations is/are balanced?

    (1) $2KCl + Pb(NO_3)_2 \rightarrow PbCl_2 + KNO_3$

    (2) $(NH_4)_2CO_3 \rightarrow NH_3 + 4H_2O + CO_2$

    (3) $Fe_2O_3 + CO \rightarrow 2Fe + CO_2$

    (a) none   (d) (1) and (2) only

    (b) (2) only   (e) (1), (2), and (3)

    (c) (3) only

19. Which pair of ions has the same number of electrons?

    (a) Ca^{2+} and Cl^- (d) Mg^{2+} and Cl^-

    (b) Ca^{2+} and Mg^{2+} (e) Li^+ and O^{2-}

    (c) Na^+ and Cl^-

20. What is the total number of atoms in the formula $Al_2(SO_4)_3$?

    (a) 3   (c) 8   (e) 17

    (b) 7   (d) 15

21. What are the formulas of the carbonate ion, the ammonium ion, and the nitrate ion?

    (a) CO_3^{2-}, NH_3^+, and NO_3^+

    (b) CO_3^{2-}, NH_3^+, and NO_3^-

    (c) CO_3^-, NH_4^+, and NO_3^-

    (d) CO_3^{2-}, NH_4^+, and NO_3^-

    (e) CO_2^{3-}, NH_4^+, and NO_3^{2-}

22. Which name and formula do *not* match?

    (a) sodium sulfide, Na_2S

    (b) magnesium fluoride, MgF_2

    (c) potassium carbonate, KCO_3

    (d) aluminum iodide, AlI_2

    (e) iron(II) oxide, FeO

23. Which of the following is a property of an acid?

    (a) It has a bitter taste.

    (b) It turns litmus paper red.

    (c) It increases the concentration of OH^- in an aqueous solution.

    (d) It has a pH greater than 7.

Short Answer

In your notebook, write a sentence or a short paragraph to answer each of the following questions.

24. Draw Lewis symbols for each of the following.

    (a) silicon   (c) strontium

    (b) sulfur   (d) argon

25. Draw Lewis diagrams for atoms of each of the following pairs of elements. Then show how atoms of each pair could form a compound, and predict the formula of the compound.

    (a) Si and H   (c) Ca and N

    (b) Be and O   (d) Al and P

26. Name the following compounds.

    (a) $Fe_2(SO_4)_3$ (c) CaI_2

    (b) $Pb(NO_3)_4$ (d) $Cr(NO_3)_2$

27. Write formulas for the following compounds.
    (a) cuprous nitrate
    (b) mercury(II) bromide
    (c) nickel(III) sulfide
    (d) calcium hydrogen carbonate

28. Which regions of Canada are most affected by acid precipitation? Give two reasons why regions may be affected differently.

29. Which acids are the main cause of acid precipitation? Write their names and formulas. What is the main source of each of these acids?

30. Make a concept map for acid precipitation. Include the following terms: types of deposition, sources, effects, controls.

31. Acids can enter streams and lakes as the result of drainage from mine wastes. For example, iron sulfide, FeS, is commonly found in the waste from coal-mining areas. Iron sulfide reacts with water and oxygen in the air to produce sulfuric acid. Balance the skeleton equation for this reaction.

$$FeS + O_2 + H_2O \rightarrow Fe_2O_3 + H_2SO_4$$

32. Give two examples to clarify the meaning of the term "rate." Then explain what the term "rate of reaction" means.

33. A large city in Canada, with a population of 1.5 million people, produces 2 kg of garbage per person per day. The garbage can be compacted into a 25 cm cube. If the garbage is to be stored on a 1 ha site (100 m by 100 m) outside the city, calculate the height of the pile of garbage in
    (a) 30 days   (b) 1 year

34. A farmer purchases chemical fertilizer for her 8 ha farm at a cost of $10.00 per bag. The instructions on the bag claim coverage of 500 m² per bag. How much will it cost the farmer to fertilize her farm?

35. For the hypothetical reaction $X(g) \rightarrow 2Y(g)$, the following experimental data was obtained.
    Note: The abbreviation "mol" stands for a unit of measurement called a mole. It describes the amount of a substance that contains a certain number of particles of the substance.

Time (s)	Concentration (mol/L)
0	1.0
10	0.6
20	0.4
30	0.3
40	0.25
50	0.2
60	0.18

    (a) Plot a graph of these data. Place time on the horizontal axis.
    (b) Calculate the rate of disappearance of X in the first 10 s.
    (c) Calculate the rate of disappearance of X from 20 to 30 s.
    (d) Why is there a difference in the two calculations?

Problem Solving

Show complete solutions for all problems that involve equations and numbers. Use the GRASP problem-solving model or a model suggested by your teacher.

36. Hydrogen sulfide is a foul-smelling gas. When the gas is bubbled through water, the solution is found to be a poor electrical conductor. Is $H_2S(aq)$ an acid or a base? Is it strong or weak?

37. Copy each of the following word equations into your notebook. Then write the balanced chemical equation, and indicate the type of reaction.
    (a) Sodium reacts with water to produce sodium hydroxide and hydrogen gas.

(b) Magnesium oxide reacts with carbon dioxide to form magnesium carbonate.

(c) When heated, ammonium chloride forms ammonia and hydrogen chloride gas.

(d) Copper(II) sulfate reacts with solid nickel to form nickel(II) sulfate and copper metal.

(e) Sodium carbonate reacts with sulfuric acid to form an aqueous solution of sodium sulfate, water, and carbon dioxide gas.

(f) Ammonia gas reacts with hydrogen chloride gas to form solid ammonium chloride.

38. Copy each of the following skeleton equations into your notebook. Then balance the equation and indicate the type of reaction.

(a) $NaClO_3(s) \rightarrow NaCl(s) + O_2(g)$

(b) $NaOH(aq) + (NH_4)_2SO_4(aq) \rightarrow$ $Na_2SO_4(aq) + NH_3(g) + H_2O(\ell)$

(c) $H_2SO_4(aq) + Al_2O_3(s) \rightarrow$ $Al_2(SO_4)_3(aq) + H_2O(\ell)$

(d) $Zn(s) + FeCl_2(aq) \rightarrow ZnCl_2(aq) + Fe(s)$

(e) $C_3H_4(g) + H_2(g) \rightarrow C_3H_8(g)$

(f) $CaCO_3(s) + HCl(aq) \rightarrow$ $CaCl_2(aq) + H_2O(\ell) + CO_2(g)$

Critical Thinking

39. Most of the chemical plants in Canada are located in Ontario and Québec. Suggest reasons to explain this.

40. Carbon monoxide, a poisonous gas, reacts slowly with oxygen to produce carbon dioxide. In the presence of rhodium metal (Rh), the reaction occurs almost instantly. Explain why.

41. Technologies are available to reduce or eliminate acidic emissions caused by human activities. Why is acid precipitation still a serious problem? Why might it increase in the future?

42. Hemoglobin is a protein molecule in blood that carries oxygen to all of the cells of the body. Carbon monoxide is produced by the incomplete combustion of fuels. It is a poison because it has the ability to attach itself to hemoglobin, instead of oxygen, with a bond that is almost 200 times stronger than the hemoglobin-oxygen bond. If a person is working in the presence of carbon monoxide (from automobile exhaust, for example), a condition called carbon monoxide poisoning may result.

(a) What would be the symptoms of carbon monoxide poisoning?

(b) How might a person with carbon monoxide poisoning be treated?

Applications

43. Pollution controls in eastern Europe are often inadequate or non-existent. To make matters worse, industries and power plants often burn poor-grade coal with a relatively high sulfur content. Why do you think these countries have not reduced acid emissions? Should Canada contribute money and technological assistance to help them? Explain your answers.

44. A number of sodium salts have important uses in industries and in homes. At a library or on the Internet, research common uses for each of the following compounds.

(a) sodium borate (common name: borax)

(b) sodium carbonate

(c) sodium hydrogen carbonate (common name: sodium bicarbonate)

(d) sodium hypochlorite

(e) sodium stearate

(f) sodium thiosulfate (common name: hypo)

45. Research the major sources of air pollution in your community. Is any of this pollution controlled in any way? What might be the human and economic costs in your community to clean up this pollution?

The Physics of Motion

"Get a move on!"
"Let's go!"
"What are you waiting for?"

Motion can bring excitement and fun. It can also be hard work. Athletes like these bobsled racers train full time to be fractions of a second ahead of a rival team. They learn the details of every aspect of their event, from the length of the track (1200 m of downhill slope) to the maximum mass of the sled and riders (630 kg). They know that every 0.1 s gained at the beginning of the course will become a 0.3 s advantage by the end.

Bobsledders sand and polish the steel runners of their sled for hours before each race to reduce friction. They know that the three people pushing the sled have less than 6 s to get it moving at up to 40 km/h. They are prepared for the shock of rocketing downhill at over 80 km/h after the first quarter of the race, on their way to a maximum speed of over 135 km/h. Accelerating around turns in the middle of the course, they experience forces over four times stronger than gravity. A few bumps later, less than a minute after they start, the race is over.

Bobsledders, like many other racers, do not guess about how to go faster. They use the scientific study of motion to measure their performance and improve their technique. In this unit, you will investigate some ways that motion is studied, described, and analyzed. You will also learn how the physics of motion applies not just to bobsledding, but to your daily life.

Unit Contents

9 What Is Motion?

Opening Ideas...

- What is the fastest moving object that you know of? How fast does it move?

- How do bats, dolphins, and autofocus cameras track moving objects?

- What are the smallest and largest moving objects that you know of? How would you describe their motion?

Science Log

Jot down your initial answers to the Opening Ideas questions. Then try to find additional information by checking with another student. Revise your answers, and record them in your Science Log. Look for more information as you explore this chapter.

Skill POWER

For tips on how to use a Science Log, turn to page 580.

Your life depends on your ability to observe and analyze motion. To ride a bicycle in traffic or cross a busy street, you must observe the path of oncoming traffic. You must predict where the vehicles will be in a few seconds and decide when and how fast you should move to avoid them. The tiniest mistake could be disastrous! Yet you do not need to make exact measurements or calculations to complete your journey safely.

Designing machines that deal with motion — such as police radar devices, air traffic control systems, and tracking systems for studying wild animals — requires a different approach. Scientists and engineers have developed systematic ways to extend the brain's automatic measuring, describing, and predicting abilities. As a result, we know an enormous amount about falling objects, speeding cars, whirling planets, and other moving objects. In this chapter, you will study how motion is measured and start to learn the scientific and mathematical language that scientists use to describe it.

Which Way Did It Go?

You have been moving and observing moving objects all your life, so you have lots of intuitive ideas about motion. How accurate are your ideas? See if your ideas about the situations below agree with those of your classmates — and with modern scientific thinking.

Key Concepts

In this chapter, you will discover

- early ideas about motion that are not currently accepted by scientists but still influence our everyday language
- how motion is described in the language of physics
- contributions that Canadians have made to the science and technology of motion

Key Skills

In this chapter, you will

- design and conduct an experiment to test a hypothesis about falling objects
- describe motion, using accepted physics symbols and quantities
- measure, describe, and graph the motion of an object without using complicated equipment
- learn about techniques and equipment for measuring motion scientifically
- interpret and draw graphs of simple motions

Key Terms

- variable pitch propeller
- conventions
- distance
- scalar
- time
- time interval
- position
- vector
- displacement
- velocity
- instantaneous
- speed
- acceleration
- precision
- readability
- linear motion
- vector sum
- vector diagram
- position-time graph
- ticker timer
- ultrasonic motion sensor
- photogate
- rate of change

Starting Point  ACTIVITY

What You Need

30–40 cm plastic or cardboard tube
1 m string
cork or stopper

What to Do

1. Work with a partner to assemble the apparatus, as shown in the diagram. Have your partner watch carefully as you swing the rubber stopper *slowly* in a circle around your head and then let go of the string. **CAUTION:** Work in a large, open space.

2. Observe the motion of the stopper carefully after you let go. Sketch or describe the path it takes (speed and direction)
   (a) immediately after being released
   (b) as it flies through the air and falls to the ground

What Did You Discover?

1. As a class, share each group's ideas about the motion you observed. If you do not agree, record the reasons why you disagree.

2. Suggest what observations or equipment could give a clearer picture of the rubber stopper's motion.

9.1 Getting Into Motion

Figure 9.1 Bicycling can be a challenging test of your natural understanding of motion.

Imagine yourself in this position: You are standing astride a sturdy mountain bike at the top of a steep gully. The ground drops away sharply in front of you. You check your helmet and elbow and knee pads one last time, take a deep breath, and push off. Bouncing and jolting at high speed among rocks and cacti, you use every muscle in your body to keep your balance. You steer the bike in a controlled plunge toward the dry river bed below. Can you catch some air to get over that ridge? Do you trust your bike to stay in one piece for the whole of this wild ride?

Extreme biking is a sport to challenge your body's understanding of motion to the limit. Bikers hurtle down mountainsides, flick their wheels around at impossible angles, or even shoot straight into the air at each end of a U-shaped ramp. This sport isn't about winning, it's about survival. It's also about physics — the physics of motion.

You might not feel ready to put your body on the line in an extreme biking event, but you can begin to explore how objects move when dropped, or rolled down a slope. In the next activity you can test some ideas about motion by making qualitative descriptions. Then, in Investigation 9-A, you will sharpen your scientific focus by making quantitative, numerical measurements of these motions.

See for Yourself

Scientists study the natural world by thinking about past observations, perhaps even from their everyday experience. Next, they form hypotheses about the patterns they think they see in natural events. Then they design and perform experiments to test their ideas. Look at two simple situations, and try to decide what you expect to happen. Then test your own ideas.

What You Need

video camera (optional)

(a) two identical sturdy empty containers, with lids
sand

(b) Hot Wheels™ track
supports and clamps
ball bearings

What to Do

1. Form a hypothesis about each of the following two situations. Give reasons for the hypothesis you make, according to the way you think falling or rolling objects behave.

    (a) How does the motion of different falling objects compare? Try using two sturdy, well-sealed plastic containers of the same size, one empty and one filled with sand. Drop them from as high a height as you can. Make sure that the surface they land on will not be damaged by the impact.

    (b) How do objects move when they roll down an incline and across a level surface? Track for toy racing cars can be made into steep or gentle inclines. Steel ball bearings make good rolling objects.

Science Inquiry ACTIVITY

2. Investigate either or both of situations (a) and (b). Make careful observations and then write a detailed description of what happened. You may want to use sketches to illustrate your observations. If you have video equipment, you could record each situation and then play back the tape at a slow speed or even frame by frame.

What Did You Discover?

1. Did your observations support your hypothesis for each situation, or did they appear to contradict it?

2. Compare your observations of each situation with that of other groups. For each situation, do all the observations support the same hypothesis, or not? Explain your findings.

3. How do scientists check their conclusions to make sure that they have not overlooked important information or made errors in reasoning?

Extension

4. Go back to your reasoning for each of your hypotheses, and review it in light of your observations. Suggest at least one improvement to your chain of reasoning.

Be Specific

If you were a judge, would you be more impressed by many reliable witnesses who gave similar testimony or by a single unsupported witness? Scientists also make judgments based on evidence. In fact, they often repeat experiments to gather more evidence. You can check your earlier qualitative observations about motion by gathering quantitative data in a simple controlled investigation.

Problem

Design and carry out a controlled investigation to answer *one* of these questions:
A. Does a heavy object fall faster than a light object of the same size?
B. When an object rolls down a U-shaped incline and then back up the other side, does it reach the same height it was released from?

Safety Precautions

Apparatus

Question A
2 identical sturdy empty containers with lids
laboratory balance
metre stick or measuring tape
stopwatch or timer

Question B
flexible I-beam curtain rail, Hot Wheels™ track, or grooved plastic rulers taped together
ball bearings or marbles of different sizes
metre stick or measuring tape
supports and clamps

Materials
Question A
sand

Procedure

1. Choose one of the two questions to investigate.

2. Make a clear hypothesis. Give reasons to support your hypothesis.

3. Design a step-by-step procedure to gather quantitative evidence that might support your hypothesis. Decide on a variable that you will manipulate and a responding variable that you will measure. Also decide how to control (keep constant) other factors that might affect your results.

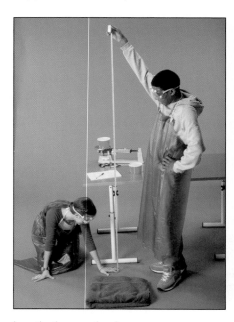

Investigating question A

Investigating question B

4 Design a data table to record your observations. Plan how you will analyze your observations to decide whether or not they support your hypothesis.

5 With your teacher's approval, conduct your investigation and analyze your results.

6 Prepare a summary of your investigation and your results in a format that your teacher approves. You could use a written lab report, a poster, or a computer presentation.

7 Present your summary to your classmates.

Computer CONNECT

If you have access to motion analysis software, you can use it to perform or extend several activities in this unit. One type of motion analysis software lets you mark the position of a video-taped moving object frame by frame. Then it automatically produces graphs of the object's position, speed, and changes in speed.

Analyze

1. How well was your hypothesis supported by your observations? Do your observations give clear evidence that the hypothesis is correct, suggest that it might be wrong, or seem inconclusive?

2. Look back at your observations and conclusions for the activity on page 285. How well does your evidence agree with your earlier qualitative observations of the same phenomenon?

3. Suggest how your investigation could be changed slightly and what might happen if it were. For example, what might happen if the falling objects were different sizes? What might happen if the U-shaped track was not symmetrical, so the ball rolled down a steep slope and up a more gradual one?

Conclude and Apply

4. Which part of the investigation did your group find the most challenging: inventing a reasonable hypothesis, designing the procedure, collecting the observations, or analyzing your results?

5. Do you personally prefer gathering quantitative data, as you did in this investigation, or making qualitative observations, as you did earlier?

6. A great deal of modern scientific work is done in research groups. Do you prefer working on your own to conduct an investigation or working in a group? Explain.

7. Identify one group-work skill that you bring to a group and one group-work skill that you need to improve.

Off the Wall

One of the best hypotheses to test is "nothing"! It is very easy to tell when you are wrong if you predict that there will be no difference between two different situations. Scientists call this a *null hypothesis*. For example, you might predict that there will be no difference in average science marks between students sitting at the front of your class and students at the back. Any significant difference, no matter who does better, could mean that your hypothesis is wrong. Philosopher Karl Popper went even further and suggested that scientific theories can only be *disproved*. Theories explain general relationships. They can never be *proved* correct by experiments, because experiments can never test all possible situations.

Karl Popper (1902–1994)

Almost all scientists now agree on the following conclusions about the motions you have been investigating. Do you think your observations supported these conclusions? Explain why or why not.

- Heavy objects and light objects, if dropped from the same height, fall to Earth in the same amount of time.
- An object rolled down an incline will return to its original height, if the incline curves back up again. If the incline levels out instead, the object will continue rolling.

Canadian Transport Technologies

The theory of motion that scientists have developed helps us to understand, describe, and predict the motion of many objects. Designing and making useful devices that move people and goods efficiently and safely is a different kind of challenge. Early craftspeople developed practical solutions, largely using trial-and-error methods. Instead of studying general theory, they learned their skills on the job by working with more experienced people. They discovered and developed a vast amount of detailed technical knowledge, much of which was never written down. Steamboats, automobiles, and even rockets were developed by skilled craftspeople. The Wright brothers, who built the first successful heavier-than-air flying machine in 1903, were bicycle mechanics by trade!

Figure 9.2 Huge distances and a harsh winter climate have driven Canadian innovations in transport.

Modern motion technology applies both scientific theory and technical knowledge to everyday problems. Modern engineers, technologists, and inventors use theory to analyze and predict how possible solutions will work. Practical skills and intuition are used to construct devices that solve problems effectively and efficiently.

Air Power

Baby buggies, bicycles, skateboards, cars, buses, ice skates, and skis — you have been using and learning about motion technology since you were born. Some of these transport devices are simple, and some are complex, but all were likely designed by other people. Can you use what you have learned to design an original vehicle?

Challenge

Use simple materials to create a balloon buggy or a hovercraft that is powered by nothing but air.

What You Need

metre stick or measuring tape
stopwatch

Hovercraft

old CD
one-hole stopper
balloons
sharp, pointed scissors or craft knife
drinking straws
masking tape
glue

Balloon Buggy

empty 2 L plastic beverage bottle
2 wooden bamboo cooking skewers
4 lids from 35 mm film canisters
balloon   masking tape

Design Criteria

A. Your vehicle must use only the materials listed or other materials approved by your teacher.
B. You must construct and test your vehicle in one class period.
C. Your vehicle must be powered only by air being released from the balloons.
D. Your vehicle is allowed to make only one official test run. You may make as many preliminary trials as you wish.
E. The hovercraft will be judged by the length of time it can hover while moving forward after a gentle push. The buggy will be judged by the distance it can travel on the test run.

Plan and Construct

1. Design and construct your chosen vehicle. Here are some hints:
   - For the hovercraft, a one-hole stopper glued over the CD hole makes a good anchor for the balloon.
   - For the balloon buggy, bamboo skewers running through straws make good axles. They can be poked through film-canister-lid wheels and fastened.

2. Do at least one preliminary test of your vehicle, and modify it if necessary.

3. Conduct your official test run. Your teacher or members of another group should certify that your measurement is correct. Measure as precisely as possible.

4. Compare your design and results with those of other groups that built the same type of vehicle.

Evaluate

1. Where did your design ideas come from — personal experiences, science courses, books or magazines, or other sources? Describe at least one design idea that you decided not to use. Why did you reject this idea?

2. What construction problems did you encounter that limited the performance of your vehicle? What single modification of your vehicle would likely make the greatest improvement in its performance?

3. Within your group, did different members do different tasks, or did everyone contribute to each task? Did one person become the group leader? How did you reach decisions?

4. What single improvement to your group's organization or approach would make the work more pleasant or productive?

Transportation in Canada

In Canada, we have two obstacles to the transportation of goods and people: a harsh climate and a population that is spread thinly over vast distances. Canadian inventors and engineers have created ingenious solutions to many of the problems associated with these obstacles. They have developed transport technologies that are so widespread and effective we often take them for granted. As you study the technologies on the next few pages, think about the following questions:

- What theoretical knowledge would be helpful for analyzing this problem?
- What technical skills would be helpful for building devices to solve this problem?
- What other problems arose as a result of the work to solve this problem? What opportunities developed for improvements or modifications?

Figure 9.3 Wallace Turnbull, inventor of the variable pitch propeller

Aviation Technology: Getting Around a Big Country

Imagine riding a bicycle which is stuck in a mid-range gear. You would have to work very hard to get started and up to cruising speed. Then, at a relatively high crusing speed, you have to keep pedalling extremely fast. The same situation would occur in a car if it did not have a transmission. The engine would have to run slow at low speeds, making a jerky, difficult start up. At high speeds, the engine would have to keep running very fast. The high speed rotations would cause wear and tear on the engine. Also, the engine would use too much fuel at these speeds.

Early aircraft had this problem. The engine drove the propeller directly, and the only way to control power output was to change the engine speed. This meant that pilots had to run the engine fast to develop enough power for takeoff, and they could not shift gears for efficient cruising. Mechanical transmissions, such as cars use, were too heavy to use on aircraft.

The solution was developed by New Brunswick inventor Wallace Turnbull (1870–1954). He made several discoveries that greatly improved the design of the newly-invented "flying machine," including one of the earliest wind tunnels in North America.

Later, in 1916, Turnbull produced a working model of a revolutionary new propeller. The pilot could change the pitch of the propeller blade. The pitch is the angle at which the blades were set into the central hub. Figure 9.4 shows how this **variable pitch propeller** could be adjusted to work well during takeoff, cruising, and landing.

The first variable pitch propeller was controlled by foot pedals operated by the pilot, a method that did not work very well. In 1927, after years of effort, Turnbull successfully demonstrated a model that used an electric motor in the propeller hub to adjust the pitch of the propeller blades. This design is one of the key inventions in aviation history.

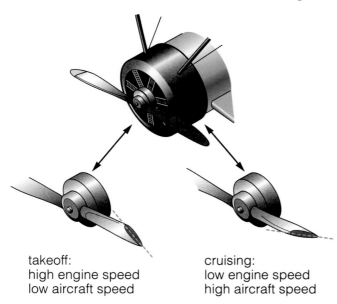

takeoff:
high engine speed
low aircraft speed

cruising:
low engine speed
high aircraft speed

Figure 9.4 Using the variable pitch propeller, pilots could match the engine's speed and power output to the varying needs of takeoff, cruising, and landing. How did an increase in pitch help during takeoff?

Elsie MacGill (1905–1980) is another outstanding figure in the history of Canadian transportation technology. The first woman electrical engineer in Canada, Dr. MacGill became famous during World War Two, when she was featured in a comic book episode called "The Queen of the Hurricane." She had managed to turn a railway boxcar factory in Thunder Bay, Ontario into an aircraft manufacturing plant which employed over 4000 workers, many of them female. Producing 23 Hawker Hurricane fighter planes each week, the factory assembled almost 1500 aircraft. These airplanes were transported to Britain, where they played a major role in winning the Battle of Britain (1940–1941) against German aircraft.

As an engineer, Dr. MacGill did much more than run a factory. She designed skis and de-icing equipment for the Hurricane, which made it more suitable for cold weather flying. She engineered production of the Curtis Helldiver airplane for the American Navy. She created the Maple Leaf trainer, an aircraft which was designed, built, and tested in just eight months. The effects of a childhood illness made it impossible for Elsie to obtain a pilot's licence. Nevertheless, she was proud of always taking part in the test flights of aircraft she designed. She also insisted that all workers in her factory receive equal pay for equal work. This was an uncommon and often unpopular idea at the time, when women were usually paid much less than men in similar jobs.

Figure 9.5 The Hawker Hurricane, built and refined at Elsie MacGill's factory in Thunder Bay

Canadians have made many other contributions to aviation technology. Here are just a few examples that you could research:

- the AVRO Jetliner, North America's first jet-propelled commercial aircraft
- the AVRO Arrow, a jet fighter that was built in the late 1950s and performed better than most military aircraft in use over the next 40 years
- bush planes, such as the Norseman, the Beaver, the Otter and Twin Otter, and the Caribou. The planes which have provided a vital link to isolated northern communities from the 1930s to the present day
- the G-suit, developed by Dr. W. R. Franks at the University of Toronto. The G-suit prevents pilots from losing consciousness during high-speed manoeuvres (more about this in Chapter 12)
- the STEM antenna for space vehicles

Figure 9.6 The prototype AVRO Arrow, designed and built in Canada, had astonishing performance but was never put into production.

Winter Transportation: Defeating the Snow

During the late nineteenth century, railways were extended rapidly across North America. Before airplanes and paved highways, railways provided the fastest, cheapest long-distance transport for passengers and freight. The first railway systems, however, were often paralyzed by severe winter weather conditions. Even today, a train with several 4000-tonne locomotives, and 100 cars weighing as much as 100 tonnes each, can be halted by a winter blizzard.

Early locomotives were fitted with wedge ploughs, which could only clear away light snowfalls. In 1869 J.W. Elliott, a Toronto dentist, patented what he thought would be a great improvement: the "compound revolving show shovel." Elliott's device contained two motor-driven metal paddle wheels that revolved in opposite directions, throwing snow aside as they turned. Elliott demonstrated his device to railway officials, but they were not interested.

Figure 9.7 Wedge ploughs can clear light snowfall, but they cannot penetrate packed drifts.

About ten years later, Toronto inventor Orange Jull added a cutting wheel to the front of Elliott's "compound shovel," to feed snow into the paddle wheels. In the winter of 1883, Jull built and tested a full-sized working model. The mechanism was still too complex, however. Jull reduced it to one revolving wheel with blades that could be adjusted to throw snow to either side. Since snow and ice that were packed between the rails could lift the whole machine, Jull added a flanger. This knife-like device cleared the space beside the rails and kept the snowplough from derailing. Between 1886 and 1888, dozens of Jull's rotary snowploughs were purchased by railroads across North America.

Winter conditions in the Rocky Mountains still defeated Jull's rotary plough. Snow is not the only material in mountain avalanches. Tree trunks, rocks, and other debris bent and broke sheet-metal plough blades. Finally, after a particularly difficult winter from 1908 to 1909, railway official George Bury designed a huge plough. The blades were of armoured steel 5 cm thick and bolted to massive cast metal rotors. Each rotor weighed 12 tonnes and was able to cut through 10 cm thick tree trunks without damage.

Rotary ploughs, similar to Bury's design, are still used today on Canadian railway lines. Household snowblowers, used in many areas of Canada, work in a similar way: a cutting knife feeds snow into a revolving wheel, which throws the snow aside through an adjustable nozzle. Lightweight motors and improved materials have reduced the size and weight of modern snowploughs, but the basic design is unchanged.

Canadian industries still lead the way in railroad technologies. Bombardier, a Montréal-based company, designs and manufactures many different trains, as well as advanced passenger airplanes (for example the airplane shown in Figure 9.2).

Canadians have made many other contributions to winter transportation technology. Here are some examples that you could research:

- ice skates, such as John Forbes' "spring skate" and James Whelpley's "long reachers"
- Armand Bombardier's snowmobile and Ski-Doo™

Figure 9.8 Rotary snowploughs can clear your driveway, but they can also keep mountain rail lines passable throughout the winter.

Figure 9.9 Lamia Orfali, an engineer at Bombardier, works on the design of a new locomotive.

DidYou**Know**?

"Space drives" may seem like the stuff of science fiction, but NASA is already developing alternatives to vehicles powered by chemical reactions. In 1998 the first ion-drive probe, *Deep Space 1*, was launched, and it later performed a successful fly-by of a remote asteroid. An *ion drive* uses electricity to ionize (charge) particles of a gas, which can then be driven magnetically out of the back of the drive at high speed. The acceleration that is produced is very low, but it can be maintained for a long time on very little fuel. As a result, the probe's eventual velocity is hundreds of thousands of kilometres per hour. Future voyages between planets may be much faster thanks to this type of technology.

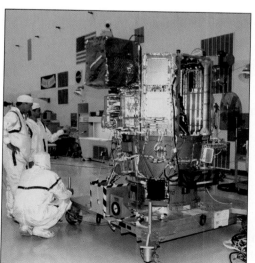

INTERNET CONNECT

www.school.mcgrawhill.ca/resources/
Ingenious and exotic transportation devices are being developed for use in space exploration. To find out about them, and about their Earth-bound ancestors, go to the web site above. Go to **Science Resources**, then to **SCIENCEPOWER 10** to know where to go next. Write a short quiz (five to ten questions) with answers, based on your findings.

Home-Grown Solutions

In this activity, you will use a library or the Internet to research a Canadian device that has contributed to the science or technology of motion. Choose a device from your existing knowledge, a preliminary survey of reference sources, or the suggestions earlier in this section. Here are some additional possibilities:

- the Jolly Jumper™, a device for bouncing infants, invented by Olivia Poole
- the Sanivan™ garbage collection truck, developed by Rinaldo Boissonault and Sicard, Inc.
- light rail transport systems, manufactured by Bombardier, Inc.
- the "giraffe truck" motorized elevated platform, developed by W. E. Thornton-Trump in Oliver, British Columbia
- the Nodwell carrier off-road cargo vehicle, developed by Bruce Nodwell of Calgary, Alberta
- fuel-cell technology, developed by Ballard Power Systems of Vancouver, British Columbia

- the Canadarm remote manipulator used on the Space Shuttle, and its successor on the International Space Station project
- the rotary internal combustion engine on which the modern Wankel engine is based

What to Do

1. Find out the following information about your chosen technology:
   - the background of the scientist or inventor
   - the particular problem being investigated
   - how and when the device was developed
   - how the device works
   - improvements or refinements that were made as the device was developed

2. Present your results as a short, illustrated feature story for a television science program or in another format approved by your teacher. Include visual aids, such as a time line and a clear diagram that shows how the device works.

Check Your Understanding

1. Write sentences comparing the motion of
   (a) two objects, one ten times heavier than the other, dropped from the same height
   (b) a marble rolled down a track that curves back up again, and a marble rolled down a track that levels out

2. Compare scientific theory and technical knowledge. In what ways are they similar? In what ways are they different?

3. Identify the problem that was solved by
   (a) Turnbull's variable pitch propeller
   (b) Jull's improved rotary snowplough

4. Identify a transport technology problem that has not yet been solved. Suggest the kind of scientific or technological breakthrough that is needed to produce a solution to the problem.

5. **Thinking Critically** In the 1960s and 1970s, automobile safety was a widespread concern. Government-imposed safety standards resulted in the development of car bumpers that could withstand moderate speed collisions with very little damage. To save weight and improve fuel economy, however, impact-resistant bumpers are not always used on today's cars. Do you think they should be? Is safety more important than fuel economy?

9.2 The Language of Motion

What would you include in a precise, scientific description of the motion of the racers in Figure 9.10? What measurements would you take? What terms would you use? What units of measurement would be appropriate? What symbols and formulas would you use if calculations were required?

Physicists have developed a specialized language to describe motion. This "physics language" has one great advantage over everyday speech: clarity. Each term has a single, precise meaning, a standard set of symbols, and a particular SI unit of measurement. Observations made in one place, by one scientist, can be understood correctly by other scientists working in other places. International groups of scientists can co-operate on large projects without confusion, since they all measure and calculate using the same **conventions:** agreements about the way that something will be done.

In fact, you already know most or all of the important words in the physics of motion. The trick is to use each word in the right situation with the right meaning. Use the next three pages to sharpen up your motion language skills.

DidYou**Know**?

Confusion about motion descriptions can lead to big and expensive problems. In 1999 NASA's *Mars Climate Orbiter* space probe disappeared, probably burning up in the Martian atmosphere. Several engineering groups had worked on the probe, which cost more than $300 million to design, construct, and launch. An investigation later found that one group had used SI units, such as metres and kilograms. Another group had assumed that data was being recorded in feet, inches, and pounds — the usual U.S. units. As a result, the computers on the probe made errors in the calculations for putting it into orbit around Mars.

Make the Right Call

For a sports event, such as a cross-country ski race, a sports commentator would use vivid language to get across the excitement of the race. A scientific description of the race might use some of the same words, but their meanings would be much more precise.

DISTANCE

Symbols: d (in this textbook) d_i (initial distance)
d_f (final distance)
Δd (distance interval, or change in distance)

Calculation: $\Delta d = d_f - d_i$

Standard unit: metre (m)

Distance measures the total length of a journey along every twist and turn of the path. Distance is a **scalar** quantity, so it has a magnitude (size) but no direction. The symbol Δ is pronounced "delta" and means "change in." Thus Δd means "change in distance."

Example: The race covered a distance of 5.62 km along the winding banks of the river.

TIME

Symbols: t t_i (initial time) t_f (final time)
Δt (time interval)

Calculation: $\Delta t = t_f - t_i$

Standard unit: second (s)

Time describes when an event occurs. Stopwatches or timers are usually reset to zero at the beginning of an experiment, so the initial time t_i is usually taken as zero. **Time interval** describes the duration of an event. Time is a scalar quantity.

Example: About 30 min into the movie (time), Amy went out of the theatre for about 5 min (time interval).

POSITION

Symbols: $\vec{d}$ $\vec{d_i}$ (initial position) $\vec{d_f}$ (final position)

Standard unit: metre (m)

Position describes an object's location, as seen by an observer from a particular viewpoint. The observer is usually assumed to be standing still on Earth's surface. In the lab, the object's initial (starting) position $\vec{d_i}$ is usually taken as the reference position or origin (zero). Position is a **vector,** so you must state both its magnitude and direction. The arrow over the letter "d" means "vector."

Example: The collision occurred 24.75 m due south of the flagpole.

Figure 9.11
Mixing science and sport

19 has constant speed, but he is still accelerating as he changes direction around the turn.

Number 19 is keeping a steady pace around the bend.

19 has taken the lead!

19 has a slightly higher average speed over the distance so far.

They're sprinting back to the finish line . . .

Displacement is decreasing, but distance travelled keeps increasing as they accelerate toward the finish line.

DISPLACEMENT

Symbol: $\Delta \vec{d}$

Calculation: $\Delta \vec{d} = \vec{d}_f - \vec{d}_i$

Standard unit: metre (m)

Displacement describes how much an object's position has changed. If the object ends up back where it started, like a runner going completely around a race-track, its displacement is zero, even if it moved a long way. Displacement is a vector.

Example: We pushed the car, producing a displacement of 4.5 m at an angle of 25° to the road.

VELOCITY

Symbols: $\vec{v}$ $\vec{v}_i$ (initial velocity) $\vec{v}_f$ (final velocity)

$\vec{v}_{av}$ (average velocity)

$\vec{v}_{inst}$ (instantaneous velocity)

Δv (change in velocity)

Calculation: $\Delta \vec{v} = \vec{v}_f - \vec{v}_i$

Standard unit: metres per second (m/s)

Velocity describes the speed and direction of motion. That is, it describes how fast an object's position is changing. The symbol $\vec{v}$ usually means the average velocity over a particular time interval. For clarity, $\vec{v}_{av}$ can be used for the average velocity, with $\vec{v}_{inst}$ representing **instantaneous** velocity (velocity at a specific instant in time). Velocity is a vector.

Example: The aircraft was travelling at 535 km/h, headed N45°W, when the weather warning was received.

SPEED

Symbol: v (in this textbook) or $|\vec{v}|$

Standard unit: metres per second (m/s)

Speed describes how fast something is moving. It has the same meaning in physics and in everyday language. Speed is a scalar and does *not* indicate direction.

Example: The cyclist reached a maximum speed of 12.00 m/s during the race.

ACCELERATION

Symbols: $\vec{a}$ $\vec{a}_{av}$ (average acceleration)

$\vec{a}_{inst}$ (instantaneous acceleration)

Standard unit: metres per second in each second (m/s^2)

Acceleration describes how much an object's velocity changes in a certain time. It results from any change in velocity: speeding up, slowing down, changing direction, or a combination. Acceleration is a vector.

Example: Earth's gravity makes objects accelerate at 9.8 m/s^2 downward.

You already know many of the technical terms that are used to describe motion because they are used in everyday speech. Other terms may be familiar from previous science courses. Try to use the terms in the following activity correctly.

Talk the Talk

To get a clear understanding of an object's motion, especially if it is changing speed and/or direction, you need to find the object's position, speed, and direction of travel many times as it moves along. The more observations you make, the better you will be able to describe the details of the motion. Use this principle to study the changing motion of a runner during a short race.

What You Need

athletic measuring tape (at least 50 m)

as many electronic timers or digital watches as possible

whistle (for starter)

What to Do

1. Predict answers to the questions at the right. Record your predictions.

2. Choose one student to be the runner and one to be the starter. The rest of the students are timers.

3. Have the runner stretch and warm up while the rest of the class sets up a 50 m or 100 m racetrack. The timers must be equally spaced along it and at least 2 m apart.

4. Have the runner run the race. Each timer must start his or her watch when the runner starts the race and stop when the runner passes his or her position.

5. Record your observations in a data table. Show the position of each timer (in metres, measured from the starting point) and the time that the runner took to reach this position.

6. Draw a line graph to show the position that the runner reached at each different time. For a graph like this, time is usually placed on the horizontal axis, and position is placed on the vertical axis.

7. Check your predictions. Correct and improve as many as possible now that you have quantitative data to work from.

Questions

A. What is the runner's *initial position* and *velocity?*

B. What is the runner's *final position* and *velocity?*

C. What is the runner's *displacement* from the beginning to the end of the race? Is it different from the *distance* that the runner travels during the race?

D. Does the runner *accelerate* at any point in the race? Where? How can you recognize when the motion is accelerated?

E. In what time intervals is the runner's *average velocity* highest and lowest?

What Did You Discover?

1. Which technical terms in the questions were least familiar to you?

2. What information was easier to obtain from your graph than your data table? What information was easier to obtain from your data table?

3. How could you change your method of collecting data to get a more detailed picture of the runner's motion?

The Rules of the Game

Over hundreds of years, physicists (and other scientists) have developed traditional ways of expressing their observations. If physics were a sport, these conventions would be the rules of the game. In physics, however, many of the rules are unwritten. Although not all physicists or physics textbooks follow the rules consistently, you should be careful to use the conventions described below unless your teacher tells you otherwise.

Figure 9.12 Clear, concise communication is an essential skill for professional scientists.

International System of Units

The International System of Units (SI) is a revised and modernized descendent of the metric system of measurement. It is used for scientific work throughout the world. Although traditional measurements are still used for everyday purposes in many places, they must be converted to SI measurements for legal and official purposes in most countries except the U.S.A.

Precision and Significant Digits

Measurements are always approximate. They depend on the **precision** of the measuring instruments that were used: that is, the amount of information that the instruments can provide. The smallest markings on most rulers, for example, indicate millimetres. You could describe the ruler's **readability** (the size of the smallest division on its scale) as 1 mm (one millimetre) or 0.001 m. You could also say the ruler is "readable to the nearest millimetre."

On most measuring scales, however, you can also estimate readings *between* the lines if you look carefully. Scientists agree to add only one additional figure to their measurements in this way. For example, examine the bicycle wheel measurement in Figure 9.13A. The metre stick shows that the wheel is about 65.38 cm, or 653.8 mm, in diameter. The first three digits of this measurement, 65.3, are said to be "certain" because they were read from the scale on the metre stick. The last digit, 8, is "uncertain" because it was estimated. The measurement has four significant digits (the certain digits plus one uncertain digit).

A machinist's micrometer, in Figure 9.13B, is much more precise (and more expensive) than a metre stick. A micrometer may show, for example, the length of a piece of metal to be 24.56 mm — a precision of four significant digits. The first three digits, 24.5, are certain. The last digit, 6, is uncertain because it was estimated or rounded by the digital display.

Skill
POWER

To review the International System of Units (*Le Système International d'Unités,* or "SI"), including standard units, prefixes, and symbols, turn to page 585.

65.38 cm or 653.8 mm

Figure 9.13 Measuring precisely with (A) a ruler and (B) a micrometer

Figure 9.14 How precise is "precise"?

If measurements are approximate, the calculations based on them must also be approximate. Scientists agree that calculated answers should be rounded so they do not give a misleading idea of how precise the original measurements were. Using the ruler measurement of 14.5 mm, for example, the calculated height of the triangle in Figure 9.14 is 12.557 368 mm. Reporting all the decimal places would give the impression that an incredibly precise instrument had been used, rather than an ordinary ruler. The answer should be rounded to 12.6 mm to reflect the precision of the ruler.

In this course, and throughout your science studies, you should always measure and calculate to the proper number of significant digits. You will often need to use scientific notation, as well. Follow these conventions:

• When measuring with a mechanical instrument, record all the digits that are marked on the instrument's scale and estimate one (and only one) more digit.

• When measuring with an electronic instrument, record all the digits on the read-out. Consider the last digit to be approximate.

• Round calculated answers only once, at the end of the calculation, so that the number of significant digits reflects the precision of the original measurements.

Skill
P O W E R

To practise calculating with scientific notation, turn to page 587.

Skill
P O W E R

For tips on working with significant digits, turn to page 605.

DidYou**Know**?

The ability to measure position accurately played a key role in the development of western Canada. Immediately after Confederation in 1867, surveyors of the Dominion Lands Survey mapped the entire western Canadian plains, using hand equipment and travelling across the country on foot. Working long before the development of aerial photography, mapping satellites, and modern electronic equipment, the surveyors prepared maps and constructed *benchmarks* (location markers). These benchmarks divided the entire western Canadian plains into a fine square grid. Railway construction and homestead settlement were able to proceed relatively smoothly because positions could be easily and precisely measured.

At least one early settler gained a fortune from careful measurements of position. H.F. "Twelve Foot" Davis noticed that the boundaries of two neighbouring gold-prospecting claims did not actually touch. Davis promptly claimed the 12 foot (3.7 m) wide strip of land between them. After becoming rich from the gold found on his tiny piece of land, Davis established a series of trading posts along the Peace River. He became a well-known and popular resident of northern Alberta.

Direction

In many experiments, objects move in a straight line in only one dimension: backward/forward or up/down. This is called **linear motion**. When this happens, vector directions can be shown using + and – signs. For position, follow the conventions below:

- A + indicates up or to the right of the starting point.
- A – indicates down or to the left of the starting point.

For displacement and velocity, follow these conventions:

- A + indicates up or toward the observer's right.
- A – indicates down or toward the observer's left.

Notice that a velocity of −20 m/s is no slower than a velocity of +20 m/s. These two motions have the same speed, but opposite directions.

When objects move vertically, the reference point from which all other heights are measured is usually taken as ground level. In other words, for an object on the ground, height equals zero. Sometimes it makes more sense to measure height from another point, such as the top of a lab table. If you do this, be sure to state the reference point for your observations in any written work.

Scalars and Vectors

Vectors, such as velocity, can be represented in several ways. In physics, the most common ways are these:

- using boldfaced type: **v** = 3.45 m/s upward
- using a vector arrow above the symbol
  (the notation used in this textbook): $\vec{v}$ = 3.45 m/s upward

Scalar quantities, such as mass, are always represented by letters in italic type, like this:

- *m* = 0.45 kg

For linear motion, position and velocity are often shown without vector notation. In this textbook, vector arrows are usually placed over the variable, but other textbooks and many teachers omit the vector arrows. Similarly, the + signs are often omitted in calculations. The final answer to a problem or calculation is most clear, however, if direction is shown by writing a + or − sign where necessary.

$\vec{d}$ = −3.7 m

$\vec{d}$ = 0.0 m

Figure 9.15 This cyclist is moving to the observer's left, so his displacement is negative.

To describe motion on a flat surface, such as a lab table or football field, you may need to work with two-dimensional vectors. This can be done using a scale drawing or diagram, as you will see in the next investigation.

Heading for Home

Think About It

Have you ever tried the sport of orienteering or used a map and compass to plot a course or find your way while hiking or sailing? If so, you are familiar with one way of using vectors. Each *leg* (straight-line section of your course) can be represented by a displacement vector. The length of each vector tells you how far you travel, and its heading tells you the direction you move. After completing one leg of the course, you set a new direction and begin the next stage of your journey.

Mathematically, you could say that the overall journey is the **vector sum** of all its individual legs: the result of adding all the individual vectors together. One way of adding vectors is illustrated in the diagram below. The vectors are drawn to scale in a **vector diagram**. They are arranged so that the end of one vector is the starting point for the next vector.

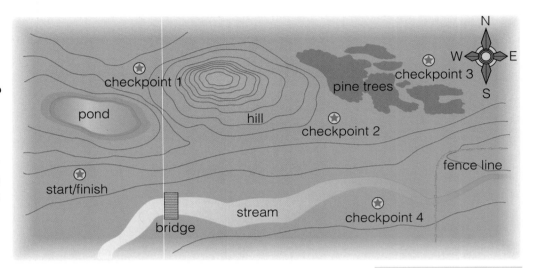

Scale: 1 cm = 250 m
        1: 25 000

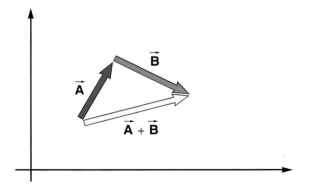

Vectors can be added by placing them "tip to tail" on a scale diagram.

What to Do

Part 1

1 Use a ruler and protractor to measure the length and heading of each leg of the orienteering course at the top of this page. The first leg goes from the starting point to checkpoint 1, the next leg goes from checkpoint 1 to checkpoint 2, and so on.

2 Use the scale on the map to calculate the "real-life" length of each leg of the course.

3 Write the displacement vector for each leg of the course using compass headings: for example, 750 m and N40°W. Call the vectors $\vec{A}$ (for the first leg), $\vec{B}$ (for the second leg), and so on.

4 The displacement from the starting point to the finishing point is the vector sum of all the individual displacement vectors. Measure and write a vector expression for this displacement.

Skill
POWER

For help with plotting points on *x*- and *y*-axes, turn to page 604.

Part 2

Starting point: (3, 4)

Leg	Magnitude (cm)	Compass direction	RCS direction
A	4.2	N	90°
B	3.1	N25°W	115°

1. Mark horizontal and vertical axes on grid paper, dividing it into four quadrants. Draw a simple cartoon figure or message composed entirely of straight lines on the grid paper.

2. Pick one vertex of your sketch to be a starting point, and find its location. On a separate page, record the location as an ordered pair of Cartesian co-ordinates (location on horizontal axis, location on vertical axis).

3. Measure the magnitude and direction of the displacement vector for each straight-line segment of your figure. Record each vector description on your list (see the diagram above). Use both systems — compass directions and RCS co-ordinates. (See the Math Connect below.)

4. Trade vector descriptions (but not grid paper) with a partner. Try to reproduce your partner's figure on another sheet of grid paper.

5. Compare your version of the figure with your partner's original figure.

Analyze

1. How close was your version to the original figure? If they were not identical, what caused the errors?

2. From your experience with compass directions and RCS descriptions of directions, which system do you prefer? Why?

Extend Your Knowledge

3. One method of creating images on computers uses "vector graphics" to describe the images. A system called "bit-mapped" or "raster" graphics is also common. Find out how one or both of these systems work and how they got their names.

Math CONNECT

When objects move over a flat surface, such as a laboratory table or level ground, compass directions are often used. On graphs and diagrams, physicists also use the rectangular co-ordinate system (RCS) to indicate direction. RCS directions specify the amount of counterclockwise rotation, in degrees, from the positive x-axis of a graph. The diagrams at the right compare the two systems.

1. Convert 160° RCS to a compass direction.

2. Convert the direction S20°W to RCS co-ordinates.

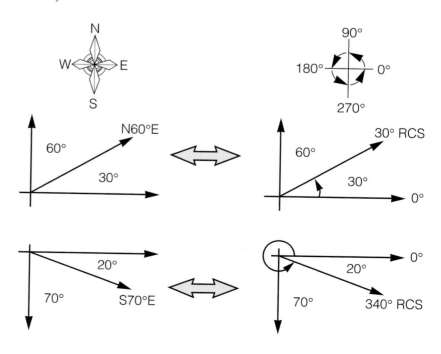

Math CONNECT

How well do you know your own country? Using the Internet or a library, find out some significant Canadian measurements. For example, what is the greatest distance between two places in Canada? What are the most western and most eastern Canadian settlements? How long is the longest river? What is the fastest wind speed ever recorded, anywhere in Canada? Think of other questions of your own. Present your findings in a report or on a poster.

Pause& Reflect

You will need to use the language of physics correctly throughout this unit. In your Science Log, make a chart to summarize the definitions and information you have just examined. Use your chart for reference as you write lab reports and solve problems.

Check Your Understanding

1. Explain the difference between
   (a) distance and displacement
   (b) velocity and speed
   (c) instantaneous and average

2. Explain the difference between the everyday use of each term below and the way it is used in physics.
   (a) acceleration   (b) initial   (c) interval

3. Examine the figure below to find each piece of information listed.
   (a) $\vec{d_i}$ (b) $\vec{d_f}$ (c) $\Delta\vec{d}$ (d) Δt

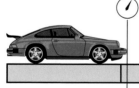

start of observations:
time = 1.34 s
position = 1.063 m

end of observations:
time = 5.63 s
position = 4.852 m

4. Copy the table below, and fill in the blank boxes. Use only the appropriate word from each pair in the right-hand column.

t_i (s)	t_f (s)	Δt (s)	$\vec{d_i}$ (cm)	$\vec{d_f}$ (cm)	$\Delta\vec{d}$ (cm)	Direction of motion
5.0	6.5		+17.3	+20.0		left/right
	8.3	2.1	+26.9		+5.3	up/down
0		105.4		+26.8	−15.4	left/right

5. **Thinking Critically** In a cycle race of several laps around a circular track, which is more meaningful: the average *speed* of a competitor, or her or his average *velocity*? Explain your answer.

9.3 Measuring Motion

Tools of the Trade

A watch, a metre stick or measuring tape, and a calculator — these are the basic tools for studying motion. From simple data about an object's position at specific times, physicists have learned how to calculate an amazing amount of data about its motion. Most high-school laboratories have at least one of the instruments described below for gathering position-time data.

Metronomes and Markers

If an object is travelling slowly in a straight line, and you do not need extremely detailed information about its motion, you can mark the object's position every second on a paper tape. Set a musical metronome to 60, so it clicks every second, and fasten a felt marker to the end of a metre stick. Stretch a paper tape along the object's path. Then walk beside the object, and mark a dot on the tape to show the position of the object each time the metronome clicks.

Figure 9.16 Race timers gather just one piece of information: the time each competitor reaches the finish line.

To analyze the data, place the end of a metre stick or measuring tape at the dot that marks the starting position of the object. Imagine that you started timing at this point, so that it represents a time of zero and a position of zero. Now measure the distance from the starting point to each successive dot, recording your observations in a data table like Table 9.1.

Figure 9.17 Using a metronome and marker to track motion

Table 9.1 Motion of a Laboratory Cart Across a Level Floor

Time (s)	Position, to the right (m)	Displacement, to the right, during interval (m)
0.0	0.000	—
1.0	1.635	1.635
2.0	2.260	0.625

Data like these are often easier to interpret if plotted on a graph. A **position-time graph** is a particular kind of graph that shows an object's position (plotted on the vertical axis) versus time (plotted on the horizontal axis). Figure 9.18 shows a graph of the data in Table 9.1.

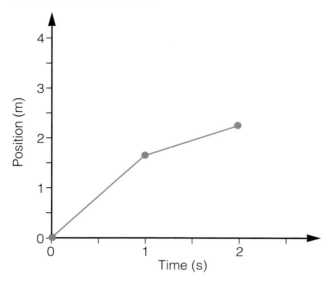

Figure 9.18 The laboratory cart keeps moving during the second time interval, but not as much as during the first interval. Can you also see this information in Table 9.1? Is it easier to see on the graph?

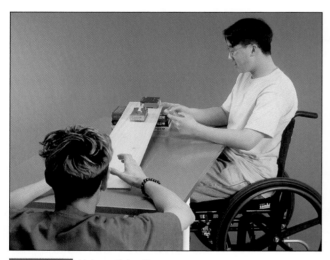

Figure 9.19 Using a ticker timer

Ticker Timers

An electrically-operated timer can mark a paper tape fast enough to make a very detailed record of the motion of a small object. A simple **ticker timer** works like an electric buzzer. It has a vibrating arm that makes a series of dots on a paper tape as the tape is pulled through the timer by the moving object. More precise timers use an electric spark to mark special paper. Most timers make 60 marks each second. For analysis, the position of every sixth dot is measured, giving a record of the moving object's location every 0.1 s. If the object started from rest, the first few dots on the tape are often too crowded together to count. Therefore measurements of position and time usually start from the first clear single dot, as shown in Figure 9.20.

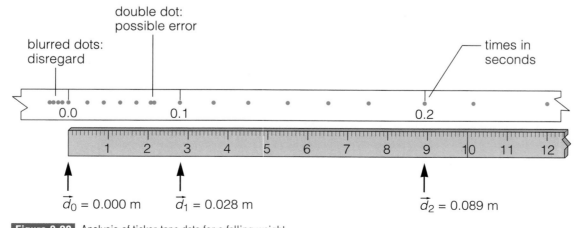

Figure 9.20 Analysis of ticker-tape data for a falling weight

Ultrasonic Motion Sensors

Like a bat, an **ultrasonic motion sensor** emits short bursts or "clicks" of high-frequency sound waves. The sensor (sometimes called a "range finder") can detect echoes of the clicks as they bounce off nearby objects. By measuring the time between a click and its echo, a calculator or computer that is attached to the sensor can calculate the distance to the object. The data can usually be viewed in a data table or converted by the computer to a graph of position, velocity, or acceleration over time (see Figure 9.22). Ultrasonic motion sensors provide a very efficient way of generating motion graphs, but they have limitations. They cannot be used for observations of very small objects or for objects that are very close to or very far from the sensor. As well, they can be confused by echoes from other moving objects or from large hard surfaces near their target.

Word **CONNECT**

The prefix "ultra" means "beyond." What is "ultrasonic" sound beyond? What other "ultra" words can you think of, and what are they beyond?

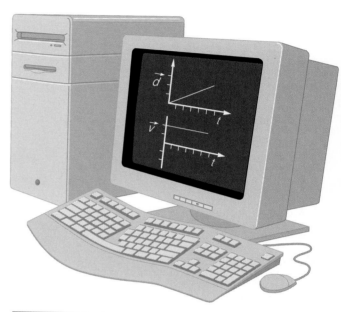

Figure 9.21 Using an ultrasonic motion sensor

Figure 9.22 Graphs that depict an object's motion can be generated far more quickly with an ultrasonic motion sensor than by hand.

Photogate Timers

A **photogate** has a light-sensitive photocell that is attached to a computer. The photocell can detect changes in light intensity as it is shaded by a passing moving object. By placing two or more photogates a measured distance apart, you can time an object's passage and calculate its average velocity over the time interval. To obtain continuous data about an object's motion, it can be attached to a "picket fence" or a Smart Pulley™. Alternating white (or clear) and black areas trigger the photocell repeatedly as the object passes by (see Figure 9.23). If you know the width of the stripes, you can set the computer to calculate or graph the object's position, velocity, or acceleration.

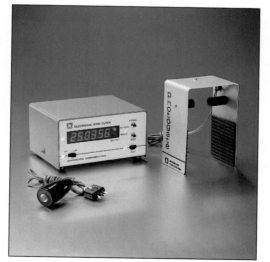

Figure 9.23 A picket fence triggers a photocell to record motion in this photogate apparatus.

Tools of Science

Ultrasonic motion sensors that are used in physics labs were originally developed for use in autofocus cameras. Today most automatic cameras use other methods to adjust for subjects at different distances. Do some research in a library, on the Internet, or at your local photographic store to find out how this is done.

Slow but Sure

Have you ever tried to march in formation with other people? Moving at a constant, steady pace is surprisingly difficult, especially if you have to keep in step with other marchers. In this investigation, you will use very simple apparatus, and a little mathematics, to detect any speed variations as you try to walk slowly and steadily.

Problem

Can you move at a constant slow speed for at least 5 s?

Apparatus

metronome
paper tape
felt pen
metre stick or measuring tape

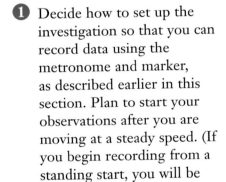

Procedure

1 Decide how to set up the investigation so that you can record data using the metronome and marker, as described earlier in this section. Plan to start your observations after you are moving at a steady speed. (If you begin recording from a standing start, you will be speeding up for the first part of your observations.)

2 Carry out a "dry run" to test your experimental set-up. If necessary, adjust the time interval, the length of the tape, or the speed at which you move so that you will obtain about ten data points.

3 Make one set of observations for each group member.

Analyze

1. Set up a data table like Table 9.1. Call the starting position "zero." Assign it time, $t = 0$ s and position, $d = 0.00$ m. Measure the positions of all the other dots on the tape to the nearest centimetre, and record your measurements in your table.

2. Use your data to make a position-time graph of your motion. Remember to follow the conventions for scientific graphing.
   - **(a)** Put the independent (manipulated) variable on the horizontal axis and the dependent (responding) variable on the vertical axis. (Hint: The dependent variable is usually the one you measure.)
   - **(b)** Set up a continuous scale on each axis, starting from zero. Choose your scales based on the measurements you made.
   - **(c)** Plot points with an error circle.
   - **(d)** Draw either a line of best fit or a smooth curve between the points (whichever seems to fit the data best).
   - **(e)** Label the axes, and give your graph a title.

Conclude and Apply

3. Write a short paragraph summarizing the experimental set-up you used. Include the following information:
    (a) the independent and dependent variables in your investigation
    (b) any other factors that you carefully kept constant (controlled variables)
    (c) any assumptions that you made about factors which could affect your results, but probably do not make enough difference to be worth considering

4. In your judgment, does your graph show that you maintained a constant speed during the investigation? Give reasons for your answer.

5. From your graph, can you identify any points that probably represent measurement errors? Explain how you identified (or could identify) these points.

Extend Your Skills

6. Identify the graph that would be produced by a person who, during the investigation,
    (a) slowed down gradually
    (b) speeded up gradually
    (c) speeded up at first and then walked at a steady pace

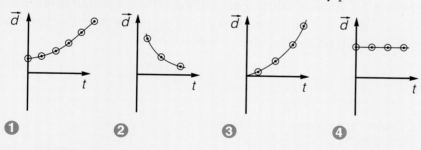

7. Repeat your observations using one of the other instruments described in this section: a ticker timer, an ultrasonic motion sensor, or a photogate timer and picket fence. You may have to adjust your speed or time interval to suit the measuring instrument, but your goal is the same — to move at constant velocity for a set length of time.

Computer **CONNECT**

If you have access to scientific graphing software, try using it to prepare your graph. Before starting, make sure that the software can produce a best-fit graph. The charting functions of most word processors are not usually adequate for scientific graphs.

Skill
P O W E R

To review scientific graphing, turn to pages 602–603.

Natural Timing

The most basic information about a moving object is its position at a particular time. Early scientists could measure position quite precisely. Before mechanical clocks were developed, however, they had great difficulty measuring time precisely. Can you manage to make accurate time measurements without using a mechanical helper?

What to Do

Use a clock or a watch to set up and practise each non-mechanical method of timekeeping described below. When you are ready, have a partner use a clock or a watch to check your accuracy while you estimate a 20 s interval, following each method. Record your results.

(a) Set up a pendulum and find its period (the time it takes for one complete swing). Then use the pendulum to estimate a 20 s time interval.

(b) Use a repeated phrase, such as "one one thousand, two one thousands, three one thousands . . ." to estimate a 20 s time interval.

(c) Sit comfortably, and find your pulse in your wrist or neck. Calculate your pulse rate in beats per minute. Then use your pulse rate to estimate a 20 s time interval.

What Did You Discover?

1. Calculate your percent error for each method, using the formula below. Use 20 s as the standard value in your calculation.

$$\text{Percent error} = \frac{\text{Measured value} - \text{Standard value}}{\text{Standard value}} \times 100$$

2. Which method was most accurate?

3. If you measured a 4 min interval using each method, by how many seconds would each measurement be incorrect?

Tricks of the Trade

A great deal of information is hidden in the results of even simple observations of motion, such as those you made in the last activity. Much of this information can be uncovered by simple mathematical analysis. If you become familiar with the symbols and algebraic expressions that physicists use in their calculations, the rest of the unit will be much easier to follow.

DidYou**Know**?

After 1500 C.E., European sailors and merchants travelled Earth's oceans more and more often, trading with and colonizing distant lands. Perhaps the toughest problem they faced was how to find their way at sea, with no landmarks to guide them.

One way to know where you are in the world depends on time measurement. If you wait for "local" noon (when the Sun is due south) and notice that your clock (which you set in London, England) reads 2:30 p.m., you can figure out that you are half way across the Atlantic. Unless your clock is accurate to within a minute, however, you could still be off course by hundreds of kilometres. It became more important to keep accurate time on board a ship at sea than almost anywhere else. It was more difficult, too, with sea-spray and a swaying deck to disturb the primitive clocks of that time. By 1714 the British government was desperate for a way to measure time accurately. They offered a prize of £20 000 (millions of dollars at modern values) for a clock that could keep time to within 3 s a day — still very inaccurate by today's standards! The story of the prize can be found in a book called *Longitude,* by Dava Sobel.

John Harrison's prize-winning watch, H-4, was made in 1770.

Change

The symbol Δ (the Greek letter "delta") is used to indicate a change in a quantity. For example, $\Delta \vec{d}$ represents a change in position (displacement). Change is always calculated by subtraction, in this order: final state – initial state. The sign of the answer gives important information about the change:

- A + represents an increase, movement to the right, or movement up.
- A – represents a decrease, movement to the left, or movement down.

Rate of Change

In mathematics, a rate describes how a quantity is changing. In this unit, we will use the term **rate of change** to mean how *fast* a quantity is changing over time. Thus we can simplify two of the definitions given earlier:

- Velocity is the rate of change of position.
- Acceleration is the rate of change of velocity.

A rate is always expressed as the change in a quantity during a single unit of time, such as 1 s or 1 h. Because actual measurements are seldom taken over precisely 1 s or 1 h, the rate of change must be calculated by division, as an average value.

$$\text{Average rate of change} = \frac{\text{Total change}}{\text{Time interval}} = \frac{\text{Final state} - \text{Initial state}}{\text{Final time} - \text{Initial time}}$$

Skill POWER

If you need to review the GRASP problem-solving method, turn to page 610.

Model Problem 1

At sunrise, the temperature was 14.5°C. After 4.0 h, the temperature had increased to 19.7°C. How fast was the temperature changing?

Given $T_i = 14.5°C$ (using T to represent temperature)
$T_f = 19.7°C$
$\Delta t = 4.0$ h

Required Rate of temperature change, r, in °C/h

Analysis Rate of temperature change $= \dfrac{\text{Change in temperature}}{\text{Time interval}}$

$$= \frac{\text{Final temperature} - \text{Initial temperature}}{\text{Time interval}}$$

Solution $r = \dfrac{\Delta T}{\Delta t} = \dfrac{(T_f - T_i)}{\Delta t}$

$$= \frac{(19.7°C - 14.5°C)}{4.0 \text{ h}} = +1.3°C/h$$

Paraphrase Temperature was increasing at an average rate of 1.3°C/h over the 4 h interval.

After taking off, a model airplane climbed for 4.5 s and reached a height of 12.5 m above the ground. The airplane then rose steadily at a rate of 0.28 m/s until it had been in the air for 1 min 20 s. What was the airplane's final height?

Given $t_i = 4.5$ s
$t_f = 1$ min 20 s
$\quad = 80.0$ s
$d_i = +12.5$ m
Rate of climb, $r = 0.28$ m/s

Required Final height, d_f

Analysis First find the increase in height, using a rate formula. Then find the final height, using the following relation:

$$\text{Final height} = \text{Initial height} + \text{Change in height}$$

Solution Find the increase in height, Δd.

$$r = \frac{\Delta d}{\Delta t}$$

$$\therefore \Delta d = r \times \Delta t$$
$$= r \times (t_f - t_i)$$
$$= 0.28 \text{ m/s} \times (80.0 \text{ s} - 4.5 \text{ s})$$
$$= +21.1 \text{ m}$$

Find the final height.
$$d_f = d_i + \Delta d$$
$$= +12.5 \text{ m} + (+21.1 \text{ m})$$
$$= +33.64 \text{ m or approximately } +33.6 \text{ m (to 3 significant digits)}$$

Paraphrase   The model airplane reached a final height of approximately 33.6 m above the ground by the end of the time interval.

Graphs

The French mathematician René Descartes discovered that graphs are a powerful tool for analyzing any numerical data. Here are three reasons why:

- *Patterns in data* can often be identified more clearly from graphs than from data tables. By analyzing the shape of a line graph, it is often possible to develop a mathematical equation that describes the data and allows accurate predications.
- Graphs can *correct for errors* in the observations. The graph line averages many observational errors. Thus, it is more accurate than the individual measurements that are used to produce it.
- *Calculating useful information* is often simpler using a graph. The slope of a line graph or the area it encloses, for example, can give important information when analyzing motion experiments. This information might otherwise be extremely difficult to calculate.

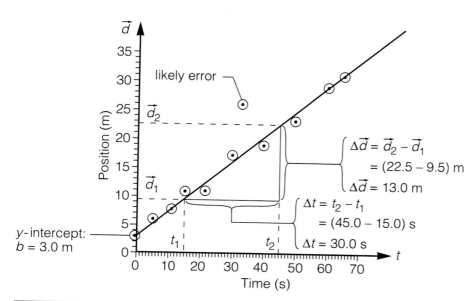

slope of line:

$$m = \frac{\Delta \vec{d}}{\Delta t}$$

$$= \frac{13.0 \text{ m}}{30.0 \text{ s}}$$

$$m = 0.433 \text{ m/s}$$

equation of line:

$$\vec{d} = mt + b$$

$$\vec{d} = 0.433t + 3.0$$

$\Delta \vec{d} = \vec{d}_2 - \vec{d}_1$
$= (22.5 - 9.5)$ m
$\Delta \vec{d} = 13.0$ m

$\Delta t = t_2 - t_1$
$= (45.0 - 15.0)$ s
$\Delta t = 30.0$ s

Figure 9.24 A line graph, with the calculation of slope

When drawing a graph that describes the motion of an object, physicists usually assume that position and speed change smoothly. The graph line is therefore drawn as a best-fit straight line or as a smooth curve between the data points. The data points on the graph, which come from measurements with experimental errors, indicate the position of the graph line. Note, however, that the line will likely not go through all the data points. The graph line shows what would happen in a nearly perfect, or "ideal," experiment with very little error.

Skill
P O W E R

To review drawing scientific graphs, turn to page 604.

Math CONNECT

In 1914 a racing pigeon in level flight reached a measured speed of 150.5 km/h. This is one of the fastest bird flights ever recorded. How fast was the bird travelling, measured in standard SI units? How long would the pigeon have taken to travel 100 m? How many times faster was the pigeon than the fastest human sprinter? Use a library or the Internet to research the current world-record speed for women and for men over a 100 m distance.

Check Your Understanding

1. Identify one advantage and one disadvantage of using each of the following devices to measure an object's motion.
   (a) ticker timer
   (b) ultrasonic motion sensor
   (c) photogate and picket fence
   (d) metronome and marker

2. Which of the measurement methods described in this section would be appropriate for measuring motion in each situation below?
   (a) changes in the speed of a ball rolling off a table
   (b) the time taken for a toy racing car to roll down a curved track
   (c) the distance moved by a lab cart each second as it rolls down a straight ramp

3. The ticker-timer tape below shows the motion of a lab cart that had very sticky wheels, which did not roll evenly. For each section of the tape, describe any changes in the cart's speed that occur.

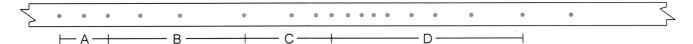

4. What is the difference between change and rate of change?

5. What three things can a + or − sign on a number represent?

6. **Apply** Examine the position-time graph, and identify or calculate each quantity below.
   (a) a point that probably represents a measurement error
   (b) direction of motion (+ or −)
   (c) initial position
   (d) final position
   (e) displacement
   (f) time interval

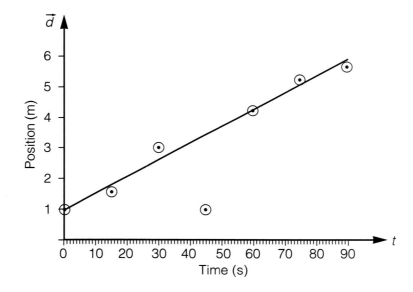

7. **Apply** High-speed passenger elevators move at speeds of up to 7.11 m/s. At this rate, how long would it take to travel up 37.5 m (about ten storeys)?

8. **Apply** A balance measurement is correctly reported as 154.36 g.
   (a) How many significant digits are in this measurement?
   (b) What is the readability of the balance?
   (c) What mass does the smallest marking on the balance represent?

Now that you have completed this chapter, try to do the following. If you cannot, go back to the sections indicated.

Summarize two ideas held by modern scientists about moving objects. (9.1)

Identify how each of the following Canadian inventions was superior to the technology that it replaced: the variable pitch propeller, the flanger on a rotary snowplough. (9.1)

Distinguish between the quantities in each pair: time and time interval, distance and displacement, velocity and speed. (9.2)

Write the formula that is used to calculate each of these quantities: time interval, displacement, change in velocity. (9.2)

Explain the difference between an instantaneous measurement and an average measurement. (9.2)

Make a chart to show differences between vector and scalar quantities. Include differences in the notation for each type of quantity. (9.2)

In your own words, describe what physicists mean by precision and readability. (9.2)

List the rules for calculating and rounding with significant digits. (9.2)

Identify possible meanings of a + sign and a − sign when describing motion in one dimension. (9.2, 9.3)

Demonstrate or describe how to use a metronome and a stopwatch or electronic timer to measure time. (9.3)

Describe how a record of motion is produced by each of the following pieces of apparatus: ticker timer, ultrasonic motion sensor, photogate. (9.3)

Identify two mathematical rates that are used to describe motion. (9.3)

Write a word equation for calculating rate of change, using total change and time taken. (9.3)

Give three reasons why data about motion is often graphed. (9.3)

Prepare Your Own Summary

Summarize this chapter by doing one of the following. Use a graphic organizer (such as a concept map), produce a poster, or write the summary to include the key chapter concepts. Here are a few ideas to use as a guide:

- Describe one situation in which it is appropriate to mentally estimate the motion of an object.
- Describe a situation in which motion must be measured with a precision instrument.
- Describe how several cold-climate transportation problems have been solved by Canadian-developed motion technology.
- Identify the main quantities that physicists observe or calculate when studying moving objects. For each quantity, give the standard symbol and unit.
- Explain how four pieces of lab apparatus are used for recording the motion of objects.
- List some physics conventions that are important when describing motion.
- What did you learn or remember about writing reports of lab activities while working through this chapter?

Reviewing Key Terms

If you need to review, the section numbers show you where these terms were introduced.

1. Turn to the list of key terms at the beginning of this chapter. Choose the term that best describes each statement below. (9.2)
   (a) Art left his home at 3:42 p.m.
   (b) His car accelerated from 0 to 40 km/h in 5.4 s.
   (c) Travelling at 50 km/h due north, Art soon reached the store.
   (d) On his way home, he followed a winding road that ended only one block from the store.
   (e) Art glanced at the speedometer, which at that moment read 47 km/h.
   (f) "Did you know you were speeding?" the police officer asked.
   (g) Finally, 44 min and 26 s after leaving, Art returned home.
   (h) The car's odometer showed that he had travelled over 15.4 km to get a loaf of bread.

2. Fill in the blanks in the statements below, using terms from the list of key terms. (9.3)

   Using a picket fence moving through a _____ , the _____ speed was measured to a _____ of three significant digits as 0.462 m/s. The timer was _____ to the nearest 0.001 m/s.

Understanding Key Concepts

Section numbers are provided if you need to review.

3. What quantitative information do you need to calculate each of these features of an object's motion? (9.2)
   (a) displacement   (c) average acceleration
   (b) average velocity   (d) average speed

4. For each measurement below, describe the readability of the instrument and the number of significant digits. (9.3)
   (a) 4.37 g   (b) 0.00630 m   (c) 4.062×10^5 s

5. Examine each measurement instrument sketched below. Record the measurement shown, the readability of the instrument, and the number of significant digits. (9.3)

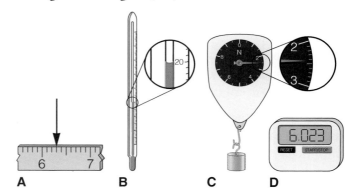

A   B   C   D

6. Describe the position and direction of travel of each object below. (9.3)
   (a) a car on level ground, position +4.5 m, velocity −10.4 km/h
   (b) an elevator, position −12.6 m, velocity +2.3 m/s
   (c) a person on a trampoline, position +1.39 m, velocity −0.52 m/s

7. Identify which of the following situations are accelerated motion. (9.3)
   (a) a runner poised at the starting line
   (b) the runner speeding up just after the starting gun is fired
   (c) the runner travelling at a steady speed around a corner
   (d) the runner slowing down after passing the finish line

8. Classify each of the following quantities as a vector or a scalar. (9.3)
   (a) speed   (c) time
   (b) velocity   (d) mass

9. Which of the following examples could best be described as instantaneous? Which examples could best be described as averages? (9.2, 9.3)
   (a) one point on a line graph
   (b) the best-fit line on a graph

(c) "Most of the district had received about 25 mm of rain by the time the storm ended."

(d) "Amy's velocity reached a maximum entering the classroom, just as the clock reached 9:00."

Developing Skills

10. Use the graph to read or calculate each quantity below. Record each answer, to one decimal place, using the proper symbols.
    (a) initial position
    (b) final position
    (c) displacement
    (d) initial time
    (e) final time
    (f) time interval from beginning to end of the observations
    (g) average velocity over the entire time interval

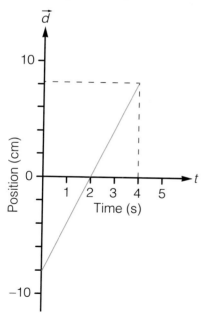

Problem Solving/Applying

11. Suppose that you had a ticker-timer tape showing the motion of a cyclist for precisely 2 s as she accelerated from rest. You want to find her average velocity during the last second of her ride. Draw an events chain to show what you need to measure and calculate.

12. The fastest-flying insect is the Australian dragonfly. It can reach a speed of 58 km/h (16 m/s) and maintain this speed for a short time. In longer flights, the fastest insects (the horsefly, the deer botfly, and the hawk moth, for example) can fly 250 m in about 23 s.
    (a) If an Australian dragonfly maintained its maximum flying speed for 7.8 s, how far would it travel in metres?
    (b) What is a horsefly's maximum flying speed?

Critical Thinking

13. Many popular sports depend on machines that have engines designed for speed or power rather than fuel efficiency or minimum pollution. Drag racing and road racing cars, "monster trucks," sport-utility vehicles, and speedboats all burn large amounts of fuel and produce correspondingly large amounts of pollutants. For example, each litre of gasoline burned produces about 2.3 kg of carbon dioxide, a greenhouse gas. Do you think that inefficient recreational vehicles should be restricted or even banned in order to protect the environment? Explain your answer.

14. Galileo, who first observed that objects with different masses fall at the same rate, was imprisoned because some of his ideas were seen as a threat to society. Do you know of times when modern scientists have been discouraged from following unpopular or possibly dangerous lines of research? Should this happen, or should scientists be able to investigate whatever they are interested in? Investigate the fate of cold fusion, human embryo clones, the mohole project, or the superconducting super-collider.

Pause& Reflect

Go back to the beginning of the chapter, on page 282, and check your original answers to the Opening Ideas questions and the Starting Point Activity questions. How has your thinking changed? Which answers have been confirmed by what you studied or remembered during the chapter? Which answers need to be changed?

10 Uniform Motion

- What is the closest thing to uniform motion that you have ever observed?

- What factors might prevent objects from moving uniformly on Earth or in space?

- What other phenomena besides uniform motion cannot be observed directly, even in the best laboratory, and must be inferred from imperfect observations?

Science Log

Recall what you already know about scientific models. How can uniform motion be a useful model for real motion, if real motion is never quite uniform? If uniform motion is not "real," why study it? Discuss these questions with a partner, and then write your ideas in your Science Log.

Slow or fast, every motion that we observe on Earth changes its direction. Big cats dodge and swerve as they run down their prey. Dancers and gymnasts follow complex paths, speeding up or slowing down continuously. Footballs and baseballs eventually slow down and stop.

Predicting the behaviour of a moving object can be very complex. If you are an athlete, you know how difficult it is to compete against someone who makes tricky moves. Navigating in busy traffic can be scary for beginning drivers. Scientists face the same problems. Measuring and analyzing motion in the real world is a challenge, whether you are tracking an aircraft by radar or trying to complete a physics investigation.

Scientists who study motion often try to simplify their task. They can imagine what **uniform motion** — motion with absolutely no change in speed or direction — would be like, even if they never actually observe it. Then, because uniform motion is quite easy to analyze, they can use it as a scientific model: a simplified way to picture or represent the real world. This will be your task in this chapter: to model the behaviour of objects that move in almost straight lines at almost constant speed.

The Sound Barrier

Trying to measure extremely fast speeds can be frustrating. The distance travelled is often small, so the time taken is extremely short. In this activity, you will attempt to measure a fairly fast speed: the speed of sound through air.

What You Need

long tape measure (at least 10 m)
2 wooden blocks
pair of gloves
set of ear plugs or defenders
several stopwatches

Key Concepts

In this chapter, you will discover

- how to interpret position-time and velocity-time graphs
- why the slope of a line on a graph is important
- how motion technology has changed over time

Key Skills

In this chapter, you will

- draw and analyze position-time and velocity-time graphs
- use mathematical techniques to solve problems about uniform motion
- design and perform experiments to measure an object's uniform motion

Key Terms

- uniform motion
- slope
- tangent line
- motion formula
- cost-benefit analysis
- multi-speed gear system
- derailleur gears
- inertial guidance systems
- Global Positioning System (GPS)
- velocity-time graph
- bob (of a pendulum)
- equilibrium position
- cycle (of a pendulum)

Starting Point ACTIVITY

What to Do

1. Work in a group of about five students. Go outside the school, and find a fairly large, flat wall. Measure a distance of 50 m away from the wall.

2. Have a designated group member stand at this distance from the wall, wearing gloves and ear protection. The other members of the group will act as timers or recorders. They should stand a few metres to one side of the designated member, but also 50 m away from the wall.

3. Have the designated member slam the two blocks together hard. The other members record the time between the production of the sound and the returning echo.

4. Repeat step 3 several times, and find an average time.

5. Repeat steps 3 and 4 for other distances, such as 75 m and 100 m.

6. Calculate the speed of sound obtained at each distance. When using the formula $v = \dfrac{d}{t}$, remember that sound travels *to* the school wall and then *back* to the group.

What Did You Discover?

1. What was the speed of sound for each distance from the school?

2. If there was a difference in times, which time would you trust the most? Why?

3. How might this activity be improved?

Extension

4. Make a position-time graph to show your average times for different distances. Put time on the horizontal axis. What shape is your graph? What does this tell you about the speed of sound?

10.1 Position, Time, and Velocity

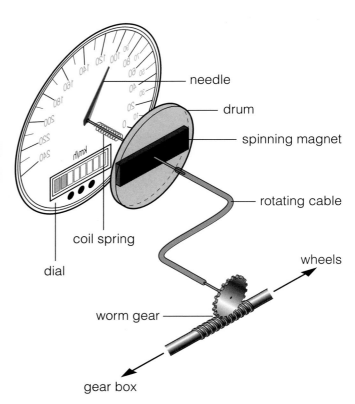

Figure 10.1 A car speedometer measures the rotation of the drive shaft. Then it converts the information into km/h on a dial or a digital display.

How can you tell whether an object is moving uniformly? You need to check whether it has constant velocity: that is, neither its speed nor its direction of motion is changing. Direction is easy to check. The object must be moving in a straight line forward or back, up or down. You can measure speed in many ways. For example, you can use a speedometer, as in a car, or observe changes in waves reflected from the object, as in a police radar gun. Even if the motion of an object is not uniform overall, you can often break down the motion into small steps. Each step *can* be modelled as uniform motion. In the next activity, you will put this idea into practice, investigating complex motions through words, graphs, and actions.

Figure 10.2 A tightrope walk, described in words and pictures

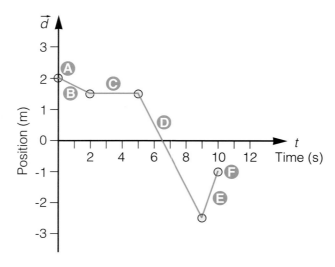

A Start 2 m to the right of the centre of the rope.

B Move very slowly to the left for 2 s.

C Stand still for 3 s.

D Move more quickly to the left for 4 s.

E Move even faster to the right for 1 s.

F End up 1 m left of the centre of the rope.

The Motion "Improv" Challenge

Drama students often practise their skills by doing an "improv" — acting out a short improvised scene. After getting only a brief description of the scene, the students create movement, actions, and dialogue while they perform. Can you do the same thing in physics — work in pairs to act out a set of motions "on the spot" from a brief written or graphical description?

What You Need

paper
pencil
stopwatch
ultrasonic motion sensor
computer (optional)

What to Do

1. The photograph in Figure 10.2 shows a tightrope walker moving back and forth, high above the ground. As you watch for 10 s, the tightrope walker changes direction four or five times. He moves at different constant speeds in each section of the tightrope walk.

2. Act out the motion of a tightrope walker while a partner writes a point-form description of each part of your motion. (The captions in Figure 10.2 give an example.) If you are planning to use an ultrasonic motion sensor, imagine that the motion stays within the region that the sensor can measure (usually from 0.5 to 4 m from the sensor). The description should include
   - the starting position: d_i metres left (negative) or right (positive) of the centre of the rope
   - the direction of motion in each section
   - the length of time, to the nearest second, that the motion in each section continues: Δt_1, Δt_2, Δt_3, . . . for the first, second, third, . . . sections
   - the speed of motion: very slow, slow, quick, very quick
   - the ending position: d_f metres left (negative) or right (positive) of the centre of the rope

3. On the other side of the paper, sketch a position-time graph of the motion you acted out. Make sure that your graph correctly represents the written description. The graph in Figure 10.2 is an example of one possible "tightrope walk."

4. If you are using an ultrasonic motion sensor, act out your motion in front of it. Make sure that your graph agrees with the sensor's graph.

5. Trade papers with another pair. Without looking at their graph, sketch a position-time graph while your partner acts out their motion according to their directions. Then check your graph against the graph they drew.

6. Trade papers with a different pair. This time, have your partner act out the motion by looking at the graph while you write a description of the motion. Then check your description against the description you were given.

What Did You Discover?

1. Which was easier to follow, the graph or the written description of the motion? Which particular movements were hardest to act out? What extra information is needed to make sure that you end up at the proper point after each set of movements?

2. **(a)** Do you think that your graphs show an overall uniform motion?
   (b) Do some parts of your graphs show uniform motion?
   (c) What feature of a position-time graph suggests uniform motion?

Extension

3. How could you adapt the techniques in this activity to record an ice-skating routine?

Graph Shapes

There are only three types of uniform motion, as shown in Figure 10.3. Study Figure 10.3 so that you can recognize each type of motion from its graph, and you can sketch the proper graph from each description.

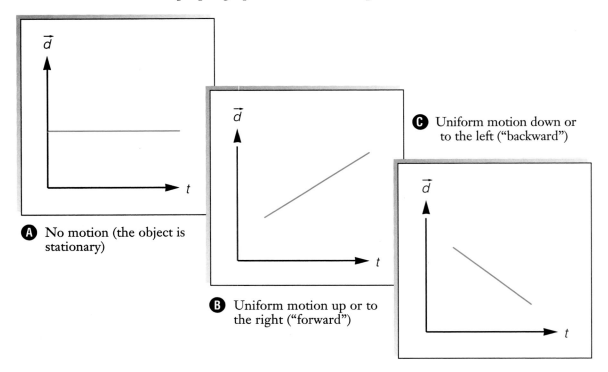

C Uniform motion down or to the left ("backward")

A No motion (the object is stationary)

B Uniform motion up or to the right ("forward")

Figure 10.3 These are the three basic types of position-time graphs for uniform motion.

The straight-line part of the graph does not always begin at the origin. If an object in an experiment starts from a standstill, for example, it has to speed up at the beginning. Its initial motion is not uniform, so the beginning of its position-time graph is curved.

If an object's speed or direction of motion changes during an experiment, its position-time graph can have several straight-line segments, as you saw in the

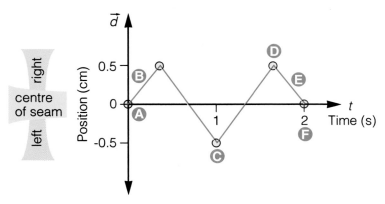

Figure 10.4 When sewing some types of stitches, the needle on a sewing machine moves sideways as well as up and down.

The motion graph shows that the needle

A starts in the centre of the line of stitches

B moves uniformly to the right until it is 5 mm from the centre line

C moves uniformly to the left until it is −5 mm from the centre line

D moves uniformly back to the right until it is 5 mm from the centre line

E moves uniformly back to the centre line

F stops

last activity. Figure 10.4 shows another example of this kind of motion. Each straight-line segment represents part of the sewing needle's motion, which is uniform. Between straight-line segments, while the needle's speed and direction are changing, the graph should really be a tight curve. For simplicity, however, graphs are often drawn without these curved portions, as though the object "jumped" straight from one velocity to another. This simplifies the graphs but also makes them less realistic.

Velocity and Slope

Graphs and hills have one similarity: both can be described by their slope. In mathematics, the **slope** of a line is calculated as

$$\text{Slope} = \frac{\text{Rise}}{\text{Run}}$$

If you are analyzing a straight-line graph, the slope is the same over any part of the graph. Therefore you can measure and calculate the slope of the whole line, or just part of it.

Remember:

- A positive slope rises as you move to the right.
- A negative slope falls as you move to the right.

In the next investigation, you will investigate how measuring the slope of a position-time graph relates to the motion the graph illustrates.

Across Canada

Have you ever dreamed of becoming an astronaut? How do you make such a dream — any impossible-sounding dream — come true? You could ask Julie Payette. On May 29, 1999, she became the 8th Canadian to fly into space, aboard the Space Shuttle *Discovery*. For Julie, this ten-day mission was just the latest stage in a long and varied journey that began in Montréal, Québec, where she was born in 1962. That journey has taken her to many different places in Europe, the United States, and Canada, in pursuit of her goals.

The first stop on Julie's quest was Atlantic College in Wales, U.K., where she won a scholarship to study at age 16. "Atlantic College helped open my mind and broaden my horizons. I met people from all over the world and shared incredible experiences." Julie returned to Montréal to earn a degree in engineering at McGill University. She then attained a Master's degree in computer processing design at the University of Toronto. This was followed by further work on computer voice recognition in Zurich, Switzerland,

and at McGill. Her astronaut training with the CSA (Canadian Space Agency) and NASA has taken her to Moose Jaw, Saskatchewan to qualify as a pilot, and to Houston, Texas to train for her role in last year's mission. Julie acted as the on-board "director" for the mission's space walks.

Julie Payette

Julie Payette has a truly global perspective. As she says, "To work while orbiting Earth, to contribute to the pursuit of scientific knowledge, and to be able to see our world from above is an extraordinary privilege. From orbit, you can't see political borders, but in a truly global fashion, you can help monitor and preserve our beautiful planet — our only home — for everyone."

What's in a Slope?

Think About It

The slope of a straight-line graph is fairly easy to calculate, but why bother? If slope were just another number, there would be little reason to calculate it. The slope of an object's motion graph, however, tells you something very useful about the object's behaviour — something that is often difficult to measure directly. By using basic algebra skills, you will discover what this "something" is.

What to Do

1 Imagine a line of people dancing the "Bunny Hop." In one part of the dance, they hop one step forward, one step back, and then forward three times. Suppose that each hop is 35 cm long. Copy and complete the position-time table below. Give your table a title.

Interval	Time (s)	Position (m)	Movement
1 {	0.0	0.00	} forward one hop
2 {	1.0	+0.35	} backward one hop
3 {	2.0	0.00	} forward one hop
4 {	2.5	?	} forward one hop
5 {	3.0	?	} forward one hop
6 {	3.5	?	} pause
	4.0	?	

2 Draw a position-time graph of the dancers' movement. If you have access to computer graphing software, print the graph. If the software permits, include the slope of the last section of the line (the hop-hop-hop).

3 Find a numerical value for the slope of the last section of the graph by following the directions below.

(a) Pick any two points on the line, and use them to draw a slope triangle. Hint: Pick whole-number time values, if possible.

(b) At the vertices of the slope triangle, label t_1, t_2, d_1, and d_2.

(c) Use the scales on the graph to find numerical values for t_1, t_2, d_1, and d_2.

(d) Calculate the slope of the graph section, using the formula

$$\text{Slope} = \frac{\text{Rise}}{\text{Run}}$$

4 Now find a formula for the slope of the same section of the line by following these directions.

(a) Use the symbols d_1 and d_2 to write two expressions for the rise (change in the vertical part) of your slope triangle. Write one expression with the Δ notation and one without it.

(b) Using the symbols t_1 and t_2, write two expressions for the run (change in the horizontal part) of your slope triangle. Write one with the Δ notation and one without it.

(c) Use your answers to directions (a) and (b) to write two expressions for the slope of the triangle: one with the Δ notation and one without it.

Skill
POWER

If you need to review determining the slope of a straight line, turn to page 604.

Analyze

1. Label each section of your graph as "positive slope" or "negative slope."

2. Recall the expressions that you wrote for the slope of the position-time graph in Chapter 9, section 9.3. What physical quantity do both these expressions define?

3. Check that your expression for slope in step 4(c) has the same units as the quantity it defines.

   (a) What is the standard unit for measuring the quantity in the numerator of your expression?

   (b) What is the standard unit for measuring the quantity in the denominator of your expression?

Conclude and Apply

4. Taken together, the numerator and the denominator of your expression give the slope of the position-time graph. According to your answers to Analyze question 3, what standard units of measurement does the slope have?

5. Which quantity is also measured in these units? What can you conclude about velocity, rate of change of distance, and the slope of a position-time graph?

Extend Your Skills

6. Draw a different slope triangle on the last section of your graph. Calculate a numerical value for its slope.

7. Do your two values for slope agree exactly? If not, could you say that they agree "within a reasonable experimental error"? Remember that, in the rules for significant digits, the last figure of any measurement is uncertain because it was estimated.

8. Draw a third slope triangle from the very beginning to the very end of your graph. Use it to calculate the *average* velocity of the dancers over the whole time interval you graphed.

9. Is the dancers' average velocity over the whole time interval equal to either of the other two velocities that you calculated in this investigation? Why or why not?

Pause& Reflect

Sketch a position-time graph of each object listed below. Describe its slope as positive or negative, and as constant, increasing, or decreasing.

(a) a stone at rest
(b) a jogger moving steadily to the right
(c) a bicycle moving to the left and slowing down
(d) a rocket moving up at an increasing speed
(e) a stone falling freely with increasing speed
(f) a parachutist drifting down at a steady speed

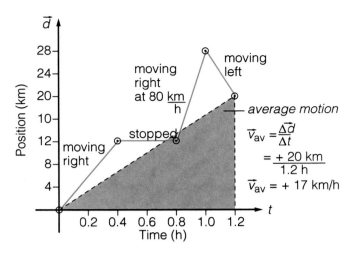

Figure 10.5 "But officer, I only travelled 17 km in the last hour. 17 km/h isn't speeding!"

Average or Instantaneous?

Can you use the language of physics to explain the driver's reasoning? A graph of his car's position over the hour can help you picture what happened. Each section of the graph has a different slope, reflecting the car's *instanta-*

neous velocity at that stage of the journey. Ignoring these stages, you can find an *average* velocity for the whole journey using just two points, one at the beginning and one at the end. Which kind of velocity did the police officer measure?

The Legal Speed Limit

How law-abiding are the drivers in your community? In this activity, you will design a method to measure the average velocity of vehicles that pass your school. Then you will use your method to look for any consistent driving patterns.

CAUTION:
- For your own safety, stay back from the road while you work on this activity.
- For the safety of the motorists, do nothing to distract them as they drive past.

What to Do

1. Devise a method to determine the average velocity (speed and direction) of vehicles that pass your school. Include the following considerations in your proposed method:
   (a) Observe a straight stretch of road. Only record vehicles travelling in one direction.
   (b) Ideally, the drivers should not know that they are being observed.
   (c) Take your measurements over a reasonably large distance.
   (d) Try to observe a stretch of road along which most vehicles travel without stopping or changing speed significantly.

Science Inquiry ACTIVITY

2. List any apparatus you will need.

3. Decide on the factors that you would like to examine. Do more drivers speed in the morning than at noon? Do more van drivers break the speed limit than drivers of family sedans? Is the driver's age a factor?

4. Discuss your method with your teacher, and then carry out your method. Be prepared to present your findings to the rest of the class.

What Did You Discover?

1. Give reasons for each of steps 1(a) to (d) in *What to Do*.

2. What percentage of drivers obey the speed limit near your school?

3. Can you see any pattern in your results? Is your pattern firm enough to be called a scientific law? Give reasons for your answer.

4. Which did you observe, the average velocity of the passing vehicles or their instantaneous velocity? Do you think there was much difference between the average and instantaneous velocities of most of the vehicles you observed? If so, why? If not, why not?

In many situations, such as getting a speeding ticket, average velocity is less important than the velocity at a specific moment — the instantaneous velocity. A car's speedometer and a police radar gun record instantaneous velocity. The slope of a position-time graph can be used to estimate instantaneous velocity, even if the graph curves as the object speeds up and slows down. You need to visualize a **tangent line**. A straight line is a tangent line if it touches the curve at just one point. Its slope matches the steepness of the graph at the point you are interested in. Figure 10.6 shows how this is done.

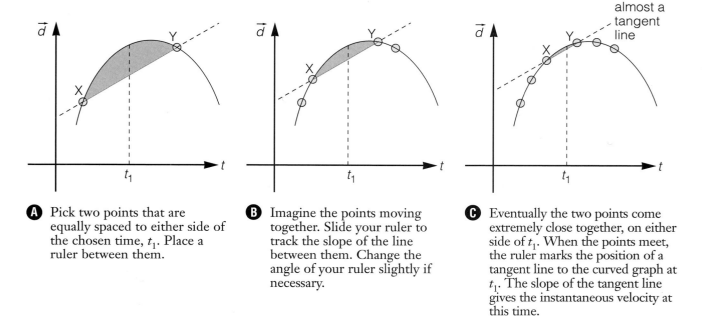

A Pick two points that are equally spaced to either side of the chosen time, t_1. Place a ruler between them.

B Imagine the points moving together. Slide your ruler to track the slope of the line between them. Change the angle of your ruler slightly if necessary.

C Eventually the two points come extremely close together, on either side of t_1. When the points meet, the ruler marks the position of a tangent line to the curved graph at t_1. The slope of the tangent line gives the instantaneous velocity at this time.

Figure 10.6 You can estimate instantaneous velocity by finding the slope of a tangent line at the time you are interested in (t_1).

In Figure 10.6, the instantaneous velocity is estimated by measuring average speeds over smaller and smaller time intervals. Think back to the activity you just completed. Try to explain why you needed to keep the time intervals for your speed measurements fairly short. Also give a reason (a different reason) why the time intervals could not be *too* short.

Using the Motion Formula

In Chapter 9, section 9.3, you learned about rates of change, and you encountered the formula

$$\text{Rate of change} = \frac{\text{Total change}}{\text{Time interval}}$$

Physicists agree to define velocity as the rate of change of position:

$$\text{Velocity} = \frac{\text{Change in position}}{\text{Time interval}} = \frac{\text{Displacement}}{\text{Time interval}}$$

$$\vec{v} = \frac{\Delta \vec{d}}{\Delta t}$$

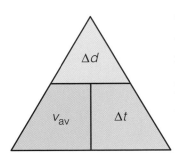

Figure 10.7 Cover up the variable that you want to find. The positions of the other two variables show you how to rearrange the motion formula.

Skill
P O W E R

If you need extra practice with the GRASP method, or with algebraic expressions, turn to page 610.

You have been thinking about two different types of velocity — average and instantaneous. Which type does the formula define? Think graphically. The formula involves a time interval, Δt, with a beginning and an end. On a position-time graph, you would usually find the velocity (the slope of the graph) using a slope triangle drawn from one end of the time interval to the other end. This would give the average velocity during the time interval. So the formula should be written as

$$\vec{v}_{av} = \frac{\Delta \vec{d}}{\Delta t}$$

(Can you see the difference?) This formula is often called the **motion formula.** The vector symbols are usually omitted for straight-line motion, because direction can simply be indicated by positive and negative signs. Sometimes you will need to rearrange the formula to find the displacement (Δd) or time taken (Δt) for a particular motion. The "formula triangle" in Figure 10.7 shows you how to do this.

The motion formula is one of the basic mathematical tools of physics. Often you will use it informally as you do lab work or analyze experiments, entering numbers directly into your calculator or making rough calculations on scrap paper. For lab reports, assignments, or tests, you need to show clearly how you did your calculations, so the reader can follow and check each step. The GRASP method of problem-solving, which you saw in Chapter 9, is one standard way to arrange mathematical work. The GRASP method is clear, complete, and helpful for organizing and communicating your thinking.

Word CONNECT

A ray of light can travel 9460 billion kilometres in one year, so astronomers call this distance a *light year.* Thus the speed of light is about 300 000 km per *second.* Even at that incredibly fast speed, our Sun's nearest stellar neighbour, Proxima Centauri, is over four light years away. To cross the Milky Way galaxy would take light about 75 000 years, more than five times as long as human civilization has existed. Obviously light speed is much too slow for science-fiction writers and filmmakers, and so they delight in proposing faster-than-light starships.

Some physicists suspect that there may be particles that can travel faster than the speed of light. They have named such particles *tachyons.* To date, no one has seen any evidence for them, such as *Cherenkov radiation* in a vacuum. Einstein's theory of relativity shows that no ordinary particle can speed up to move faster than the speed of light in a vacuum, but this does not rule out particles that *always* move faster than light.

Where does the name "tachyon" come from, and who invented it? What is Cherenkov radiation? Is it usually seen in a vacuum? What ideas have science-fiction writers invented to break the light-speed barrier? Do you think any of these ideas could work?

The blue glow of Cherenkov radiation in a nuclear reactor

Math CONNECT

Suppose that a car is travelling at 72 km/h. What is its speed in m/s? Find a standard *conversion factor* (the number that you must divide by) for converting km/h to m/s.

So far in this chapter, you have been using the concept of uniform motion as a model for real-life motion. The idea of combining theory and observations has a long history. Over 2000 years ago, the Greek philosopher Plato argued that nothing in the natural world can be understood completely using observations alone. All observations have slight errors, so they cannot be trusted completely. To find the truth, we must picture an ideal, error-free situation by thinking logically.

Plato taught that *everything* we observe is like an imperfect shadow of a perfect ideal. Every horse is enough like an ideal horse (the "form" of a horse) that we can recognize and classify it. Plato also said that these ideal forms must be as "real" as anything we can touch or see. Otherwise, how could we all learn to recognize and classify in the same way, and to agree that a particular animal really is a horse? What do you think?

1. Review your Science Log entry for page 318. Did you agree with Plato or not? Would you change your answer now?

2. Modern scientists rely heavily on experiments to learn about nature. Does this mean that Plato was wrong and that experiments can be trusted? Explain.

Plato and Aristotle, as painted by Raphael

Check Your Understanding

1. What are the special features of uniform motion?

2. Examine each position-time graph below, and describe the following features.
   (a) slope of the graph (positive/zero/negative; increasing/constant/decreasing)
   (b) speed (increasing/constant/decreasing)
   (c) direction of motion (to observer's right or left)
   (d) velocity of the object

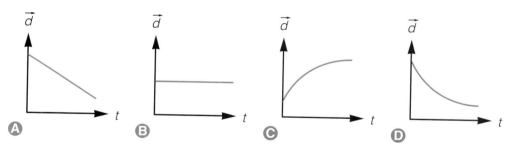

3. Compare the average slope of a position-time graph with the slope at a particular point.
   (a) What does each slope tell you about the motion?
   (b) How is each slope measured?
   (c) For what shape of graph are the two slopes always identical? What kind of motion is this?

4. **Apply** Copy the table opposite, and use the motion formula to fill in the blanks. Write out each calculation in proper form, and round your answer appropriately.

5. **Thinking Critically** Refer back to the Stretch Your Mind above. Why did Plato argue that observations and experiments could not be trusted completely?

d	t	v_{av}
10.5 m	4.3 s	
	8.2 s	25 m/s
164 km		110 km/h

10.2 Getting Around

Figure 10.8 What does being late for an English class have to do with physics?

DidYouKnow?

One of the world's worst air disasters occurred on the ground. On March 27, 1977, two fully-loaded Boeing 747 airplanes collided on a runway at Tenerife in the Canary Islands. Special systems failed which should have told each pilot where the other plane was at all times, and 583 lives were lost.

Panic! Your last-period teacher kept talking after the class ended, you are stuck in a congested hallway, and there is less than a minute before the next class begins. Can you possibly make it on time?

Getting to class on time may not seem like a physics problem, but it is certainly a matter of distance, time, and velocity. So are many other aspects of everyday life, although the quantities may not be as precise as the quantities you use in science class. In athletics, for example, speed is often inferred from a competitor's time for an event, rather than being calculated exactly. If you read that Donovan Bailey ran 100 m in 9.84 s at the 1996 Summer Olympics in Atlanta, Georgia, you immediately realize that this is very fast. You do not have to work out that it represents an average speed of 36 km/h — faster than a car in a school zone, and a world record at the time.

Pause& Reflect

Think about controlling air traffic at airports, routing trains that run in opposite directions on a single track, or planning a vacation. Scheduling any form of transport involves relationships between distance, speed, direction, and time. In a group or with a partner, brainstorm as many different scheduling situations as possible. Estimate the precision of measurement that you think would be appropriate for each situation. Also describe any particular measurement problems that might affect it.

Check Out the Route

Solving a practical motion problem differs from a physics experiment in several ways. Imagine planning a car trip, for example. You might say, looking at Figure 10.9, "I think we can make it from Edmonton to Calgary in less than 3 h. The distance looks like about 300 km. On the main highway, where the speed limit is 110 km/h, I've heard that traffic usually moves pretty steadily all the way."

In the example below, notice that the map scale in Figure 10.9 is treated as exact. Therefore it does not affect the number of significant digits in the answer.

0 10 20 30 40 50 60 70 80 90 100

kilometres

scale : 1 : 2 000 000
1 cm = 20 km

A *Distance (d) and speed (v) are used instead of displacement and velocity.* Direction is likely to keep changing, and it is determined by the road. You can show this by writing the motion formula without vector symbols, as

$$v = \frac{\Delta d}{\Delta t} \text{ or simply } v = \frac{d}{t}.$$

B *Speeds are difficult to predict in advance.* Any vehicle speeds up and slows down as weather and traffic conditions change. You can use speed limits and average speeds to estimate travel times roughly, but actual times vary a great deal.

C *Distances are often estimated from a map.* Either use a ruler or lay a piece of sewing thread along the route and then straighten and measure the thread. Using the map scale, you can calculate the actual distance in kilometres.

Figure 10.9 How long should you allow for a journey like this?

Model Problem

On the map in Figure 10.9, the measured distance along Highway 2 from the northern edge of Calgary to the southern edge of Edmonton is 13.5 cm. What is the actual distance between the two cities?

Given   measured distance = 13.5 cm
map scale: 1 cm = 20 km

Required   actual distance, d, in km

Analyze   Use the map scale to write the ratio.
$$\frac{\text{Actual distance}}{\text{Map distance}} = \frac{20 \text{ km}}{1 \text{ cm}}$$

Solution $\dfrac{\text{Actual distance}}{\text{Map distance}} = \dfrac{d \text{ km}}{13.5 \text{ cm}} = \dfrac{20 \text{ km}}{1 \text{ cm}}$

So $d \text{ km} = 20 \text{ km} \times \dfrac{13.5 \text{ cm}}{1 \text{ cm}}$

$= 270 \text{ km}$

Paraphrase   From the map, the distance from the northern edge of Calgary to the southern edge of Edmonton, along Highway 2, is about 270 km.

Math CONNECT

Use a road map or an atlas to find the distance from Saint John, New Brunswick, to Montréal, Québec. Estimate an average speed, and work out how many hours of driving this trip would take. How long should you allow for the trip, including rest and food breaks? Would it be practical and safe to make the trip in a single day? Explain your answer.

Are We There Yet?

In this activity, you will estimate distances from a map. You will use the motion formula to work out travel times between different places and by different routes. Then, you will use your calculations to plan a sightseeing trip in Cape Breton, Nova Scotia.

What You Need

ruler   sewing thread
map of Cape Breton (provided by your teacher)

What to Do

1. Decide on a method to measure each distance below on the map of Cape Breton, and to calculate the actual distances in kilometres.
   (a) the straight-line distance ("as the crow flies") between Port Hastings and Sydney
   (b) the distance from Port Hastings to Sydney along the northern route, following Highways 105 and 125
   (c) the distance from Port Hastings to Sydney along the southern route, following Highways 104 and 4

2. Most road maps, including this one, include actual driving distances between marked points.
   (a) Find these driving distances on the map. Total them along the northern and southern routes between Port Hastings and Sydney.
   (b) Compare the totals with the distances you calculated in step 1 by working out a percent difference.
   (c) Does the method you used in step 1 seem to be accurate enough for estimating travel distances? Justify your answer.

3. A travel guide lists the driving distance between Port Hastings and Sydney as 165 km and gives 2 h as the average driving time.
   (a) Is the guide using the northern or southern route? Explain your answer.
   (b) Calculate an average driving speed based on the figures in the guide.
   (c) Assume that you could travel at the same speed on the other route. Work out how long the trip would take.

4. The Cabot Trail is a very scenic route around the northern part of Cape Breton Island. Answer the questions below to plan a trip along the Cabot Trail. Support your answers with appropriate calculations.
   (a) Assume that you enter the trail, heading north from Highway 105 and going toward Middle River, at 10:00 a.m. You want to stop for a picnic lunch some time between 12:00 and 1:00 p.m. Suggest an appropriate place to stop and eat.
   (b) If you take 1 h for lunch, when will you likely arrive in St Ann's?
   (c) If you spend 45 min shopping for souvenirs in St Ann's, what time will you reach the campground at Baddeck?
   (d) Will you have time to tour the Alexander Graham Bell Museum at Baddeck before supper at 6:00 p.m.?
   (e) Suppose you follow a similar schedule the next day, leaving Baddeck at 10:00 a.m. and returning by 6:00 p.m. How long could you spend at the National Historic Site at Louisbourg?
   (f) If you want to allow at least 4 h to tour Louisbourg, should you plan on returning to your campsite at Baddeck? Would it be better to leave this campsite, drive to Louisbourg, and camp there for the night?

Faster and Farther: Improving Motion Technology

Are people in Western cultures addicted to high-speed travel? Modes of transport in pre-industrial societies tend to remain unchanged for centuries. Loads are carried by people or hauled by animals. In Europe and North America, however, the industrial revolution brought immense efforts by scientists and engineers to develop faster and more powerful motion technologies. People and goods could move at ever greater speeds over longer and longer distances.

For example, think again about the journey between the cities of Toronto and Ottawa in Ontario. Figure 10.10 shows how this journey has changed over the last century or so. Can you find a similar example in your own part of Canada?

A In the late nineteenth century, stagecoach service between Toronto and Ottawa dramatically shortened the journey, to only 5–6 days.

B Gasoline-powered automobiles and an all-weather gravel road reduced the travel time to about 12 h by 1920.

C Long-distance driving was still a challenge, however. Many people preferred to use one of the frequent passenger trains, which in 1940 took only 8 h to go between the cities.

D By the late 1950s, the convenience of automobile transport had caused a great increase in inter-city traffic. The road was made into a modern highway. Driving time was around 4–5 h. People abandoned the railway passenger service, which was eventually cancelled.

E Highway traffic continued to increase, and maintenance and congestion became major problems in the 1980s and 1990s.

Figure 10.10 Evolution of a journey

As each change in Figure 10.10 occurred, people debated its benefits and its costs. Figure 10.11 sets out some of the perspectives that can be used in such a debate.

In the next activity, you will have the chance to debate a transport issue from some of these perspectives. You will weigh the advantages (benefits) and disadvantages (costs) of different courses of action. This process is sometimes called a **cost-benefit analysis**.

An *ethical* perspective tries to determine whether the change is right or wrong, according to generally accepted beliefs and values. How will the change affect the quality of people's everyday lives? Do we have the right to change the world in this way?

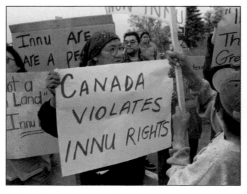

A *legal* perspective focusses on responsibilities and fair treatment, according to current laws and past decisions. What laws and regulations apply to the change? Who will be affected, and how will these people and groups be compensated?

A *technological* perspective focusses on manufacturing processes or devices. What machinery will be involved in the change? How can its efficiency and performance be improved?

A *political* perspective focusses on the role of the government. Should public funds help to pay for the change? Is it popular with voters?

An *economic* perspective focusses on money. How much will the changes cost? Who will pay for them?

An *ecological* perspective is concerned with relationships between living things and their environment. How will the change affect the natural environment? Are its effects reversible?

Figure 10.11 Perspectives on change

A *scientific* perspective tries to understand, explain, and predict the effects of the change. What problems might arise from it? What future technologies are possible, according to current scientific theory? Should these technologies be taken into account in current planning?

Just a Minute Now . . .

High-speed transport is a fact of life in our society. Rapid changes in motion technology are taken for granted. Many people — perhaps you — assume that faster travel is "better" and that newer technologies are preferable to existing ones. Here is a chance to develop and apply a more critical view.

What to Do

1. Refer to Figure 10.10. In your group, pick one of the changes in land transport as an issue. Imagine that it is a current issue, so you do not know how the change will turn out.

2. Brainstorm costs and benefits of the change from at least four of the perspectives outlined in Figure 10.11. Keep track of your ideas in a table, similar to the one below.

Change: Paving the Highway

Perspective	Benefit	Cost
political	popular with travellers	Fewer stops are required. It may put hotels and restaurants out of business.
ecological		

3. Divide your group into pairs, and pick one perspective for each pair to develop. In each pair, one person should argue for the change and the other person should oppose it. Support your position with examples, logical arguments, or personal experiences. Be dramatic and convincing, but make sure that your presentation is properly thought out and takes no longer than 2 min.

Science Inquiry ACTIVITY

4. In your group, sum up each pair's arguments on an overhead transparency or flip chart.

5. Be ready to present your group's discussion of the issue to the class. Use your visual aid to summarize the arguments.

6. Listen to each group's presentation in turn, recording which side of each argument you agree with. After each group is done, record whether you are generally in favour of the change or opposed to it.

7. Tally the class responses to each argument. Also tally the number of people in favour of and opposed to the change itself.

What Did You Discover?

1. Which perspectives did you find most convincing? Which were not important to you?

2. How did your responses to the arguments compare with those of your classmates? Did you tend to hold the majority or minority position?

3. Describe how you felt when you were presenting your perspective to your classmates.

Extension

4. Have you ever taken a public stand to oppose or favour a proposed technological change? For example, you might have signed a petition, written a letter, attended a meeting, or telephoned a radio or television program. Describe what happened, and explain why you took this stand.

As you found out in the last activity, a technological change can raise major societal issues. What causes a technological change? How is it linked to scientific discoveries and technical innovations? How do developments in a particular technology affect other related fields? Historians of science have studied the growth of many technologies, with these questions in mind. In the following investigation, you will take a historical viewpoint, tracing and analyzing the development of a particular motion technology over time.

The Better Bicycle

Think About It

The time line on the next three pages shows some important events in the development of the bicycle. Use it as your primary reference for this investigation. You may also need to consult other reference sources, however.

What to Do

1. Study the time line, and summarize the following information from the time line in your notebook. Use point form.

   • changes in materials as the bicycle developed

   • ideas that were not adopted at first but were later used or re-invented
   • ideas that completely changed people's idea of how a bicycle could be built
   • new technologies that improved the design or performance of the bicycle
   • societal changes caused by the bicycle: for example, changes in women's fashions

2. Compare summaries with a partner, and add any information you overlooked.

3. Discuss the Analyze questions on page 339 with your partner, and then answer the questions.

1645
Jean Theson (France) takes out a patent on a four-wheeled machine that is propelled by two seated men. Not until 1779 is a large, slow machine, similar to Theson's design, seen on the streets of Paris.

1791
The Conte de Sivrac drives the *Célérifère*, a two-wheeled wooden device, through the streets of Paris. There is no easy way to steer it, however.

1818
Baron Karl de Drais de Sauerbrun astonishes citizens of Paris by exhibiting his riding machine, called the *draisienne*. It has a steerable front wheel, arm rests, a padded seat, and a brake on the rear wheel. The seated driver propels the device by pushing his feet against the ground. Copies are made in Britain and the U.S.A., but it never becomes popular.

1839
Kirkpatrick Macmillan, a Scottish blacksmith called "daft Pete" by his neighbours, constructs a bicycle with *swinging foot pedals* attached by levers to a crank on the rear wheel. In 1842, Macmillan outraces a horse-drawn carriage on his *hobbyhorse* but accidentally hits a child. He is fined for reckless driving, thus becoming the first law-breaking cyclist.

1894
American adventurer Annie Londonberry bicycles around the world.

1890
Combining an inexpensive diamond-shaped frame with pneumatic tires and effective brakes, the *Humber bicycle* establishes a basic design that is still used today. In France, a folding bicycle is developed for military use.

1873–1885
H. J. Lawson builds the first modern bicycle. Called the *safety bicycle*, it has a rear chain drive. Lawson spends the next 11 years perfecting his design. In 1885, John Starley (nephew of James) shows his version of the safety bicycle, which has brakes on both the front and rear wheels.

1888
John Dunlop, an Irish veterinarian, invents the *pneumatic (inflated) tire*, using linen from his wife's old dresses to strengthen the rubber tube.

1870
James Starley (England) tries to reduce the weight of a bicycle by using a very small rear wheel and a large front wheel. Because his device has no freewheel, it has footrests where the rider's feet can be placed while coasting. Starley's *penny farthing*, or *old ordinary*, is unstable and difficult to ride, but Starley continues working to improve it. (The name "penny farthing" comes from the names of two British copper coins of the time. A farthing was worth only one quarter of a penny and was much smaller.)

1861
Pierre and Ernest Michaux (France) start building the *boneshaker* or *vélocipède*, a wood-and-iron bicycle with a *pedal-driven front wheel*. Within four years, they are hand-making over 400 a year, and copies are being manufactured in Britain and the U.S.A.

1868–1869
J. Hastings makes *solid rubber tires* for his steam-driven bicycle. The *first recorded track race* for bicycles is held in France and is won by James Moore. The *first bicycle show*, in Paris, features machines with primitive gear systems and freewheels, which allow the wheels to keep turning while the driver's feet remain still.

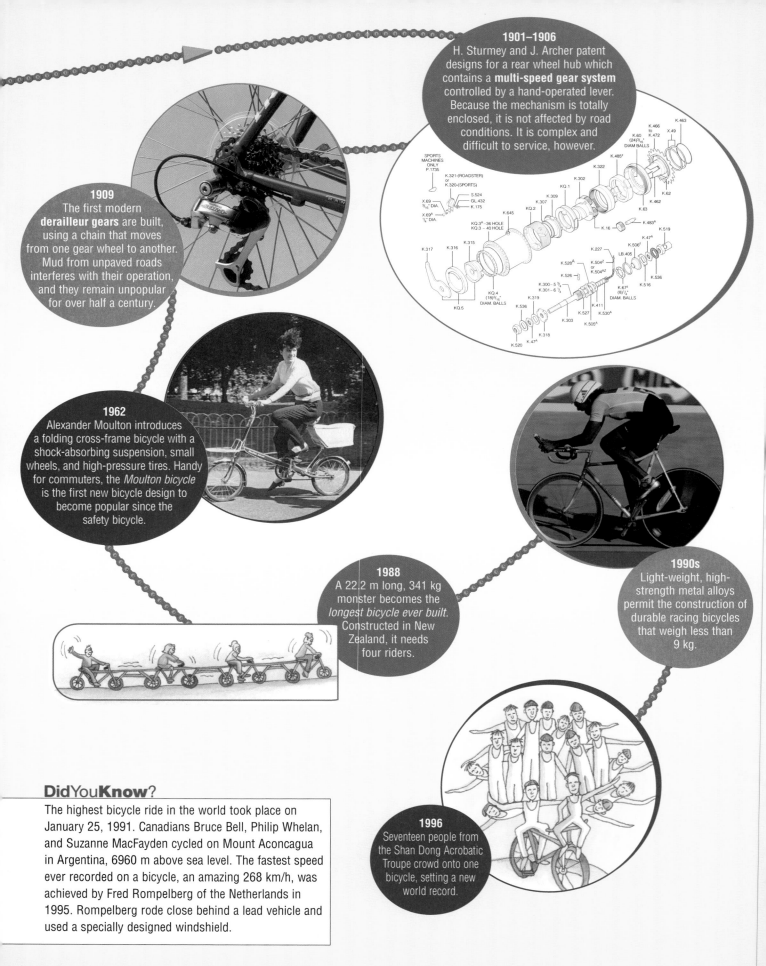

1901–1906
H. Sturmey and J. Archer patent designs for a rear wheel hub which contains a **multi-speed gear system** controlled by a hand-operated lever. Because the mechanism is totally enclosed, it is not affected by road conditions. It is complex and difficult to service, however.

1909
The first modern **derailleur gears** are built, using a chain that moves from one gear wheel to another. Mud from unpaved roads interferes with their operation, and they remain unpopular for over half a century.

1962
Alexander Moulton introduces a folding cross-frame bicycle with a shock-absorbing suspension, small wheels, and high-pressure tires. Handy for commuters, the *Moulton bicycle* is the first new bicycle design to become popular since the safety bicycle.

1988
A 22.2 m long, 341 kg monster becomes the *longest bicycle ever built*. Constructed in New Zealand, it needs four riders.

1990s
Light-weight, high-strength metal alloys permit the construction of durable racing bicycles that weigh less than 9 kg.

1996
Seventeen people from the Shan Dong Acrobatic Troupe crowd onto one bicycle, setting a new world record.

DidYou**Know**?

The highest bicycle ride in the world took place on January 25, 1991. Canadians Bruce Bell, Philip Whelan, and Suzanne MacFayden cycled on Mount Aconcagua in Argentina, 6960 m above sea level. The fastest speed ever recorded on a bicycle, an amazing 268 km/h, was achieved by Fred Rompelberg of the Netherlands in 1995. Rompelberg rode close behind a lead vehicle and used a specially designed windshield.

Analyze

1. Decide on your "top five" developments in the history of bicycle technology. Write a brief overview of these developments. Justify your choices by explaining the importance of each.

2. Some people question the value of "pure" scientific research, which does not have any obvious application. History shows, however, that this apparently "useless" information often leads to dramatic technological breakthroughs. Review how the performance of bicycles was improved as inventors tackled the following two problems. Then suggest at least two pieces of basic scientific knowledge that underlie the solutions to each problem.

   (a) finding an efficient way to allow a bicycle to travel at a variety of speeds, while the rider's feet move at a comfortable pace

   (b) reducing the weight and increasing the strength of early bicycle frames and wheels

3. Improvements in technology often introduce unexpected new problems. What new problems were caused by each innovation below? Describe at least one solution that has been developed for each problem.

   (a) inflatable tires that make bicycles much more comfortable to ride on rough roads

   (b) gear systems that allow bikers to reach much higher speeds

4. Any technology brings both benefits and costs. For example, off-road biking is an exciting and non-polluting sport (benefit). In sensitive river-bank ecosystems, however, it compacts soil, increases erosion, damages plants, and causes other ecological damage (costs). Make a cost-benefit analysis of the widespread use of modern bicycles, thinking particularly about environmental and safety issues.

5. Changing technologies have significant effects on attitudes, laws, and ways of thinking. For example, safety problems developed as bicycle speeds increased, but these problems did not prevent people from using bicycles. Instead, people learned to manage and accept the risks of this new mode of transport. Identify at least one effect that the development of modern bicycles has brought in each area listed below.

   (a) laws

   (b) individual attitudes

   (c) technologies to help cope with the risks of bicycling

Extend Your Knowledge

6. Use a library or the Internet to research the development of one subsystem of a bicycle: for example, the frame, gears, suspension, or brakes. Report your results as a time line, or in another form approved by your teacher.

7. Consumers expect products they buy, including bicycles, to be well-constructed and designed to give adequate safety and performance. In Canada, the Canadian Standards Association (CSA), government departments, the Consumer's Association of Canada, and special interest magazines and user groups are all involved in testing or regulating consumer products. Use a library or the Internet to research what standards bicycles have to meet. Who sets the standards and makes sure they are met? Where can consumers find accurate information to help them compare and evaluate competing bicycle models?

8. Skateboards, wheelchairs, hydrofoil boats, skis, and many other transportation technologies have well-documented histories. Choose another transport technology that interests you, and prepare a time line to show its development. Use the bicycle time line you have been studying as a model for the sort of information to seek.

Off the Wall

How can you ride a bicycle lying down? Believe it or not, there is an unusual and innovative bicycle that allows you to do this — the *recumbent bicycle.* The pedals and seat are placed to support the rider's weight much more evenly than a regular bicycle saddle does, and the rider's head does not have to bend back on the neck. Riding a "recumbent" is nearly as comfortable as sitting on a sofa!

Check Your Understanding

1. Which perspective would you expect a person in each occupation below to bring to a debate as a result of special training and experience?

   (a) business owner
   (b) Member of Parliament
   (c) research scientist
   (d) religious or spiritual leader

2. Give examples to explain what is meant by each of the following terms.

   (a) a *cost* of a technology
   (b) a *benefit* of a technology
   (c) cost-benefit analysis

3. **Apply** Advertisers have found that labelling a product "new" is a very powerful way to increase sales. From the information in this section, give at least two reasons and examples why consumers might not assume that "new" technologies are automatically better than established methods.

4. **Thinking Critically** Describe differences between scientific research and technological problem-solving in terms of

   (a) the type of questions that each activity starts with
   (b) the type of results that each activity produces

5. **Thinking Critically** Read this newspaper report on traffic problems 100 years ago. Then answer these questions.

   (a) Make a table comparing the problems caused by horse-drawn vehicles 100 years ago, and the problems of modern road traffic.
   (b) Do you think the introduction of motor vehicles improved city life, or made it worse? Justify your answer.

Horse-drawn carriages: an eco-disaster

The beginning of the twentieth century brought cries to reduce pollution by prohibiting the horse in American cities. Streets were beginning to be paved, and wheels and hooves ground sun-dried horse dung into a fine dust. The fecal dust in the air often caused chronic respiratory problems.

Traffic posed another problem. Horses and wagons clogged the roads. Pedestrians had to watch out for runaways, careless drivers, and the hooves of skittish animals. In one study, a total of 7912 horse-drawn vehicles passed a busy intersection in a 12 h period.

The cities, in turn, created a harsh environment for the horse. Some poor animals were beaten with whips, starved, and housed in filthy stalls. Urban horses became sick, or broke their legs stumbling on cobbles, and were left to die in the streets. In 1880, New York City dragged 15 000 dead horses off its streets.

The Hamilton Spectator, January 12, 2000

10.3 Velocity-Time Graphs

Driving down a twisting, foggy road can be a frightening experience. You can easily become lost, even though the speedometer tells you how fast you are going. Early sailors faced the same problem. They could estimate or measure their speed, but without landmarks, how could they determine their position?

The motion formula helped. Speed and direction of travel (in other words, velocity), together with the time spent travelling, were used to calculate displacement. Knowing where they had started from, sailors were then able to keep track of their current position. The measuring instruments necessary to obtain this information — compasses and chronometers that kept accurate time on an unstable ship — gave European sailors the physical technology they needed to venture out of sight of land and cross Earth's oceans. Figure 10.12 shows sailors using sextants: devices for observing the position of the Sun. For centuries, sailors have used these devices to find how far north or south they are, and to identify local noon.

Figure 10.12 Sextants have been used for hundreds of years and are still popular today.

Did You Know?

Long before the age of European exploration, the Polynesian people of the Pacific Ocean successfully explored and colonized a vast region of Earth. Beginning around 1500 B.C.E., the Polynesians migrated eastward from southeast Asia.

First they colonized the Fiji, Tonga, and Samoa island groups, and then they moved on to settle in New Zealand and the Hawaiian islands around 1000 C.E. How did they do it?

For transport, they probably used sturdy, ocean-going *voyaging canoes,* with twin hulls hollowed out of tree trunks and sails made from matted leaves. For navigation, or *wayfinding,* they studied the stars, the ocean swells, the flight patterns of birds, and other natural signs. They even carried plants and livestock on their voyages, since the islands they hoped to settle were too isolated to have ecosystems rich enough to support farming. A typical voyaging canoe might be 15 to 20 m long, with room for 20 people or more.

INTERNET CONNECT

www.school.mcgrawhill.ca/resources/

Through projects such as the Polynesian Voyaging Society, modern Polynesians are recreating and rediscovering their ocean-going past. To learn more, go to the web site above. Go to **Science Resources**, then to **SCIENCEPOWER 10** to know where to go next.

Figure 10.13 For less than the price of a good tent, back-country travellers can buy miniature GPS receivers that calculate position to an accuracy of 15 m anywhere on Earth!

In the twentieth century, electronic technology and satellites revolutionized navigation. **Inertial guidance systems** now use gyroscopes, rather than compasses, to sense changes in direction. In the **Global Positioning System (GPS)**, receivers on Earth use precisely timed signals from a network of satellites to calculate position.

Measuring instruments are only part of navigation technology, however. Techniques for using the measurements are just as important. Early sailors relied on geometrical methods, together with information from standard tables and charts, to determine their positions and plot courses. Today the graphs and formulas that are used by physicists allow you to do the same thing. From data about velocity and time, you can determine an object's past position and predict its location in the future.

The Shape of Velocity-Time Graphs

If an object is moving in a straight horizontal path along a level surface, or rising or falling in a vertical direction, its velocity can be shown on a **velocity-time graph**. In this kind of graph, time is marked on the horizontal axis and velocity is marked on the vertical axis. Like position-time graphs, velocity-time graphs are drawn with a best-fit line or curve.

Figure 10.14 shows velocity-time graphs for three basic kinds of motion. **Remember:** Positive and negative signs represent the direction of motion as it appears to a stationary observer on the ground.

Be careful! Velocity-time graphs do *not* show an object's position. Think of them as showing a speedometer reading for the object. By looking at the graph, you can describe changes in speed and direction. To tell precisely where the object *is*, you need to do extra analysis — just as in a car you need to glance away from the speedometer and check the surroundings in order to find your location.

DidYou**Know**?

Mount Everest just got taller! Using small but highly accurate GPS receivers, Bill Crouse and Pete Athans, of Colorado, led a seven-person team to climb Everest in May 1999. Crouse and Athans spent an hour taking careful measurements on the summit, as their receivers communicated with GPS satellites overhead. It was not until they had returned home, however, that they learned the results of their scientific expedition: the height of Everest had been calculated (to within 1 m) as 8850 m above sea level. This is just a little higher than the previous figure of 8848 m, which had been accepted for almost half a century but had a 5 m error margin. It is thought that Everest is moving northeastward at the rate of 3 to 6 mm per year, and perhaps upward as well, because the Indian continental plate is pushing into Tibet.

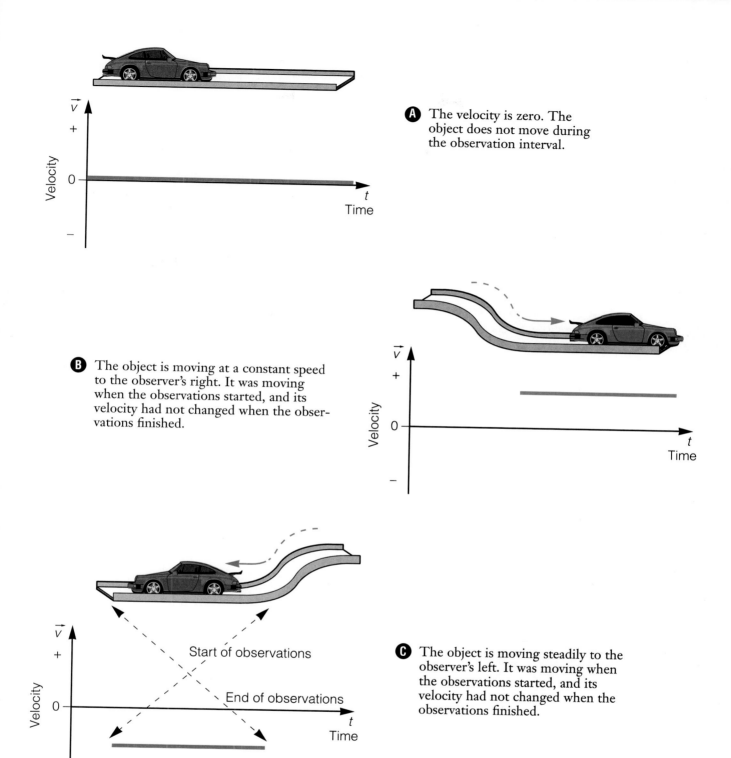

A The velocity is zero. The object does not move during the observation interval.

B The object is moving at a constant speed to the observer's right. It was moving when the observations started, and its velocity had not changed when the observations finished.

C The object is moving steadily to the observer's left. It was moving when the observations started, and its velocity had not changed when the observations finished.

Figure 10.14 Velocity-time graphs of simple motions

Velocity-time graphs may have several sections, just like the position-time graphs you studied earlier. If the details of speeding up or slowing down are not important, the graphs are usually "idealized," as though the complete velocity change took place all at once. In the real world, of course, velocity changes take a little time, giving graphs with rounded corners and curved sections.

Pick Up the Pace

Have you ever competed in a middle-distance or long-distance race? If so, you know that it can be hard to keep the same pace throughout the race. Sometimes you even need to change your speed on purpose: for example, as you sprint for the finish line.

Problem

Make a hypothesis about which parts of an 800 m or 1500 m race will be the fastest and which parts will be the slowest. Then test your hypothesis by measuring the speed of an athlete at each stage of a real track race. This might be either a school event or a specially staged race in which some of your classmates compete.

Apparatus

stopwatch
clipboard
pencil
warm clothing and rain gear
(if weather conditions are poor)

Materials

graph paper

Procedure

1 Make a table like the one below to record your observations. Give your table a title.

Distance past start line (m)	Time (s)	Lap number

2 Each group should choose a different athlete to observe. Members of your group should stand at the side of the track next to each of the four 100 m lines. In the top left box of your table, enter 100 if you are standing 100 m beyond the start line, or 200, 300, or 400 (if you are on the start line), as appropriate. For the rest of the entries in this column, add 400 m to each previous entry until you reach the total distance for the race.

3 When the beginning of the race is signalled, start your stopwatch (wherever you are standing). Use a visual cue, such as a dropped flag or smoke from the starting gun, to record the start.

4 Each time your athlete passes you, click the "split time" button. This gives you the time from the beginning of the race until the moment when the athlete passes you. Record this split time and the lap number in your table.

5 Click the "split time" button a second time. You will see that your stopwatch is still counting the time from the beginning of the race.

6 Repeat steps 4 and 5 for each remaining lap.

Analyze

1. Make another table, like the one below, for your results. Give your table a title.

Stage of race	Start time (s)	Finish time (s)	Δt (s)	Δd (m)	v_{av} (m/s)
0 m – 100 m	0.00				
100 m – 200 m					

2. Use your observations table (from the Procedure) and the motion formula (page 328) to complete your results table.

3. On graph paper, draw a velocity-time graph of your results. Mark the horizontal axis at each 100 m interval, and choose an

appropriate scale for the vertical axis. For each 100 m section of the race, plot the speed of your athlete as a horizontal line at the appropriate height.

4. Was your hypothesis about the athlete's speed during the race supported? Explain your answer.

Conclude and Apply

5. Why did you use a visual cue for the start of the race?

6. Do you think that your graph gives a realistic picture of the athlete's speed through the race? If so, explain why. If not, can you explain how the graph might still be valuable?

7. Based on your velocity-time graph, sketch a continuous graph of the athlete's speed at every moment of the race. (You may have to use your imagination a little!)

Extend Your Skills

8. The following graphs are idealized examples of a car's motion through a school zone. Analyze each section of each graph separately and then create a complete description of the car's motion. Graph (A) has been completed for you. (*Italic* type shows information that cannot be obtained by just looking at the graph.)

Skill
POWER

For tips on scientific graphing, turn to pages 602–604.

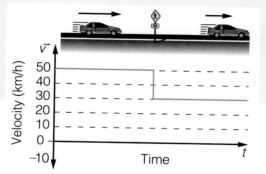

The car was travelling to the right at a steady speed of 50 km/h. Then it slowed to 30 km/h *as it entered the school zone* and travelled at this speed until the end of the observations.

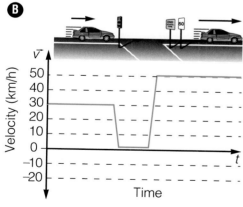

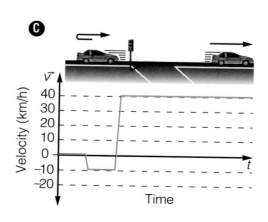

Interpreting Velocity-Time Graphs

Horizontal lines on a velocity-time graph show uniform motion: that is, constant speed and direction. Inclined lines show changes in speed or direction, or both: in other words, accelerated motion. Graphs of accelerated motion can be quite tricky to interpret, so study the examples in Figure 10.15 carefully.

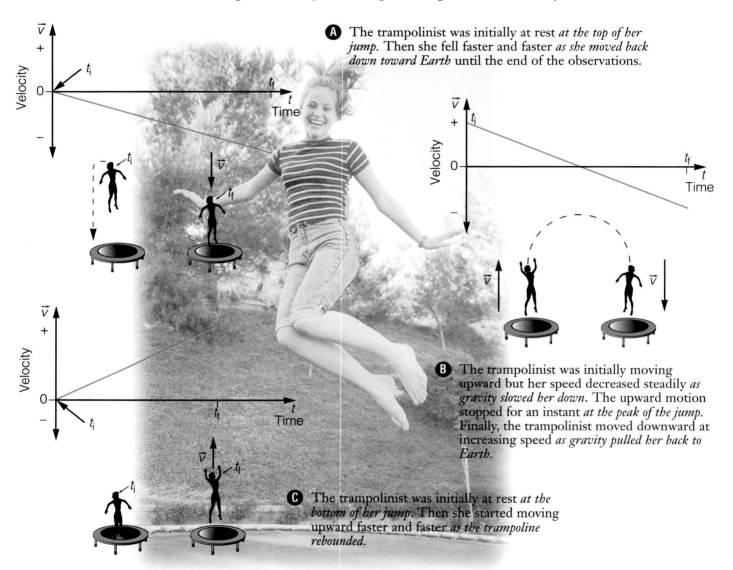

A The trampolinist was initially at rest *at the top of her jump*. Then she fell faster and faster *as she moved back down toward Earth* until the end of the observations.

B The trampolinist was initially moving upward but her speed decreased steadily *as gravity slowed her down*. The upward motion stopped for an instant *at the peak of the jump*. Finally, the trampolinist moved downward at increasing speed *as gravity pulled her back to Earth*.

C The trampolinist was initially at rest *at the bottom of her jump*. Then she started moving upward faster and faster *as the trampoline rebounded*.

Figure 10.15 These velocity-time graphs show a trampolinist's accelerated motion. *Italic* type indicates information that cannot be obtained by just looking at the graph. How does graph (B) show a change in direction?

The next investigation will allow you to apply what you have learned about motion, by studying the motion of a pendulum. You will measure the motion of the pendulum **bob:** a small mass that hangs from the end of a taut string. The bob's displacement is usually measured from its **equilibrium position,** hanging directly below the pendulum's support. One **cycle** of a pendulum's motion is shown by the curved arrow in Figure 10.16.

Figure 10.16 Describing a pendulum

The Pendulum's Path

A child on a playground swing, the moving weight in an old-fashioned clock, a heavy load swinging back and forth as it is lifted by a crane — each of these objects is a pendulum, moving with a characteristic back-and-forth motion.

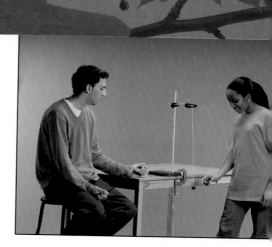

Problem

How accurately can you translate the motion of a pendulum into the position-time and velocity-time graphs used by physicists?

Apparatus

small mass (50 to 100 g)
string (1 m)
support
ultrasonic motion
   detector (optional)

Procedure

❶ Make a pendulum by suspending the mass from the support with the string.

❷ Let the pendulum come to rest at its equilibrium position. Identify and sketch the bob's position for positive and negative displacements. Make sure that everyone in your group looks at the pendulum from the same direction!

❸ Pull the bob about 10 cm to the right, keeping the string taut. Then release it and let it move through one cycle of its motion. Let the pendulum swing several times, watching carefully how the bob's position changes over time. Does it change smoothly or suddenly? Does it come all the way back to its starting point? Hint: Do not worry about the

bob's slight change in height as it swings. Concentrate on its movement left and right.

❹ On the top half of a sheet of graph paper, sketch a position-time graph that shows the pendulum's motion for two complete cycles.

❺ Repeat step 3, but this time concentrate on the pendulum's velocity. Where is it moving the fastest and the slowest? Does its speed change smoothly or

suddenly? Where is its velocity positive, and where is its velocity negative?

❻ On the bottom half of your graph paper, sketch a velocity-time graph of the pendulum's motion for two complete cycles. Use the same scales on the time axes of both your graphs.

❼ If you have access to an ultrasonic motion detector, compare your graphs with the graphs it produces.

Analyze

1. Identify any differences between your graphs and those you used for checking. If your graphs were not correct, describe features of the pendulum's motion that were not properly shown on your graphs.

2. Label the following points on your graphs.
   (a) maximum displacement (two points)
   (b) minimum displacement
   (c) maximum velocity
   (d) minimum velocity (two points)
   (e) changes in direction of motion (two points)
   (f) equilibrium position
   (g) one complete cycle of the pendulum's motion

Taking Control

An air traffic controller must keep track of every airplane in a particular area and make sure that all the airplanes stay a safe distance apart, horizontally as well as vertically. This is a very challenging task. Positions are constantly shifting as the airplanes move toward and away from each other, some entering and some leaving the controller's area. A radar screen provides these trained professionals with the exact location, height, speed, and direction of each airplane they are watching.

To keep everyone in the right place, the air traffic controller talks to the pilots of the airplanes via radio to tell them if they need to change their positions. The controller also gives the pilots other information. Are they cleared for takeoff or landing? Does the flight path need to be altered to go around a storm? Has the flight been rerouted to a different airport?

To become an air traffic controller, you need to finish high school and then complete a special training program. Not everyone gets into the training program. An aptitude test helps to determine which applicants have the necessary qualities to become successful air traffic controllers. Some of these qualities are listed below. Think about why each quality is important in this career.

- good eyesight
- excellent hearing and diction
- good communication skills
- ability to handle stress
- good basic mathematics skills
- good judgment and quick thinking

Check Your Understanding

1. Suppose that you want to determine where a moving object used to be located, and to predict where it will be in the future.
   (a) What information do you need?
   (b) What measuring instruments do you need?
   (c) How will you calculate answers from the results of your measurements?

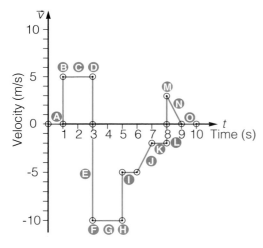

2. Examine the graph at left. Identify all the lettered sections that indicate
   (a) uniform motion
   (b) movement to the observer's left
   (c) the object slowing down
   (d) the object +10 m from its starting point
   (e) motion to the observer's right at 5 m/s

3. Sketch, and describe in words, the appearance of
   (a) position-time graphs of uniform motion
   (b) position-time graphs of accelerated motion
   (c) velocity-time graphs of uniform motion
   (d) velocity-time graphs of accelerated motion

4. **Thinking Critically** What do we mean when we say a velocity-time graph is "idealized?" Why would a graph be idealized?

5. **Thinking Critically** Many motion technologies are first developed for military purposes and then adapted for civilian use. For example, cruise missiles compare computerized map data to radar observations in order to track their position. This technology may well be adapted within the next 20 years to control cars on automated highway lanes. Discuss or write about military technology research from some of the perspectives listed on page 334. Are you opposed to this type of research, or would you make a case for continuing to fund it? Justify your answer.

Now that you have completed this chapter, try to do the following. If you cannot, go back to the sections indicated.

Identify two key features of *uniform* motion. (10.1)

Sketch a position-time graph that shows
(a) a stopped object
(b) uniform motion up or to an observer's right
(c) uniform motion down or to an observer's left
(10.1)

Sketch a position time-graph with a positive slope. Mark on it a slope triangle with the following features labelled: $\Delta\vec{d}$, Δt, rise, run. (10.1)

Write directions for using a position-time graph to determine an object's average velocity and its instantaneous velocity. (10.1)

Write the motion formula in three different forms, and explain when you would use each form. (10.1)

List the steps that you need to follow if you want to use a road map to estimate the driving time between two cities. (10.2)

List the possible perspectives that might be used when discussing a proposal to enlarge a student parking lot at a high school. Choose two perspectives, and give an example of a statement that reflects each one. (10.2)

Give examples of how the development of a personal transportation technology (such as inline skates) has brought both costs and benefits, and has changed the laws or attitudes in your community. (10.2)

Sketch a velocity-time graph that shows an object
(a) standing still
(b) moving up at a constant speed
(c) moving down at a constant speed
(d) changing direction (10.3)

Label a drawing of a pendulum to show
(a) the equilibrium position
(b) one cycle of the pendulum's motion
(c) points at which speed is a maximum and a minimum (10.3)

Prepare Your Own Summary

Summarize this chapter by doing one of the following. Use a graphic organizer (such as a concept map), produce a poster, or write the summary to include the key chapter concepts. Here are a few ideas to use as a guide:

• What were some of Plato's ideas about observing and studying the natural world?
• How is the slope of a graph calculated?
• Describe what you can infer about an object's motion from the slope of its
  (a) position-time graph
  (b) velocity-time graph

• Explain when and how you would measure an object's
  (a) instantaneous velocity
  (b) average velocity
• What are the key features of the motion of a pendulum?
• How can you determine the actual distance between two locations from a map?
• What typical features of technological change are illustrated by the history of the bicycle?
• From what perspectives can people evaluate the costs and benefits of a scientific or technological development?

Reviewing Key Terms

If you need to review, the section numbers show where these terms were introduced.

1. Explain how the slope of a curved line at a given point is related to the tangent to the curve at this point. (10.1)

2. Distinguish between a technological perspective and a scientific perspective. (10.2)

3. Suppose that you were debating whether tax money should be used to help develop very high speed passenger airplanes, even faster than today's supersonic Concorde. Give an example of a statement that you might make if you were arguing from each perspective listed below. (10.2)
   (a) economic
   (b) technological
   (c) ecological
   (d) ethical

Understanding Key Concepts

Section numbers are provided if you need to review.

4. Describe how you could determine each quantity below from a position-time graph of an object's motion. (10.1)
   (a) average velocity
   (b) instantaneous velocity

5. Are measurements ever exact numbers? Justify your answer, and explain its implications for calculations with measurements. (10.2)

6. What is the meaning of each of the following features of a velocity-time graph? (10.3)
   (a) a horizontal section of the graph
   (b) an inclined (slanted) section of the graph
   (c) a line above the horizontal axis
   (d) a line below the horizontal axis
   (e) a point where the line crosses the horizontal axis

Developing Skills

7. Suppose that each position-time graph below represents the motion of a train travelling over level ground. The reference point for position is the station from which the train departed.
   (a) Give a mathematical description of the slope of each graph or graph section (increasing/decreasing/constant; positive/negative/zero).
   (b) Give an example of a scenario that would produce each graph.

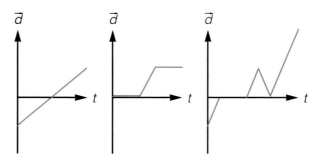

8. Suppose that you were analyzing the following aspects of a sprinter's 100 m run:
   • speed as the runner reached the halfway point
   • maximum speed reached during the race
   • a single number that best represents speed over the entire race
   (a) Would you use average or instantaneous velocity to describe each feature of the race?
   (b) Would you use the average slope or the slope at a particular point to calculate each quantity?

9. A high diver (A) stands motionless at the end of a platform. Suddenly (B) she leaps upward. A second later (C) she seems to be suspended motionless high in the air, and then (D) she falls faster and faster toward the water below. As she slices into the water (E), her speed drops quickly and (F) continues to slow more gradually. Finally (G) she comes to within a few centimetres of the bottom of the pool. Arcing upward (H), she rises steadily to the surface (I) and swims slowly to the side.
   (a) Sketch a velocity-time graph that shows the vertical motion of the diver. Label points A to I above.

(b) Sketch a position-time graph that shows the height of the diver. Take the surface of the pool as your reference point, where height equals zero.

10. Use the motion formula in an appropriate form to find each quantity below.

    (a) the speed of sound, given that a clap of thunder is heard by an observer 1.5 km away, 4.6 s after the lightning that produced it is seen

    (b) the distance in kilometres from Earth to the Moon, given that radio waves travelling at the speed of light (3.0×10^8 km/s) take 1.28 s to cover this distance

    (c) the time that light from the Sun takes to reach Earth if it must travel 1.5×10^8 km at the speed of light

Problem Solving/Applying

11. Jan lives nine-and-a-half blocks from his school, which starts at 8:30 a.m. One day he leaves his house at 8:15 a.m. He walks steadily until 8:25 a.m., when he has three blocks left to cover. He speeds up and jogs the rest of the way at a uniform pace, arriving just as the bell rings.

    (a) Sketch a position-time graph of Jan's motion, assuming that each block is 60 m long.

    (b) What does the slope of each section of the graph indicate?

    (c) Find the velocity during each section of Jan's trip.

    (d) Find Jan's average velocity over the entire trip.

12. An athlete on an interval training program alternates jogging 100 paces, which takes 41 s, and walking 50 paces, which takes 27 s. Each jogging pace is 0.9 m long, and each walking pace is 0.6 m long.

    (a) Calculate
    - the jogging velocity
    - the walking velocity
    - the average velocity over the entire interval

    (b) Sketch a velocity-time graph of the motion.

Critical Thinking

13. A car moves at 100 km/h along a highway, slows down quickly to 60 km/h while passing through a town, and then speeds up quickly to 100 km/h at the town boundary.

    (a) How would a velocity-time graph of this motion be idealized (simplified)?

    (b) What advantages might an idealized graph have over a precise graph of the motion?

    (c) When would this simplification not be sensible?

14. When you plot a graph based on experimental data, the points seldom lie exactly on a straight line. Sometimes, however, the points can be used to indicate the position of a best-fit line, which fits between them as closely as possible.

    (a) Why do scientists draw a best-fit line instead of joining the points exactly? Are there any disadvantages to drawing a best-fit line?

    (b) In what way is drawing a best-fit line when graphing data similar to finding the average of a number of measurements?

Pause& Reflect

1. Go back to the beginning of the chapter, on page 318, and check your original answers to the Opening Ideas questions and the Starting Point Activity questions. How has your thinking changed? Use physics terms and ideas to explain or justify your answers.

2. Many social critics believe that our society must reduce the speed of technological (and social) change in order to survive. One possible way to do this might be to reverse common ways of thinking about the kinds of changes that are desirable. At present, new technologies and products are usually considered to be worthwhile unless they have obvious and serious *disadvantages*. Would it be better to adopt new technologies and products only if they had obvious and significant *advantages* over present ones? Write your reaction to this proposal in your Science Log. Use examples you have studied in this chapter, or other examples you are familiar with, to support your position.

11 Accelerated Motion

Opening Ideas...

- Describe different examples, in everyday life, of motions that involve acceleration.

- Has your body ever been injured (or at least affected) by rapid changes in speed or direction? Explain how.

- If you are in an elevator or a car at night, how do you sense that you are accelerating?

Science Log

List three examples of accelerated (changing) motion that you have observed or experienced recently. For each example, describe exactly how the motion changed. What other effects did the acceleration produce, besides changing the speed and/or direction of motion? Write your descriptions in your Science Log.

*S*peed kills!
Slow down and live!

These catchy slogans are good advice for drivers, but they leave out an important fact: high speed by itself is not necessarily dangerous. Passengers in the Concorde supersonic airliner, for example, travel at over 2300 km/h, yet they are not harmed in any way by their high speed. Right now, as you sit "still" reading, you are being whirled around rapidly as Earth spins on its axis, at a speed of over 1100 km/h if you live near the Canada-U.S. border. At the same time, you are moving at over 100 000 km/h as Earth and everything on it orbits around the Sun.

Rapid *changes* in speed, however, are always dangerous. As the athlete in the photograph accelerates, the forces that change her speed or direction put her body under great stress. This stress may be enough to damage her bones, muscles, or joints. Slowing down rapidly can be equally punishing.

In everyday life, **accelerated motion** (changing speed or direction) is far more common than uniform motion (constant speed and direction). Precise measurements of accelerating objects allow scientists and engineers to predict the forces that accompany changing motion. Transport technologies — cars, aircraft, and even running shoes — are designed to stand up to the stresses they will experience. In this chapter, you will be introduced to various laboratory instruments, graphs, and formulas that are used to study accelerated motion.

Build Your Own Accelerometer

As you walk or run, you can sense when your motion changes. You can also use a simple **accelerometer** (a device to measure acceleration) to study changes in motion.

What You Need

clean, empty plastic bottle or jar with a tight-fitting lid

small cork or piece of foam plastic to act as a float

thread

waterproof tape or silicone glue

water

data table (provided by your teacher)

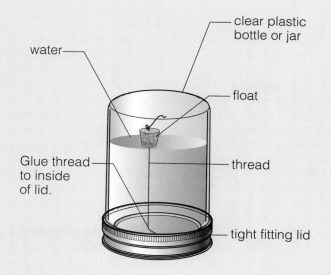

water — clear plastic bottle or jar

float

Glue thread to inside of lid.

thread

tight fitting lid

Key Concepts

In this chapter, you will discover

- how acceleration is defined, measured, and expressed
- how acceleration, displacement, and certain features of velocity-time graphs are related
- how some common technologies increase and decrease acceleration

Key Skills

In this chapter, you will

- calculate acceleration from measurements of velocity, position, and time
- use velocity-time graphs to find the acceleration and displacement of moving objects
- design and perform experiments to create and measure accelerated motion

Key Terms

- accelerated motion
- accelerometer
- average acceleration
- instantaneous acceleration
- theoretical physics
- stroboscope
- air brake
- drag

What to Do

1. Build an accelerometer that is similar to the one above.

2. Everyone in your group should watch the same side of the accelerometer, so you will all agree on the direction in which the liquid and the float move.

3. Observe the float and the liquid as you move the accelerometer in different directions and at different speeds. Record your observations.

What Did You Discover?

1. Explain how your accelerometer shows whether motion is
   (a) uniform or accelerated
   (b) changing rapidly or slowly

2. How does your accelerometer indicate the direction of a change in motion?

3. Does circular motion seem to be accelerated or uniform? Give evidence to support your answer.

4. Is this type of accelerometer useful for studying vertical motion? If you did not try vertical motion, do so before answering.

11.1 Describing and Measuring Acceleration

To control a rocket, scientists need accurate, detailed information about how the rocket's motion is changing. Accelerometers like the one you used in the Starting Point Activity are not nearly precise enough. Using similar but more accurate equipment, however, scientists have made the following observations.

- Motion with no change in speed or direction (uniform motion) does not affect accelerometers.
- Any change in speed — speeding up or slowing down — affects accelerometers.
- Changes in direction affect accelerometers.
- More rapid changes in speed or direction produce greater effects.
- Acceleration is not always in the same direction as the object's motion.

From these observations, scientists have made the following inferences:

Acceleration

1. Acceleration involves changes in *velocity*. Recall, from Chapter 10, that velocity describes both the speed and direction of motion. Changes in speed or direction, or both, involve acceleration.
2. Acceleration is the *rate of change* of velocity. In other words, faster changes in velocity involve greater acceleration. Expressed as a mathematical equation,

$$\text{Acceleration} = \frac{\text{Change in velocity}}{\text{Time interval}}$$

Figure 11.1 Accelerating the huge mass of a fully fuelled rocket is very difficult. As the fuel is burned, however, the rocket becomes lighter and its upward acceleration increases.

In algebraic symbols, this definition of acceleration becomes

$$\vec{a} = \frac{\Delta \vec{v}}{\Delta t} \qquad \text{or} \qquad \vec{a} = \frac{(\vec{v}_f - \vec{v}_i)}{(t_f - t_i)}$$

where v_f = final velocity
v_i = initial velocity
t_f = time at the end of the observations
t_i = time at the beginning of the observations

The symbol $\vec{a}$ is often used to represent acceleration that is measured over a certain time interval. A more precise symbol is $\vec{a}_{av}$, which stands for **average acceleration.** Acceleration can also be measured at a specific instant in time. This gives an object's **instantaneous acceleration** ($\vec{a}_{inst}$). Can you recall another quantity that has both average and instantaneous values? Which is it?

Vector symbols are used to show that velocity and acceleration have both magnitude (size) and direction. Recall that, if an object is moving in a straight line, you can show the direction of motion by using + and − signs for the velocities, following the usual conventions:

- A + sign indicates motion up or to the right of an observer.
- A − sign indicates motion down or to the left of an observer.

Similarly, when you calculate acceleration, your answer will be either positive or negative. The sign gives important information about the motion, so you should include it in your answer.

> Be careful! When physicists study linear motion (motion back and forth in a straight line), they often omit the vector signs in their equations. To calculate correct answers, however, you *must* indicate directions by using + and − signs for displacements, velocities, and accelerations.

Calculating Acceleration

The problems that follow apply a mathematical model of acceleration in simple, "ideal" situations. As you work through them, think about the problems of calculating acceleration in the "real world," as well. You would need to observe an object's velocity at the exact start and end of an observing interval. In other words, v_i and v_f are *instantaneous* velocities. These cannot simply be measured with a stopwatch and a metre stick. Could you use mathematics techniques to infer acceleration values from simpler observations? Would you need special measuring equipment?

Model Problem 1

A study of the cheetah, the fastest land animal, reported that one cheetah had reached a speed of 19 m/s in 2.0 s from a standing start. What was the cheetah's acceleration? (Assume that the cheetah was moving to the right.) If you need to review the units of acceleration, turn to page 297 in Chapter 9.

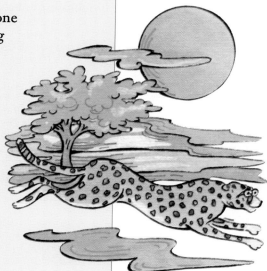

Given Velocity at the start of the measurements, $\vec{v}_i = 0$ m/s
Velocity at the end of the measurements, $\vec{v}_f = +19$ m/s
Time taken, $\Delta t = 2.0$ s

Required Acceleration, $\vec{a}$, in m/s²

Analysis Use the acceleration formula $\vec{a} = \dfrac{\Delta \vec{v}}{\Delta t}$, in the form

$$\vec{a} = \frac{(\vec{v}_f - \vec{v}_i)}{\Delta t}.$$

Solution $\vec{a} = \dfrac{(\vec{v}_f - \vec{v}_i)}{\Delta t}$

$$= \frac{(+19 \text{ m/s} - 0 \text{ m/s})}{2.0 \text{ s}}$$

$$= +9.5 \text{ m/s}^2$$

Paraphrase The cheetah accelerates at +9.5 m/s² (to 2 significant digits).

Model Problem 2

Find the acceleration, in m/s², of a car as it slows down from 50 km/h to 30 km/h in 3.5 s. (Assume that the car is moving to the observer's right.)

Given Velocity at the start of the measurements, $\vec{v}_i = +50$ km/h

Velocity at the end of the measurements, $\vec{v}_f = +30$ km/h

Time taken, $\Delta t = 3.5$ s

Required Acceleration, $\vec{a}$, in m/s²

Analyze First convert the velocities from km/h into m/s.

$$\vec{v}_i = \frac{+50 \text{ km}}{1 \text{ h}} \times \frac{1000 \text{ m}}{1 \text{ km}} \times \frac{1 \text{ h}}{3600 \text{ s}}$$

$$= +13.89 \text{ m/s}$$

$$\vec{v}_f = \frac{+30 \text{ km}}{1 \text{ h}} \times \frac{1000 \text{ m}}{1 \text{ km}} \times \frac{1 \text{ h}}{3600 \text{ s}}$$

$$= +8.33 \text{ m/s}$$

Then use the acceleration formula, $\vec{a} = \dfrac{\Delta \vec{v}}{\Delta t} = \dfrac{(\vec{v}_f - \vec{v}_i)}{\Delta t}$

Solution $\vec{a} = \dfrac{(\vec{v}_f - \vec{v}_i)}{\Delta t}$

$$= \frac{(+8.33 \text{ m} - (+13.89 \text{ m}))}{3.5 \text{ s}}$$

$$= -1.589 \text{ m/s}^2$$

Paraphrase The car accelerates at about −1.6 m/s² (to 2 significant digits) as it slows down.

Word ⬦ CONNECT

Were you surprised by the wording of the paraphrase at the end of Model Problem 2: "The car *accelerates* . . . as it slows down"? In everyday language, "acceleration" almost always means "speeding up." The opposite change, slowing down, is often called "deceleration." In physics, however, the definition of acceleration includes both speeding up and slowing down. Both actions are changes in velocity, so they are both accelerations. There is nothing special about slowing down — it is just another way to change the velocity.

The prefix "de-" is used to mean "the opposite of" in other contexts, besides physics. Think of examples in as many different areas as you can.

Positive and Negative Acceleration

In the model problems, you calculated a negative acceleration when a car's forward motion slowed down. How do you think an acceleration calculation would turn out if an object moved down, or to your left, so that it had a changing *negative* velocity? What about a velocity that changed from positive to negative, such as the velocity of a ball that was thrown upward, slowed down, stopped, and then started to fall back down? Would its acceleration change from positive to negative along with its velocity?

May the Force Be with You

Positive acceleration can mean speeding up, but not always. Negative acceleration can mean slowing down, but it can also mean just the opposite. Work through this activity to discover the real meaning of positive and negative acceleration.

What to Do

(a) $\vec{v}_i = +20$ cm/s $\Delta\vec{v} = ?$ $\Delta t = 10$ s

$\vec{v}_f = +40$ cm/s

$$\vec{a} = \frac{\vec{v}_f - \vec{v}_i}{\Delta t}$$

$$= \frac{(+40 \text{ cm/s}) - (+20 \text{ cm/s})}{10 \text{ s}}$$

$$\vec{a} = +2.0 \text{ cm/s}^2$$

(b) $\vec{v}_i = +40$ cm/s $\Delta t = 10$ s

$\vec{v}_f = +20$ cm/s $\Delta\vec{v} = ?$

(c) $\Delta\vec{v} = ?$ $\vec{v}_i = -20$ cm/s^2

$\Delta t = 10$ s

$\vec{v}_f = -40$ cm/s

(d) $\vec{v}_i = -40$ cm/s

? $\Delta t = 10$ s

$\vec{v}_f = -20$ cm/s

1. Copy the four vector diagrams above. Complete each diagram by drawing a vector arrow to represent the change in velocity.

2. Calculate the acceleration for each diagram. Calculation **(a)** is completed as an example.

3. Remember that vectors pointing to the observer's right are considered positive and vectors pointing to the observer's left are considered negative. Mark the sign (+ or −) of all the vectors in the diagrams.

4. Which one of the vectors in the diagrams always has the same sign as the acceleration?

What Did You Discover?

1. Explain, in clear sentences, what you can infer about the change in an object's velocity if it has
   (a) positive acceleration
   (b) negative acceleration

Extension

2. In earlier grades, you may have learned about the three laws of motion suggested by Sir Isaac Newton over 300 years ago. Newton's second law states that a moving object only changes its motion (accelerates) when a force acts on it. The amount of acceleration depends on the strength of the force and the mass of the object.
   (a) Imagine that you are pushing on the object in each diagram to cause its motion to change as shown. In your notebook, add a force vector to each diagram, to show which way you are pushing.
   (b) Compare the direction of the force causing each acceleration with the sign of the acceleration you calculated. Write a clear statement to explain the relationship.

The following statements sum up how physicists interpret positive and negative accelerations.

- Positive acceleration means that the force causing the acceleration points up or to the observer's right.
- Negative acceleration means that the force causing the acceleration points down or to the observer's left.
- On a vector diagram, the sign of the object's acceleration tells the direction of the change in velocity, $\vec{\Delta v}$.

In your Science Log, compare your conclusions in the Science Inquiry Activity with the summary statements listed above. Did you interpret positive and negative accelerations in the same way that physicists do? If you discovered different relationships between the directions of acceleration, force, and change in velocity, explain how you reached them. Identify any errors in your reasoning. Then summarize the key scientific ideas about acceleration that you learned or remembered as you worked through this section.

Check Your Understanding

1. Imagine explaining the scientific concept of acceleration to a friend who has not studied physics. List the key points in your explanation.

2. **Apply** The most powerful production car in the world in 1999 (a McLaren F1) could reach a speed of 26.8 m/s (over 96 km/h) from a standing start in 3.2 s.
   (a) Find the car's average acceleration.
   (b) If the car could maintain this acceleration, how long would it take to reach a speed of 200 km/h?

3. **Apply** A new world acceleration record for electrically powered motorcycles was set, in 1999, by a motorcycle that started from rest and took 14.57 s to reach a maximum forward velocity of +18.3 m/s (almost 66 km/h).
   (a) Find the motorcycle's average acceleration.
   (b) At its maximum speed, how long would the motorcycle have taken to travel once around a 400 m track?

4. **Thinking Critically** Some textbooks give the following rule for finding the direction of acceleration:
   - If an object is speeding up, its acceleration is in the same direction as its motion.
   - If an object is slowing down, its acceleration is in the opposite direction to its motion.

   Use this rule to find the direction of acceleration (+ or −) in each situation below. Then sketch a velocity vector diagram to support your answer.
   (a) v_i = 2.5 m/s to the observer's right
       v_f = 5.5 m/s to the observer's right
   (b) v_i = 0.46 m/s down
       v_f = 0.14 m/s down
   (c) v_i = 6.6 m/s to the observer's left
       v_f = 4.3 m/s to the observer's right

5. **Thinking Critically** How are acceleration and velocity similar? How are they different?

11.2 Using and Picturing Acceleration

Figure 11.2 This Boeing 747 has accelerated along the runway until it is moving quickly enough to lift into the air.

A flight in a modern passenger airplane is a series of accelerations. Powerful jet engines accelerate the airplane until air passes around the wings fast enough to lift it upward. On landing, mechanisms that reverse the jet exhausts, together with control surfaces on the wings and tail, help to slow the airplane rapidly and safely.

Athletes also depend on acceleration. Basketball and hockey players accelerate by changing velocity to get a clear shot. Tennis, baseball, and Ping-Pong™ players make balls suddenly slow down or change direction. Sprinters and bobsledders try to speed up faster than their opponents. A huge industry designs, produces, and sells sports equipment — such as footwear, bats, and rackets — designed to increase acceleration. Have you ever wondered how effective some of this equipment actually is? Measurements of acceleration can help you find out.

Sensors that track motion in the controlled setting of a lab are one thing, but imagine equipment that could do the same for professional athletes during a football, hockey, or basketball game! A system to do this was demonstrated in 1999 and first tested by the Boston Bruins hockey team. Miniature sensors and radio transmitters worn by the players send data about the players' speed and acceleration. As well, data on the force of their impacts is relayed to receivers around the edge of the playing surface.

The Definite Difference

Numbers are easy to compare. Product-testing laboratories often use specially designed and very ingenious equipment to gather quantitative (numerical) information. This information makes it possible to compare the performance of different brands or designs of equipment. You can use a stopwatch, a measuring tape, and a calculator — and the ideas you have studied in this chapter — to obtain the same type of data about athletic footwear.

Problem

What effects do different starting conditions and footwear have on a sprinter's acceleration?

Apparatus

metre stick or tape
stopwatch
set of photogates
digital, video, or Polaroid™ camera
(optional)

Materials

starting blocks, or different types of
athletic footwear, or multi-gear
bicycle

Procedure

❶ As a group, brainstorm different methods that sprinters use to get a good start. Pick two methods to compare: for example, running shoes versus bare feet, two different brands of running shoes, running shoes with or without spikes, or a starting block versus no starting block. With your teacher's approval, you can investigate something other than a sprinter: for example, a cyclist starting in different gears.

❷ Choose one group member to be the sprinter. This student will accelerate as rapidly as possible using the two different methods you have chosen. Also choose a timer and a starter.

❸ Do a preliminary trial to find out where to place the timer with the stopwatch. A distance of 5 to 10 m is usually suitable for a sprinter. You may have to adjust this distance so that the sprinter is still accelerating at the timing position.

❹ Use the photogates to determine the velocity of the sprinter at the timing postion. Put one photogate 0.5 m before the timing position and the other 0.5 m after the timing position.

❺ Measure and record the distance from the starting position to the timing position as precisely as possible.

❻ Time several trials as the sprinter uses one method of starting and then the other. Remember to allow the sprinter some recovery time between trials. Record your data in a data table.

❼ Choose another group member to be the sprinter, and repeat step 5.

Analyze

1. Use your measurements of distance and time for the whole sprint to find the sprinter's average velocity, in each trial.

2. Using the time interval data from the photogates and the distance between them, calculate a value for the sprinter's final velocity, v_f.

3. Calculate the sprinter's average acceleration in each trial. Use your measured value of Δt for the whole sprint, your value of v_f from question 2, and the value $v_i = 0$ m/s. Average your results for each sprinter and starting method.

Conclude and Apply

4. How consistent are your results? Do both sprinters show similar differences for the two methods? Are the results for each sprinter similar for different trials?

5. How might your results be affected by the sprinter's increasing tiredness as the investigation continued? Does this actually show up in your results? How does this affect the trustworthiness of your results?

Extend Your Knowledge

6. Running-shoe manufacturers spend a lot of money telling consumers that their products improve performance. Find or describe at least one advertisement that does this. If you investigated different types of footwear, do your results support the manufacturer's claims? Does footwear make much difference in a sprinter's performance?

7. Laboratory tests of a consumer product do not always reflect the way that the product is actually used outside the lab. In what ways is the design of your investigation different from what happens when athletic equipment is used in regular competition? Do these differences make your results useless? Support your answer with examples and logical reasons.

8. Use a library or the Internet to research the results of experiments by consumer-testing organizations on running shoes or other athletic equipment. How well do your results agree with any published results that you find? What might be causing any differences?

Picturing Acceleration

Physicists reuse ideas. If an idea or model helps to describe or analyze one situation, scientists try using it in other, similar situations. Copy the graphic organizer in Figure 11.3, and try to fill in the blanks before reading further. Reuse ideas you learned in Chapters 9 and 10.

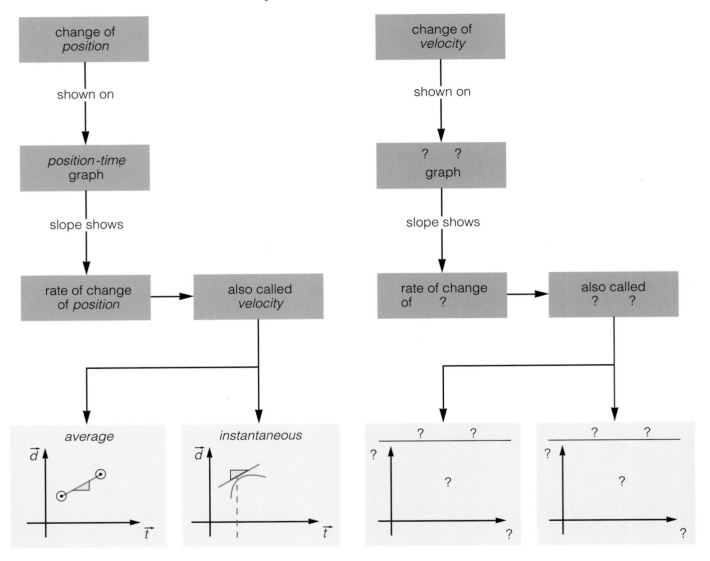

Figure 11.3 Graphic organizer for velocity and acceleration

Rate of Change: Slope

Whenever a quantity changes over time, the changes can be pictured on a graph, with time along the horizontal axis. The *rate* of change is shown by the slope of the graph. You have already seen two examples of this important use of graphs.

- Velocity (rate of change of *position*) is shown by the slope of a *position-time* graph.
- Acceleration (rate of change of *velocity*) is shown by the slope of a *velocity*-time graph.

Figure 11.4 shows some examples of these relationships.

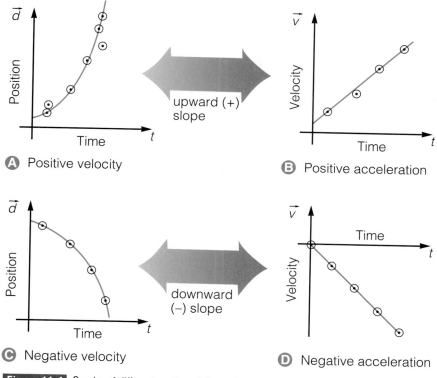

A Positive velocity

upward (+) slope

B Positive acceleration

downward (−) slope

C Negative velocity

D Negative acceleration

Figure 11.4 Graphs of different motions: interpreting the slope

The same method can be used to find the slope of any graph. For example, you can calculate the slope of a velocity-time graph (to find acceleration) in the same way that you calculated the slope of a position-time graph (to find velocity).

- Average acceleration $(\vec{a}_{av})$ is the slope of a straight line drawn between the beginning and the end of a time interval on a velocity-time graph (see Figure 11.5A).

- Instantaneous acceleration $(\vec{a}_{inst})$ is the slope of a tangent line (a straight line that just touches a curve) at a particular instant on a velocity-time graph (see Figure 11.5B).

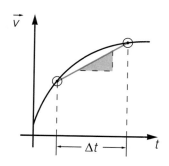

Figure 11.5A Finding average acceleration over a time interval, Δt

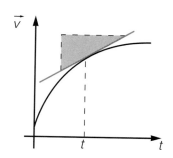

Figure 11.5B Finding instantaneous acceleration at time, t

Brush Up Your Graphing Skills

Think About It

Psychologists who study learning have found that even the best-learned skills are not automatically transferred to new and unfamiliar situations. In physics, this is especially true of mathematical skills. Skills that you learned when you were studying velocity, for example, may not come to mind when you are trying to solve a problem about acceleration — unless you practise first.

What to Do

Go back to Chapter 10, and review the methods you learned for finding the slope of a position-time graph. Then use similar methods to answer the following questions.

1 Describe the slope of each velocity–time graph below as positive, zero, or negative. State whether the graph shows positive acceleration, zero acceleration, or negative acceleration.

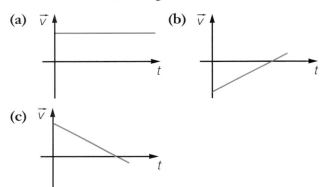

2 Use a ruler to sketch a graph that shows each motion described below. Remember your sign conventions!

  (a) motion to an observer's left with no acceleration

  (b) motion to an observer's left with positive acceleration

  (c) motion to an observer's left with negative acceleration

  (d) motion to an observer's right with negative acceleration

3 Below each graph for question 2, draw vector arrows to show

  • the direction of the initial velocity
  • the direction of the change in velocity
  • the direction of the final velocity
  • the direction of the force causing the acceleration

4 Copy the table below, and sketch an appropriate velocity-time graph on each set of axes. One graph is completed as an example.

	Positive acceleration	Negative acceleration
Motion up (positive velocity)	$\vec{v}$	$\vec{v}$
Motion down (negative velocity)	$\vec{v}$	$\vec{v}$

Math CONNECT

The exact location of a point on a graph is often written in brackets as an *ordered pair* (also called *Cartesian co-ordinates*).

In the graph below, the point (7.5, 5) is located 7.5 units to the right along the *x*-axis and 5 units up the *y*-axis. Where would the point (7.5, −5) be located on this graph?

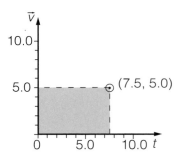

5 Use the co-ordinates marked on the graph below to find the value of

(a) $\vec{v}_f$ (final velocity)

(b) $\vec{v}_i$ (initial velocity)

(c) t_f (end of the time interval)

(d) t_i (beginning of the time interval)

(e) $\Delta\vec{v}$ (change in velocity)

(f) Δt (time interval)

(g) $\vec{a}$ (acceleration)

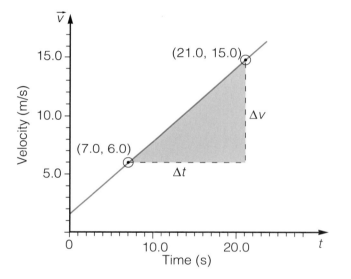

6 Use the co-ordinates marked on the graph below to find the instantaneous acceleration of the moving object at time P.

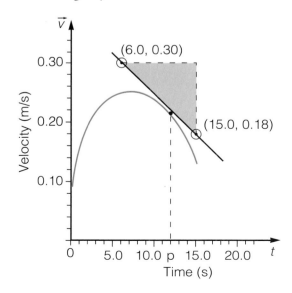

7 Use grid paper to draw a properly scaled graph of constant-acceleration motion, based on the following information.

- The initial velocity is 0 m/s.
- The final velocity is 4.5 m/s.
- The observations start at time 3.6 s.
- The observations end at time 6.6 s.

Draw a slope triangle on the graph, and use it to find the average acceleration of the object during the observation interval.

8 Study the graph below. Identify points that show

(a) zero acceleration

(b) positive acceleration

(c) negative acceleration

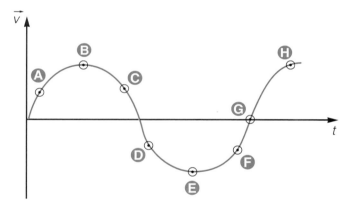

Analyze

1. Write a mathematical formula that shows how to find average acceleration using $\vec{v}_f$, $\vec{v}_i$, t_f, and t_i.

2. Look back at your graph for question 7 above. How can you tell that the slope represents constant acceleration?

3. Go back to the graph for question 8. How can you tell that the slope does not represent constant acceleration?

Estimating Final Velocity

A model rocket waits on the launch stand. The engines ignite, and the rocket accelerates skyward. In almost no time, the model is level with the top of a nearby flagpole. You might wonder how fast the rocket is going as it clears the flagpole. This is not difficult to find out, using only a tape measure, a stopwatch, and a little math.

In an earlier activity, you studied the motion of balls rolling down a ramp. By calculating a ball's average velocity, you were able to find its velocity at the instant it passed an observer. You can use a similar method to find the velocity of the model rocket as it passes a particular point (the top of the flagpole), assuming that the rocket's acceleration is constant. You need to know three values:

- the rocket's initial velocity (it was standing still, so $\vec{v}_i = 0$ m/s)
- the height of the flagpole (this is the rocket's displacement, $\Delta\vec{d}$)
- the time the rocket took to clear the flagpole (Δt)

Figure 11.6 Model rocketry is a popular hobby. Powered by solid-fuel engines, model rockets can reach very high speeds and considerable altitude before parachuting back to Earth. Larger models can carry computerized sensors to measure height, as well as cameras and even television equipment.

Using these values and the motion formula, you can calculate the rocket's average velocity as it rose to the height of the flagpole.

$$\vec{v}_{av} = \frac{\Delta\vec{d}}{\Delta t}$$

Average velocity can also be found from initial and final velocity.

$$\vec{v}_{av} = \frac{(\vec{v}_i + \vec{v}_f)}{2}$$

Since the rocket started from rest, $v_i = 0$ m/s. Therefore you can write

$$\vec{v}_{av} = \frac{(0 + \vec{v}_f)}{2}$$

or

$$\vec{v}_{av} = \frac{\vec{v}_f}{2}$$

Rearranging this formula, you can find the rocket's final velocity, v_f.

$$\vec{v}_f = 2 \times \vec{v}_{av} \quad \text{or} \quad \vec{v}_f = 2\vec{v}_{av}$$

In other words, when an object starts from rest and accelerates uniformly, its final velocity is exactly double its average velocity (which is often more easily found). This can be shown on a velocity-time graph, such as Figure 11.7. Final velocity, v_f, is instantaneous, which makes it tricky to measure. Average velocity, however, can be found easily from displacement and time observations. So the formula $v_f = 2v_{av}$ is a very useful tool for practical motion problems. Be careful to use it only when you know the acceleration is constant, however.

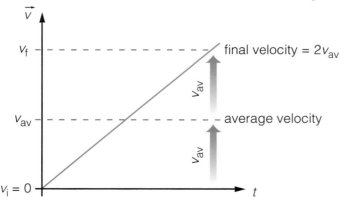

Figure 11.7 The relation between initial, final, and average velocity

Formulas and Graphs, Patterns and Relationships

Developing mathematical formulas and interpreting graphs, as you have just been doing, can be quite different from the practical challenge of measuring an object's motion in a laboratory. Both of these ways of studying nature are used in physics, however. **Theoretical physics** is the search for patterns and relationships, using data obtained from studies and experiments. Because numerical data are so useful in physics, the patterns and relationships that theoretical physicists discover are often expressed in mathematical forms, such as graphs and formulas.

Theoretical physicists seldom conduct experiments with laboratory equipment. Their tools are computers, chalkboards, and pencils and paper. Their work involves ideas, symbols, and mathematical techniques, rather than experimental apparatus. Success, to a theoretical physicist, can mean uncovering a pattern that no one had previously suspected. It could also mean finding a mathematical model that helps other scientists represent the important features and relationships of their observations. Theoretical physicists spend a lot of time reading about other people's ideas, solving mathematical equations, making testable predictions, and showing how experimental data support or cast doubt on scientific theories.

Figure 11.8 Stephen Hawking (b. 1942) has developed important ideas about black holes and the history of the universe, using advanced mathematics. He has written several best-selling books, which explain his ideas in everyday language. Overcoming the effects of chronic illness, Stephen Hawking remains one of the most influential and well-known modern theoretical scientists.

Pause & Reflect

Examine Figure 11.7 carefully. How can you tell that it shows constant acceleration? What would it look like if the acceleration was not constant? If the rocket's acceleration was increasing or decreasing, could the average velocity still be found in the same way? Discuss these questions with a partner. Then write your conclusions in your Science Log. Sketch a few graphs to make your explanation clearer.

DidYou**Know**?

Albert Einstein (1879–1955)

Albert Einstein revolutionized theoretical physics in the early twentieth century by creating mathematical explanations for many puzzling observations. When young, Einstein was not an outstanding student. He disliked high school and left early. He worked as a clerk in the Swiss patent office while developing his early theories. After they were published, he began working as a university teacher and researcher.

INTERNET CONNECT

www.school.mcgrawhill.ca/resources/

Find out more about the lives, interests, and accomplishments of important scientists and engineers by going to the web site above. Go to **Science Resources**, then to **SCIENCEPOWER 10** to know where to go next.

Tools of Science

The Black Brant research rocket was developed in Canada and manufactured near Winnipeg, Manitoba. Versions of the Black Brant have been used by scientists in Canada and the United States for over 30 years to gather data about the upper atmosphere, study comets, and conduct experiments in low-gravity conditions.

Check Your Understanding

1. Explain how the size and direction of acceleration can be calculated using the slope of an object's velocity-time graph.

2. (a) Sketch a velocity-time graph of a bus trip, showing these stages in the trip.

    A initial velocity of zero while passengers board the bus

    B constant acceleration leaving the bus-stop

    C uniform motion at the speed limit

    D slight slowdown when approaching heavy traffic

    E rapid slowdown and stop at the next bus stop

    F final velocity of zero while passengers get on and off

    (b) Identify stages of the trip with positive, negative, and zero acceleration.

    (c) Identify sections of the velocity-time graph with positive, negative, and zero slope.

    (d) Classify each stage of the trip as uniform or accelerated motion.

3. **Apply** *The Guiness Book of World Records* once reported that a person had survived a fall from a 56.4 m cliff (as high as an 18-storey building). After falling for 3.1 s, the person had come to a stop about 0.015 s after hitting the ground.

    (a) The average downward velocity during the fall would have been about 15.2 m/s. What was the person's final velocity just before impact?

    (b) What was the person's average downward acceleration while falling?

    (c) How large was the person's average acceleration after hitting the ground? In what direction was this acceleration?

    (d) Sketch a velocity-time graph that shows the fall. Use the usual convention of downward velocity being negative.

4. **Thinking Critically** A speed skater starts a race with an initial velocity of zero. She speeds up, travels at constant speed, slows down, and ends up with a final velocity of zero.

    (a) What is the skater's overall change in velocity? What is her average acceleration during the race?

    (b) If the skater stops and finishes at the same point on an oval track, how does her average acceleration resemble her displacement during the race? Explain your answer.

Canadian speed skater Catriona Le May Doan

11.3 Inferring Acceleration

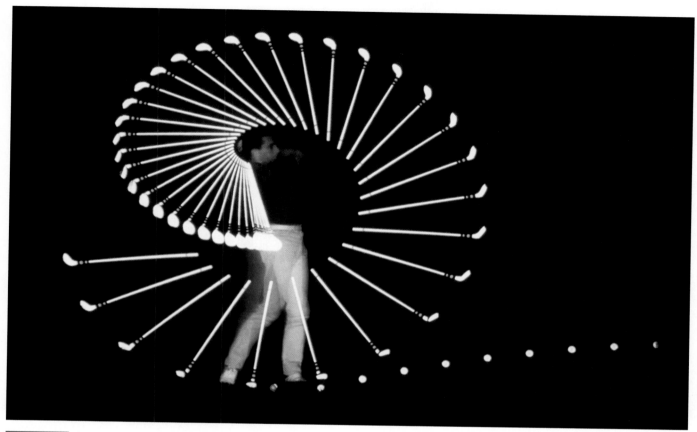

Figure 11.9 A stroboscopic image of a golf swing

Have you ever watched dancers moving under a strobe light? The smooth, rhythmic movements take on a strange, jerky appearance as they are "frozen" for an instant by the rapid flashes of light. Scientists use a similar method to record rapidly changing motion.

Photographs like the one on this page are made with a **stroboscope:** a rapidly blinking light that records a series of pictures on the same piece of photographic film. Careful examination of the film can reveal useful qualitative (non-numerical) information: for example, how a tennis player can improve his or her stroke. If quantitative (numerical) information is needed, just measure the distance between one image of the moving object and the next one. Knowing how fast the stroboscope was flashing, you can calculate detailed information about the object's velocity and acceleration. **Note:** people with certain medical conditions, such as epilepsy, can suffer seizures if exposed to strobe lighting.

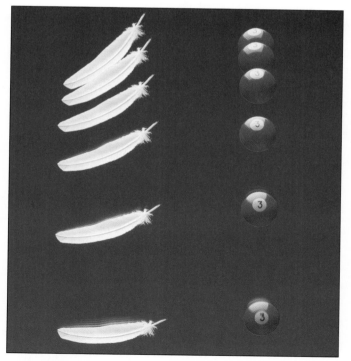

Figure 11.10 This falling billiard ball and feather were photographed several times each second.

Free Fall

Think About It

Is the falling ball in the photographs accelerating or moving uniformly? In this investigation, you will use measurements, calculations, and graphs to find out.

What You Need

calculator
graph paper

What to Do

1 Prepare a data table similar to the one below, but with no data. Give your table a title.

Interval	Displacement, Δd (m)	Time, Δt (s)	Average velocity, v_{av} (m/s)	Change in velocity, Δv (m/s)	Acceleration, a (m/s²)
1			2.31		
2			2.63	} 0.32	9.6
3				}	
11					

2 Calculate the average velocity of the ball in each interval. Record your answers in the data table.

Hint: You can use the formula $\vec{v}_{av} = \dfrac{\vec{\Delta d}}{\Delta t}$, since both the displacement and the length of the time interval are shown in the photograph.

3 Draw a velocity-time graph of the ball's downward motion, using the graph opposite as a model. Notice that the average velocity during each interval is plotted as a dot halfway between the beginning and the end of the interval. A falling object behaves like a smoothly accelerating object, such as a ball rolling down a slope, which you learned about earlier. It reaches its average speed over an interval at the midpoint of the interval.

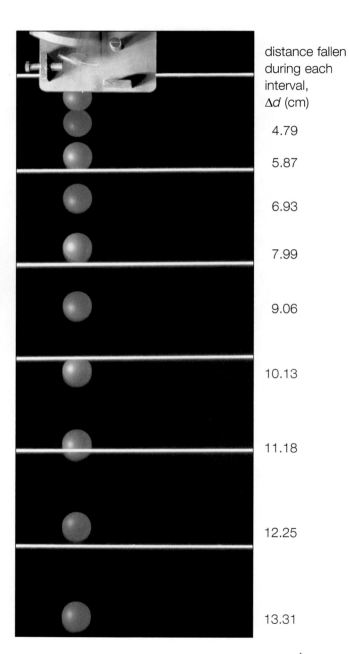

distance fallen during each interval, Δd (cm)

4.79

5.87

6.93

7.99

9.06

10.13

11.18

12.25

13.31

These stroboscopic images of a falling billiard ball were taken $\dfrac{1}{30}$ of a second (0.033 s) apart. After the first few overlapping images, the distance that the ball fell in each interval was carefully measured and marked beside the photograph.

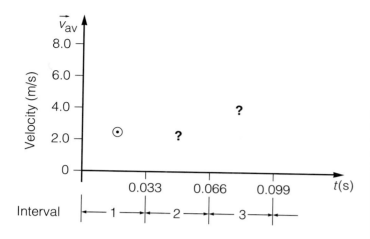

Interval

4 Calculate the change in velocity from the midpoint of each time interval to the midpoint of the next one. Hint: You can read the values from your velocity-time graph, or you can use your average velocities from step 2 in the formula $\Delta v = v_f - v_i$.

5 Find the average acceleration of the ball during its fall, using the velocity-time graph you drew in step 4. Hint: Remember that average acceleration is given by the slope of a velocity-time graph.

Tools of
Science

Stroboscopic photography is not the only way to study rapidly moving objects. Repeating motion, such as the rotation of a fan or a reciprocating (back-and-forth) movement, can appear much slower when you look through a hand stroboscope like the one pictured here. As you turn the stroboscope wheel, its slots reveal a brief glimpse of the moving object every few hundredths of a second. If your school does not have a hand stroboscope, it is not difficult to make one from particleboard or thin plywood.

Analyze

1. Find and describe evidence that the ball is accelerating by examining
   (a) the distance it fell in successive intervals
   (b) the average velocity in each interval
   (c) the velocity-time graph

2. Find and describe evidence that the ball shows *constant* acceleration by examining
   (a) the velocity-time graph
   (b) the changes in velocity that you calculated in step 4

3. What force was causing the ball's motion to accelerate?

4. Review your earlier observations about the motion of falling objects (Chapter 9, section 9.1). Then re-examine the stroboscopic photograph in Figure 11.10 (page 369). Does the photograph support your observations?

Extend Your Skills

5. Calculate the average acceleration of the ball in the photograph from the midpoint of each time interval to the midpoint of the next interval. Use the formula $\vec{a}_{av} = \dfrac{\Delta \vec{v}}{\Delta t}$, with the changes in velocity that you calculated in step 4. Record the average accelerations in your data table. Do your calculations show that acceleration was constant as the ball fell? Do they agree with your answer to question 2?

Velocity-Time Graphs and Displacement

The velocity of a moving object can be determined very easily by using computer programs to analyze data from ultrasonic rangefinders, photogate timers, or videotapes of its motion. The experimenter does not have to calculate velocity from measurements of position or displacement, the way you did in the last investigation. Once you have a velocity-time data table or graph, however, you can extract a lot of information from it, with either pencil and paper or computer analysis. For example, the graph in Figure 11.11 shows the motion of a falling billiard ball. Recall, from previous sections, how to analyze this velocity-time graph to find

- the acceleration of the object
- the average velocity of the object during a time interval
- the instantaneous velocity of an object at a particular instant of time

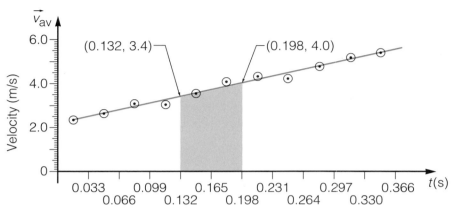

Figure 11.11 How far did the falling ball move during the shaded time interval?

From a velocity-time table or graph, you can also determine how far an object moved (its displacement) during a time interval, even if the object's velocity was changing. The steps below show you how, using data from the graph in Figure 11.11. **Be careful:** Use this method only if you know (or can safely assume) that the object's velocity was changing steadily — in other words, that the object had constant acceleration.

Finding the Displacement of an Accelerating Object

1. Read the initial time (t_i) and initial velocity ($\vec{v}_i$) at the start of the interval.

$$t_i = 0.132 \text{ s} \qquad \vec{v}_i = 3.4 \text{ m/s}$$

2. Read the final time (t_f) and final velocity ($\vec{v}_f$) at the end of the interval.

$$t_f = 0.198 \text{ s} \qquad \vec{v}_f = 4.0 \text{ m/s}$$

3. Find the average velocity during the interval using the following formula:

$$\vec{v}_{av} = \frac{(\vec{v}_i + \vec{v}_f)}{2}$$

$$\vec{v}_{av} = \frac{(3.4 + 4.0)}{2} \text{ m/s}$$
$$\vec{v}_{av} = +3.7 \text{ m/s}$$

4. Find the time interval by subtraction:
$$\Delta t = t_f - t_i$$

$$\Delta t = 0.198 \text{ s} - 0.132 \text{ s}$$
$$\Delta t = 0.066 \text{ s}$$

Computer **CONNECT**

Using mathematical models, a computer can graph and illustrate the motion of an object almost instantly, according to conditions that you set. *Simulation* programs require you to construct a situation that will produce a certain motion graph. *Analysis* programs graph the motion of an object in a videotape after you mark the position of a selected point in each frame of the digitized video. Using these tools, you can learn to interpret complex motion graphs in a short time — a task that was very difficult for even the most brilliant physicists in the past.

5. Find the displacement using the formula $\vec{\Delta d} = \vec{v}_{av} \times \Delta t$.

$\vec{\Delta d} = (3.7 \text{ m/s}) \times (0.066 \text{ s})$

$\vec{\Delta d} = +0.24 \text{ m}$

Skill POWER

If you need practice rearranging formulas, turn to page 611.

In the given time interval, the object travels about 0.24 m forward. Steps 3 and 5 are often combined into one mathematical formula for displacement:

$$\vec{\Delta d} = \frac{(\vec{v}_i + \vec{v}_f)}{2} \times (\Delta t)$$

For motion in a straight line, this formula is often written without vector symbols. Positive (+) and negative (−) signs are used to indicate the direction of the velocity and displacement in any calculations. The concluding statement, or paraphrase, usually describes the directions in words, however. For example, you would write "The object had a velocity of 4.5 m upward" if your calculated velocity was +4.5 m and the object was moving vertically.

STRETCH Your Mind

1. Use your knowledge of mathematics to explain how the formulas from steps 3 and 5 were combined by substitution to produce the new formula for displacement:

$$\vec{\Delta d} = \frac{(\vec{v}_i + \vec{v}_f)}{2} \times (\Delta t)$$

2. The formula for displacement can be rearranged to isolate any of the variables in it. Complete these different versions of the formula.

   (a) $\Delta t = ?$

   (b) $\vec{v}_i = ?$

   (c) $\vec{v}_f = ?$

Figure 11.12 shows a velocity-time graph of constant-accelation motion. The average velocity during a time interval is exactly halfway between the initial and final velocities for the interval. This suggests another way of finding displacement, as the area under a velocity-time graph. You will learn more about this idea in Chapter 12.

Pause& Reflect

Carefully examine the shaded part of the graph on the right in Figure 11.12. What shape is it? Would you think of Δt as its length or its width? What about $\vec{v}_{av}$? When you multiply $\vec{v}_{av}$ and Δt, what are you finding out about the graph? What does $(\vec{v}_{av}) \times (\Delta t)$ tell you about the motion of the object? What feature of the velocity-time graph indicates the displacement of the moving object? Write your ideas in your Science Log.

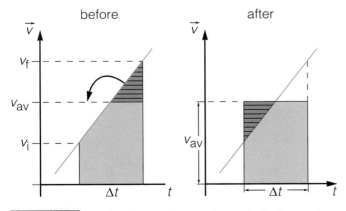

before   after

Figure 11.12 Imagine cutting and rearranging a velocity-time graph, as shown above, to find the displacement of a moving object.

Hit the Brakes!

Slowing down a heavy, fast-moving aircraft or racing car in a short distance can be too much for drum or disc brakes, like those used on most vehicles. Although the brakes could be made powerful enough to stop the wheels from turning, the skidding tires would be quickly worn away or destroyed as they scraped across the ground. **Air brakes** are parachutes or surfaces that can turn or pivot to increase **drag** (air resistance). Air brakes help to produce the acceleration needed to stop a vehicle. **Remember:** Slowing down is also acceleration, because it is a change in velocity.

The Space Shuttle *Atlantis*, slowing from over 350 km/h at touchdown

Challenge

Design and construct an effective air brake for a small vehicle, and measure its acceleration.

Materials

small moving vehicle, such as a lab cart or a large toy car
starting ramp to get the vehicle moving
construction materials, such as wood, cardboard, cloth, string, glue, and fasteners
stopwatch or photogate timer
metre stick or tape

Design Criteria

A. Your vehicle must gain initial velocity by moving down the ramp without any braking action.

B. The air brake must be triggered in some way that does not slow the vehicle significantly.

C. The air brake may be a separate structure that the vehicle runs into, but it must end up attached to the vehicle.

D. The air brake must not cause the vehicle to tip over, spin, or turn significantly.

E. After constructing your air brake, you must conduct several trials to determine
  • the velocity of the vehicle after it rolls off the ramp, just before the air brake is triggered
  • the average acceleration from the time that the air brake is triggered until the time that the vehicle comes to a complete stop

Plan and Construct

1 Work in a small group to brainstorm possible designs for an air brake, such as parachutes, movable sails, or spoilers that change the shape of the vehicle to increase air resistance. Consider how to keep your air brake from slowing the vehicle as it goes down the ramp. How will your air brake fold or turn when activated? How will you attach it to the vehicle? What sort of trigger mechanism will you use?

2 Obtain the materials you need, and construct a prototype of your air brake.

DidYou**Know**?

Power skaters increase their strength by skating against the resistance of a braking parachute.

③ Conduct preliminary trials, and modify your air brake until it satisfies the design criteria.

④ Decide what measurements you need and how you will use them to calculate

(a) the velocity of the vehicle just as the air brake is triggered

(b) the average acceleration of the vehicle while it brakes (Hint: You need to know the vehicle's change in velocity as it brakes and the time interval required for it to stop. The final velocity of the vehicle is zero, because it has stopped. The initial velocity is its speed just as the air brake is triggered. You can measure the stopping time directly, or you can calculate it from the stopping distance and the average velocity.)

⑤ Create a data table for your observations.

⑥ Conduct several trials, so that you can average your results to increase their reliability.

Evaluate

1. Average your results, and complete the calculations listed in the Design Criteria.

2. Prepare a concise summary of your observations and calculations. Include a sketch or photograph of your air brake.

3. What problems did you observe when you tested your prototype? What modifications did you make to overcome these problems?

4. How does the effectiveness of your design compare with the effectiveness of other groups' designs?

5. What changes would you make if you designed a second-generation version of your air brake?

6. What single change could most improve the efficiency of your work group?

Across Canada

Dr. Donath Mrawira was born in Tanzania on the slopes of Africa's highest mountain, Kilimanjaro. At about age 10, he took a train to his uncle's home. The steam locomotive fascinated him. "Looking at those moving parts," he says, "I knew I wanted to create and work with that kind of stuff."

Young Donath followed his dream, studying civil engineering at university in Dar-es-Salaam, Tanzania, and Waterloo, Ontario. Today he is Assistant Professor of Civil Engineering at the University of New Brunswick. He is also Director of the D.C. Campbell Chair in Highway Construction and Pavement Research. "Pavements are made of asphalt and crushed stone," Donath explains. "They are flexible to a certain extent, but in the cold Canadian winter, they get hard and can break like glass. In summer, they soften. When heavy trucks roll over, we get rutting. In our asphalt labs, we look at the properties, throw in polymers, and try to come up with better pavements for Canadian extremes."

Road salt is another of Dr. Mrawira's concerns. "We use it to keep Canadian roads passable in winter," he says. "It lowers the freezing point of water, but it's a toxic substance that affects water bodies. In our labs, we model the behaviour of road pavement, determining exactly when it freezes. This helps us use road salt to the best advantage, which reduces our need for it."

Dr. Donath Mrawira

Like many other scientists, Donath travels a lot. Among the countries where he does pavement management projects is Tanzania — where a chugging, whistling locomotive first inspired him to make motion and transportation his life's work.

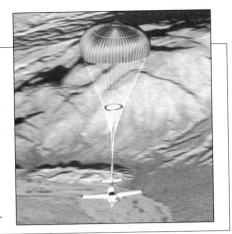

Off the Wall

A parachute supporting an entire airplane? Not exactly standard emergency equipment, but the SR-20 is a small, single-engine airplane equipped with just that — an emergency parachute for the airplane itself. If the plane goes out of control, the parachute can be extended from its roof by a manually fired rocket. Although the parachute would probably not save the plane, it would stop an uncontrolled downward spiral and slow the plane enough for the passengers to survive a crash. The parachute system has never been used in an actual emergency, but it has been successfully tested. Similar systems have been effective for ultralight recreational aircraft. In fact, the final stage of early space missions, before the Space Shuttle, was a gentle parachute descent of the astronauts' capsule into the ocean.

Check Your Understanding

1. List the information or measurements that you need when analyzing a stroboscopic photograph to find
   (a) the velocity of the moving object
   (b) the acceleration of the moving object

2. **Apply** Modern strobe equipment can easily take photographs $\frac{1}{1000}$ of a second apart. At this rate, if you were photographing a cheetah (the fastest land mammal) moving at its maximum speed of about 27 m/s, how far would it move between any two flashes of the strobe light?

3. **Apply** Some birds endure tremendous accelerations as they dig insects out of trees. A bird's beak can be moving as fast as 5.8 m/s (almost 21 km/h), but its speed is reduced to zero within 0.0059 s by the impact with the tree.
   (a) What acceleration does the bird's brain withstand?
   (b) How far into the tree bark does the bird's beak travel as it stops?
   (c) Suppose that the bird's head started from rest and travelled 6.0 cm forward just before reaching its maximum velocity and striking the tree. How long would the forward motion take?

4. **Apply** Some insects withstand even larger accelerations than birds. The tiny click beetle has been measured jumping 29.8 cm into the air to escape a predator. It lands again at a speed of about 2.42 m/s and stops in about $\frac{1}{10\,000}$ of a second (1.07×10^{-4} s).
   (a) What acceleration does the beetle withstand as it lands? Hint: Is the insect speeding up or slowing down? What is its initial and final velocity?
   (b) How big a dent does the beetle make in the soil it lands on? Assume that the beetle does not bend its legs, so the depth of the dent is equal to the distance it travels while stopping.
   (c) The beetle's mass is only about 0.004 g. How does this explain why your answer to part (b) is so small?

5. **Thinking Critically** Careful measurements of objects falling through the air show that their speed does not continue to increase indefinitely. A ball, similar to the one photographed in Figure 11.10, reaches a maximum ("terminal") downward velocity of about 40 m/s. What keeps the ball from moving faster? Why do you think a 7.3 kg shot-put has a terminal velocity of about 145 m/s downward, while a Ping-Pong™ ball's terminal velocity is only about 9 m/s downward?

CHAPTER at a glance

Now that you have completed this chapter, try to do the following. If you cannot, go back to the sections indicated.

Give two specific examples of
(a) positive acceleration
(b) negative acceleration (11.1)

List all the types of changes in an object's motion that produce acceleration. (11.1)

Make sketches to show how a liquid level accelerometer shows the size and direction of acceleration. (11.1)

Write a simple mathematical formula that relates acceleration to change in velocity and time interval. Rearrange the formula in three ways, so that it can be solved for each variable in it. (11.1)

Write a point-form procedure for finding an object's acceleration if you can time its travel over a measured distance several times along its path of motion. (11.1)

Sketch velocity-time graphs that show the difference between finding average acceleration and finding instantaneous acceleration. (11.2)

Sketch velocity-time graphs that show positive, negative, and zero acceleration. (11.2)

Describe what a theoretical physicist does. (11.2)

Explain how an electronic stroboscope "stops" motion. (11.3)

Show how an object's average velocity is related to its initial and final velocities
(a) using a graph
(b) using a diagram (11.3)

Identify what is shown by the area under a velocity-time graph. (11.3)

Describe two methods of increasing drag to slow down a vehicle. (11.3)

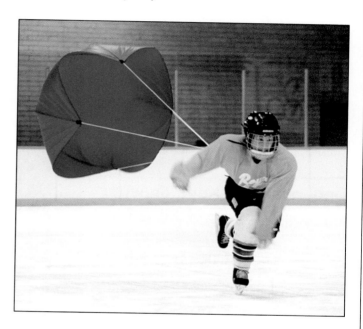

Prepare Your Own Summary

Summarize this chapter by doing one of the following. Use a graphic organizer (such as a concept map), produce a poster, or write the summary to include the key chapter concepts. Here are a few ideas to use as a guide:
• What do physicists mean by acceleration? Include
  (a) a definition in words
  (b) standard units
  (c) whether acceleration is a vector or scalar quantity
  (d) examples of accelerated motion

  (e) methods of measuring and calculating acceleration
• Contrast average and instantaneous acceleration.
• Describe the connection between acceleration and the net force acting on an object.
• Explain how you can decide whether or not an object's motion is accelerated, using
  (a) a data table giving its velocity at different times
  (b) a velocity-time graph
  (c) a position-time graph

Reviewing Key Terms

If you need to review, the section numbers show you where these terms were introduced.

1. In your notebook, match the description in column A with the correct term in column B.

A
• device that produces rapidly repeated views of an object, which show details of its motion
• device that measures acceleration
• force that slows moving objects by friction with the air
• slope of a tangent to a velocity-time graph

B
• accelerometer (chapter opener)
• instantaneous acceleration (11.2)
• air brake (11.3)
• drag (11.3)
• stroboscope (11.3)
• accelerated motion (chapter opener)

Understanding Key Concepts

Section numbers are provided if you need to review.

2. Give examples to show that large acceleration is more dangerous than large constant velocity. (chapter opener)

3. A car is leaving a city and travelling north at 15 m/s (about 55 km/h). As it enters a highway the driver accelerates at +4.0 m/s² for 5 s. (11.1)

   (a) List the car's speed after each second of acceleration.

   (b) Describe how the car's motion would differ if it had accelerated at −4.0 m/s². List the car's speed after each second of this acceleration.

4. Explain how a graph of constant *acceleration* is similar to a graph of constant *velocity*. In what way are the graphs different? (11.2)

5. Suppose that you were taking a stroboscopic photograph of a bird flying, to study the movement of its wings. (11.3)

   (a) How would the appearance of your photograph change if the strobe light flashed more times each second?

   (b) Which photograph would give more detailed information about the wing motion, a photograph with a fast flash rate or one with a slower flash rate? Justify your answer.

   (c) How could you obtain the same effect as a faster flash rate using a hand stroboscope?

6. In your notebook, correct the errors in the following statements. (11.1–11.3)

   (a) $\vec{v}_{av} = -10$ m/s²

   (b) $\vec{v}_{av} = \dfrac{(\vec{v}_f - \vec{v}_i)}{2}$

   (c) $\vec{a}_{av} = +3.5$ m²/s

   (d) The direction of acceleration is always opposite to the direction of the velocity change on a vector diagram.

   (e) On velocity-time graphs, the average velocity is always plotted at the end of a time interval.

7. Why are air brakes used to help stop fast-moving vehicles quickly? Why are larger, more powerful disk or drum brakes, like those on an automobile, not used? (11.3)

Developing Skills

8. Act out the motion of a skater accelerating, as described below.

(a) moving uniformly in the positive direction and then accelerating positively

(b) moving uniformly in the negative direction and then accelerating negatively

(c) moving uniformly in the negative direction and then accelerating positively

Problem Solving/Applying

9. An activity that is similar to bungee jumping occurs in the New Hebrides Islands. Men jump from a platform with a vine tied to their ankles. After falling freely for about 1.50 s, they reach a velocity of −15 m/s (downward). The vine arrests their fall just above the ground, stopping them in a few milliseconds with an acceleration estimated at +1070 m/s². (The force of the vine is upward, in the positive direction, so the divers' acceleration is also positive.)

(a) Find the time that the divers take to stop.

(b) How far does the vine stretch as it stops the diver? In other words, find the diver's displacement as he stops.

10. U.S. Air Force Colonel John Stapp, a medical doctor, took several dozen test rides on a rocket-driven sled in the early 1950s. After reaching a maximum velocity of over 1000 km/h on a 2 km track, the sled hit a long trough of water, which slowed it very rapidly. The graph below shows a typical sled run.

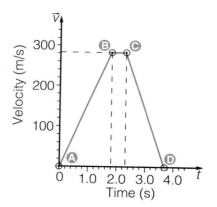

(a) Describe what is happening to the sled at points A, B, C, and D.

(b) Calculate the acceleration of the sled in the intervals between A and B and between B and C.

(c) How far did the sled travel as it slowed down?

Critical Thinking

11. Travelling to a distant planet or star in a reasonable length of time requires a very high velocity. A present-day space probe reaches this velocity using powerful rocket engines, which produce very large accelerations for a short period of time. After the engines run out of fuel, the probe coasts to its destination.

(a) List some disadvantages of using very large accelerations for a short period of time to speed up a space probe.

(b) How would it be possible to reach the necessary high velocity using less powerful engines, which would produce smaller accelerations?

12. Galileo was the first scientist to observe that heavy objects and light objects fall (or roll down an incline) at the same speed. Why do you think the mass of a falling object does not affect its acceleration, at least in the situations you studied, where friction is unimportant?

Galileo Galilei (1564–1642)

Pause & Reflect

Go back to the beginning of the chapter, on page 352, and check your original answers to the Opening Ideas questions. How has your thinking changed? How would you answer those questions now that you have investigated the topics in this chapter?

12 Life in Motion

- Do you like midway rides? If so, which ones do you find most enjoyable? Why?

- Why do you feel weightless when falling?

- How do police officers measure the speed of cars?

Science Log

In your Science Log, make a list of careers that require an ability to describe or measure motion. Do any of these careers interest you? If so, what makes them interesting?

Midway rides can be a lot of fun. You swoop upward, twist, spin, and fall. Sometimes you lose your sense of up and down. All of these motions involve acceleration: a change in velocity. After all, a ride would be boring if it moved at a nice steady speed. Midway rides are very popular. They are found in small-town fairs, major exhibitions, and even some shopping malls.

The sensation of being thrown around in a safe environment is exciting. Great care must be taken, however, to make sure that the envi-ronment does remain safe. Otherwise excitement becomes terror. The engi-neers who design these rides must know just how much acceleration is safe for the human body. They must also be able to predict the motions that the ride will produce and deter-mine the stresses within the structure of the ride. Next the ride must be designed and built to withstand these stresses. After that, the responsibility falls to the operator of the ride. The operator must inspect the ride regu-larly and keep it in good condition. Then we can all have fun.

Thrills Without Spills

What makes rides exciting? In many cases, there is no one answer. For some people, just being up high is exciting. For others, speed and acceleration are a large part of the fun. In this activity, you will analyze the speeds and accelerations involved in two rides.

Starting Point ACTIVITY

What to Do

1. Copy the following diagram of a roller coaster into your notebook.

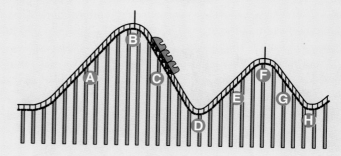

2. Identify any points along the track where the cars are undergoing nearly uniform motion.
   Remember: Uniform motion has constant speed *and* direction. Going around in a circle is not uniform motion. The direction is constantly changing.

3. Identify points where the acceleration is
   (a) due only to a change of speed (little or no change of direction)
   (b) due mainly to a change in direction

4. At which points are seat belts most necessary? Explain your choice.

5. Where do you think the greatest thrill on a roller coaster ride occurs? Why?

6. Select any ride that you enjoy. Sketch part of the path that you follow on the ride. Then locate points of high speed and high acceleration. Explain why you enjoy the ride.

What Did You Discover?

1. Suppose that your eyes were closed. How would you know whether you were accelerating?

2. What relationship is there between the thrill of a ride and the accelerations involved?

3. Are there any other factors, besides acceleration, that add to the thrill of a ride?

12.1 The Drop Zone

Figure 12.1 "Free fall" can be exciting, but it also has a practical aspect. The plants at top left are part of an experiment to study weightless growth.

Daring midway riders try a ride that lifts a car to a great height and then allows it to fall. Of course, the car is deflected before it smashes into the ground. During the fall, the riders feel weightless. This is because everything is falling along with them, at the same rate. If you were in the falling car with a huge professional wrestler, both of you would stay side by side on the way down. If either of you held out a pen and released it, the pen would also fall at the same rate. It would seem to hover weightless in the air in front of you.

Astronauts in space experience the same effect. A spacecraft in orbit has not escaped Earth's gravity. The spacecraft's speed (as much as 29 000 km/h) carries it around Earth in a continuous "free" fall. This produces an effect called **microgravity**: a near-weightless environment in orbit. There is still some gravitational effect, but an accelerometer is needed to detect it. Microgravity feels a little like falling in the midway ride described above, except that you never get to the bottom!

In television broadcasts from space, astronauts sometimes spin objects in midair or chase water bubbles and swallow them. Microgravity has more serious uses, however. Scientists can use it to study the growth of plants and other organisms. They can also use it to study the behaviour of the human body in almost perfect weightlessness.

The **acceleration due to gravity** on Earth (often represented by the letter g) is close to 9.8 m/s² in a downward direction. This means that a freely falling object gains 9.8 m/s downward velocity for each second that it falls. Table 12.1 shows the velocity of an object at the end of each second, if it starts at rest.

Table 12.1 Rate of Fall in Earth's Gravity

Time after release (s)	Downward velocity (m/s)
0.00	0.00
1.00	9.80 (1.00 s × 9.8 m/s²)
2.00	19.6 (2.00 s × 9.8 m/s²)
3.00	29.4 (3.00 s × 9.8 m/s²)

Measuring the Acceleration Due to Gravity

The acceleration due to gravity (*g*) is an important physical quantity. It affects how fast we fall, how much we weigh, and how high we can kick a football. It also affects how quickly satellites orbit Earth. Mineral deposits can be found by looking for a local increase in the value of *g*. The increase is caused by a dense mass of ore just beneath Earth's surface.

Problem

In this investigation, you will use a ticker timer to record the motion of a dropped object. You will then analyze your observations and use them to find a value for *g*. You may want to review what you learned about this timing technology in Chapter 9, page 306.

Part 1

The Drop

Safety Precautions

The student who drops the mass must ensure that it will not strike any other member of the group.

Apparatus

robust object, such as a 1 kg mass

small board or other cushioning
   substance, such as an old
   mouse pad

C-clamp

support stand

ticker timer with 1.5 m of tape

clamp to attach the timer to the
   support stand

ruler (accurate to 0.1 cm)

Procedure

❶ Clamp the base of the support stand close to the edge of a desk or table.

❷ Clamp the timer near the top of the support stand. Make sure that the timer overhangs the edge of the desk. It must face downward and be at least 1.5 m above the floor. If possible, set the timer to 10 Hz.

❸ Place the board or cushioning material on the floor, directly under the timer.

❹ Thread the tape through the timer.

❺ Attach the leading edge of the tape to the object that will be dropped.

❻ Hold the object steady. Turn on the timer.

❼ Release the object.

❽ Turn off the timer as soon as the tape has passed through it. Check that the timer has left distinct dots on the tape. If necessary, adjust the timer according to your teacher's instructions.

CONTINUED ▶

Part 2
Graphing Position

All the directions are downward in this part of the investigation. Remember that negative values represent downward vectors.

Procedure

① Make a table like the one below. Copy the headings, but leave the rest of your table blank. (The entries in the table below are examples of how your table should be completed.) Give your table a title.

② Spread out the tape. Examine the end where the dots are closest together. Find the first distinct dot, and circle it.

③ If the timer makes dots at the rate of 60 Hz, circle every sixth dot. Count from the first marked dot (zero), as shown in the photograph. If the timer makes dots at the rate of 10 Hz, circle every dot. Begin with the first distinct dot. In either case, the time interval between circled dots is 0.10 s. Ask your teacher if you are unsure about your timer's speed.

④ Measure the distance from the first circled dot to each of the other circled dots. Record the values in the "Position" column of your table. Record all the values to the nearest 0.1 cm.

⑤ Plot a position-time graph of the data in the first two columns. Describe, in your own words, the shape of the curve.

Time, t (s)	Position, $\vec{d}$ (cm)	Displacement, $\Delta\vec{d}$ (cm)	Time interval, Δt (s)	Velocity, $\vec{v}_{av}$ (cm/s)	Change in velocity, $\Delta\vec{v}$ (cm/s)	Acceleration, $\vec{a}_{av}$ (cm/s²)
0.0	0.0	} −1.1	0.1	−11		
0.1	−1.1	} −10.2	0.1	−102	} −91	−910
0.2	−11.3	} −19.7	0.1	−197	} −95	−950
0.3	−31.0	} −29.6	0.1	−296	} −94	−940
0.4	−60.6					

Part 3
Graphing Velocity

Procedure

① Find the displacement, $\Delta\vec{d}$, from one circled dot to the next. Either measure from the tape, or subtract the position values in the second column of your table. Place your displacement values in the "Displacement" column. Also complete the "Time" and "Time interval" columns. Remember that you are measuring in steps of 0.1 s.

② Calculate the average velocity for each interval. Use the formula

$$\vec{v}_{av} = \frac{\Delta\vec{d}}{\Delta t}$$

Place these values in the "Velocity" column.

③ Plot a velocity-time graph of your data. If the acceleration is constant, then (as you saw in Chapter 11) the average

velocity over an interval should be the same as the instantaneous velocity at the midpoint of the interval. This means that you should plot the first velocity at a time of 0.05 s, the second velocity at 0.15 s, the third velocity at 0.25 s, and so on.

④ Describe, in your own words, the shape of the graph.

Part 4

Finding the Acceleration Due to Gravity

1 Determine the values for the change in velocity, $\Delta \vec{v}$, by subtracting the velocity values in the fifth column of your table. Enter your $\Delta \vec{v}$ values in the "Change in velocity" column.

2 For each change in velocity, calculate the acceleration for the time interval. Use the formula

$$\vec{a}_{\text{av}} = \frac{\Delta \vec{v}}{\Delta t}$$

Place your acceleration values of the last column of the table. The time interval is still 0.1 s. Why?

Skill
P O W E R

To practise your graphing skills, turn to page 604. For help with calculating errors, turn to page 598.

Analyze

1. If an object is falling freely, what does the graph of position against time look like?

2. If an object is falling freely, what does the graph of velocity against time look like?

3. In this investigation, did the acceleration of the falling object appear constant? Give evidence from your graphs and calculations.

Conclude and Apply

4. Calculate an average value for the acceleration due to gravity, g. Use the values from the right-hand column of your table. Remember to convert your units from cm/s^2 to m/s^2.

5. The acceleration due to gravity on Earth is 9.8 m/s^2 downward, or –9.8 m/s^2. What is your percent error?

6. Was your value for g different from –9.8 m/s^2? If so, suggest some possible reasons for this difference. Also try to estimate how much difference each reason might make.

Extend Your Knowledge

7. Think of a method that you could use to measure the acceleration due to gravity from the velocity-time graph. Try your method, and calculate the percent error. Compare your measured value with the average that you calculated in question 4.

DidYou**Know**?

Slight variations in Earth's gravity can be very revealing. Examine the different colours in the map at the right. They show a pattern of variations in the Yucatán peninsula, Mexico. Most scientists now believe that this is the place where a massive comet or asteroid struck Earth 65 million years ago. The impact may have triggered the extinction of the dinosaurs and many other species.

The ripple pattern reveals shock waves in Earth's crust. The shock waves cannot be seen directly. They are preserved as changes in rock density. These changes create slight increases or decreases in the acceleration due to Earth's gravity, which a satellite in orbit can detect. This evidence of the Yucatán impact is sometimes called the "smoking gun."

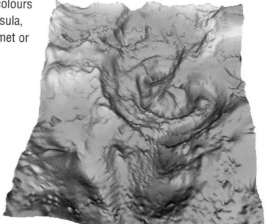

This computer-enhanced gravity map shows the "splash" of the Yucatán impact.

Swing It 🧪

For many years, scientists did not drop an object in order to measure the acceleration due to gravity. Instead, they set a pendulum swinging. Recall, from Chapter 10, that one cycle of a pendulum is the time for the bob to swing down through the vertical, swing back, and return to its starting position. As long as the swing is not too big, the time in seconds for each cycle, T, can be given by the formula

$$T = 2\pi\sqrt{\frac{l}{g}}$$

In this formula, $\pi = 3.14$ (as usual), l is the length, in m, of the pendulum (the distance from the pivot point to the centre of the swinging mass), and g is the acceleration due to gravity, in m/s^2. You will learn more about the pendulum formula if you continue your study of physics in Grade 11.

What to Do

1. Design a procedure to measure the acceleration due to gravity, using the pendulum formula. You should be able to carry out your procedure at home. Have your teacher approve your procedure.

2. Carry out your procedure at home, with the supervision of an adult. Make all the necessary observations.

What Did You Discover?

1. Calculate the percent error for your value for g.

2. Suggest sources of error in your procedure. Estimate how much difference each source of error might make.

3. Is your value closer to the accepted value, -9.8 m/s^2, than your value in Conduct an Investigation 12-A? Recommend one of the two methods for finding g. Give reasons for your recommendation. Also state any drawbacks to this method.

Extension

4. What length of pendulum gives a period of $T = 1.0$ s?

DidYou**Know**?

Relative to our closest neighbours, Earth has a large acceleration due to gravity.

Object	Acceleration due to gravity at the surface (m/s^2 downward)
Earth	9.8
Moon	1.7
Mercury	3.7
Venus	8.6
Mars	3.7
Jupiter	26.5
Saturn	9.0 (at the equator) 12.1 (at the poles)
Uranus	8.7
Neptune	11.2
Pluto	0.6

Suggest a reason why Earth's surface gravity produces a higher acceleration than Uranus' surface gravity. Why do you think Saturn's surface gravity varies so much?

Solving Problems Involving Gravity

We know that the acceleration due to gravity is constant near Earth's surface. Therefore we can use the basic acceleration formulas from Chapter 11. The fundamental formula is

$$a = \frac{\Delta v}{\Delta t} \qquad \text{Formula 1}$$

In terms of v_i and v_f, we can write the formula as

$$a = \frac{v_f - v_i}{\Delta t} \qquad \text{Formula 2}$$

Sometimes this is not the most convenient way to write the formula. We can rearrange Formula 2 as

$$\Delta t = \frac{v_f - v_i}{a} \qquad \text{Formula 3}$$

Then we can rearrange Formula 3 as

$$v_f = v_i + a\,\Delta t \qquad \text{Formula 4}$$

Formulas 3 and 4 represent exactly the same relation between acceleration, velocity, and time as Formulas 1 and 2. They are useful, however, because they provide shortcuts for many problems. You will see this in the first model problem below.

Skill POWER

To practise algebra techniques for handling formulas, turn to page 611.

Model Problem 1

A tennis player throws a ball upward at 15 m/s. What is its velocity after 2.0 s?

Given
Initial velocity, $v_i = +15$ m/s
Time interval, $\Delta t = 2.0$ s
Acceleration, $a = -9.8$ m/s²

Required
Final velocity, v_f, in m/s

Analysis
The formula that expresses v_f in terms of the other three variables is
$v_f = v_i + a\,\Delta t$

Solution
$v_f = v_i + a\,\Delta t$
$\quad = (+15 \text{ m/s}) + (-9.8 \text{ m/s}^2) \times (2.0 \text{ s})$
$\quad = +15 \text{ m/s} - 19.6 \text{ m/s}$
$\quad = -4.6 \text{ m/s}$

Paraphrase
The velocity of the ball after 2.0 s is 4.6 m/s downward (to 2 significant digits).

A dime is flipped upward with a speed of 5.0 m/s. To what maximum height does it rise?

Given
Initial velocity, $v_i = +5.0$ m/s
Acceleration, $a = -9.8$ m/s^2

Required
Displacement, Δd, in m

Analysis
First notice that the problem gives a third piece of information. At its highest point, the coin is no longer climbing. It is stationary for an instant. Therefore final velocity, $v_f = 0.0$ m/s.

No formula will solve the problem right away. We will start with

$$a = \frac{v_f - v_i}{\Delta t}$$

We can rearrange this formula to calculate Δt:

$$\Delta t = \frac{v_f - v_i}{a}$$

Then we can use a formula from Chapter 11, page 373:

$$\Delta d = \frac{(v_i + v_f)\,\Delta t}{2}$$

Solution

$$\Delta t = \frac{v_f - v_i}{a}$$

$$= \frac{(0.0 \text{ m/s} - 5.0 \text{ m/s})}{(-9.8 \text{ m/s}^2)}$$

$$= 0.5102 \text{ s}$$

Using the second formula,

$$\Delta d = \frac{(v_i + v_f)\,\Delta t}{2}$$

$$= \frac{(5.0 \text{ m/s} + 0.0 \text{ m/s}) \times (0.5102 \text{ s})}{2}$$

$$= 1.2755 \text{ m}$$

Paraphrase
The maximum height of the coin is 1.3 m above its initial height (to 2 significant digits). (Notice that the answer is rounded to 2 significant digits only at the end. This helps to keep the calculation accurate.)

Terminal Velocity

You learned that all objects fall at the same rate. Why is the skydriver in the photograph using a parachute? Obviously the skydiver believes that the parachute will provide a slow, controlled fall. What if the skydiver were falling toward the surface of the Moon or an airless planet such as Mercury? The parachute would be useless. Here on Earth, however, parachutes work well because of an effect called terminal velocity.

As the skydiver falls faster and faster through the atmosphere, air friction increases. Eventually, as you saw in Chapter 11, the forces of air friction (or drag) balance the force of gravity. After that, the skydiver neither speeds up nor slows down. This steady speed is called **terminal velocity**. For humans, terminal velocity without a parachute is about 240 km/h, or 67 m/s. With the parachute open, a typical terminal velocity is about 30 km/h, or 8.3 m/s. This is roughly the same velocity that you would reach if you jumped off the roof of a one-storey building. You would need training to land without hurting yourself, but it is reasonably safe.

Math **CONNECT**

High accelerations are often expressed in terms of the acceleration due to Earth's gravity, g. If you are accelerating at 5.0 g, or "five gees," this represents 5.0 × 9.8 m/s² or 49 m/s². The acceleration due to gravity at the surface of Mars is 3.7 m/s². How many "gees" is this?

Figure 12.2 Once a parachute is opened, its large surface generates high air resistance. The skydiver's terminal velocity is much slower than it would be without the parachute.

Terminal Velocity

The terminal velocity of an object depends, to a large extent, on the object's shape and density. A snowflake has a much lower terminal velocity than a raindrop. A dandelion seed has a lower terminal velocity than a pine cone. Yet when these objects begin to fall, they all start by accelerating at 9.8 m/s^2 downward. Once they reach terminal velocity, they fall at a steady speed, without accelerating. For some objects, like the dandelion seed and the snowflake, a slow terminal velocity is reached early. This means that the acceleration period is very short.

Problem

If a Styrofoam™ sphere is dropped from ceiling height, will it reach terminal velocity before it hits the floor? If it does, what is its terminal velocity?

Apparatus

Styrofoam™ sphere
appropriate motion sensing and timing equipment, including ultrasonic motion sensor, stopwatch, metre rule, measuring tape, and/or video camera

Procedure

1. To design your procedure, work in groups of about four members. You need to think about the following questions:
   (a) How will you obtain position and time data for the falling sphere?
   (b) How will you display your data?
   (c) How will you tell from your data if the sphere has reached terminal velocity?
   (d) If the sphere reaches terminal velocity, how will you calculate the value of the terminal velocity?
   (e) If you are using a video camera, how will you obtain distance and time information from it?

2. Choose a timing procedure. You will need to record many position and time values for the dropped sphere.

3. If the Styrofoam™ spheres come in a range of sizes, arrange with another group to test the same size of sphere. This will allow you to see if your results are reproducible.

4. Have your teacher approve your procedure. Then carry out your investigation.

Analyze

1. Did your sphere reach terminal velocity? If so, what was the value of its terminal velocity?

2. How consistent were the data you obtained?

3. How do your results compare with the results of other groups that tried the same size of sphere?

4. If other groups used different sizes of spheres, which size has the largest terminal velocity? Suggest a reason for this.

Conclude and Apply

5. How could you improve the investigation?

Extend Your Skills

6. Form a hypothesis about the factors that affect terminal velocity. Think about factors such as mass, density, and shape. Adapt your procedure to test your hypothesis.

Protecting the Human Body from Acceleration: The G-Suit

A key contribution to aviation technology was made by a medical research scientist at the University of Toronto, Dr. Wilbur Franks (1901–1986). Franks' research sometimes involved spinning glass test tubes in a centrifuge. (A centrifuge is a rotating chamber that uses high accelerations to separate substances.) The fragile test tubes tended to break. Franks noticed that they could be protected by placing them in water-filled "jackets." In 1939, war broke out. Franks realized that the same principle could be used to design a suit that would keep pilots from blacking out in high-acceleration manoeuvres.

Franks tested his suit himself in 1939. It worked by applying hydraulic pressure to the pilots' legs and lower torso. The hydraulic pressure maintained blood pressure to the chest and brain. Franks' invention became known as the **G-suit**. Variants have been a key element of NASA's space program. Canadian innovation still leads the field in this technology. The new CF-18 G-suit uses a technique called "positive pressure breathing." It works by matching the increased pressure about the chest with a pressurized oxygen mask system. The CF-18 G-suit allows trained pilots to function without strain at accelerations of up to 7.5 g.

Figure 12.3 The G-suit, a fashion essential for fighter pilots and astronauts

Check Your Understanding

Note: In these questions, assume that thrown or falling objects accelerate at a constant $g = -9.8$ m/s^2 throughout. Also assume that objects do not reach terminal velocity, unless stated otherwise.

1. An arrow is fired straight upward at 50 m/s. Calculate its velocity after

   (a) 3.0 s   **(b)** 8.0 s

2. A monkey in a tree throws a banana straight down at 2.0 m/s. What is the velocity of the banana after 1.5 s?

3. There is a famous (and probably untrue) legend about why Sir Isaac Newton first started to think about gravity. According to the legend, he was awakened from an afternoon nap under a tree by an apple falling on his head. If the apple struck Sir Isaac with a speed of 6.0 m/s, for how long had it been falling?

4. **Apply** State three reasons why knowledge of the acceleration due to gravity is important.

5. **Apply** The graph at the right shows the position of a parachutist who has just jumped out of a hovering helicopter and is going straight down. Describe what is happening to the parachutist in each of the following regions.

   (a) up to A

   (b) between A and B

   (c) between B and C

   (d) between C and D

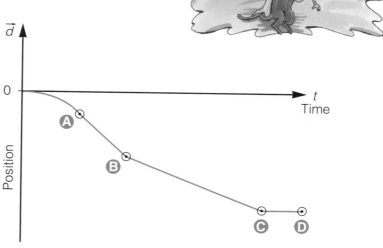

12.2 The Mathematics of Acceleration

In Chapter 11, you created velocity-time graphs of an object's motion. You used the following ideas:

- The *slope* of a velocity-time graph gives the object's acceleration (average or instantaneous).
- The *area* under a velocity-time graph gives the object's displacement during a time interval.

Physicists have analyzed velocity-time graphs with many different shapes. They have used their analyses to develop mathematical formulas for calculating displacement. You can use these formulas to calculate answers to many common problems, as an alternative to drawing or measuring graphs.

More About Area

The "area under the graph" is actually the area between the graph line and the horizontal axis (see Figures 12.4A to 12.4C). If the graph line is below the horizontal axis, the area calculation gives a negative answer — a negative displacement (Figure 12.4D). This means that by the end of the time interval, the object had moved in the negative direction. During the time interval, the object had a negative velocity.

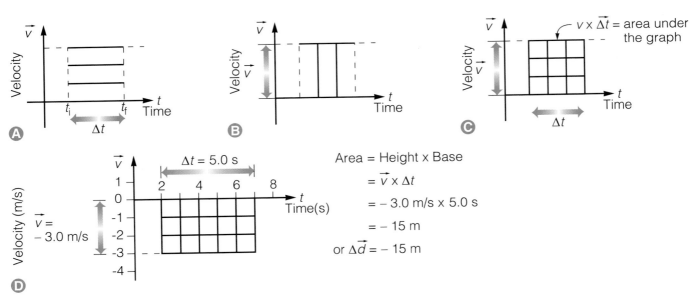

Area = Height x Base

$= \vec{v} \times \Delta t$

$= -3.0 \text{ m/s} \times 5.0 \text{ s}$

$= -15 \text{ m}$

or $\Delta \vec{d} = -15 \text{ m}$

Figure 12.4 The "area" under a velocity-time graph gives the displacement during the time interval. Lines below the horizontal axis give a negative area "under" the graph. This means that the object moved in the negative direction during the time interval.

The area of a rectangular region is easy to calculate. On a velocity-time graph, it tells the displacement of an object that is moving with constant velocity. The area under the graph has the same meaning even if it is not a rectangle, however.

> The area under a velocity-time graph always tells the displacement of the object during a particular time interval. You can use any appropriate mathematical formulas or methods that you know to find the area under a complex graph.

Figure 12.5 shows how to find the areas under graphs with the most common shapes. Notice that the displacement units must match the velocity units. For example, metres are used with *metres* per second, and centimetres are used with *centimetres* per second. (The graphs in the illustration are too small to read precisely. Therefore the calculated answers have not been rounded using the rules for significant digits.)

Skill
P O W E R

To review how to find the areas of different shapes, turn to page 595.

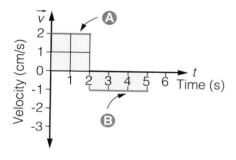

Total area = Area A + Area B
= (2 cm/s) × (2 s) + (−1 cm/s) × (3 s)
= 4 cm + (−3 cm)
= 1 cm
The displacement during the time interval was +1 cm.

Triangular area = $\dfrac{\text{Base} \times \text{Altitude}}{2}$

= $\dfrac{10\ \text{s} \times 5\ \text{m/s}}{2}$

= 25 m
The displacement during the time interval was +25 m.

Total area = Area A + Area B
= $\dfrac{(\text{Base of A}) \times (\text{Altitude of A})}{2}$ + (Base of B) × (Altitude of B)

= $\dfrac{4\ \text{h} \times 2\ \text{km/h}}{2}$ + 4 h × 4 km/h

= 4 km + 16 km
= 20 km
The displacement of the object during the time interval was +20 km.

Area by counting squares = 12 squares

In general, count only the squares that have half or more of their area under the graph. Here each square has height 10 cm/s and width 1 s. This gives an area of 10 cm.

Total area of the region = 12 × 10 cm
= 120 cm
The displacement of the object during the interval was about +120 cm.

Figure 12.5 Finding the areas under graphs with some common shapes

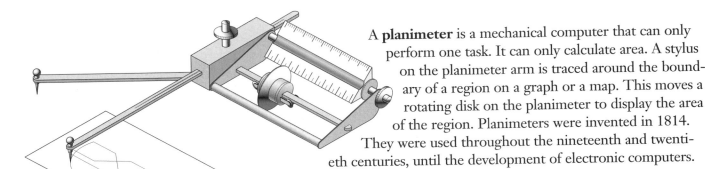

A **planimeter** is a mechanical computer that can only perform one task. It can only calculate area. A stylus on the planimeter arm is traced around the boundary of a region on a graph or a map. This moves a rotating disk on the planimeter to display the area of the region. Planimeters were invented in 1814. They were used throughout the nineteenth and twentieth centuries, until the development of electronic computers.

Figure 12.6 A planimeter, a mechanical device for measuring area

From Graph to Displacement Formula

You have just been calculating the area under a velocity-time graph. You cut the graph into geometric shapes. Then you added the areas of the shapes to find the total area. This gave the displacement of the object. You can use the same technique to work out a general formula for the displacement of an accelerating object. Look at the steps in "Stretch Your Mind" on the next page. You will see that the formula turns out to be

$$\Delta d = v_i \, \Delta t + \frac{a \, (\Delta t)^2}{2}$$

This formula will save you from drawing a lot of graphs. Be careful when using it, however. First, it applies only if the acceleration is *constant*. Second, remember to use positive (+) and negative (–) signs for the directions of the velocity and acceleration.

Model Problem 1

A coin is dropped from the roof of a tall building. How far does it fall by the end of 3.0 s?

Given
Initial velocity, $v_i = 0$ m/s (The coin was *dropped*.)
Acceleration, $a = -9.8$ m/s^2
Time interval, $\Delta t = 3.0$ s

Required
Displacement, Δd, in m

Analysis
The formula that expresses Δd in terms of v_i, a, and Δt is

$$\Delta d = v_i \, \Delta t + \frac{a \, (\Delta t)^2}{2}$$

Solution

$$\Delta d = v_i \, \Delta t + \frac{a \, (\Delta t)^2}{2}$$

$$= (0 \text{ m/s}) \times (3.0 \text{ s}) + \frac{(-9.8 \text{ m/s}^2) \times (3.0 \text{ s})^2}{2}$$

$$= -44.1 \text{ m}$$

Paraphrase
The coin falls 44 m (to 2 significant digits) in 3 s.

Study the diagram and explanation below. They show the steps in developing the formula for the displacement of an accelerating object. Try to follow and understand these steps.

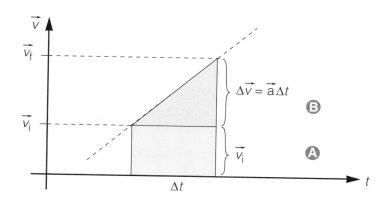

Displacement	=	Area under graph		
	=	Area of region A	+	Area of region B
	=	(Base of A) × (Height of A)	+	$\dfrac{\text{(Base of B)} \times \text{(Height of B)}}{2}$
	=	$\Delta t \times v_i$	+	$\dfrac{\Delta t \times \Delta v}{2}$

Both terms in this equation are usually written with Δt at the end. The equation becomes

Displacement	=	$v_i \times \Delta t$	+	$\dfrac{\Delta v \times \Delta t}{2}$

The second term can be rewritten without using Δv. Use the definition of acceleration:

$$a = \frac{\Delta v}{\Delta t} \quad \text{or} \quad \Delta v = a \times \Delta t$$

So the equation for the area under the graph becomes

Displacement	=	$v_i \times \Delta t$	+	$\dfrac{a \times \Delta t \times \Delta t}{2}$
Δd	=	$v_i \times \Delta t$	+	$\dfrac{a \times (\Delta t)^2}{2}$
	=	$v_i \Delta t + \dfrac{a (\Delta t)^2}{2}$		

Now that's mathematics!

Model Problem 2

A car that is moving east at 20 m/s (about 70 km/h) starts to brake. Its speed drops by 2.5 m/s each second. How long does the car take to stop? How far does it move during this time?

Given

Assume that east is positive.

Initial velocity, $v_i = +20$ m/s

Acceleration, $a = -2.5$ m/s² (The car is slowing down.)

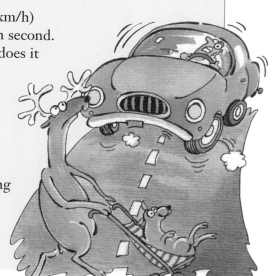

Required

(a) Time interval, Δt, in s

(b) Displacement, Δd, in m

Analysis

The car is moving in the positive direction (east), but it is slowing down. Thus the acceleration is negative. When the car stops, its velocity is zero: $v_f = 0$ m/s.

(a) The time interval can be found using the definition of acceleration:

$$a = \frac{\Delta v}{\Delta t}$$

So $\quad \Delta t = \frac{\Delta v}{a}$

Or $\quad \Delta t = \frac{v_f - v_i}{a}$

(b) One way to find displacement is by using the formula

$$\Delta d = v_i \, \Delta t + \frac{a \, (\Delta t)^2}{2}$$

Solution

(a) First we need to find Δt:

$$
\begin{aligned}
\Delta t &= \frac{v_f - v_i}{a} \\
&= \frac{0 \text{ m/s} - (+20 \text{ m/s})}{-2.5 \text{ m/s}^2} \\
&= \frac{-20 \text{ m/s}}{-2.5 \text{ m/s}^2} \\
&= 8.0 \text{ s}
\end{aligned}
$$

(b) Then we can use the formula for Δd:

$$
\begin{aligned}
\Delta d &= v_i \, \Delta t + \frac{a \, (\Delta t)^2}{2} \\
&= (+20 \text{ m/s}) \times (8.0 \text{ s}) + \frac{(-2.5 \text{ m/s}^2) \times (8.0 \text{ s})^2}{2} \\
&= +160 \text{ m} + (-80 \text{ m}) \\
&= +80 \text{ m}
\end{aligned}
$$

Paraphrase

The car takes 8.0 s to stop. In this time, it travels 80 m east.

Model Problem 3

A rabbit and a fox ran a race. They started in the same direction, from the same place. The rabbit accelerated at 5.0 m/s² for 4.0 s up to its maximum speed. It then ran at this speed for another 4.0 s. The fox accelerated at 2.0 m/s² for 8.0 s. Who was ahead at the end of 8.0 s, and by how much?

Given

For the rabbit during acceleration,
$v_i = 0.0$ m/s
$a = 5.0$ m/s²
$\Delta t = 4.0$ s

For the rabbit during constant velocity,
$v_f = ?$
$\Delta t = 4.0$ s

For the fox,
$v_i = 0.0$ m/s
$a = 2.0$ m/s²
$\Delta t = 8.0$ s

Required

Δd, in m, for the rabbit and for the fox

Analysis

For the first part of the rabbit's run, the final velocity can be found using
$v_f = v_i + a \, \Delta t$

The rabbit's displacement during the first 4 s (constant acceleration) can be found using a formula from Chapter 11:

$$\Delta d = \frac{(v_i + v_f) \times \Delta t}{2}$$

For the constant velocity part of the rabbit's run, we can use
$\Delta d = v_f \times \Delta t$

For the displacement of the fox, we can use

$$\Delta d = v_i \, \Delta t + \frac{a \, (\Delta t)^2}{2}$$

Solution

First part of the rabbit's run:
$v_f = v_i + a \, \Delta t$
$\quad = 0.0$ m/s $+ (5.0$ m/s²$) \times (4.0$ s$)$
$\quad = 20$ m/s

$$\Delta d = \frac{(v_i + v_f) \times \Delta t}{2}$$

$$\quad = \frac{(0.0 \text{ m/s} + 20 \text{ m/s}) \times 4.0 \text{ s}}{2}$$

$$\quad = 40 \text{ m}$$

Second part of the rabbit's run:

$$\Delta d = v_f \times \Delta t$$

$$= 20 \text{ m/s} \times 4.0 \text{ s}$$

$$= 80 \text{ m}$$

Total displacement of the rabbit $= 40 \text{ m} + 80 \text{ m}$
$$= 120 \text{ m}$$

For the fox:

$$\Delta d = v_i \, \Delta t + \frac{a \, (\Delta t)^2}{2}$$

$$= 0.0 \text{ m} + \frac{(2.0 \text{ m/s}^2) \times (8.0 \text{ s})^2}{2}$$

$$= 64 \text{ m}$$

Difference in displacements $= 120 \text{ m} - 64 \text{ m}$
$$= 56 \text{ m}$$

Paraphrase
The rabbit is ahead of the fox by 56 m.

Check Your Understanding

1. Suppose that you are calculating the area under an object's velocity-time graph.
   (a) What must be true about the units on the axes?
   (b) How can you tell from the graph that the calculated area will be negative?
   (c) How do you interpret an area calculation that gives a negative answer?

2. British racing driver David Hurley survived an acceleration estimated at -1730 m/s^2 when he crashed at 172 km/h (47.8 m/s). His car stopped in about 0.028 s. Hurley had 29 fractured bones and 3 dislocated joints.
   (a) How far did Hurley's car travel while coming to a rest?
   (b) The acceleration that Hurley experienced is far higher than John Stapp's acceleration in question 10 on page 379. Why did Hurley survive it?

3. **Thinking Critically** Parachutists land at speeds of between 5 m/s and 9 m/s. This is 7.0 m/s, on average. If they stiffen their knees, they accelerate to a stop in about 0.019 s. If they flex their knees while landing, stopping takes much longer — about 0.050 s.
   (a) Sketch a velocity-time graph for each method of landing. Put both graphs on the same axes.
   (b) Predict which method of landing involves a smaller acceleration and thus less chance of injury. Justify your answer. Do *not* do any calculations.
   (c) Suggest some other situations in which the same principle is used to reduce the accelerating forces that are needed to stop an object.

12.3 Tracking Technologies

Very rarely do scientific discoveries remain unused. They lead to new devices or technologies that we can use to help us solve problems. Indeed, technology is often described as the practical application of scientific knowledge. For example, the discovery of the Doppler effect in sound waves eventually led to motion detectors. Motion detectors rely on this effect to measure speed. You may have already used motion detectors in your motion experiments. In this section, you will learn about technologies that are based on scientific phenomena, such as the Doppler effect and optical reflection.

Radar Ranging

Many motion technologies depend on the electromagnetic spectrum. (You likely studied this in earlier grades.) Visible light, infrared radiation, and radio waves are often used for motion detection and measurement.

Figure 12.7 Radar is a motion technology with many different uses.

Speed measurement can be very simple. It can involve sending out short pulses of electromagnetic radiation and timing how long they take to return. In a vacuum (and in air), the speed of this radiation is 3.00×10^8 m/s. Radar pulses are usually timed in microseconds, or millionths of a second. (One microsecond is written as 1 μs = 0.000 001 s = 10^{-6} s.) Suppose that a radio wave is sent toward a jet fighter and returns 40.0 μs later. The total distance travelled by the radio wave is

$$\Delta d = v \times \Delta t$$
$$= (3.00 \times 10^8 \text{ m/s}) \times (40.0 \times 10^{-6} \text{ s})$$
$$= 120 \times 10^2 \text{ m}$$
$$= 12\ 000 \text{ m}$$
$$= 12.0 \text{ km}$$

The total distance to the fighter and back is 12.0 km. Therefore the fighter must be 6.00 km away. This technique for finding distances is called **radar ranging**.

Word CONNECT

Scientists had attempted to develop radar systems early in the twentieth century. There were no major developments until the Second World War (1939–1945), however. Then radar became crucial to aerial warfare. The word "radar" is an *acronym*. It was made up from the beginning letters of the words "RAdio Detecting And Ranging," which describe it. Who invented the word "radar"? Do you know of any other technological words that are acronyms?

Skill POWER

If you need to review SI units of measurement, turn to page 586.

Tools of Science

For some time now, hand-held radar guns have been used in baseball to measure the speed of a pitch. Now there are range-finding devices that can help a golfer know the distance to a flag stick or across a water hazard. Do you think these devices should be allowed? Write a brief defence of your opinion.

Suppose that a second pulse is sent out 1.00 s later and returns after 37.0 μs. The new total distance is

$$\Delta d = v\, \Delta t$$
$$\Delta d = (3.00 \times 10^8 \text{ m/s}) \times (37.0 \times 10^{-6} \text{ s})$$
$$= 111 \times 10^2 \text{ m}$$
$$= 11.1 \text{ km}$$

The fighter is half of this distance, or 5.55 km, away. Its speed is given by

$$v = \frac{\Delta d}{\Delta t}$$

$$v = \frac{(6.00 \text{ km} - 5.55 \text{ km})}{1.00 \text{ s}}$$

$$= 0.45 \text{ km/s}$$

The fighter is travelling at 0.45 km/s, or about 1600 km/h. This is nearly 1.5 times the speed of sound, or Mach 1.5.

Radar in Action

Many distance or ranging devices depend on sending out a wave and timing how long it takes to return. This approach is used to measure the distance between a space shuttle and a satellite during an orbital rendezvous. On Earth, small, hand-held devices are used to measure the distance between ships or between a ship and the dock. Even cameras come equipped with range-finding devices for automatic focus. Some of these devices emit ultrasound. Others send out infrared radiation.

Police officers have long used radar guns to catch speeders. Then radar-jamming devices came on the market to foil the police radar. These were declared illegal, and the police began to use radar detectors to identify cars that were using the jammers.

Figure 12.8   The space shuttle in the photograph is using radar ranging to "capture" a satellite for repairs. This capture has to be centimetre-perfect. There are billions of dollars at stake.

Figure 12.9   A highway pile-up — the frequent result of too much speed.

One problem with the use of radar by traffic police is that it spreads out quickly. At a distance of 300 m, the beam is about 30 m wide. If several cars are close together, the radar cannot tell them apart. The problem was solved by introducing laser speed guns. These speed guns generally give off infrared radiation. At a distance of 300 m, the beam spreads out to be only 1 m wide. Thus police officers can measure the speed of individual cars in a group at this distance.

There are two types of laser speed guns. The first type sends out pulses and measures the time interval before the wave returns. By doing this several times per second, the car's speed can be determined. The second type depends on the **Doppler effect.** This is a change in the observed frequency of a wave. It is caused by the motion of the source of the waves toward or away from the observer. When the source begins to move, the waves in front of it have a higher frequency than when it was at rest (see Figure 12.10). The waves behind it have a lower frequency than when it was at rest. You have probably observed the Doppler effect many times. Whenever a firetruck or an ambulance sweeps past you, the drop in pitch of its siren is a Doppler effect.

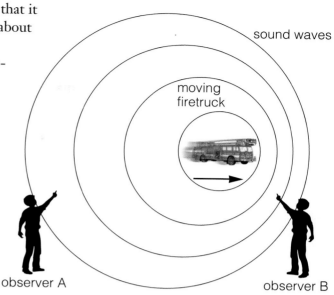

sound waves

moving firetruck

observer A

observer B

Figure 12.10 Waves ahead of a moving source become "bunched up." They pass an observer at a higher frequency. Waves behind a moving source are more spread out. An observer measures a lower frequency.

The Doppler effect is often used in **Doppler radar** devices for measuring velocity. A police laser gun can use the Doppler effect to calculate the speed of a vehicle. Doppler radar is also used to study tornadoes. Until recently, weather radar sent out radio waves and timed how long it took them to return from the raindrops in a storm. This told meteorologists (weather scientists) how far away the storm was and how large it was. Now many weather stations use Doppler radar. If a tornado develops in a storm, the reflecting radio waves are Doppler-shifted. Where the raindrops in the rotating storm are heading toward the radar, the reflected waves are shifted to higher frequencies. Raindrops on the other side of the storm, rotating away, give reflected signals that are at lower frequencies. When meteorologists see this frequency spread, they know that they have located a tornado. From the size of the frequency shifts, they can also estimate how strong the winds are in the funnel.

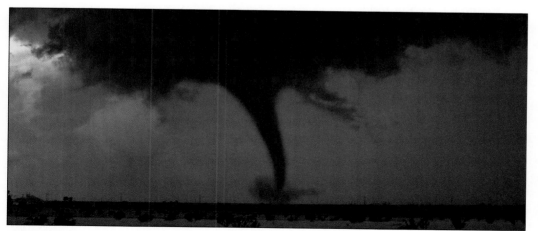

Figure 12.11 Wind speeds in this tornado may exceed 300 km/h.

The Doppler effect is extremely important in astronomy. A shift toward lower frequencies indicates motion away from Earth. This is called a "red shift" because stars and galaxies appear slightly redder. A "blue shift" shows motion toward Earth. The fact that all galaxies appear red-shifted, was first observed by the American astronomer Edwin Hubble (1889–1953). Hubble also observed that the red shift increases with the distance from Earth. Hubbles' observations are key evidence for an expanding universe.

Speeding, Safety, and Modern Life

Think About It

Ever since Henry Ford began the mass production of automobiles, people have been driving at ever-increasing speeds. Superhighways allow us to cross Canada by land in a matter of days. This increase in personal speed is not limited to highways. Recent years have seen a dramatic increase in the use of snow-mobiles and high-speed water craft.

Unfortunately there has also been a corresponding increase in accidents, injury, and death as a result of these technologies. The number of deaths world-wide due to traffic accidents alone is equal to several jumbo jets crashing every single day. In addition, pollution of the ground, air, and lakes and rivers has been linked to automobiles. By some estimates, approximately 50 percent of air pollutants are pro-duced by automobile engines.

In this investigation, you will examine the costs and benefits of these high-speed methods of transportation. Then you will present what you have learned in a forum about the impacts of high-speed travel on modern life.

INTERNET CONNECT

www.school.mcgrawhill.ca/resources/

Transport Canada's web site is a valuable source of data on accidents and other traffic-related topics. You can gather data on pollution from Environment Canada's web site. Go to the web site above. Go to **Science Resources**, then to **SCIENCEPOWER 10** to know where to go next.

What to Do

1. As a class, brainstorm both positive and negative effects of high-speed travel. Make a table to record all the major effects.

2. Divide into groups to research the major effects.

   (a) To investigate the positive effects, develop a questionnaire on vehicle use. Survey people in your school and community.

   (b) You can obtain accident information for Canada from the web site of Transport Canada.

   (c) You can obtain local accident information from the web site of your provincial ministry or department of transportation.

   (d) You can obtain pollution information from the web site of Environment Canada. With your teacher's permission, you may also want to search the Internet using key words, such as "automobile environmental impact."

   (e) Other departments in your school may have additional information.

3. Each group will have 5 min to present their findings as part of a forum on the topic. If possible, videotape the presentations. Archive them in your school library so that others can benefit from what you learned.

Analyze

1. How well did your group work together?

2. How well did your group contribute to the forum, compared with other groups? What were the strengths of your presentation? How could you have made your presentation better?

3. Did any obvious conclusion come out of the forum?

Following Migration

Until recently, it has been very difficult to track the movements of animals, especially migrating birds. New techniques have simplified this. Collars that contain tiny radio transmitters (weighing less than 20 g) can be attached to birds. Changes in the birds' positions are then tracked by satellites. The satellites receive the radio waves that are broadcast by these transmitters.

Migrating flocks of birds also appear on the Doppler radar of weather stations. The radar provides information about the location of the birds. It also shows how fast they are moving. These studies show that migrating birds often wait for a tailwind before setting off on their trek for the day.

Figure 12.12 Motion-tracking technologies are now used by biologists to track the migration of birds, such as these Canada geese.

Collaring Wildlife

Keeping track of animals in the wilderness can be extremely difficult, too. Imagine trying to watch over a herd of elk in order to find out which parts of their range are most important to them. Such information is needed if scientists decide to help a herd in distress. This information is also needed to assess the impact of human farming and industries on elk herds. Biologists can now collect data by attaching radio-transmitting collars to the elk in order to track them.

Radio collars can be used to track any large animal. For example, there is much that we do not know about the habits of bears. If a radio collar is attached to a bear (while tranquillized, of course), biologists can learn much about its movements. They can see where it feeds in the spring. They can also see whether it moves to a different range for the warmer months. Then they can find out where it hibernates in winter. This knowledge can lead to a better understanding of bears and perhaps a happier co-existence of humans and bears.

Figure 12.13 Biologist Gordon Stenhouse prepares to put a radio collar on a tranquillized grizzly bear.

Moving Mountains

The devastating power of volcanoes has always been a threat to humans. A volcano can fill the air with superheated steam, toxic gases, and a rain of ash and glowing rock. Lava pours down the volcano. It buries towns and changes the whole landscape of a region. Mudslides can sweep away obstacles such as trees, houses, and even people.

Figure 12.14 Volcanoes have caused some of the most devastating disasters in history. One of the earliest to be accurately recorded was the eruption of Mt. Vesuvius in 79 B.C.E. This eruption destroyed the Roman town of Pompeii and buried many of its citizens alive.

Volcanologists (scientists who study volcanic eruptions) know there is little that can be done to tame a volcano. They do hope to become better at predicting when a volcano will erupt, however. During an eruption, molten rock or magma rises up through the network of fissures and tubes beneath a volcano. As it does, it pushes gases out of fissures in the rock of the volcano. This changes the composition of gases around a volcano. It indicates a forthcoming eruption. In addition, the pressure of the magma causes the volcano to swell. In order to detect the swelling, scientists place instruments around the volcano. *Tiltmeters* detect changes in the slopes of the sides of the volcano. *Geodimeters* detect changes in the positions of points around the volcano. They measure the time for laser beams to reflect back to the laser gun.

A fairly new technology is replacing geodimeters. Points can now be tracked by means of the Global Positioning System (GPS), which you studied in Chapter 10 (page 342). In the next activity, you will model this method of determining position.

Using the Global Positioning System

To an increasing extent, we rely upon the Global Positioning System (GPS). We use it to tell us where we are and how we can get to our destinations. A GPS locator listens for radio signals that have been emitted simultaneously from at least three satellites. The signals arrive at different times, however. The arrival times depend on how far the receiver is from each satellite. The receiver uses these different arrival times to plot location on Earth. In this activity, you will simulate this location system.

What You Need

2 ropes, each at least 4 m long and marked off at 10 cm intervals
3 stools or chairs to act as antennas
protractor
masking tape
2 different-coloured markers

What to Do

1. Work in groups of four or five. Using the tape, label the stools "antenna A," "antenna B," and "antenna C." Place the stools such that
   • A is 3 m due north of B
   • C is 2 m due east of B

2. Imagine that the stools are radio antennas that transmit a signal at exactly the same moment. You are somewhere in the region. Your locator unit does not know the precise instant when the signals were given off. It can tell, however, that the signal from B arrived 1.33 ns later than the signal from C ("n" or "nano" means 10^{-9}). In addition, the signal from A arrived 2.00 ns later than the signal from C. Since radio waves travel at 3.00×10^8 m/s, these times mean that
   • B must be 0.40 m (40 cm) farther from you than C is, and
   • A must be 0.60 m (60 cm) farther from you than C is

   Verify that these distances are correct.

3. Using the ropes, find at least six points that are 40 cm farther from B than from C. For example, you could hold the rope from B at the 200 cm mark while holding the rope from C at the 160 cm mark. You should be able to find two points where both ropes are stretched taut. Place coloured tape on the floor at these points. Use the same colour for both points.

4. Using the ropes, find at least six points that are 60 cm farther from A than from C. Place different-coloured tape at each of these points.

5. Drape one rope over the points from step 3. This rope traces the curve for all the points that are 40 cm farther from B than from C.

6. Drape the second rope over the points from step 4. This rope traces the curve for all the points that are 60 cm farther from A than from C. The point of intersection of these curves is your location, as given by the time differences. Report this location relative to antenna C (distance and direction).

What Did You Discover?

1. According to the time differences, where were you relative to antenna C?

2. Suppose that the GPS unit had been able to listen to four antennas. How might this have affected your result?

3. Do you think that you could have obtained the same result by using the time differences between B and A and between B and C? If you have time, try it.

Skill
P O W E R

For help with SI units and scientific notation, turn to page 585.

Tools of Science

All objects give off infrared radiation. Warm objects give off more radiation than cool ones. Humans are usually warmer than their surroundings. Therefore they are clearly "visible" to an infrared detector. Such a detector can be used to switch on lights when a person enters a room or switch them off when the person leaves. In either case, the detector responds to a sudden change in the amount of infrared radiation it receives. Outside lights can also be equipped with infrared detectors. The motion sensors that are used in burglar alarms operate exactly the same way. So do some automatic-flush toilets and "tapless" washbasins.

An infrared detector can also be used on a television set. If no motion is observed by the detector for a set time interval, it switches off the television since the viewer is probably asleep or absent. Of course, the family cat might keep the television on all night with its rambles!

Check Your Understanding

1. In your own words, explain how radar can detect a tornado.

2. How far does infrared radiation travel in 100 μs?

3. Sound travels at 330 m/s on a cold day. A mountain climber shouts and then hears the echo 3.6 s later. How far away is the reflecting surface?

4. **Apply** Propose some applications of range-finding that were not mentioned in this chapter.

5. **Apply** Propose some applications of Doppler radar that were not mentioned in this chapter.

6. **Thinking Critically** A cloud of insects reflects radio waves and shifts them to lower frequencies. Which way is the cloud of insects moving? Explain your answer.

Career CONNECT

Teri MacDonald-Cadieux is a professional road-racing driver. Her job demands special physical and mental qualities. She must pilot her car around complex, twisting courses. Her first racing experience came at the age of 11, behind the wheel of a go-kart. Teri's worst moment in racing came in 1997. Her car crashed into a wall at over 200 km/h. It rolled several times before coming to a stop. In the accident, Teri fractured a vertebra in her neck. Within three months, however, she was back in the driver's seat.

Teri's love of driving goes beyond her role as a driver. She teaches race-driving techniques, runs car-care clinics, and is a certified child safety seat inspector. As well, she presents a television feature called "Car Sense." In this feature, she aims to demystify the automobile.

List the qualities that you think would be needed in Teri's work. In what other careers might these qualities be valuable?

Teri MacDonald-Cadieux

Now that you have completed this chapter, try to do the following. If you cannot, go back to the sections indicated.

Analyze position-time data to determine velocities and accelerations. (12.1, 12.2)

Draw and interpret position-time graphs. (12.1, 12.2)

Draw and interpret velocity-time graphs. (12.1, 12.2)

Solve problems that involve displacement, velocity, and acceleration. (12.1, 12.2)

Explain why falling objects reach a terminal velocity. (12.1)

Use sketches to show two ways that a velocity-time graph of accelerated motion can be subdivided to find its area. Beside each sketch, write the associated displacement formula. (12.2)

Explain how to find the area under each velocity-time graph below. (12.2)

Explain how a planimeter is useful when studying motion graphs. (12.2)

Give formulas for finding the displacement of an accelerating object without knowing its
(a) final velocity
(b) acceleration (12.2)

Solve ranging problems involving echoes. (12.3)

Describe how the Doppler effect is used in various speed measurements. (12.3)

Describe motion technologies that are involved in observing
(a) car speeds
(b) volcanoes
(c) migrating birds (12.3)

Explain briefly how the Global Positioning System works. (12.3)

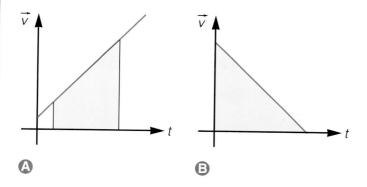

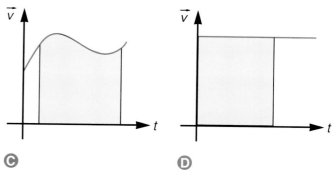

A   B   C   D

Prepare Your Own Summary

Summarize this chapter by doing one of the following. Use a graphic organizer (such as a concept map), produce a poster, or write the summary to include the key chapter concepts. Here are a few ideas to use as a guide:
- What types of calculations could you use to predict the displacement or velocity of a falling object or an object that has been thrown straight upward?

- List the types of information you can determine from a velocity-time graph of an object's motion. Explain how to find each piece of information.
- Briefly describe two ways that electromagnetic radiation is used in position and velocity measurements.

12 Review

Reviewing Key Terms

If you need to review, the section numbers show you where these terms were introduced.

1. In your notebook, match the description in column A with the correct term in column B.

A
• fastest speed of a falling object
• mechanical device that calculates area
• near-weightless conditions found in orbit
• shift in frequency due to speed
• system that locates positions on Earth

B
• Doppler effect (12.3)
• microgravity (12.1)
• GPS (12.3)
• planimeter (12.2)
• terminal velocity (12.1)
• radar ranging (12.3)

Understanding Key Concepts

Section numbers are provided if you need to review.

2. The acceleration due to gravity on Mars is -3.7 m/s^2. In your notebook, complete the following table of time and velocity for a rock dropped from rest. (12.1)

Time (s)	Velocity (m/s)
0.0	
1.0	
2.0	
3.0	
4.0	

3. **(a)** If a box is dropped from an airplane at a high altitude, it will not keep accelerating all the way to the ground. Explain why. (12.1)

   (b) On what sort of planet would an object keep accelerating all the way to the ground? (12.1)

4. Think about the phrase "area under a velocity-time graph." (12.2)

   (a) Why is the phrase misleading?

   (b) What information about an object's motion is shown by the area under its velocity-time graph?

5. Predict what you might learn by studying the area under an *acceleration*-time graph of an object's motion. (12.2)

6. State two advantages of a laser speed gun over a radar speed gun. (12.3)

Developing Skills

7. **(a)** Sketch a graph of position against time for a falling object. (Ignore terminal velocity.)

   (b) Sketch a graph of velocity against time for a falling object. (Ignore terminal velocity.)

   (c) Sketch a graph of velocity against time for a falling object if it eventually reaches terminal velocity.

   (d) Indicate which aspects of the graph in part (a) and the graph in part (b) represent displacement.

   (e) An object that reaches terminal velocity does not travel as far in a given amount of time as an object that keeps on accelerating. Use the graphs from parts (b) and (c) to show this.

8. Use your local library or the Internet to research some of the motion technologies mentioned in section 12.3.

Problem Solving/Applying

9. A rock is dropped over a cliff. Determine its velocity after
   (a) 6.0 s
   (b) 9.2 s

10. A squirrel throws an acorn down from a tree with a speed of 3.0 m/s. Calculate the velocity of the acorn after
    (a) 0.50 s
    (b) 1.8 s

11. A defender throws a boulder from the top of a very high tower. The velocity of the boulder is 6.0 m/s downward. How far does the boulder fall by the end of 4.0 s?

12. A golf ball is thrown straight upward with a speed of 19.6 m/s.
    (a) At its maximum height, the ball's velocity is zero. How long does the ball take to reach its maximum height?
    (b) What is its maximum height?
    (c) Suppose that the ball was thrown upward at the same speed on Pluto. How high would it rise? (See the table on page 386.)

13. A car is travelling at 12 m/s (about 45 km/h). It approaches a stop sign and decelerates at 4.0 m/s^2.
    (a) How long does the car take to stop?
    (b) How far does the car travel while stopping?

14. A car is travelling at 25 m/s (about 90 km/h). It approaches a stop sign. If it decelerates at 4.0 m/s^2, how far will it travel while stopping? Compare this distance with the distances in question 13(b). Does twice the speed require more or less than twice the stopping distance?

15. Ultrasound travels through air at about 340 m/s. Suppose that a camera sends out an ultrasound pulse and the pulse returns 0.060 s later. How far away is the object that is being photographed?

16. A laser gun sends out an infrared pulse. The pulse returns from a car 0.400 μs later. After 1.0 s, the laser sends out another pulse. It returns after 0.200 μs. If the speed limit is 80 km/h (22 m/s), decide whether or not the car is speeding.

Critical Thinking

17. How might Doppler radar be used to measure the acceleration of a car?

18. Suppose that you have been asked to compare the performance of two different brands of tennis rackets. Describe some ways that you could test them. What characteristics would you look for?

19. Amusement park roller coasters use changing acceleration to thrill their riders. For safety reasons, however, the acceleration is usually kept smaller than 40 m/s^2. A roller coaster called "The Flight of Fear" accelerates its riders smoothly from 0 m/s to 24.6 m/s in 3.9 s. Suppose that on one run, a safety device then caused the cars to brake and come to a stop in 7.80 m.
    (a) How long would the cars take to stop?
    (b) What would be the average acceleration of the cars as they stopped?
    (c) Would the ride exceed the usual maximum acceleration starting or stopping?
    (d) What would be the average acceleration of the ride from start to stop?

Pause& Reflect

1. Go back to the beginning of the chapter, on page 380, and check your original answers to the Opening Ideas questions. How has your thinking changed? How would you answer those questions now that you have investigated the topics in this chapter?

2. At the beginning of this chapter, you were asked to list careers that involved an ability to describe or measure motion. List any other careers that you learned about in this chapter. Are there any careers on your original list that were not mentioned in this chapter?

Ask an Expert

There was a time when cars did not even have seat belts to protect their passengers. Times have changed. Today car manufacturers continually use the physics of motion to improve the systems we rely on as drivers and passengers. Brad Hedderson, from the product and manufacturing engineering at Quality Safety Systems Company, explains how seat belts are evolving.

Q **What exactly do you do?**

A Our company supplies seat belts to certain North American automobile manufacturers. We work with a group of about a dozen engineers. We design the products that the company makes and sells.

Q **Can you explain how a seat belt protects a person in a car crash?**

A Well, there are different types of seat belts. The standard belt you'll find in most cars, since 1974, is a three-point system. A strip of webbing is fixed to the car near the bottom of the seat. It runs up, over the passenger's lap, and slides through a slot in the metal tongue (the part that locks into the buckle). The seat belt carries on, up over the shoulder and back down to a mechanism called the retractor. The retractor is hidden away behind some plastic trim.

Q **What is the retractor?**

A It's a spool that rolls out and winds up the webbing, similar to a window shade. The retractor spins to allow the webbing to unwind as you fasten the seat belt. In a crash, however, the retractor locks, so no webbing can unwind. This prevents a person from being thrown into the steering column or windshield by his or her own forward momentum.

Q **What makes the retractor lock in a crash?**

A Attached to the retractor frame is a smooth, moulded plastic cup that holds a chrome-plated sensor ball. Hinged to the sensor ball is another component called a sensor "pawl." Any sudden change in acceleration, such as a crash, causes the ball to rise up within the cup. This pushes the pawl to interface with a gear on the retractor. A sequence of events is started, to lock the retractor so that it cannot turn and release webbing. In a crash, the mechanism locks the retractor about 20 ms after impact, before a person can even be thrown forward.

Q Do you make other types of seat belts?

A Yes. We've developed one new seat-belt system. It works together with the air bag to minimize the possibility of certain crash injuries.

Q How does the new system differ from the standard one?

A The new system works in two separate stages if there's a crash. In the first stage, sensors in the car send a signal to an add-on mechanism in the retractor, called a "pre-tensioner." The pre-tensioner begins operating within 2 ms. Within 20 ms, it has wound in any slack in the seat belt, pulling the person snuggly back against the seat and out of the way of the expanding air bag.

In the second stage, as the car slows, the person's forward momentum applies a force against the seat belt. A sensor measures the force on the belt. When the force reaches a predetermined level, a mechanism in the retractor allows it to release the appropriate amount of webbing, based on the person's size and the severity of the accident. This allows the person to move forward into the air bag in a more controlled way. Adding a degree of slack to the seat belt allows the chest and hips to move a little. This minimizes some of the whiplash injuries that can occur when the head alone snaps forward.

Q These systems sound pretty complicated. How do you test them to be sure they work properly?

A For many of our tests, we use a small deceleration sled. Our engineers mount a retractor, in its proper position, onto steel plates that are bolted together. We mount the whole assembly onto the sled and use compressed air to shoot the sled forward. Electronic sensors on the sled measure the speed of the velocity change. Other diagnostic equipment measures how much webbing can be pulled out.

The ball in the retractor reacts to any rapid change in velocity. So even though we are accelerating the unit, we can test for what happens in the major deceleration of a crash.

EXPLORING Further

Safely Does It

1. How much do you know about the safety systems of the cars you ride in? Find out about the seat-belt system and/or air-bag system in the car of someone you know. What is the year and model of the car? Does the car's manual tell you anything about the seat-belt system? Does the car have an air bag? What are the limitations of use on the air bag? Are certain people supposed to avoid sitting in a passenger seat because of the air bag?

2. Analyze the safety systems at work when a person rides a bicycle. What other systems do you think could be designed to improve the safety of this mode of transport? Write a detailed explanation, including some sketches, to explain how these systems could work.

High-Tech Highway

The use of remote sensing technology on our highways is expanding. Radar and laser beams clock our speeds. Signs on curves warn us if we are approaching too quickly. Some bridges flash a warning for overheight trucks. Recent innovations allow the operators of toll highways to identify our  licence plates as we enter and exit the highways. If they wished, the operators could also compute our average speed. Television cameras monitor traffic conditions, so problems can be identified instantly.

With the sensors, monitors, and computers that are now available, do you think it is possible to design road and vehicle systems that could take over many of the drivers' tasks and provide for greatly increased safety?

Challenge

As part of an engineering development team, you are to prepare a proposal for the creation of a high-tech "safe highway." This highway will take over most of the drivers' responsibilities for driving their vehicles.

Materials

2 sheets of Bristol board or other poster-quality cardboard art materials, such as markers and fine-line felt pens

Design Criteria

A. Your design should address these points:

- Do vehicles need to "know" the speed limit? If so, how will they obtain this information?
- Should the system be able to change the speed of vehicles to match driving conditions?
- How will each vehicle be kept in its proper lane?
- How will adequate space be maintained between vehicles?
- How will vehicles receive warnings about accidents and blockages, which may require sharp braking, farther along the highway?

B. Create two posters for your design. The first poster should illustrate the network of sensors, computers, and communication links required for your system. The second poster should advertise the benefits of your system.

C. Produce a pamphlet, at least four pages long, to explain your system in greater depth than is shown on the poster.

Plan and Construct

1. Working in groups of four, discuss how the motion of vehicles could be controlled by a network of computers, sensors, and communication links. As a starting point, consider the questions in Design Criterion A. Add any other questions you can think of. Use your ideas to make a list of specifications for your network.

2. Create an engineering proposal, based on your specifications.

3. Prepare the posters and pamphlet for your engineering proposal.

4. Prepare a questionnaire to be given out after your presentation. The rest of the class should be able to use this questionnaire to rate the posters, the pamphlet, and your presentation. They should also be able to provide constructive suggestions. Members of your group should complete the questionnaire, as well.

5. Give a 5 min presentation, in which your engineering development team explains the proposal to a group of elected officials represented by the rest of your class.

Evaluate

1. Based on the questionnaire responses, identify the strong parts in your proposal and presentation. Also identify parts that could be improved.

2. Are there aspects of other proposals and/or presentations that you wish you had used in yours?

A DEBATE

Who's in the Driving Seat?

Think About It

The technology now exists to control the motion of vehicles remotely, using systems like the one you just designed. Such systems would ensure that vehicles could not travel at unsafe speeds, tailgate, or jump lanes too quickly. Reaction times for braking could be measured in milliseconds. No cars would run red lights or make improper turns. Should such technology be used?

Resolution

"Be it resolved that the driving of vehicles on highways should be controlled by a remote system."

What to Do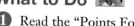

1. Read the "Points For" and "Points Against" on this page. Think about other points that you could make in favour of and against the resolution.

2. Two teams, made up of two students each, will debate the resolution. One team will speak in support of the resolution, and the other team will speak against it. **Note:** If you are on one of the teams, you must try your best to convince the audience of the side that you team is defending — no matter which side you actually believe in.

3. Two other students will be assigned to work with each team. These students will gather the background information needed to make a strong case for the side that the team is defending.

4. The rest of the class will judge the debate. In preparation for the debate, students should do their own research in order to understand the science and technology behind the issues. They should also survey themselves to find their original stand on the resolution.

5. Your teacher will provide you with the proper *Debating Procedures* to follow.

Points For

- Such a system would drastically reduce traffic accidents, injuries, and deaths.
- Insurance rates would drop, since fewer vehicles would be damaged.

Points Against

- The system could be considered to be an infringement of individual choice. Situations that require a human response could arise. Such situations could even require drivers to break traffic regulations.
- Systems are fallible. What would happen if a traffic computer crashed while drivers were on a highway?

Analyze

1. For the audience:

   (a) Based on the number of people who changed their stand on the topic, which team won the debate?

   (b) What made this side more convincing, the team's research or its delivery?

2. For the debaters:

   (a) How well did your team work together?

   (b) Which of your opponents' points were the hardest to refute?

Now that you have completed Chapters 9, 10, 11, and 12, you can assess how much you have learned about motion by answering the following questions. Before you begin, you may find it useful to return to each Chapter at a Glance and each Chapter Review.

True/False

In your notebook, indicate whether each statement is true or false. Correct each false statement.

1. Scalar quantities have both a magnitude and a direction.

2. For downward motion, velocities are usually written as negative numbers.

3. Acceleration can be determined by finding the slope of a position-time graph.

4. If an object's motion is uniform, its average velocity and its instantaneous velocity are equal.

5. If a journey takes you back to your starting point, both your displacement and the distance you travelled equal zero.

6. A very massive falling object always accelerates faster than a less massive object.

Completion

In your notebook, complete each statement with the correct term or phrase.

7. A _____ experiment generally has one manipulated variable and one responding variable.

8. Just like bats and dolphins, an experimenter using an _____ determines the position of an object by observing reflected sound waves.

9. Information from a _____ analysis can be helpful for choosing among alternative solutions to a societal problem.

10. Theoretical physicists try to develop scientific _____ to represent complex phenomena in a simplified way.

11. An object's speed and direction of travel never change if the object's motion is _____.

12. Jet pilots wear a _____ so they can withstand very high accelerations.

Matching

13. In your notebook, copy the descriptions in column A. Beside each description, write the term from column B that best fits the description. A term may be used once, more than once, or not at all.

A	B
• theoretical physicist who increased our understanding of black holes and the history of the physical universe	• terminal velocity
• path followed by a projectile	• planimeter
• term that means "expressed in numbers"	• equilibrium position
• highest downward speed reached by a falling object	• Doppler radar
• instrument used to find the wind speed in violent storms	• quantitative
• used to find the slope at a particular point on a graph	• qualitative
• position where a pendulum comes to rest	• tangent line
• motion in a straight line	• midpoint
• instrument used to reveal the details of rapid motion	• parabola
	• stroboscope
	• Albert Einstein
	• Stephen Hawking
	• linear

Multiple Choice

In your notebook, write the letter of the best answer for each of the following questions.

14. If a position-time graph has zero slope, you can infer that the object being observed was
    (a) moving at uniform velocity
    (b) moving to the right and accelerating
    (c) moving uniformly to the left
    (d) moving to the left and accelerating
    (e) not moving at all

15. Position and velocity are related in the same way as
    (a) position and displacement
    (b) position and acceleration
    (c) velocity and acceleration
    (d) displacement and velocity
    (e) displacement and acceleration

16. Which quantity cannot be calculated from a velocity-time graph?
    (a) the object's initial position
    (b) the direction of the object's motion
    (c) how fast the object is moving
    (d) whether the object is accelerating
    (e) the object's displacement

17. A student tries to write the motion formula in three forms:
    (1) $\Delta d = v\Delta t$
    (2) $v = \dfrac{\vec{\Delta d}}{t}$
    (3) $\Delta t = \dfrac{\vec{v}}{\vec{\Delta d}}$

    Which forms are correct?
    (a) all three forms
    (b) forms (1) and (2) only
    (c) forms (1) and (3) only
    (d) forms (2) and (3) only
    (e) only form (1)

18. Suppose that you are studying cars travelling across an intersection. You decide to measure each car's initial velocity, final velocity, and time taken to cross the intersection. Which quantity below could you calculate from these data, assuming that the car's acceleration is constant?
    (a) only position at any given time
    (b) only average velocity
    (c) only average acceleration
    (d) both average velocity and average acceleration
    (e) neither average velocity nor average acceleration

19. Read the following statements about Earth's gravity.
    (1) Gravitational acceleration varies slightly from place to place on Earth's surface.
    (2) There is no gravitational acceleration in an orbiting spacecraft.
    (3) Gravitational acceleration on Earth is smaller than it is on the other inner planets.

    Which statement or statements are correct?
    (a) only (1)
    (b) only (2)
    (c) only (3)
    (d) only (1) and (2)
    (e) only (2) and (3)

20. What does the area "under" a velocity-time graph represent?
    (a) displacement
    (b) acceleration
    (c) time interval
    (d) change in velocity
    (e) initial and final position

Short Answer

In your notebook, write a sentence or a short paragraph to answer each of the following questions.

21. Identify two differences between studying motion in a physics laboratory and in everyday situations.

22. Classify each quantity listed below as a vector or a scalar.
    (a) mass
    (b) time
    (c) position
    (d) speed
    (e) velocity
    (f) acceleration

23. What three things can be represented by a + sign or a − sign with a measurement of position or velocity?

24. How many significant digits are in each measurement below?
   (a) 4.00 cm   **(c)** 104 kg
   (b) 0.0063 s   **(d)** 4.60×10^3 L

25. Which of the following situations are examples of uniform motion, and which are examples of accelerated motion?
   (a) a runner poised at the starting line
   (b) the runner speeding up just after the starting pistol is fired
   (c) the runner travelling at a steady speed around a corner
   (d) the runner slowing down after passing the finish line

26. Suppose that you had a ticker-timer tape showing the motion of a cyclist for precisely 3 s, as she accelerated from rest. You want to find her average velocity during the third second of her ride. Draw an events chain to show what you need to measure and calculate.

27. Identify two key differences in transport technology used by pre-industrial and by industrial societies.

28. Complete a chart that lists all the mathematical formulas used in this unit. Write each formula, make sure that you know the meaning of each symbol in it, and describe any special conditions that must be met before the formula can be used.

29. Identify two methods for measuring gravitational acceleration. For each method, describe the measurements needed and the mathematical formula used to calculate g from the measurements.

30. How do you know when a falling object has reached its terminal velocity? What features of the object affect its terminal velocity?

31. List three ways in which motion-tracking technology is used outside a physics laboratory.

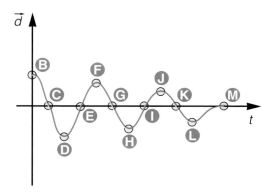

32. Examine the position-time graph above of a pendulum's motion. Identify, by letter, the time(s) when the pendulum is
   (a) completing its first cycle
   (b) at maximum displacement
   (c) passing through its equilibrium position
   (d) moving at maximum speed
   (e) moving at minimum speed
   (f) no longer moving

33. Sketch the shape of a velocity-time graph of a pendulum's motion to match the position-time graph in question 32.

34. The worst recorded elevator disaster occurred in South Africa, when a mine elevator dropped 487 m before hitting the bottom of the mine shaft.
   (a) If an object fell freely for this distance, how long would the fall take? Assume an initial velocity of 0 m/s.
   (b) How fast would the object be travelling at the end of the fall?
   (c) Your calculations probably do not correctly describe the actual motion of the elevator. Identify several reasons why this is so.

Problem Solving/Applying

Show complete solutions for all problems that involve equations and numbers. Use the GRASP problem-solving model or a model suggested by your teacher.

35. High-speed passenger elevators move upward at speeds of up to 7.1 m/s. At this rate, how long would an elevator take to climb 37 m (about ten storeys)?

36. Examine the sketch of a trip on a carnival bungee ride. Read or calculate each quantity below.

(a) $\vec{\Delta d}$ from initial position to position A

(b) $\vec{v}_{inst}$ at position A

(c) $\vec{v}_{av}$ between position A and position B

(d) $\vec{v}_{inst}$ at position B

(e) $\vec{a}_{av}$ between position A and position B

(f) $\vec{\Delta d}$ from the initial position to position B

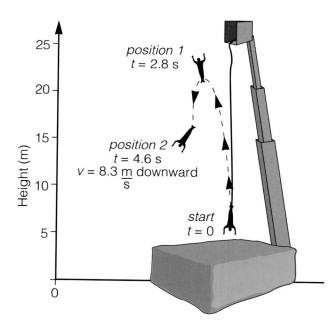

position 1
t = 2.8 s

position 2
t = 4.6 s
v = 8.3 $\frac{m}{s}$ downward

start
t = 0

Height (m)

37. A baseball pitcher, who is standing 18.5 m from the batter, throws a fastball moving at 40.0 m/s (close to 140 km/h). The batter swings, contacts the ball for 0.030 s, and sends it straight back to the pitcher at 50.0 m/s. Assume that air resistance has little effect over the short distance that the ball travels, so the velocities are constant.

(a) How long does the pitch take to reach the batter?

(b) What is the ball's change in velocity when it is hit? (Hint: Think of the initial velocity of the pitch as positive. How should you represent the final velocity of the ball after its direction is reversed?)

(c) What is the ball's average acceleration while it is being hit?

(d) How long does the ball take to return to the pitcher?

(e) Draw a properly scaled velocity-time graph of the ball's motion.

(f) On your graph, mark a line to represent the ball's average acceleration from the time it is thrown until it reaches the pitcher again. Use a slope triangle, or another method, to find a value for the average acceleration.

Critical Thinking

38. Noise pollution is a serious problem when developing high-speed transport technologies. The Concorde passenger jet, for example, can only travel at supersonic speeds on routes above oceans and unpopulated areas. This is because of the "sonic boom" it creates and the noise of its engines at full power. For a technology of your choice, compare and contrast a pure scientific approach to noise pollution with a technological problem-solving approach.

Application

39. Many safety devices work by increasing the time during which an object comes to a stop. For example, air bags in cars slow a passenger's forward motion more gradually than impact with a rigid surface. Longer stopping times reduce acceleration, which lessens the injury-producing forces experienced in an accident. Find out how air bags work. How long do they take to inflate? How much do they reduce accelerations in an accident? What safety problems do air bags cause?

Weather Dynamics

"It sounded like a train was coming toward the house, only metres away! We ran to the window. We saw the longest, strangest funnel cloud that you could ever imagine in your wildest dreams. But it was real. So we raced to the basement and took cover."

Scenes like this happen hundreds of times every spring. They have been happening for thousands of years. You may live where tornadoes are rare. No matter who you are or where you live, however, you cannot escape weather. Harsh weather, in some form, affects everyone.

In ancient times, many cultures explained severe weather events as the wrath of angry gods. Pictured here is Zeus, the Greek god of the sky. The tornado in the photograph makes it easy to see why ancient cultures believed as they did. People would pray to the gods and even make sacrifices. They believed that the gods would have mercy and protect them from the dangers of the weather. People also performed rituals to persuade their gods to send rain for their crops. Their efforts were not very successful. Weather continued to dominate their lives.

Today most people do not believe that severe weather is caused by angry gods looking down on Earth. Instead, we have weather satellites that "look down" and track weather events all over the world. Meteorologists can explain what causes thunderstorms and tornadoes. They can predict weather several days in advance, with good accuracy. They can also track hurricanes and send out warnings so that people can prepare for the worst. With all of our scientific knowledge and advanced technology, however, we are no more successful than the ancient cultures. We cannot control the weather any more than they could. The best we can do is forecast the weather and prepare for it.

Science
Log

Using what you already know about thermal energy and fluids, write answers to the questions above. Try to think of the first time you ever wondered about wind. What did you think caused wind? Have your ideas changed? As you read this chapter, look for answers to these questions and see if your current ideas will change.

Imagine this. It is a hot summer day, and you are at the beach. Lying on a beach towel, you close your eyes and turn your face toward the Sun. You feel the soothing warmth on your skin. When a breeze wafts by, you feel cool. The breeze subsides, but the Sun continues to beat down and you become uncomfortably warm. You decide to go for a swim, stand up, and step off of your beach towel. The hot sand nearly burns your bare feet, so you run to the water as fast as you can. The water feels almost chilly, but you quickly adapt and enjoy the swim. When you get out of the water, you feel so cool that you start to shiver. Grabbing a towel, you dry yourself off and feel comfortable once again. Eventually you notice that the shadows are getting longer and the Sun does not feel quite as warm. It is time to head for home.

In the scene above, you imagined experiencing many of the fundamental principles that are responsible for weather. How does solar energy interact with air, water, and solid ground? In this chapter, you will investigate how these interactions cause wind, rain, and snow. You will learn about some unique properties of water that affect weather and climate. You will be then ready to learn about weather around the world later in this unit.

Weather

Key Concepts

In this chapter, you will discover

- how energy from the Sun reaches Earth
- why one substance may become hotter than another when both are in the Sun
- how the evaporation of water helps to control the temperature of lakes, rivers, and oceans
- what the structure of the atmosphere is

Key Skills

In this chapter, you will

- test materials for their ability to absorb radiant energy
- simulate wind
- determine the dew point
- infer the effects of global warming on weather

Key Terms

- conduction
- convection
- radiation
- solar constant
- specific heat capacity
- heat of vaporization
- heat of fusion
- saturated
- condensation nuclei
- humidity

- absolute humidity
- relative humidity
- water cycle
- troposphere
- stratosphere
- mesosphere
- thermosphere
- ionosphere
- aurora
- atmospheric pressure

Feel the Heat

What do you see and what do you feel when you are near an electrical element as it heats up? What can you infer about solar energy by observing an electrical element?

CAUTION:

- Do not touch the electrical element.
- Keep loose clothing away from the electrical element, and tie back long hair.

What You Need

toaster or hot plate with coil
watch or clock with second hand

What to Do

1. Make sure that the electrical element is turned off. Sit or stand in a comfortable position, with your hand about 30 cm from the element. Note the colour of the element.

2. Turn on the electrical element. Make four observations at 15 to 20 s intervals. Note
   (a) the colour of the elements
   (b) the sensation you feel on your skin.

3. Remaining in the same position, turn off the element. Over a period of about 2 min, make four more observations. Note the colour of the element and any sensations you feel on your skin.

What Did You Discover?

1. Which did you observe first, a visible change in the element or a sensation on your skin?

2. Describe the visible change.

3. How do you think the visible colour travelled from the element to your eyes?

4. Air is not a good conductor of heat. Infer how the heat travelled to your skin.

5. How do you think the colour you see is related to the heat you feel?

6. From your observations of electrical elements, infer how energy travels from the sun.

13.1 Earth's Energy Budget

The warmth that you felt on your skin in the Starting Point Activity is very similar to the warmth that you feel when lying in the Sun. Energy travels from an electrical element to your skin in the same way that it travels from the Sun to Earth. What is this mechanism of energy transport?

Energy Travelling from the Sun

In previous science courses, you learned that thermal energy is the energy of motion of particles — such as atoms, ions, and molecules — in a substance. Heat is thermal energy transferred from one object to another. How does the energy of motion of particles in the Sun travel through empty space to Earth? To answer this question, examine Figure 13.1. The three photographs illustrate the three mechanisms of heat transfer: **conduction**, **convection**, and **radiation**.

From Figure 13.1, you can see that both conduction and convection require matter to transport thermal energy. Since there is very little matter in space, radiation is the only mechanism that can carry energy from the Sun to Earth. After the energy reaches Earth, conduction and convection become important mechanisms for distributing the energy throughout Earth's surface and atmosphere.

A Conduction is the mechanism of heat transfer in which highly energetic atoms or molecules collide with less energetic atoms or molecules, giving them some energy. In this photograph, the atoms in the stove element are moving extremely rapidly. They collide with the atoms in the skillet, giving thermal energy to the skillet. To hold a cast iron skillet, you must use a hot pad because the atoms in the skillet are transferring the energy throughout the entire skillet by conduction. All of the atoms remain in their own place, however. Only the energy moves.

B Convection is the mechanism of heat transfer in which highly energetic molecules move from one place to another. In the photograph, the water molecules at the bottom of the pan are receiving thermal energy by conduction. The water expands as it warms, becoming less dense. The less dense water rises, and denser, cooler water moves down to take its place. This movement creates convection currents. You can see these convection currents because water at different temperatures bends light to a different extent.

C Radiation is the mechanism of heat transfer in which atoms or molecules emit electromagnetic waves. These waves carry the energy through space and deposit it only when they interact with some form of matter. In the photograph, radiant energy from the stove element is carrying energy to the hand. The radiant energy is converted back to thermal energy when it interacts with the hand.

Figure 13.1 Mechanisms of energy transfer

Solar Radiation

Recall, from your previous science courses, that radiant energy takes the form of electromagnetic waves. These waves have a great range of wavelengths. As shown in Figure 13.2, the electromagnetic waves that carry radiant energy from the Sun to Earth contain only a very narrow range of wavelengths. Included in this range are a little ultraviolet radiation, all wavelengths of visible light, and some infrared radiation. All forms of life on Earth depend on solar energy (radiant energy from the Sun) for their survival. In addition, solar energy drives all weather systems.

DidYouKnow?

Only about 0.023 percent of the solar energy that reaches Earth is captured by green plants and used for photosynthesis. The remainder is available to drive weather systems.

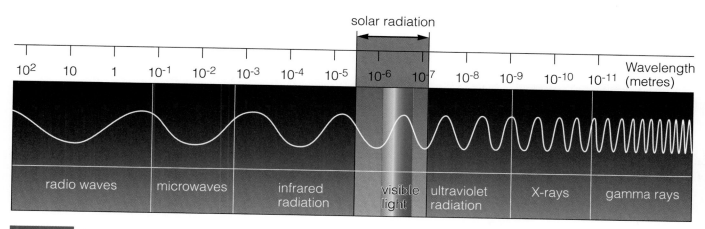

Figure 13.2   Nearly all the radiant energy from the Sun lies within the range of wavelengths shown here. Only a very small percentage of radiant energy has wavelengths outside this range.

DidYouKnow?

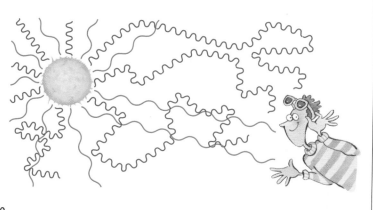

Since the Sun emits radiation with all the wavelengths of visible light, you might expect it to look white. Why, then, does it look yellow to orange? Why does the sky look blue, and why do the clouds appear white?

When sunlight reaches the atmosphere, gases and particles in the air scatter some of the light. The tiny droplets of water in the clouds scatter all the wavelengths of light, so the clouds look white. Thick clouds look grey because they scatter so much light that only a small amount penetrates the clouds. Oxygen gas, which is evenly distributed throughout the atmosphere, scatters the shorter wavelength blue light more readily than the longer wavelength red light. Therefore more red, orange, and yellow light remain in the beam that comes directly from the Sun to your eyes. This makes the Sun appear yellow to red. The blue sky is blue light from the Sun that has been scattered several times by oxygen in the air before finally reaching your eyes.

Radiant Energy Reaching Earth

Because space contains very little matter, the solar energy that arrives at Earth's outer atmosphere is essentially the same as it was when it left the Sun. The amount of energy that reaches Earth's outer atmosphere is often described by the **solar constant,** 1367 J/m²s. The solar constant is the amount of radiant energy that hits 1 m² of Earth's outer atmosphere every second. Figure 13.3 illustrates the fact that the solar constant applies only to rays that arrive perpendicular to the surface.

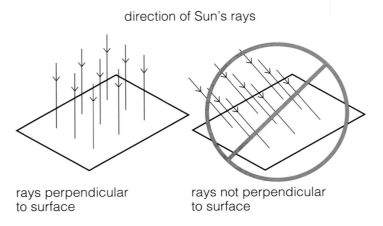

direction of Sun's rays

rays perpendicular to surface

rays not perpendicular to surface

Figure 13.3 Since the amount of energy differs depending on the direction of the incoming rays, the solar constant is defined for the situation in which the Sun's rays arrive perpendicular to the surface of Earth. This is shown on the left side of the illustration.

When solar energy penetrates the atmosphere, two different interactions occur. Some of the energy is reflected back into space, unchanged. The remainder of the energy is absorbed, either by the atmosphere or Earth's surface. Figure 13.4 shows how solar energy is distributed. The percentages in the figure represent the average conditions for the entire planet over a typical year.

Figure 13.4 Half of the solar energy that enters Earth's atmosphere is absorbed by Earth's surface. What happens to the other half? About 20 percent is absorbed by the hundreds of kilometres of atmosphere as it passes through. The remaining 30 percent is reflected and leaves the atmosphere. Thus it is lost to Earth.

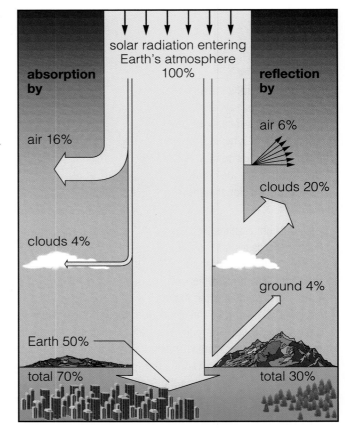

solar radiation entering Earth's atmosphere 100%

absorption by

air 16%

clouds 4%

Earth 50%

total 70%

reflection by

air 6%

clouds 20%

ground 4%

total 30%

Absorption or Reflection

What characteristics of an object cause it to absorb or reflect solar energy? In this activity, you will investigate one of these characteristics.

CAUTION:

- Be careful when using scissors.
- Be sure that the cans have no sharp edges.
- Handle thermometers with care.

What You Need

2 aluminum cans (identical, clean, and empty)
black construction paper
white construction paper
scissors
cellophane tape
laboratory thermometer
water
graduated cylinder

What to Do

1. Using the graduated cylinder, determine the amount of water that will nearly fill one can. Empty the can.

2. Cut the black and white construction paper to fit the outside of the cans. Tape the black paper on one can and the white paper on the other can. Be sure that the paper fits tightly.

3. Measure the amount of cool water that you determined in step 1. Pour it into one can.

Measure the same amount of cool water again, and pour it into the other can.

4. Measure and record the temperature of the water in each can.

5. Cut a piece of black construction paper and a piece of white construction paper to fit the tops of the cans. Tape the white piece on the top of the white can and the black piece on the top of the black can.

6. Place the cans in direct sunlight, and let them stand for about 1 h.

7. Measure and record the temperature of the water in each can.

What Did You Discover?

1. In which can did the water show the greater temperature increase?

2. What would you infer about the characteristic that caused absorption of solar energy? What caused reflection of solar energy?

Extensions

3. Look at the photographs of snow. Which snow would probably melt faster in sunlight?

4. If you lived in a hot, sunny climate, would you choose to own a white car or a black car? Why? What colour of upholstery would you choose?

Earth's Constant Temperature

Imagine that an ocean, 5 km deep, entirely covered Earth. If all the solar energy that is now absorbed by Earth and the atmosphere were absorbed by this ocean, and none of the energy escaped, the entire ocean would begin to boil in about 25 years. We know, however, that the average temperature of Earth has not changed substantially over thousands of years. How can Earth maintain a nearly constant temperature? From year to year, Earth must lose, on average, as much energy as it absorbs. Where does this "lost" energy go? What happens between the time the energy is absorbed and the time it is "lost?"

Earth, the Moon, and other planets do not emit visible light like the Sun and stars do. When you see the Moon and planets in the night sky, you are seeing sunlight reflected from them. Although the Moon and planets do not emit visible light, this does not mean that they do not emit electromagnetic radiation. All objects, including rocks and even icebergs, emit radiation. Objects that are cooler than about 1000 K (about 727°C), however, emit radiation with wavelengths longer than the wavelengths of visible light. Figure 13.5 is similar to Figure 13.2, but it includes the range of wavelengths of electromagnetic waves that Earth emits. As you can see, Earth's radiation lies within the infrared range.

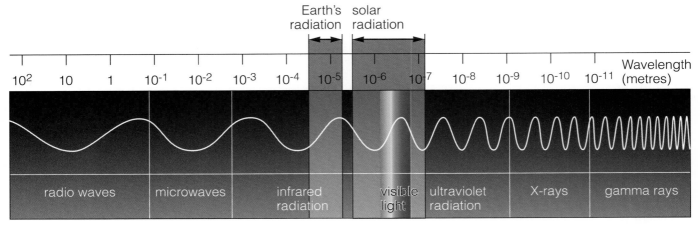

Figure 13.5 Most of Earth's radiation lies in the range shown here. These infrared rays continually carry energy away from Earth, out into space.

Earth maintains an energy balance and a temperature balance by radiating as much energy out into space as it absorbs from the Sun. The energy transformations that occur between the time solar radiation is absorbed and the time it is re-emitted as infrared radiation are the transformations that drive weather systems. You will investigate these transformations in the next section.

Check Your Understanding

1. What is the only way that energy can travel from the Sun to Earth? Explain why.

2. Name the categories of electromagnetic waves that make up radiant energy from the Sun.

3. Define the term "solar constant."

4. How does Earth maintain its relatively constant temperature?

13.2 Energy and Water

Only about 30 percent of Earth's surface is land, and clouds cover much of this land. Therefore most of the incoming solar radiation that penetrates the atmosphere strikes water. As a result, the interactions between solar energy and water have a major influence on weather. Is it any wonder that some people have said "Planet Water" would be a more appropriate name than "Earth?"

Word CONNECT

Meteorologists use the term *insolation* to mean "incoming solar radiation." Examine the term and its meaning to see if you can determine how the term was formed.

Interactions of Water and Radiant Energy

The type of interaction that occurs between solar radiation and water depends on the state of the water. For example, fresh, white snow reflects as much as 90 percent of the incoming radiation, and ice reflects about 50 percent. Liquid water, however, reflects only 7 percent of the radiation that strikes its surface. Thus lakes, rivers, and oceans absorb 93 percent of the incoming solar radiation that reaches their surfaces. Nevertheless their temperatures do not vary a great deal. Why?

DidYouKnow?

Water is the only substance on Earth that occurs in nature in all three states — solid, liquid, and gas.

Figure 13.6 What prevents lakes and oceans from boiling?

The temperatures of oceans and very large lakes are relatively constant for several reasons. Some of these reasons are related to water's unique properties, such as its large **specific heat capacity**. Specific heat capacity is defined as the amount of heat that is required to raise the temperature of one gram of a substance one degree Celsius. Chemists have measured the specific heat capacity (c) of many substances. Using these measured values, and the formula below, you can calculate the amount of heat (Q) required to raise the temperature of an amount of a substance (m) by a given temperature change (ΔT). Table 13.1 shows the specific heat capacities of several common substances.

$$Q = mc\Delta T$$

DidYouKnow?

The greek letter delta, Δ, is often used in equations to represent "change."

Table 13.1 Specific Heat Capacities (J/g•°C)

Substance in nature	Specific heat capacity	Liquid	Specific heat capacity
pure water	4.18	water	4.18
sea water	3.89	methanol	2.55
dry air	1.00	ethanol	2.46
wet mud	2.51	hexane	2.26
brick	0.84	toluene	1.80
granite	0.79		
limestone	0.92		

Model Problem 1

Compare the increase in the temperature of 1.0 g of water and 1.0 g of ethanol when they each absorb 10 J of thermal energy.

Given

Mass of water, m = 1.0 g
Mass of ethanol, m = 1.0 g
Specific heat capacity of water, c = 4.18 J/g•°C
Specific heat capacity of ethanol, c = 2.46 J/g•°C
Energy absorbed, Q = 10 J each

Required Temperature change, ΔT

Analysis Use the relationship $Q = mc\Delta T$. Solve for ΔT.

Solution For water, $Q = mc\Delta T$

$$10 \text{ J} = 1.0 \text{ g} \times \frac{4.18 \text{ J}}{\text{g}•°C} \times \Delta T$$

$$\frac{10\text{J}}{4.18 \text{ J/°C}} = \frac{\cancel{4.18 \text{ J/°C}} \times \Delta T}{\cancel{4.18 \text{ J/°C}}}$$

$$\Delta T = \frac{10\text{J}}{4.18\text{J/°C}}$$

$$= 2.4°C$$

For ethanol, $Q = mc\Delta T$

$$10 \text{ J} = 1.0 \text{ g} \times \frac{2.46 \text{ J}}{\text{g}•°C} \times \Delta T$$

$$10 \text{ J} = 2.46 \text{ J/°C} \times \Delta T$$

$$\frac{10\text{J}}{2.46\text{J/°C}} = \frac{\cancel{2.46 \text{ J/°C}} \times \Delta T}{\cancel{2.46 \text{ J/°C}}}$$

$$\Delta T = \frac{10\text{J}}{2.46 \text{ J/°C}}$$

$$= 4.1°C$$

Paraphrase When 1.0 g of water absorbs 10 J of energy, the temperature increases by 2.4°C. When 1.0 g of ethanol absorbs 10 J of energy, the temperature increases by 4.1°C. The temperature of ethanol increases more than the temperature of water, under the same conditions.

Word CONNECT

What does the word *latent* mean? If you do not know, look it up in a dictionary. Explain why it is a good word to describe the energy that is used to evaporate a liquid.

Chemists have made many comparisons and have shown that the temperature of water increases much less than the temperature of most similar substances after absorbing the same amount of energy. Thus a larger specific heat capacity results in a smaller temperature increase. Water's large specific heat capacity helps to moderate its temperature because the temperature change is relatively small when water absorbs a large amount of energy. Nevertheless, if water absorbs energy and this energy remains in the water as thermal energy, the temperature of the water will rise to some extent. There must be other factors that prevent the temperatures of large bodies of water from continually rising.

STRETCH Your Mind

1. Use the equation $Q = mc\Delta T$ to calculate the amount of heat absorbed by each can of water in the activity on page 425. (To convert from volume to mass of water, recall that 1 mL of water has a mass of 1 g.)

2. Assume that the black can absorbed 100 percent of the sunlight that hit its surface. What percentage of the sunlight that hit the surface of the white can was reflected?

3. Imagine that you had used ethanol instead of water in the activity. Assume that the masses of ethanol were the same as the masses of water that you used. Also assume that the amounts of energy absorbed by the cans of ethanol were the same as those you calculated in question 1 for the cans of water. Determine the temperature changes of the cans of ethanol.

The second unique property of water that helps it maintain constant temperatures is its **heat of vaporization**. Heat of vaporization can be defined as the amount of energy that is required to convert 1.0 g of a substance from the liquid state into the gaseous state. If the gas condenses back into a liquid, the same amount of energy is released as heat. Scientists often call this energy the *latent* heat of vaporization because the thermal energy that is used to evaporate a liquid does not become thermal energy again until the gas condenses back to a liquid and releases the energy. Table 13.2 lists the heats of vaporization for several common liquids.

When water absorbs solar energy, some of the solar energy is used to evaporate the water. This energy is not available to increase the temperature of the water. You can calculate the amount of heat that is required to evaporate a given mass (*m*) of liquid by using the values in Table 13.2 and the following formula. The symbol $\Delta H°_{vap}$ represents the heat of vaporization of 1.0 g of a substance.

$$Q = m\Delta H°_{vap}$$

Table 13.2 Heats of Vaporization

Liquid	Heat of vaporization (J/g)
water	2260
methanol	1076
ethanol	855
hexane	335
toluene	363

Model Problem 2

Imagine that there is a large hole in your school driveway, where rainwater always collects. If the hole contains 2.7 kg of water, how much energy is required to evaporate all of the water?

Given Mass of water, m = 2.7 kg
Heat of vaporization of water, $\Delta H°_{vap}$ = 2260 J/g

Required Heat, Q

Analysis Use the relationship, $Q = m\Delta H°_{vap}$.
Solve for Q.

Solution
Convert the mass of water from kilograms to grams.

$$2.7 \text{ kg} \times \frac{1000 \text{ g}}{\text{kg}} = 2700 \text{ g}$$

$$\begin{aligned} Q &= m\Delta H°_{vap} \\ &= 2700 \text{ g} \times 2260 \text{ J/g} \\ &= 6\,102\,000 \text{ J or } 6.1 \times 10^6 \text{ J} \end{aligned}$$

Paraphrase 6.1×10^6 J of energy are required to evaporate 2.7 kg of water.

STRETCH Your Mind

How much energy is required to evaporate 2.7 kg of toluene? How many times as much energy is required to evaporate the same amount of water?

A third unique property of water is its large **heat of fusion**. Heat of fusion is the amount of heat that is required to melt 1.0 g of a solid into a liquid. In reverse, the heat of fusion is also the amount of energy that is released when 1.0 g of a liquid freezes or becomes a solid. Once again, water's heat of fusion is larger than the heats of fusion of other substances, as you can see in Table 13.3.

Table 13.3 Heats of Fusion of Several Solids

Substance	Heat of fusion (J/g)
water	333
methanol	100
ethanol	109
hexane	152
toluene	72

You can calculate the amount of heat, Q, required to melt a given mass, m, of a solid into a liquid by using the values in Table 13.3 and the following formula. The symbol $\Delta H°_{fus}$ represents the heat of fusion of 1.0 g of a substance. Notice that this formula is almost the same as the formula for calculating the heat of vaporization. The only difference is that you use the heat of fusion instead of the heat of vaporization.

$$Q = m\Delta H°_{fus}$$

Model Problem 3

Imagine that a snowplough went by your school and pushed a large pile of snow into the front yard. There must be at least 750 kg of snow in the pile! How much energy is required to melt 750 kg of snow?

Given Mass of water (solid), $m = 750$ kg
Heat of fusion of water, $\Delta H_{fus} = 333$ J/g

Required Heat, Q

Analysis Use the relationship $Q = m\Delta H^\circ_{fus}$ to solve for Q.

Solution Convert the mass of water from kilograms to grams.

$$750 \text{ kg} \times \frac{1000 \text{ g}}{\text{kg}} = 750\ 000 \text{ g}$$

$$\begin{aligned} Q &= m\Delta H^\circ_{fus} \\ &= 750\ 000 \text{ g} \times 333 \text{ J/g} \\ &= 249\ 750\ 000 \text{ J or } 2.5 \times 10^8 \text{ J} \end{aligned}$$

Paraphrase 2.5×10^8 J of energy are required to melt 750 kg of snow.

STRETCH Your Mind

A large icicle is hanging from the corner of a roof. If the icicle has a mass of 365 g, how much energy is required to melt it?

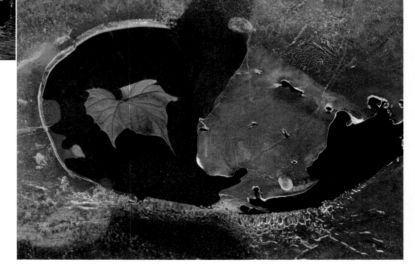

A In the spring, days become longer and the Sun begins to warm the land. If large amounts of snow and ice remain from the winter, however, much of the Sun's energy is used to melt them. Therefore the temperature does not rise as much as it would in the absence of snow and ice.

B As winter sets in, the days get shorter and the Sun provides less heat than in summer. As liquid water freezes, however, it releases heat. Therefore the temperature does not drop as much as it would if there were no water to freeze.

Figure 13.7 Water's large heat of fusion moderates temperature changes in both spring and fall.

Water in the Air

Can liquid water continue to evaporate until it is all converted into a gas? If not, what conditions would determine the amount of water that could exist as a gas in the air? What would happen if the air could not hold any more water vapour but water continued to evaporate from a source of liquid water? Analyze the two photographs in Figure 13.8 to see if you can find any clues that will help you answer these questions.

Figure 13.8 Clouds in the sky and the mist over a kettle both consist of extremely tiny droplets of liquid water.

Compare the states of water in the two photographs. In both photographs, liquid water is absorbing energy from a source of heat — the Sun or a stove element. The air just above the surface of the ocean and just above the cap of the kettle is clear. Therefore, if any water exists in this air, it is in the gaseous state. High above the ocean, you see clouds. Just beyond the clear region above the cap of the kettle, you see mist. Clouds and mist are made of liquid water. There is, most likely, water in the clear regions of air, which condenses into droplets. Does this help you answer the questions above?

As the water evaporated from the liquid state, some of the water existed as vapour. Then, because the air could not hold all of the vapour that was collecting in it, some of the water vapour condensed back into a liquid in the form of clouds or mist. What characteristic of the air, which might affect the state of the water, changed as the distance from the water increased?

In both photographs, the temperature of the air became lower as the distance from the liquid water increased. Warm air can hold more water vapour than cool air.

When there is as much water vapour in the air as possible at a given temperature, we say that the air is **saturated**. Table 13.4 shows how many grams of water 1.0 kg of saturated air contains at various temperatures. For example, at 20°C, 1.0 kg of saturated air contains 15.0 g of water in its gaseous state. If the air becomes cooler, or if more water evaporates, some of the water vapour will condense. Water droplets form around tiny particles, such as dust and salt, in the air. Particles that stimulate droplet formation are called **condensation nuclei**. Droplets also form on the surface of solids. Have you ever walked through grass in the early morning, when the temperature was cool, and discovered that the grass was wet? To learn more about the formation of dew, try the next activity.

Table 13.4 Amount of Water Vapour in Saturated Air at Standard Atomspheric Pressure

Temperature (°C)	Grams of water vapour in 1.0 kg of air
40	49.8
38	44.4
36	39.5
34	35.1
32	31.2
30	27.7
28	24.6
26	21.7
24	19.2
22	17.0
20	15.0
18	13.2
16	11.6
14	10.1
12	8.9
10	7.8
8	6.8
6	5.9
4	5.1
2	4.4
0	3.84
-2	3.31
-4	2.85
-6	2.45
-8	2.10
-10	1.79
-12	1.53
-14	1.30
-16	1.10
-18	0.93
-20	0.78
-22	0.66
-24	0.55
-26	0.46

What Is the Point? (The Dew Point)

How can you predict when dew will form? What conditions cause dew to form?

CAUTION:

- When the lid is removed from a can by a can opener, the can often has sharp edges. Be careful when handling the can.

- Stir with a stirring rod, not a thermometer. Laboratory thermometers often have mercury sealed inside. Stirring with a thermometer could break it and release the toxic mercury.

What You Need

laboratory thermometer
stirring rod
aluminum can
room-temperature water
ice

What to Do

1. Measure and record the temperature of the air in the room.

2. Fill the can half full of room-temperature water.

3. Measure the temperature of the water.

4. Add a small amount of ice, and stir gently with the stirring rod. Watch for moisture to appear on the can. (You may have to add more ice.)

5. At the first sign of moisture on the outside of the can, read and record the temperature of the water in the can. Label this temperature "dew point."

What Did You Discover?

1. Why did moisture condense on the outside of the can?

2. What do you think the term "dew point" means?

3. Use Table 13.4 to find and record the amount of water vapour that the room air would hold if it were saturated.

4. Find the actual amount of vapour in the room air. (Hint: When the temperature of the water reached the temperature that would make the air saturated, condensation began to form on the can.)

5. What percentage of the total amount of vapour that the air could hold is actually in the air?

   Hint: $\dfrac{\text{Amount of vapour in the air}}{\text{Amount of vapour the air could hold}} \times 100\%$

6. In your own words, explain the conditions that are necessary for dew to form.

Extension

7. Imagine that the dew point of air was −10°C and you were able to make the water in your can cool to below this temperature. What would form on your can?

When you performed the calculation in step 5 of the last activity, did you know that you were calculating the relative humidity of the air in your room? **Humidity** is the amount of water vapour in the air. **Absolute humidity** is the actual amount of water vapour in the air, expressed in units such as grams of water vapour per kilogram of air. **Relative humidity** is the percentage of water vapour in the air compared with the amount of water vapour that the air would contain if it was saturated.

The humidity can influence the way you feel. For example, does your skin tend to dry out in the winter even if the weather report says that the relative humidity is 75 percent? Have you ever heard someone say, "As soon as you turn on the furnace, the air dries out"? How can the air be dry if the humidity is not low? What is the relationship between cold weather and dry air? How does "turning on the furnace" affect the humidity? Consider the following case.

The outdoor temperature is −12°C and the relative humidity is 75 percent. According to Table 13.4 on page 431, saturated air at this temperature would contain 1.53 g of water vapour per 1.0 kg of air. So at 75 percent humidity, the air would contain 0.75 × 1.53 g of water per 1.0 kg of air, or 1.15 g of water per 1.0 kg of air. A ventilation system, as well as open doors, brings outdoor air into your home, and the furnace heats the air to +20°C. What is the relative humidity now? Table 13.4 says that air, at 20°C, can hold 15.0 g of water per 1.0 kg of air. So the relative humidity is

$$\frac{1.15 \text{ g}}{15.0 \text{ g}} \times 100\% = 7.7\%$$

No wonder your skin feels dry!

Figure 13.9 In the winter, every time someone goes into or out of a building, warm indoor air is exchanged with the cold air outside.

The Water Cycle

Evaporation and condensation are occurring throughout the world, at all times. About 23 percent of all incoming solar radiation causes liquid water to evaporate into water vapour. Most evaporation comes from oceans, of course. Water also evaporates from rivers, lakes, and moist ground. Another very important source of water vapour is living plants. Plants draw water from the ground with their roots. The water rises through the plants and evaporates out of their leaves in a process called transpiration. Nearly everywhere on Earth, air contains water vapour. The amount of water vapour varies with local weather conditions.

The movement of air into cooler regions, or the lowering of air temperature, causes the water vapour to condense into water droplets, forming clouds. If the air is cold enough, ice crystals form instead of liquid droplets. If the droplets or crystals coalesce and become large enough, they fall to Earth. Local conditions (which you will study in more detail in Chapter 15) determine whether the droplets or crystals reach the ground in the form of rain, snow, sleet, or hail. When moisture falls to the ground, it may run off into rivers or lakes, or it may go directly back into the oceans. Water may seep deep into the ground and flow in underground rivers back to the surface. The overall process, called the **water cycle**, is illustrated in Figure 13.10.

DidYouKnow?

Transpiration from plants causes more moisture to enter the air than does evaporation from other sources.

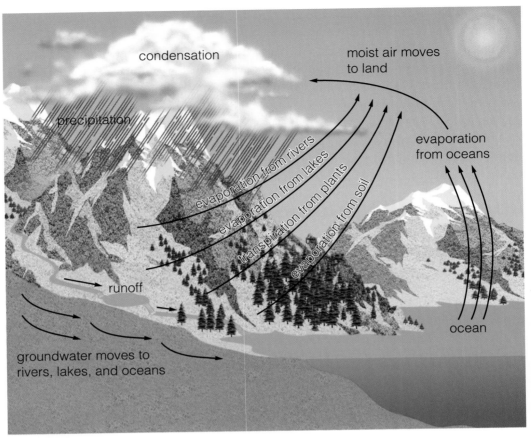

Figure 13.10 The total amount of water in the air, in the form of vapour or clouds, is enough to cover Earth with a layer about 2.5 cm deep. This water has a residence time of approximately 9 days. Residence time is the time that is needed for all the atmospheric water to fall to Earth as rain or snow and to be replaced by evaporation. Since solar energy causes evaporation, we can say that the Sun is the engine that drives the water cycle.

Check Your Understanding

1. Explain how the specific heat capacity of water influences the temperature of a large lake.

2. Define "heat of vaporization."

3. What type of energy change occurs when liquid water freezes?

4. What happens when saturated air cools?

5. Explain what a weather reporter means by "The relative humidity is 62 percent."

6. **Thinking Critically** If steam condenses on skin, it can cause a very serious burn. Use the concept of heat of vaporization to explain the cause of the burn.

7. **Apply** Assume that a small fish pond contains 4000 kg of water. If it absorbs 6.15×10^7 J (61 500 000 J) of solar energy in one day, and none of the energy is lost to evaporation, how much will the temperature of the water rise?

8. **Apply** If all 6.15×10^7 J of energy absorbed by the fish pond in question 7 were used to evaporate water, how much water would evaporate?

13.3 Interactions of Solar Energy with Land and Air

You have learned how oceans and very large bodies of water maintain a relatively constant temperature. You know from experience, however, that land and air can have widely varying temperatures, even from day to night. How does the interaction of solar energy with dry land and with air differ from its interaction with water? How do these different types of interactions account for weather processes?

Heating Dry Land

In the introduction, you imagined yourself stepping off of a beach towel onto hot, dry sand and your feet burning on the sand. Then, when you stepped into the water, it felt chilly. Both the sand and the water were exposed to the same amount of incoming solar radiation. Thus the nature of each substance must account for the large difference in the temperatures.

Water's large specific heat capacity is part of the explanation. If one gram of water and one gram of dry sand absorb the same amount of radiant energy, the temperature of the sand will increase five times as much as the temperature of the water. The second reason for the difference in the temperature of the sand and the water is the depth to which light penetrates the two substances. All the radiant energy that reaches the sand is absorbed in the top few centimetres. Radiant energy penetrates much more deeply into water, so the energy is spread through the water and not concentrated at the surface. Our next step is to determine how these differences in temperature affect the air just above the land and the water.

 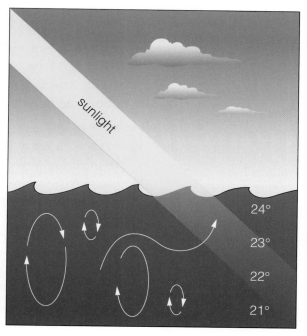

Figure 13.11 The only mechanism that heats the soil below the very top layer is conduction. Not only does light penetrate deeper into the water and deposit energy over many centimetres of depth, but any movement in the water will also mix the water and make the temperature more uniform.

Comparing the Properties of Soil and Water

The different responses of soil and water to radiant energy are responsible for many aspects of weather. In this investigation, you will observe and analyze the temperature changes of water and soil. You will also note the rate of change of their temperatures, when exposed to the same amount of radiant energy.

Problem

How does the interaction of solar energy and soil compare with the interaction of solar energy and water?

Safety Precautions

- Use thermal gloves when touching the lamp.
- Do not let the lamp or its cord make any contact with the water.

Apparatus

support stand
overhead light with clamp
metre stick
2 clear plastic boxes
4 thermometers
2 small wood blocks (about 1 cm × 1 cm × 5 cm)

Materials

water
dry, dark soil
masking tape

Skill

P O W E R

For tips on working in groups, turn to page 584.

Procedure

1 Assume that the soil and water will be exposed to the same amount of radiant energy. Formulate a hypothesis about the temperature change for soil compared with the temperature change for water. Base your hypothesis on what you have learned about the properties of water and on your own experiences. Include your ideas about the rate at which the temperature changes as well as the amount it changes.

2 Make a table like the one below for recording your data. Remember to give your table a title.

Time (min)	Temperature 1 cm water (°C)	Temperature 3 cm water (°C)	Temperature 1 cm soil (°C)	Temperature 3 cm soil (°C)
0				
3				
6				
9				
12				
15				
Lamp off				
18				
21				
24				
27				
30				

3 Fill one plastic box with water, 5 cm deep. Fill the other box with 5 cm of soil. Gently pack down the soil to remove most of the air.

4 Tape the small wooden blocks to the inside of the boxes, near the top. These blocks will hold the thermometers away from the sides of the boxes.

5 Insert and tape two thermometers in each box, as the student is doing in the photograph. The bulb of one thermometer should be just below the surface of the water or soil. The bulb of the second thermometer should be 3 cm below the surface of the water or soil. When inserting the thermometer into the soil, do not use pressure. Make a hole with a pencil, and put the thermometer in the hole. Then gently pat the soil so that it is in contact the bulb of the thermometer.

6 Attach the lamp to the support stand. Position the lamp so that it is no more than 30 cm from the soil and water. Ensure that both boxes receive the same amount of light.

7 Read and record the temperatures registered by all four thermometers.

8 Turn on the lamp. Read and record all four temperatures every 3 min for a total of 15 min.

9 Turn off the lamp. Read and record the temperatures every 3 min for a total of 15 min.

Analyze

1. In which substance, soil or water, is the temperature change greater near the top?

2. In which substance is the temperature change greater at a depth of 3 cm?

3. In which substance is the difference greater between the temperatures at the top and the temperatures at a depth of 3 cm?

4. In which substance is the rate of change of temperature greater? Was the rate of change the same for warming and for cooling?

Conclude and Apply

5. What would you conclude about the specific heat capacity of dry soil compared with the specific heat capacity of water?

6. Did your results support or contradict your hypothesis? Explain.

7. The water in a swimming pool often feels cooler than the surrounding air during the day, and warmer at night. Use your results to explain why this is the case.

8. Describe one feature of weather that you have noticed in your personal experiences and you can now explain, based on your results.

Heating the Air

You have just learned that solar radiation is the principle source of energy for heating land and water. Is the absorption of solar energy the predominate method of warming air? You now have the tools to find out. Use your knowledge of specific heat capacities to perform the following Science Inquiry Activity.

Science Inquiry ACTIVITY

Does Solar Energy Heat the Air?

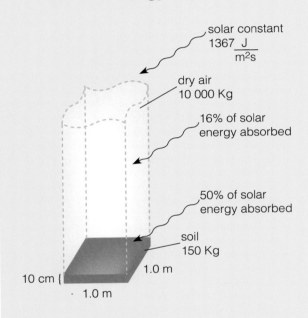

solar constant
$$1367 \frac{J}{m^2 s}$$

dry air
10 000 Kg

16% of solar
energy absorbed

50% of solar
energy absorbed

soil
150 Kg

10 cm {

1.0 m

1.0 m

Consider a column of dry air, with a cross section of 1.0 m², extending from sea level to the top of the atmosphere. Assume that an amount of solar energy, equivalent to the solar constant, reaches the top of this column. What are the changes in the temperatures of the air and the soil over a period of 1 h?

What You Need

pencil
paper
calculator

Skill
POWER

For tips on reviewing how to rearrange formulas, turn to page 611.

What to Do

1. Determine the total amount of solar energy that reaches the top of the column of air in a period of 1 h. Hint: The area of the top of the column is 1.0 m², and the solar constant is 1367 J/m²s. Thus 1367 J of energy are reaching the top of the column of air every second. Multiply 1367 J by the number of seconds in an hour.

2. Suppose that the air absorbs 16 percent of this energy as it passes through. Calculate the total amount of energy that is absorbed by the air.

3. Now suppose that the top 10 cm (approximately) of soil absorbs 50 percent of the solar energy. Calculate the total amount of energy that is absorbed by the soil.

4. Use the formula $Q = mc\Delta T$ to calculate the temperature changes of
   (a) the air
   (b) the soil
   Note: The masses of the soil and air are given in the figure. The specific heat capacity of dry air is $c = 1.0$ J/g °C. The specific heat capacity of soil varies depending on the type of soil. Use the approximate value of $c = 0.85$ J/g °C.

What Did You Discover?

Compare the temperature changes that you calculated for soil and air. Would you conclude that the absorption of solar energy is the primary source of energy for heating air? Explain why you would or would not.

You probably discovered that if the absorption of solar energy were the only source of energy for heating air, the air would be extremely cold. What heats the air?

At the beginning of this chapter, you read that radiation was the only way that solar energy could travel through empty space and reach Earth. After the land and water absorb the radiant energy, however, the other two mechanisms of energy transfer play a role in heating the air. First consider conduction. Energetic molecules in land or water collide with molecules in the air that are close to the surface. These collisions give the molecules in the air some of the energy. The temperature of this lowest level of air eventually comes close to the temperature of the land or water beneath it. Then convection steps in. As the lowest layer of air warms, it expands, becoming less dense. Recall, from your earlier studies of fluids, that less dense fluids rise and more dense fluids fall. So, as the warm air rises, cooler air descends and takes its place close to the ground.

Finally, you cannot rule out radiation as a mechanism of energy transfer to the air. You have discovered that all components of air are very inefficient at absorbing the short-wavelength solar radiation. Water vapour and carbon dioxide in the air, however, very effectively absorb the longer wavelength, or infrared, radiation emitted by Earth (review Figure 13.5). This absorption of long-wave radiation from Earth is the major source of thermal energy for the air close to the surface. Figure 13.12 summarizes the mechanisms for distributing solar energy. The differences between the mechanisms for the warming of land, water, and air, and their differing specific heat capacities, result in a variety of different temperatures for substances on and just above Earth's surface. What happens when these substances interact with each other? To find out, perform the following investigation.

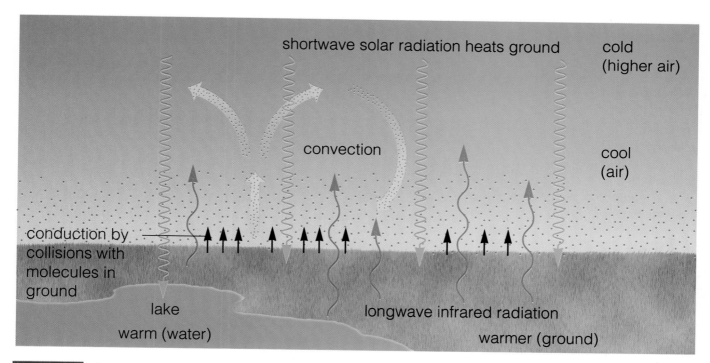

Figure 13.12 Short-wave solar radiation penetrates the atmosphere and is absorbed by the ground and water. Here the radiant energy is converted into thermal energy. The ground and water then transfer some thermal energy to the air by conduction. As well, some of Earth's thermal energy is converted into long-wave infrared radiation, which is absorbed by components of the air.

Blowing in the Wind

When a substance is moving, even air in the form of wind, it has kinetic energy. What is the source of the kinetic energy of air in wind? You have seen that substances can absorb solar radiation and convert it into thermal energy, the random motion of atoms and molecules. Wind, however, is not random but co-ordinated movement of air in a specific direction. How is thermal energy related to wind?

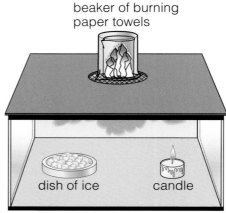

beaker of burning paper towels

dish of ice   candle

aquarium

Problem

How do the interactions between ground, water, and air result in wind?

Safety Precautions

- Handle matches carefully.
- Wear thermal gloves when handling the beakers with the burning paper.
- Keep loose clothing away from flames and long hair tied back.

Apparatus

aquarium
screened top for aquarium
100 mL beaker
1000 mL beaker
Petri dish
scissors

Materials

piece of cardboard that is larger than aquarium lid
ice
short, fat candle
matches
paper towels
tape

Procedure

1 Cut the cardboard so that it is just a little larger than the aquarium lid. In the centre of the cardboard, cut a hole that

is slightly larger than the 1000 mL beaker.

2 Put ice in the Petri dish. Place the Petri dish at one end of the aquarium.

3 Place the candle at the other end of the aquarium.

4 Light the candle.

5 Put the screened lid on the aquarium, and put the cardboard on top of the lid.

6 Fold up a small piece of paper towel, and put it in the 100 mL beaker. Place the beaker on the screened lid, in the centre of the hole in the cardboard.

7 Light the paper towel. Turn the 1000 mL beaker upside down, and place it over the beaker with the lighted paper towel.

8 For several minutes, observe and record what happens inside the aquarium.

Analyze

1. Describe the motion of the smoke in the aquarium.

2. Based on your previous knowledge about fluids, explain the effect that the ice has on the air near it.

3. Explain how the candle affects the air.

4. Based on the condition of the air near the ice and near the candle, explain the motion of the air.

Conclude and Apply

5. How does the motion of the air in the aquarium model wind?

6. Describe conditions in nature that are similar to the conditions in the aquarium.

Hot Air Goes Up

In your investigation, you demonstrated a very important principle of weather — the source of wind. Uneven heating of air creates wind. When air is heated, the molecules in the air move faster and collide with greater forces. Consequently, they push each other farther apart, making the air less dense. If cool air is located beside the warm air, the cool, dense air exerts pressure on the warm, less dense air, and pushes it upward, out of the way. This motion of air is wind.

Land and sea breezes provide an excellent example of wind. When the Sun is shining, solid ground is warmer than water. Therefore the air just above dry land is warmer than the air above water. Both regions are warmer than the air farther above the ground. The warm air over the land rises while the cooler air over the water moves in to replace it. As well, the cool air above then sinks down. Once again, this air is warmed by conduction. What happens to the warm air that rose? As the warm air rises, it expands and cools. As it cools, it becomes more dense. The overall result is the closed path of the convection current, as shown in Figure 13.13A.

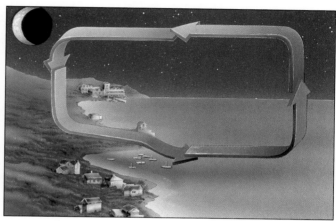

Figure 13.13 During the day, a sea breeze blows toward the land. At night, a land breeze flows out to sea.

At night, dry land cools faster than water, due to water's large specific heat capacity. Soon the air above the land and water take on their temperature characteristics. Since the land cools faster than the water, the air above the water is now warmer and less dense than the air above dry land. Therefore the path of the convection current is the opposite of the daytime current. Warmer air above the water is rising, drawing in the cooler air from the land. The result is the convection current shown in Figure 13.13B.

Regions of the Atmosphere

The mechanisms that you read about for heating the air and creating wind affect only for the first few kilometres above Earth's surface. Above this level, changes in the characteristics of the atmosphere are gradual. Although there are no distinctive lines between layers, scientists have named four general regions according to temperature profiles. These regions are illustrated in Figure 13.14.

The region of the atmosphere from Earth's surface up to about 10 km is named the **troposphere**. All of the interactions discussed above occur in this region.

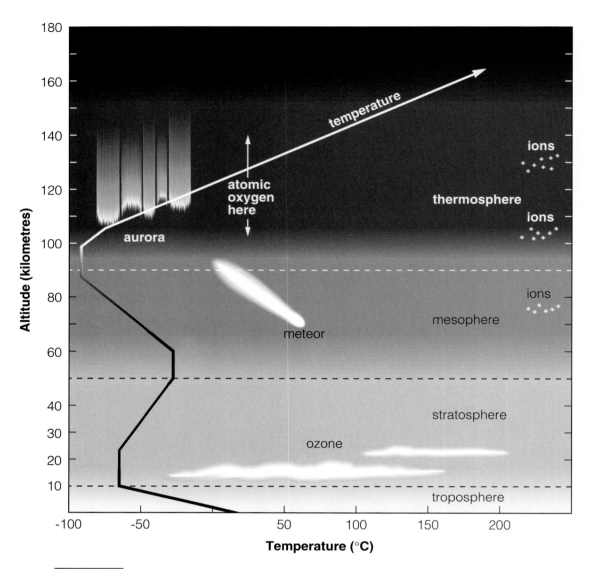

Figure 13.14 The four layers of the atmosphere are distinguished by their temperature profiles.

You could say that all weather occurs in the troposphere. As you know, temperatures at ground level vary a great deal. As the altitude increases, however, the temperature becomes more uniform and tends to decrease. At about 10 to 11 km, the temperature levels off at a chilly −57°C.

As the altitude increases, the temperature begins to rise once again. This region of rising temperature, which continues to about 50 km, is named the **stratosphere.** The reason for the temperature increase is the presence of ozone. Ozone molecules consist of three oxygen atoms (O_3), whereas common oxygen molecules have two atoms (O_2). Due to the chemical properties of ozone, it absorbs ultraviolet radiation from the Sun. This causes the temperature of the region to rise. If this ozone layer were not present, the amount of ultraviolet radiation that reached Earth's surface would be hazardous to living organisms. The ozone layer makes life on Earth possible.

Between 50 and 60 km above sea level, the temperature levels off at about −2°C, marking the top of the stratosphere. The next region, of decreasing temperature, is called the **mesosphere.** The top of the mesosphere extends to about 90 to 100 km, where the temperature levels off at a frigid −90°C to −100°C. Meteors

DidYouKnow?

Over the past several years, the ozone layer has been thinning due to the release of a class of chemicals called CFCs. These chemicals were commonly used as refrigerants until scientists discovered that when they escaped into the atmosphere, they stimulated the breakdown of ozone in the stratosphere. Although the use of CFCs has been drastically reduced, some still remain in the atmosphere. Since the ozone layer is thinner, people need to wear sunglasses and sunscreen to block the damaging ultraviolet light.

Word CONNECT

In your previous science sources, you may have seen several terms with the prefixes, "tropo," "strato," "meso," and "thermo." Look up the meaning of these prefixes. Explain why each one is appropriate for the layer of the atmosphere it denotes. Think of at least three other terms you have learned that have one of these prefixes.

from outer space often penetrate the atmosphere this far, but they burn up due to air friction before reaching the bottom of the mesosphere.

At an altitude of 100 km, the temperature begins to rise and becomes much higher than at any other level. Because of the high temperature, scientists call this region the **thermosphere**. What could cause transformations of radiant energy into thermal energy at these exceedingly high altitudes, where the air is extremely thin? Meteorologists discovered that oxygen molecules, absorbing very high energy ultraviolet light, account for most of the temperature increase. At an altitude of 150 km, the temperature reaches 180°C. At altitudes of 500 km, the temperature reaches 600°C. The extremely high temperatures are deceptive, however. Since there are so few atoms and molecules, collisions are rare. Objects passing through the thermosphere collide with so few high-energy particles that the result is not the same as it would be for more dense air. For example, a gas molecule might travel 500 km between collisions. The very small number of collisions means that the energy of the molecules is rarely passed from one object to another.

A layer of charged particles called the **ionosphere** lies within the thermosphere and upper mesosphere. The ionosphere is created when atoms and molecules in the atmosphere absorb high-energy ultraviolet radiation from the Sun. The absorbed energy causes electrons to be ejected from atoms, creating ions. The ionosphere has a direct effect on radio and satellite communications. As illustrated in Figure 13.15, the layer of ions bends, or reflects, the very long wavelength electromagnetic waves used in radio transmission. This bending allows you to receive radio transmissions in locations that are a great distance from a transmission tower. Due to this reflection of radio waves by the ionosphere, radio waves cannot be used for satellite transmissions. Microwaves, with wavelengths much shorter than radio waves, are unaffected by the ionosphere and therefore can penetrate this region, undisturbed. Consequently, any signals that are sent to or from satellites must be carried by microwaves.

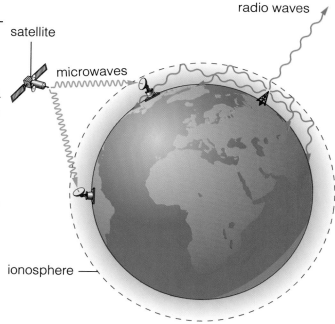

Figure 13.15 The ionosphere bends radio waves, making it possible to pick up signals at great distances from a radio transmitter. However, this bending of waves makes it impossible to use radio waves for satellite communication.

Solar Energy and Weather **443**

The thermosphere is the location of the magnificent display of the northern and southern lights called the **aurora.** This array of lights is created by clusters of charged particles with extremely high energy, coming mainly from the Sun. These particles, which are sometimes called solar wind, collide with gases in the atmosphere, causing atoms to become excited. As the atoms return to their stable ground state, they emit the excess energy in the form of light. The collisions occur mainly near the North and South Poles because Earth's magnetic field diverts incoming particles. As illustrated in Figure 13.16, only those particles directed toward the poles are likely to reach the atmosphere.

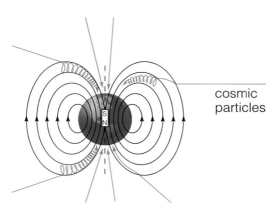

cosmic particles

Figure 13.16 Earth's magnetic field directs particles in the solar wind to the poles, where they excite oxygen and nitrogen molecules in the air. Excited oxygen molecules emit green light when they return to their ground state. Excited nitrogen molecules emit pink light, accounting for the variety of colours in the aurora.

Atmospheric Pressure

If all weather occurs in the troposphere, what effect do the upper layers have on conditions in the troposphere? Every layer of air exerts pressure on the layer below because every molecule in the air is pulled toward Earth by the gravitational force. Consequently, the lower layers are compressed by all of the layers above, as illustrated in Figure 13.17. We call this **atmospheric pressure.** Although pressures vary, scientists have chosen a standard for reference. Standard atmospheric pressure is 101 300 Pa — the atmospheric pressure in dry air at sea level when the temperature is 25°C.

Figure 13.17 As the altitude increases, the layer above is smaller. Therefore the atmospheric pressure is lower and the air is less dense.

The number 101 300 Pa sounds rather large. So why do we seem to be so unaffected by and unaware of it? One reason is that we are used to it. Also, as you may recall from your study of fluids, pressure is exerted in all directions. Atmosphere is not just pushing down on us, it is pushing equally all over our bodies. Another reason that we are unaware of the large pressure is that the atmosphere consists mainly of gases. We move through it and it moves around us. Figure 13.18 illustrates one way to develop a sense to how much pressure the atmosphere exerts on you. Figure 13.18 A, shows how air moves around your hand as you lift it. Try to imagine what it would be like if there were an invisible wall around your hand that went all the way to the top of the atmosphere. This wall would prevent the air from moving around your hand. If you were standing at sea level, and tried to lift a column of air the size of your hand, it would feel like you were lifting a 100 kg mass. How does the pressure change as you go to higher altitudes? To make the same observation on the top of Mt. Everest, you would only have to lift about 35 kg of mass. Atmospheric pressure decreases rapidly as the altitude increases because there is a smaller layer of air above to create pressure. Table 13.5 lists the atmospheric pressures at a variety of altitudes.

A When you raise your hand, air moves around it.

B If air did not flow around your hand, you would have to lift the entire column of air in order to lift your hand. Then you would realize that the atmosphere is exerting a very large pressure on you.

Figure 13.18 How much pressure?

As you know, close to Earth's surface, the air is heated different amounts by contact with the ground, radiation from the ground, and convection. These temperature differences cause small differences in pressure over limited regions. Therefore local atmospheric pressures vary above and below the standard atmospheric pressure.

Table 13.5 Atmospheric Pressure and Altitude

Altitude (km)	Atmospheric pressure (kPa)
0.0	101.3
1.0	88.5
2.0	77.3
3.0	67.6
4.0	59.0
5.0	51.6
7.5	36.8
10	26.2
15	13.3
20	6.8
25	3.5
50	0.1

Gases in the Atmosphere

How do the individual gases in the atmosphere affect the interaction of the atmosphere with radiant energy? As you have already read, oxygen in the thermosphere and ozone in the stratosphere absorb much of the ultraviolet radiation that enters the atmosphere, protecting us from high levels of this dangerous radiation. There is very little other absorption of incoming solar radiation by gases in the atmosphere. The atmosphere, however, efficiently absorbs the longer wavelength, re-radiation from Earth. The gases that are most responsible for the absorption of this long-wave infrared radiation are carbon dioxide and water vapour. As you know, the amount of water vapour varies a great deal from day to day and from place to place.

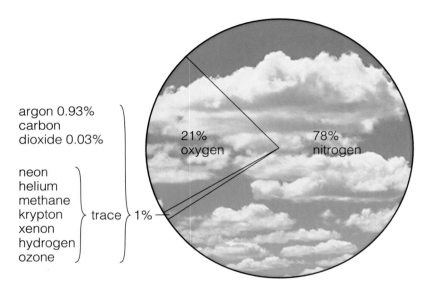

Figure 13.19 Only two gases, nitrogen and oxygen, make up 99 percent of the atmosphere. Water vapour is not included in the graph because of the large variation in amounts present.

In Unit 1, you learned that carbon dioxide is a greenhouse gas. Now you can understand why. Along with the other greenhouse gases — methane, dinitrogen oxide, and the chlorofluorocarbons (CFCs) — carbon dioxide traps infrared radiation from Earth and warms the atmosphere before the energy escapes out into space. Although carbon dioxide makes up only 0.03 percent (three ten-thousandths) of the gases in the atmosphere, its presence is critical to the average temperature of the troposphere. If there were no greenhouse gases at all, Earth's average temperature would be approximately 35°C lower than the current average. Since very few plants could grow in these conditions, life could not be sustained. Greenhouse gases are necessary.

Why, then, are scientists concerned about the greenhouse effect? The concentration of carbon dioxide in the atmosphere is critical. If there were too little, Earth would be too cold. If there were too much, however, Earth's temperatures would rise to a potentially dangerous extent. In Unit 1, you learned why carbon dioxide levels were rising and what some of the effects might be. Now consider how an increase in Earth's average temperatures might affect the weather. The following Think & Link Investigation will guide you to some possible answers.

Weather After Global Warming

Think About It

Meteorologists at Environment Canada have developed one of the most advanced computer models for forecasting weather. Data are entered into the computer and the model then provides a forecast for temperatures, atmospheric pressures, winds, humidity, and other properties of weather. The model can provide data other than basic forecasts. By entering imaginary data, the model can predict possible outcomes.

Meteorologists have used the program to predict the effects of doubling the concentration of carbon dioxide in the atmosphere. The computer model predicted an overall increase in world-wide average temperatures of 3.5°C. However, the temperature increases vary considerably from one region to another. The following diagrams show the projected temperature increases for the entire Earth in summer and in winter.

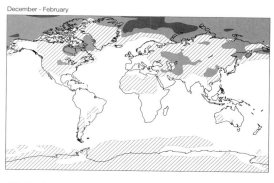

December - February

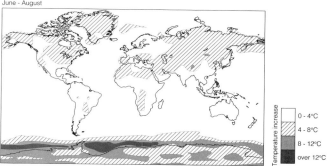

June - August

	Temperature increase
	0 - 4°C
	4 - 8°C
	8 - 12°C
	over 12°C

How might such temperature increases affect the weather throughout the world? Scientists have made a few predictions. See if you agree with them?

What to Do

1. Read the following predictions that various scientists have made.

   - Glaciers will retreat more rapidly.
   - The number and severity of thunderstorms, tornadoes, and hurricanes will increase.
   - Water levels in the Great Lakes will be reduced.
   - Ice caps will recede.
   - There will be a water shortage.
   - The average humidity will be lower.
   - Permafrost will begin to melt.

2. Within your group, discuss whether or not the projected temperature changes would or would not cause the predicted outcomes listed in step 1.

3. Choose three predictions to research. Assign different members of your group to research the individual predictions. Use library resources and the internet.

4. Discuss your research with the whole group. Decide whether your findings support of or contradict the three predictions you selected.

5. Present your findings and conclusions in the form of a poster.

Analyze

1. Make all of the posters available to the class as a whole. Read the posters prepared by other groups.

2. Compare the cases in which different groups chose the same prediction to evaluate. How similar or different were the findings and conclusions of different groups?

3. With the entire class, have a discussion about the probable effects of global warming on the weather in Canada with a special emphasis on the region where you live.

There's Something in the Air

You are an atmospheric chemist who has recently completed your masters degree. Below is a portion of your résumé, outlining your education and experience:

Education
- Masters of Science, Atmospheric Chemistry, York University, 1999
- Bachelor of Science, Combined Honours Chemistry and Earth and Atmospheric Science, York University, 1997, including courses in chemistry and meteorology, as well as atmospheric radiation and thermodynamics, synoptic meteorology, cloud physics, and numeric weather prediction
- Honours Secondary School diploma, Grantham Secondary School, 1993

Experience
- junior research assistant north of Churchill, Manitoba, summer 1996, assessing levels of pollution in ground water
- assistant to on-air meteorologist of television station CHNR, summer 1995
- junior developer, PhotoPlus photography store (part-time 1990–1993)
- winner of Science Fair 1992, provincial level, for project exploring the rate and intensity of combustion of various materials

Interests
- wilderness camping
- amateur photography and developing

On an employment web site, you have found the following two positions that you would like to apply for. To accompany your résumé and university transcripts, you need to write a covering letter to each potential employer. Keep in mind that you may want to highlight different information for each position.

Environmental consulting company has an opening within the Atmospheric Studies Group for a staff scientist to carry out air-quality studies. This full-time entry-level position requires a masters degree in environmental or atmospheric science, with course work in meteorology.

Atmospheric Chemist needed to work with government research scientists in the Arctic, measuring ozone levels and assessing atmospheric change. A masters degree is required. Some related experience would be an asset. Job requires a commitment to live in a remote location for a minimum of three years.

Check Your Understanding

1. Explain why the temperature of dry land increases faster during the day and decreases faster during the night than the temperature of the water in lakes, rivers, and oceans.

2. Explain the role of conduction in the heating of air.

3. Describe three mechanisms by which air is heated.

4. Name one important feature of each of the four layers of the atmosphere.

5. Why is it necessary to use microwaves to send signals to and from communication satellites.

6. What is the relationship between greenhouse gases and global warming?

CHAPTER at a glance

Now that you have completed this chapter, try to do the following. If you cannot, go back to the sections indicated.

List the three mechanisms of heat transfer, and explain why only one can be used to transfer solar energy to Earth. (13.1)

Describe the nature of solar energy as it travels to Earth. (13.1)

Make a diagram that shows the distribution of solar energy after it reaches the upper atmosphere. (13.1)

Explain how Earth maintains a relatively constant average temperature. (13.1)

Describe the three properties of water that help to moderate Earth's temperature. (13.2)

Explain the conditions that determine the amount of water vapour in the air. (13.2)

Make a diagram that shows the major processes in the water cycle. (13.2)

Describe the differences between the interaction of solar energy with water and with dry land. (13.3)

Explain, step by step, the cause of a sea breeze. (13.3)

Describe the ways in which all three mechanisms of heat transfer are involved in heating air. (13.3)

Make a table that describes the four layers of the atmosphere. Include temperature, causes of the temperature, altitude, and unique occurrences in each layer. (13.3)

Describe the fundamental cause of atmospheric pressure. (13.3)

Discuss the benefits and potentially harmful effects of greenhouse gases. (13.3)

Prepare Your Own Summary

Summarize this chapter by doing one of the following. Use a graphic organizer (such as a concept map), produce a poster, or write the summary to include the key chapter concepts. Here are a few ideas to use as a guide:
- What is the form of solar radiation as it travels through space to Earth?
- What influences the absorption or reflection of radiant energy?
- What effect does water's high specific heat capacity have on the temperature of the water in lakes, rivers, and oceans?
- How does the evaporation of liquid water help to cool the water?
- How is energy used in the water cycle? What is the source of this energy?
- What happens when the air above the land heats more than the air above a nearby ocean?
- What is the ionosphere?
- What condition does standard atmospheric pressure describe?

CHAPTER 13 Review

Reviewing Key Terms

If you need to review, the section numbers show you where these terms were introduced.

1. Use the list of key terms at the beginning of the chapter to fill in the blanks in the following sentences.
   - **(a)** The amount of energy that is required to convert one gram of liquid water to the gaseous state is called the ____________________. (13.2)
   - **(b)** When there is as much water vapour in the air as it can hold, the air is ____________________. (13.2)
   - **(c)** The land warms the air close to the land by ____________________. (13.3)
   - **(d)** All weather happens in the ____________________. (13.3)
   - **(e)** The ______________ bends radio waves. (13.3)
   - **(e)** If there were no ____________________, the temperature of Earth would probably be too cold to support life. (13.3)
2. In your notebook, write a sentence that correctly uses each of the following terms.
   - **(a)** radiation (13.1)
   - **(b)** condensation nuclei (13.2)
   - **(c)** relative humidity (13.2)
   - **(d)** atmospheric pressure (13.3)
   - **(e)** global warming (13.3)

Understanding Key Concepts

Section numbers are provided if you need to review.

3. How can energy travel through empty space? (13.1)
4. Compare the radiation emitted by the Sun with the radiation emitted by Earth. How are they similar, and how are they different? (13.1)
5. Since Earth continually absorbs solar energy, why does it not keep getting warmer? (13.1)
6. How do the interactions differ when solar energy reaches the surfaces of snow, ice, and liquid water? (13.2)
7. Water has a relatively large heat of fusion. How does this property of water affect the temperature of an area in which a lake freezes in the winter and thaws in the spring? (13.2)
8. Describe the conditions that cause rain or snow to fall. (13.2)

9. Describe 4 different energy transformations that are taking place in this picture. (13.2)
10. Describe the conditions that cause a sea breeze. (13.3)
11. Explain two reasons why the temperature increase for water is quite different from the temperature increase for soil when they are exposed to the same amount of solar radiation. (13.3)
12. Name the two regions of the atmosphere in which the temperature rises with an increase in altitude. Explain what causes the warming in each region. (13.3)
13. List some potential causes of global warming. (13.3)

Developing Skills

14. Use the data in Table 13.5 to make a line graph or a bar graph of atmospheric pressure versus altitude.
15. Trace the path of a unit of solar energy from the time it enters the atmosphere until the time it leaves the atmosphere. Assume that it is absorbed and not reflected directly back into space. Include at least three different energy transformations that it might undergo. Describe its effect on the substance that absorbs it.

16. Design and, if possible, carry out an experiment to measure the specific heat capacity of granite, limestone, or some other type of rock. Hint: You know the specific heat capacity of water, so you can measure its temperature change and calculate the heat transfer when water absorbs heat. Use the water to change the temperature of another substance, such as a rock.

Problem Solving/Applying

17. How much heat is required to increase the temperature of 750 g of seawater by 30°C?

18. A technique called "cloud seeding" is sometimes used to try to cause rain. Airplanes spray silver iodide crystals into clouds. Why do you think this might cause rain?

19. How much energy is required to convert 3.2 g of liquid hexane into a gas? If the same amount of energy was used to evaporate liquid water, what amount of liquid water would be converted to its gaseous form?

20. How much energy is required to melt 78 g of solid methanol?

21. Explain two reasons why putting ice in a soft drink makes it cool. Use correct technical terms.

22. Assume that the temperature outside is -22°C and the relative humidity is 90%. If the temperature in the house is 18°C, what is the relative humidity in the house?

23. Under normal conditions, air is about 1°C cooler for every 100 m increase in altitude. Assume that the outside air has a temperature of 22°C and you measured the dew point to be 14°C. How high would you expect clouds to be forming?

Critical Thinking

24. When any fossil fuel is burned to produce heat or electricity, or to run a vehicle, carbon dioxide is a natural product. Think of a way to slow the rise of carbon dioxide concentrations in the atmosphere.

25. Why do you think that there are almost no clouds in the stratosphere?

26. The relative amounts of different gases are much the same throughout the atmosphere. That is, oxygen makes up 21% of the gases at all altitudes. Why, then, do people find it hard to breathe at high altitudes?

Pause& Reflect

1. Go back to the beginning of the chapter, on page 420, and check your original answers to the Opening Ideas questions. How has your thinking changed? How would you answer those questions now that you have investigated the topics in this chapter?

2. By answering the Opening Ideas questions, you probably uncovered some misconceptions you had about solar radiation and the way that it affects Earth. Think of one more misconception you had before studying this chapter.

3. In your Science Log, write a paragraph about the most surprising concept you learned in this chapter.

14 Air, Water, and Solar

- What causes the temperature differences between the winter and the summer?

- Why do storms always seem to come from the west?

- What is El Niño?

Science
Log

In your *Science Log*, write answers to the questions above based on your current knowledge about weather. Then write some other questions about general weather patterns that you would like answered. While you study this chapter, look for the answers to your questions. Also check to see if your answers to the Opening Ideas questions are correct.

If you live in Canada, you have most likely been caught in a blizzard. Hopefully you have never been caught in one as severe as this blizzard in April of 1997 in Manitoba. This Winnipeg man is trying to dig his car out of a one metre snow drift.

Some people who have never lived in Canada believe that it is cold and snowy all the time. You know, however, that summers here can be very mild and beautiful. In fact, the weather can become excessively warm. Extreme heat and lack of rain sometimes cause a drought. The photograph above shows conditions near Old Wives Lake in Saskatchewan in 1958.

Our weather is extremely variable. For example, in one small part of Ontario, near Lake Superior, temperatures have been reported as low as −58.3°C and as high as 42.2°C. What causes these extreme variations in temperature? Are weather conditions as variable in all parts of the world as they are here? In this chapter, you will learn how the shape, movement, and structure of Earth create seasons and influence weather patterns. You will see how Canada's location in North America determines its climate.

Energy

What's Your Angle?

How does the angle of the Sun affect the amount of solar energy that reaches each square metre of Earth's surface area?

What You Need

flashlight with a strong, narrow beam
black construction paper
scissors
tape
ruler
protractor
white paper
pencil

Key Concepts

In this chapter, you will discover

- how Earth's spherical shape affects temperature and wind patterns
- why the tilt of Earth's axis causes seasons
- how Earth's rotational motion affects wind and water currents
- how the continents influence ocean currents
- how the continents and oceans affect the air above them

Key Skills

In this chapter, you will

- determine lengths of days and seasons for a chosen location
- predict general wind patterns
- determine the cause of water currents

Key Terms

- longitude
- latitude
- Arctic Circle
- Tropic of Cancer
- Tropic of Capricorn
- Antarctic Circle
- polar zone
- temperate zone
- tropical zone
- Coriolis effect
- prevailing westerlies
- jet stream
- ocean currents
- gyres
- upwelling
- El Niño
- air mass

Starting Point ACTIVITY

What to Do

1. Roll a piece of black paper into a tube and attach it to the flashlight.

2. In another piece of black paper, cut a square that is 1.5 cm on each side. Attach the paper to the end of the tube.

3. Point the flashlight directly at a piece of white paper, with the end of the tube about 5 cm from the paper. Trace the lighted square on the paper.

4. Tilt the flashlight so that it makes angles of 30°, 45°, 60°, and 80° from the vertical, as shown in the diagram. Trace the lighted spot for each angle on the paper.

5. Measure the dimensions of each lighted spot, and calculate the area. Then calculate the ratio of the first area to each of the other areas.

What Did You Discover?

1. One square metre of Earth's surface absorbs 685 J of energy every second when the Sun is directly overhead. How much does one square metre absorb when the Sun is at angles of 30°, 45°, 60°, and 80° from the vertical? Hint: Multiply 685 J by the ratios that you calculated in step 5.

2. Write a paragraph describing how the angle of the Sun affects the amount of energy absorbed per square metre of Earth's surface.

14.1 Solar Energy and a Spherical Earth

Figure 14.1 Earth is constantly in motion. Although our senses do not detect this motion, or Earth's shape, these factors have a tremendous influence on our weather and climate.

In Chapter 13, you learned about interactions between solar radiation and Earth's atmosphere, water, and dry land. You did not learn about the effects of any properties of Earth itself. The Sun, however, shines on a spherical, rotating, orbiting Earth. These properties determine the amount of solar radiation that different regions of Earth absorb.

Before reading about the effects of Earth's properties, study Figure 14.2 to learn two terms: **longitude** and **latitude**. Scientists use these terms to describe specific locations on Earth's surface.

DidYou**Know**?

The term "longitude" was chosen because the lines are all the same length and longer than any line of latitude. Even the equator is shorter because Earth is not a perfect sphere. Instead it is pear-shaped.

A Latitude is a measure of the distance north or south from the equator. Latitude is not measured in kilometres but in degrees of the angle shown here. The lines that form the angle start at Earth's centre. One line goes to the equator and the other line goes to the desired location.

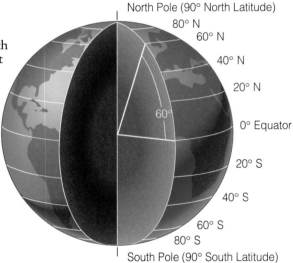

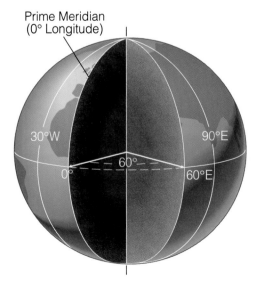

B Longitude is a measure of the distance east or west from a reference line called the *prime meridian*. The prime meridian runs from the North Pole to the South Pole, and it passes through Greenwich, England. To determine the longitude of a location, draw another line from the North Pole to the South Pole so that it passes through the location. The measure of the angle that is made by lines from the centre of Earth to the prime meridian, and to the line through the location, is the longitude of the location.

Figure 14.2 You can specify any point on Earth by its latitude and longitude.

Hot and Cold

How does the spherical shape of Earth influence the climate of different regions? To answer this question, consider what you learned in the Starting Point Activity. As shown in Figure 14.3, a beam of sunlight that strikes the equator is perpendicular to Earth's surface. Consequently Earth's surface absorbs the maximum amount of energy from the Sun at this location. What happens when an identical beam of sunlight reaches a region that is located at a latitude of 45°? The energy is spread over an area that is nearly one-and-a-half times as large as the area on the equator. Therefore each square metre of ground or water absorbs only about two thirds as much energy as it would absorb if it were located on the equator. Near the poles, another identical beam of sunlight is spread over a much larger area. As a result, Earth's surface near the poles heats up much less than it does at the equator.

If the conditions shown in Figure 14.3 never changed, temperatures throughout the world would be much the same at all times during the year. You know, however, that average temperatures change with the seasons. What is missing in the diagram?

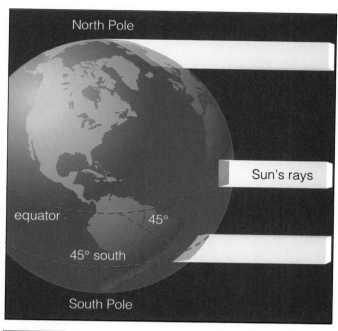

Figure 14.3 How does this diagram resemble the diagrams you drew in the Starting Point Activity?

The Four Seasons

To understand why seasons change, consider Earth's orbit around the Sun and Earth's orientation in this orbit. Figure 14.4 shows that Earth is spinning or rotating on its axis (an imaginary line from the North Pole to the South Pole) while orbiting around the Sun. The axis of rotation is tilted with respect to the plane of the orbit. Imagine a line going through the centre of Earth, perpendicular to the orbital plane. The angle between the axis of rotation and this perpendicular line is $23\frac{1}{2}°$. When Earth is oriented as it is in Figure 14.4, the Sun's rays that strike Earth perpendicular to the surface are not hitting the equator but are, instead, hitting Earth's surface $23\frac{1}{2}°$ north of the equator. Thus, in this orientation, the Northern Hemisphere receives more direct sunlight than the Southern Hemisphere. Therefore it is summer in the Northern Hemisphere.

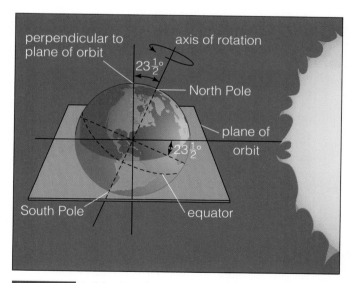

Figure 14.4 In this orientation, Earth's surface $23\frac{1}{2}°$ north of the equator absorbs the maximum amount of solar energy. Therefore it has the highest average temperatures.

Pause&
Reflect

Study Figure 14.4. Picture, in your mind, the rotation of Earth around its axis. Convince yourself that, as Earth turns, the direct rays of the Sun will always be perpendicular to the surface at a point $23\frac{1}{2}°$ north of the equator.

To understand how the seasons change, analyze Figure 14.5. Earth's tilt on the left is the same as it is in Figure 14.4, causing summer in the Northern Hemisphere. As Earth progresses around the Sun, the angle between the axis of rotation and the orbital plane stays the same. When Earth moves counterclockwise, as shown in Figure 14.5, summer changes into fall in the Northern Hemisphere. The Sun's rays strike the equator perpendicular to Earth's surface, so the amount of sunlight that reaches the two hemispheres is the same. Three months later, when Earth is at the right end of its orbit, its tilt causes the Sun's rays to strike perpendicular to its surface south of the equator. This causes summer in the Southern Hemisphere and winter in the Northern Hemisphere. Finally, at the top of the diagram, the most intense sunlight is, once again, at the equator. Thus the two hemispheres are receiving the same amount of sunlight. Spring has come to the Northern Hemisphere.

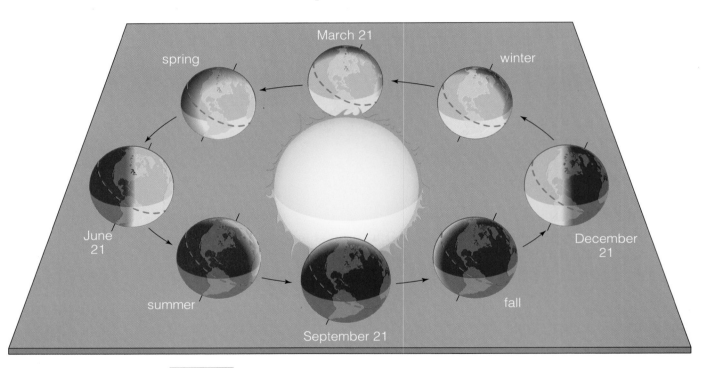

Figure 14.5 When it is summer in the Northern Hemisphere, it is winter in the Southern Hemisphere. The labels represent conditions in the Northern Hemisphere.

Day and Night

When Earth makes one complete revolution around the Sun, it rotates on its axis 365 times. This is just another way of saying that there are 365 days in a year. How does the tilt of Earth's axis affect day and night? How do the seasons affect the length of the days? To answer these questions, complete the following investigation.

Skill
P O W E R

To review how models can help convey scientific concepts, turn to page 606.

Hours of Daylight

The Sun's rays strike the Northern Hemisphere at a steeper angle in the winter than they do in the summer, and the days are shorter in winter. Both effects are caused by the position and tilt of Earth as it revolves around the Sun.

Problem

How short is the shortest day of the year in the community where you live? How long is the longest day?

Apparatus

globe
strong flashlight with a good
    parabolic reflector
protractor
metre stick
holder to support the flashlight (lab
    jack, or support stand and clamp)

Materials

removable adhesive dots
masking tape

Procedure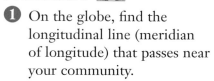

1. On the globe, find the longitudinal line (meridian of longitude) that passes near your community.

2. Use adhesive dots, or very small pieces of masking tape, to label the following points on the line you identified in step 1.
   (a) 60°N latitude
   (b) your community
   (c) 30°N latitude
   (d) equator
   (e) 30°S latitude
   (f) 60°S latitude
   (g) North Pole
   (h) South Pole

3. Assign one dot to each person in your group, to record information about the location represented by this dot when you start to take data. If your group is large enough, have more than one person record information about each dot.

4. Earth rotates 360° in 24 h. Determine the number of degrees it rotates in 1 h.

5. As a group, decide on a method to measure the distance that the globe must be turned to represent the passing of 1 h (the number of degrees you determined in step 4).

6. Put the globe on a table, and set up the flashlight about 2 or 3 m away. Position the flashlight so that it shines directly on the centre of the globe. Position the globe so that the top of the axis of rotation is directed away from the flashlight.

CONTINUED ▶

7 Rotate the globe so that the "Sun" (flashlight) shines directly on the International Date Line (180°W or E longitude). The prime meridian (0° longitude) should be in the centre of the dark area. It is now midnight in Greenwich, England. Make the room very dark to have a good contrast between light and dark regions on the globe. (Scientists use the time in Greenwich, England, as a reference time. This time is sometimes called "Greenwich Mean Time.")

8 Record information about your dot. Write down the reference time (midnight), and state whether your dot is in daylight, dark, dawn, or dusk. (Hint: You will be turning the globe counterclockwise when looking at the North Pole. If your dot is in a shadow but about to move into light, it is dawn.)

9 Tape a small strip of masking tape (about 2 mm wide) on the exact top and bottom of the globe. These are the locations that are just between darkness and light.

10 Estimate the point at the very centre of the globe, where the "sunlight" is striking perpendicular to the surface of the globe. Place a small strip of masking tape at this point.

11 Rotate the globe the equivalent of 1 h (the number of degrees you determined in

step 4) so that it is 1:00 a.m. Greenwich Mean Time. Write down the reference time, and state whether your dot is in daylight, dark, dawn, or dusk.

12 Repeat steps 8, 9 and 10.

13 Continue to turn the globe the equivalent of 1 h, until you have completed one full "day." Record the data for each position, and tape strips of masking tape as directed in steps 8, 9, and 10.

14 Re-orient the globe so that the axis of rotation is perpendicular to the incoming "sunlight." Repeat steps 6 through 12, but do not tape the strips of masking tape to the top, centre, or bottom of the globe.

15 Re-orient the globe so that the top of the axis of rotation is slanting directly toward the "Sun." Repeat steps 6 to 12, including steps 9 and 10 (taping the strips of masking tape).

Analyze

1. Make 3 tables (one for each orientation of the globe) with the following headings: "Location (longitude and latitude) of dot," "Reference time," and "Condition at dot (dark, dawn, or dusk)."

2. Put all of the data that your group collected in the tables. Give each table a title. Each member of your group should make their own copy of the tables.

3. Decide what season of the year, in the Northern Hemisphere, is simulated by each orientation of the globe. (Each orientation represents the first day of a season.) For each orientation, determine the day length at each location represented by a dot. Also record the latitude of each location (dot).

4. Use the values you determined in question 2 to plot three graphs, one for each orientation of the globe. Put "Day length" on the vertical axis and "Latitude" on the horizontal axis. For units on the horizontal axis, start with 90°N, go down to 0° for the equator, and then continue to 90°S. Plot a point for each location (dot) on the globe. Name each graph "First Day of ▬▬▬," and fill in the season(s).

Conclude and Apply

5. Which regions on Earth have the greatest extremes in day length? Explain.

6. Do the regions that have the longest day also have the warmest summers? Explain why or why not.

7. Which regions have the least variation in day length? Describe the climate in these regions.

8. Which regions do you think have the greatest temperature differences between winter and summer? Explain your reasons for your choices.

9. What are the extremes in day length, throughout the year, in your community?

10. The first day of summer is called the summer solstice. What is unique about this day?

11. The first day of winter is called the winter solstice. What is unique about this day?

12. The first day of spring is called the vernal equinox, and the first day of fall is called the autumnal equinox. What is unique about these two days?

13. The photograph below was taken by exposing the same film approximately once every hour for most of a day. At what location and at what time of year to you think the photograph was taken? Explain what is happening in the photograph.

14. The strips of masking tape that you taped at the top, centre, and bottom of the globe form circles. These circles create five regions, or zones, of the globe. Describe the characteristics of day length and angle of the Sun that make each zone different from the other zones.

Extend Your Knowledge

15. Imagine that Earth's axis of rotation lies in the orbital plane and remains in the same orientation as Earth revolves around the Sun. Describe how this orientation of Earth's axis would affect day length at several of the locations that you investigated.

Look up the meaning of the terms "solstice," "equinox," and "vernal" in a dictionary or on the Internet. Explain why these terms are appropriate for the days they describe.

Circles and Zones

In Conduct an Investigation 14-A, you created lines that encircled the globe. From north to south, these lines are named the **Arctic Circle, Tropic of Cancer, Tropic of Capricorn,** and **Antarctic Circle.** The regions that are defined by these lines are called "zones." They are named according to their general **climates:** their average weather conditions over many years. Figure 14.6 summarizes the climates in the **polar, temperate,** and **tropical zones.** Compare the information in the captions with your answer to Conclude and Apply question 13 in the investigation.

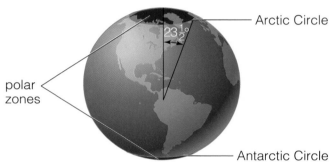

A The polar zones receive 24 h of darkness during parts of the winter and 24 h of sunlight during parts of the summer. The 24 h of sunlight, however, do not cause significant warming. This is because the Sun's rays make such a small angle with Earth's surface that the energy is spread over a very large area.

B The Sun's rays are never perpendicular to Earth's surface in the temperate zones. The temperature and weather conditions are quite variable. There is usually a significant difference in the weather during the summer and the winter.

C The Sun's rays are perpendicular to Earth's surface at some location in the tropical zone throughout the entire year. Therefore the average temperatures in this zone are generally warmer than those in the other zones.

Figure 14.6 Life in the different climate zones presents some very different challenges.

Check Your Understanding

1. How does the spherical shape of Earth influence the amount of solar radiation that is absorbed by different regions on Earth?

2. Describe the position of Earth with respect to the Sun when it is winter in the Northern Hemisphere.

3. **Apply** Name two different reasons why Canada is colder in the winter than in the summer.

4. What condition determines the location of the line called the Tropic of Cancer?

5. **Thinking Critically** Certain places on Earth are sometimes called "the land of the midnight Sun." Where are these places, and how do they earn this name?

14.2 Worldwide Wind Currents

Figure 14.7 The meteorologist has studied many, detailed weather maps and data to create a forecast. The report that you see on television is a condensed summary of this forecast that is easy to understand.

If you watched weather forecasts on television in British Columbia, Manitoba, and Nova Scotia, you would probably notice at least one thing in common. The forecaster would say that a weather system was coming from the west. Why do weather systems generally move from west to east in Canada? Do weather systems move from west to east in all parts of the world?

Wind Patterns on a Spherical Earth

In Chapter 13, you discovered that uneven warming and cooling of Earth's surface causes the air above it to have different temperatures. When air warms, it expands and becomes less dense. Cool air is more dense than warm air and therefore exerts more pressure on the surroundings. Since fluids always flow from a region of higher pressure to a region of lower pressure, cool air flows toward and under warm air, pushing it up and away.

In section 14.1, you learned that the spherical shape of Earth causes Earth's surface to be heated more near the equator than near the poles. These patterns of high and low temperatures initiate worldwide movements of air. Examine Figure 14.8 to see how global wind patterns begin. These are the patterns that would prevail if Earth were not rotating on its axis.

Earth's surface near the equator becomes warmer, on average, than at all other latitudes. There the air that is close to Earth's surface warms to nearly the same temperature as the land or water. As the air warms, it expands, becomes less dense, and begins to rise. Cooler air moves in below. The very cold air at the poles is quite dense. Therefore it moves along Earth's surface toward the warmer regions, pushing the air ahead of it. If Earth were a small sphere, the patterns shown in Figure 14.8A would probably predominate. However, when air rises upward from the equator and starts its northward or southward it cools. By the time the air reaches

A If Earth were a small sphere, and global movements of air followed the same pattern that sea and land breezes do, the wind pattern shown here would occur.

Figure 14.8 If Earth did not rotate, the prevailing wind patterns would be to the North or South.

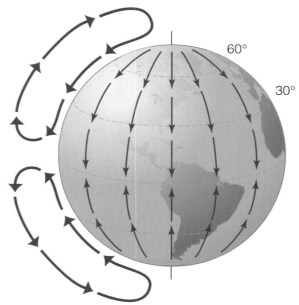

north or south latitudes of about 30°, it has cooled so much and become so dense that it begins to drop back to Earth's surface again. When it reaches the surface, some goes back toward the equator and some moves toward the poles. At the same time, cold air is flowing from the poles toward the equator. By the time this air reaches a latitude of about 60°, it has warmed enough to begin to rise. The overall result is the three closed patterns of air movement that you see in Figure 14.8B. If the shape of Earth and the excess heating at the equator, compared with the poles, were the only factors that determined air movement, the arrows on the globe would show the patterns of movement. Earth's rotation, however, is another factor influencing air movement.

Wind Patterns on a Rotating Earth

If the atmosphere were standing still while Earth was rotating underneath it, you would constantly feel a strong wind moving at about 300 m/s. The fact that you do not feel this wind indicates that the atmosphere is moving with Earth. So, aside from local winds, each molecule of air is moving at essentially the same speed as the point on Earth beneath it. Different points on Earth's surface are moving at quite different speeds, however. You can visualize these different speeds by examining Figure 14.9. Lines A and B represent the same longitudinal line at two different times. Every point on line A moves to line B in about 6 h. You can see that a point on the equator moves farther and therefore faster than a point at 30°N latitude. It moves much farther and faster than a point at 60°N latitude. How does this rotational motion affect the northerly or southerly movement of air caused by convection?

When air begins to move north or south due to convection, it continues to move east at the same speed that it was moving before. Figure 14.10 shows the resulting motion of air when these two different movements occur at the same time.

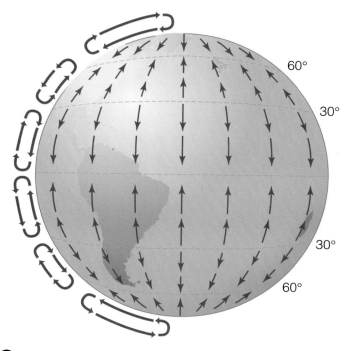

B Earth is a very large sphere, so the winds would have a long way to travel if they followed the pattern shown in diagram A. As air travels north or south, its temperature and density change. Upper air drops and lower air rises before the pattern shown in diagram A is complete. The result is the three closed patterns shown here.

DidYouKnow?

If you live in the southern part of Canada, you and the air around you are moving with a speed of about 300 m/s due to Earth's rotation.

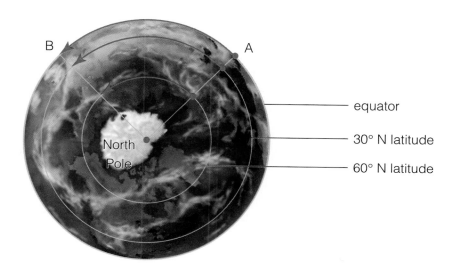

equator

30° N latitude

60° N latitude

Figure 14.9 The three arrows represent the distance that three different points on Earth's surface move in 6 h.

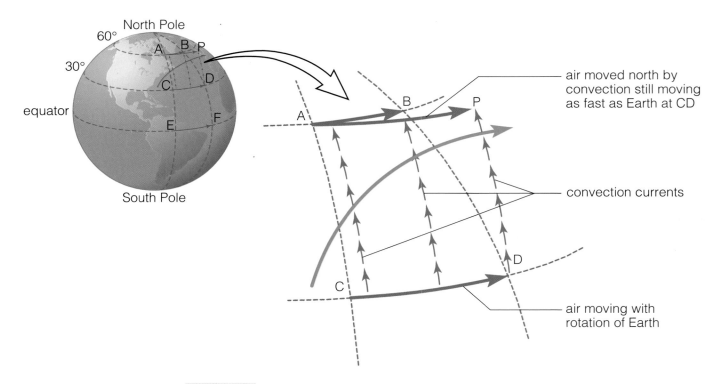

Figure 14.10 The combination of movements, due to convection and Earth's rotation, causes air between 30°N and 60°N to move in a westerly direction: that is, from west to east.

The two lines of longitude show the locations of points on Earth's surface, roughly 2 h apart. Examine the air in the enlarged part of the diagram. The air at point C is moving with Earth, so it should reach point D in 2 h. The air above point C never reaches point D, however, because convection currents carry it northward. Since the air is still travelling east at the same speed that point C on Earth's surface is travelling, the air goes to point P. During the same period of time, point A on Earth's surface reaches point B. The air at point P is moving faster than the ground beneath it. This movement of air is felt as a wind blowing from the west to the east. The red arrow shows the combined effect when convection and rotation act on the air at the same time. The influence of Earth's rotation on air, or on any object moving on Earth's surface, is called the **Coriolis effect.**

In the central part of the Northern Hemisphere, including most of Canada and the United States, the Coriolis effect causes winds to blow from west to east. These winds, called the **prevailing westerlies,** are the reason why weather systems in Canada generally move out of the west and toward the east. Notice that the direction used to describe a wind is the direction *from* which it is blowing. Do all of the prevailing winds throughout the world blow from west to east? Try the next investigation to find out.

DidYou**Know**?

The Coriolis Effect is named after the French mathematician Gustave Gaspard de Coriolis (1792–1843). Coriolis developed the mathematical description of motion on a rotating sphere (Earth). He also proposed the terms "work" and "kinetic energy" as they are currently used in physical science.

Determining the Direction of Prevailing Winds

Think About It

By studying Figure 14.10, you discovered that the Coriolis effect caused westerly winds to prevail between 30°N latitude and 60°N latitude. In this investigation, you will determine the direction of the winds at other latitudes. First, however, predict the direction of the prevailing winds in each region of Earth separated by the equator and the 30° and 60° lines of latitude.

What to Do

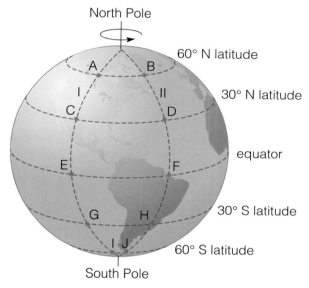

North Pole

60° N latitude

30° N latitude

equator

30° S latitude

60° S latitude

South Pole

1 Study the diagram. Notice that the two lines of longitude are labeled I and II. These lines represent the distance that a longitudinal line would move in roughly 2 h. You will use the diagram to determine the direction of the prevailing winds at different latitudes.

2 Obtain an enlarged copy of section CDEF on the diagram. (Your teacher may give you a copy or may ask you to make your own. Be sure to draw the section to scale if you make your own copy.)

3 Refer to Figure 14.8B to determine the direction that convection currents move in the region between the equator and 30°N latitude. Sketch short "convection" arrows on your copy of section CDEF to show this direction.

4 Draw two more arrows, just above line EF and just below line CD.

5 Look at the two arrows that you drew in step 4. Select the arrow that is at the tail of the convection arrows, similar to line CD in Figure 14.9. Imagine that you are moving this arrow along the direction of the convection arrows. Keeping the tail of the arrow on line 1, continue moving until it reaches the second arrow that you drew. Draw another arrow here to represent the "moved" arrow. (The moved arrow is similar to arrow AP in Figure 14.9.) Label the tip of the moved arrow "P."

6 Draw a horizontal arrow *from* longitudinal line II *to* point P. Label this arrow "prevailing winds."

7 Obtain an enlarged copy of the section from AB to the North Pole. Repeat steps 3 through 6.

8 Obtain an enlarged copy of section EFGH. Repeat steps 3 through 6.

Analyze

1. For each section of the diagram, explain why the last arrow you drew is labelled "prevailing winds."

2. Predict the direction of the prevailing winds for section GHIJ and the section from IJ to the South Pole.

3. Compare the results of the Coriolis effect in each section you drew and with Figure 14.10. Examine the diagrams, starting at the tails of the arrows that indicate the direction of the convection currents. Then turn in the direction of the prevailing winds. Do the winds always turn left or right, or are they different in each section?

Conclude and Apply

4. Write a concluding statement about the Coriolis effect and prevailing wind patterns.

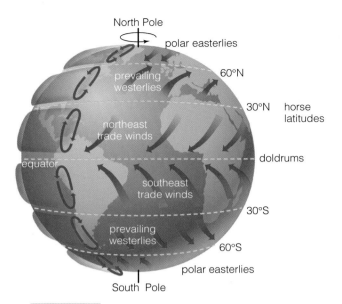

Figure 14.11 If the shape and rotation of Earth were the only factors that affected winds, then winds would continuously blow in the directions shown by the arrows.

Compare your results in Think & Link Investigation 14-B with Figure 14.11. Did you conclude that the Coriolis effect causes winds to veer to the right in the Northern Hemisphere, as shown in Figure 14.11? In the Southern Hemisphere, winds curve to the left. These changes in direction occur regardless of the original direction of the wind. Coriolis used the laws of physics to derive his mathematical equations, which give the results that you found using diagrams.

Jet Streams

On November 4, 1944, 94 B-29 Superfortress bombers took off for a mission over the Pacific. The airplanes climbed to an altitude of nearly 10 km. When the pilots saw the prearranged landmark, they turned east. Suddenly they all discovered that they were flying at speeds of approximately 750 km/h with respect to their targets on the ground. The B-29 is not a jet. Its top speed is supposed to be about 600 km/h. How could the planes be flying 150 km/h faster than their top speed?

When the pilots made their final turn, the planes were caught in a wind that carried them along at speeds higher than the planes could normally fly. This wind is now called a **jet stream.** The speed of the B-29s caused the mission to fail, but it led to detailed studies of this important weather phenomenon.

Jet streams are ribbons of extremely fast moving air near the top of the troposphere. They are caused by contact between cold and warm air. Therefore they are found at the boundaries between the polar and temperate zones and between the temperate and tropical zones. The polar jet stream, which affects Canada's weather, forms at the junction of the prevailing westerlies and polar easterlies. When the prevailing westerlies are far enough north, they encounter the cooler polar easterlies. The cooler, denser air pushes beneath the warmer westerlies and forces them upward. As the air rises, it encounters fewer barriers, such as hills or mountains. With nothing to hinder it, the air picks up speed. The combination of convection and the Coriolis effect intensifies the speed of the air and eventually creates a jet stream.

Figure 14.12 B-29 aircraft are capable of flying at high altitudes. The pilots in World War II flew high enough to learn about jet streams by experiencing them.

Figure 14.13 You cannot see jet streams, but sometimes they cause water to condense, forming clouds that reveal their position.

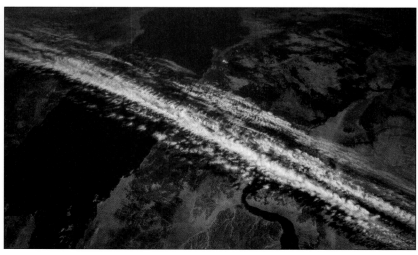

Wind speeds in a jet stream vary from 100 km/h to 300 km/h. Jet streams are thousands of kilometres long, and they can be a few hundred kilometres wide. They are usually two or three kilometres thick. Jet streams are not perfect circles around Earth. They continually curve and meander to the north and south, as shown in Figure 14.14. In general, the weather north of a jet stream is cold while the weather south of the jet stream is warmer.

The wind patterns in Figure 14.11 occur in the spring and fall. Thus, the jet stream forms near 60°N latitude. What happens to jet streams when the seasons change? A look at Figure 14.15 will help you answer this question. Remember that the polar jet stream forms where the polar easterlies meet the prevailing westerlies. In the summer or winter, the tilt of Earth causes the Sun's rays to strike perpendicular to Earth, slightly north or south of the equator. This change in the heating patterns of Earth's surface causes the wind patterns to shift somewhat. Consequently the general location of the polar jet stream shifts with the wind patterns.

Figure 14.14 Jet streams often dip south below the prairies or sometimes south of the Great Lakes.

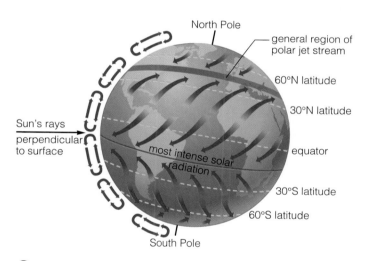

A In the winter, the wind patterns shift south and, with them, the jet stream.

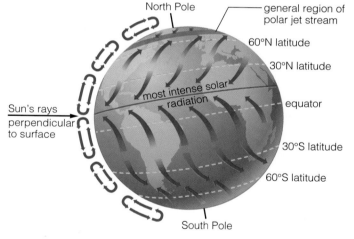

B In the summer, the jet stream retreats far to the north.

Figure 14.15 Prevailing winds in the different seasons in the Northern Hemisphere

Although Figure 14.15 shows how the polar jet stream shifts to the north in the summer and to the south in the winter, it does not explain the meandering. At first, the jet stream appears to guide the cold fronts and thus the storms. Storms often occur just to the south of the polar jet stream because the warm air is rising, creating the right conditions. If a thunderstorm is especially intense, however, the rapidly rising air seems to move the jet stream. Since both jet streams and frontal systems influence each other, it is very difficult to predict precisely where and how fast a jet stream will meander. Meteorologists and atmospheric scientists have a lot to learn before they can predict the movement of jet streams.

Aye, Aye Captain

Imagine that you are the captain of a trading ship in the eighteenth century. In the early spring, you will leave Spain and head toward the New World. While there, you will do some exploring and as much trading of goods and trinkets as possible. You will head for home in the early fall. Because your ship depends entirely on wind for power, you must plan your route based on the prevailing winds. (Sea captains did not know about convection and the Coriolis effect. They learned about wind directions from experience and from other sea captains.)

What to Do

1. Use the information you have learned about prevailing wind patterns and the way they shift with the seasons to plan your route. Make a sketch of your route.

2. Sea captains always tried to avoid the doldrums and the horse latitudes (see Figure 14.11). Conduct research to find out what happened if ships were caught in these latitudes. Find out why these latitudes were given their names.

3. Why were the trade winds given their name?

Mix It Up

Air is continually on the move, throughout the world. Although Earth's surface absorbs much more solar energy in the tropical zone than it does in the temperate or polar zones, all the thermal energy does not remain in the tropical zone. Circulating winds carry thermal energy to the cooler regions of the world and carry cooler air down from the poles.

Check Your Understanding

1. Why does air over the equator tend to rise?

2. How do you know that the atmosphere rotates with Earth and does not remain stationary while Earth rotates under it?

3. What property of Earth causes the Coriolis effect?

4. Describe the overall result of the Coriolis effect in the Northern and Southern Hemispheres.

5. Where would you expect to find a jet stream?

6. **Analyze** A round-trip airplane ticket between Calgary (Alberta) and Toronto (Ontario) states that the actual flying time in the air is 3 h 38 min from Calgary to Toronto and 4 h 6 min from Toronto to Calgary. From your knowledge about winds, explain why it takes half an hour longer to fly from Toronto to Calgary than from Calgary to Toronto, in the same type of airplane.

14.3 Rivers in the Sea

Windswept seas and crashing waves can be beautiful or frightening, depending on where you are standing. Wind has a powerful effect on open water. Since water covers about 70 percent of Earth, and winds are blowing much of the time, the effect of winds on the oceans influences weather all over the world. How, exactly, do the oceans respond to the prevailing winds?

Surface Currents

Surface winds start a process that creates giant rivers in the seas. Some of these rivers, or **ocean currents,** carry warm waters from points close to the equator all the way to the Arctic Sea. Other ocean currents carry the cool Arctic or Antarctic waters toward the equator. The large specific heat capacity of water allows it to absorb large amounts of solar energy. The ocean currents distribute this energy around the world.

Winds start the ocean currents flowing, but two other major factors influence the final patterns. Unlike winds that flow above the land, ocean currents are blocked and diverted by the continents. As well, the Coriolis effect influences ocean currents in the same way that it influences winds. Ocean currents turn to the right in the Northern Hemisphere and to the left in the Southern Hemisphere.

Figure 14.16 This lighthouse has probably saved the lives of many sailors on these rough seas.

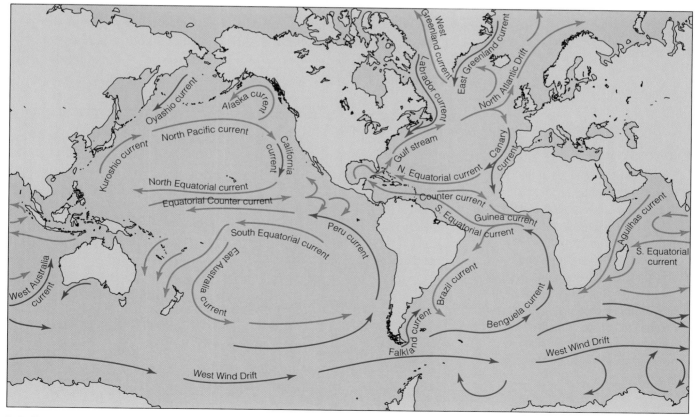

Figure 14.17 Look for patterns in the directions of flow and the temperatures of the major ocean currents shown here.

Figure 14.18 The Atacama Desert runs along the coasts of Chile and Peru. Although it is located near the ocean, the air is cool and dry.

The combined result of all of the factors that act on the oceans is the network of ocean currents shown in Figure 14.17. When you look at the network, the first thing you will probably notice is a pattern of nearly circular currents. These circular currents, called **gyres,** flow clockwise in the Northern Hemisphere and counterclockwise in the Southern Hemisphere. Another pattern is found within the gyres. Notice that on the right or east side of the gyres, the currents are cool. Look for the California current, Peru current, Benguela current, and Canary current. As a result of the cool temperature of the water, the air above these currents is also cool. Cool air does not hold as much water vapour as warm air. Consequently, if this air moves ashore, there is little condensation and very few clouds form. Some of these coastal regions are even desert-like due to the small amount of rain.

On the left, or west, side of most gyres, the currents are warm. Thus there is a lot of water vapour in the air. When this warm, humid air moves ashore, rain often follows. Look for the Brazil current, the East Australia current, the Kuroshio current, and the Gulf Stream. These warm currents warm the air. Therefore the climate of some northerly regions is warmer than expected for the latitude.

There is no complete ocean current circling the Northern Hemisphere because the continents are in the way. The West Wind Drift, just north of Antarctica, is the only ocean current that goes all the way around the world. Notice how branches of the West Wind Drift veer to the left. These branches bring cold Antarctic water to the west coasts of Australia, South America, and Africa. The cold water makes its way nearly to the equator. The West Wind Drift is the largest of all of the surface currents, transporting 125 million cubic metres of water per second. A flow of water this great could fill all of the Great Lakes in just two days!

DidYou**Know**?

Captains of sailing ships in the late seventeenth century had no satellite data and no sophisticated, electronic measuring equipment on their ships. Yet they knew all about the Gulf Stream. If there was little wind to propel their ships, the captains would seek out the Gulf Stream and "hitch a ride" from the east coast of North America to Europe. Timothy Folger, captain of a whaling ship and cousin of Benjamin Franklin, drew this map in 1770.

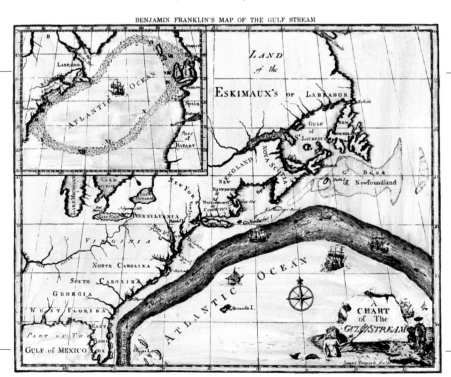

BENJAMIN FRANKLIN'S MAP OF THE GULF STREAM

The Gulf Stream and Climate

Without the Gulf Stream, history might have been quite different. Find out why by answering the following questions and doing the required research.

What You Need

world map with city names and latitudes

What to Do

1. Study Figure 14.17. Name the two major currents that combine to form the Gulf Stream.

2. As the Gulf Stream turns toward the northeast, with what current does it merge?

3. Describe the main path of this current when it reaches Europe.

4. Using a map of the world, find at least three pairs of cities (or towns) that fit the following criteria.
   (a) The two cities must be at nearly the same latitude.
   (b) One of the cities in the pair must be in northern Europe, including Great Britain, near the ocean current you named in step 2.
   (c) The second city of the pair must be in central or eastern Canada.

For example, Trondheim in Norway and Iqaluit in the Northwest Territories are both at 63°N latitude.

5. Research the average monthly temperatures of these three pairs of cities or towns. Record the average temperatures in a data table.

6. For each pair of cities or towns, compare the average temperatures month by month. Calculate and record the temperature differences for each month of the year.

What Did You Discover?

1. How do the temperatures of these pairs of cities or towns compare? Are the differences in average temperatures greater at one time of the year than another? If so, infer why.

2. Write a paragraph about how the Gulf Stream affects the climate of the regions it flows near.

Extension

3. Northern Europe would be very different if the Gulf Stream and the North Atlantic Drift had not influenced its climate. Write a paragraph that describes what you think northern Europe would be like if its climate was similar to that of central or Eastern Canada.

The size and speed of ocean currents vary but, in general, warm currents are faster, deeper, and narrower than cold currents. For example, the warm Gulf Stream flows at about 1.5 m/s while the cold California current flows at only about 0.1 m/s. The Gulf Stream is about 75 km wide and 2 km deep. The California current is over 1000 km wide but only 0.5 km deep. While these currents are flowing across the surface of the oceans, what is happening down below?

Deep Currents

Ocean water below a depth of 100 m is not directly affected by winds. Slow-moving currents exist in the deep ocean water, however. Ocean water also moves vertically: that is, up and down. To find out what factors influence the motion of deep ocean water, complete the following investigation.

Moving Mountains of Water

Winds cannot directly move water that is well below the surface of the oceans. Some properties of the seawater itself, however, can induce motion. In this investigation, you will simulate these properties and learn why they cause ocean currents.

Part 1
Temperature and Water Currents

Temperature differences in air cause differences in density, and differences in density cause motion. Since air and water are both fluids, does water respond in a similar way?

Problem

What happens when water that is one temperature comes in contact with water that is a very different temperature?

Safety Precautions

Use care when working with hot water.

Apparatus
clear plastic storage box
dropper
rock or other heavy weight

Materials
room-temperature water
hot water (not boiling)

plastic bag	ice cubes
food colouring	cloth
tape	twist tie

Procedure

1. Fill the plastic box about three-quarters full of room-temperature water.

2. Pour hot water into the plastic bag, and add the rock. (The rock should be as hot as the water, so it does not cause the water to cool.) Close the bag with a twist tie (or zip lock). Place the bag in a corner of the box of water.

3. Wrap four or five ice cubes in a piece of cloth. Put the cloth with the ice cubes in the box of water, in the corner diagonal to the hot-water bag. Tape the cloth to the end of the box, so the ice cannot float away.

4. Use the dropper to drop three or four drops of food colouring into the water, just beside the ice.

5. Watch patiently for several minutes. Observe any movement of the food colouring.

6. Select another place to add more food colouring. Predict what will happen when you add the food colouring there.

7. Test your prediction.

Analyze

1. Describe the movements of the food colouring. Explain why you think these movements occurred.

2. Explain how temperature differences can cause these movements.

Conclude and Apply

3. How might temperature differences occur in ocean water? Using the information you obtained, infer how temperature differences in ocean water cause ocean currents.

Part 2

Salt Concentration and Water Currents

Seawater is very salty, but the concentration of salt varies from place to place.

Problem

How does the concentration of salt affect the motion of water?

Safety Precautions

Use care when handling scissors or other sharp objects.

Apparatus

clear plastic storage box
scissors or other sharp object for punching holes

Materials

tap water
salt water with food colouring
thin, clear, disposable plastic cup
tape

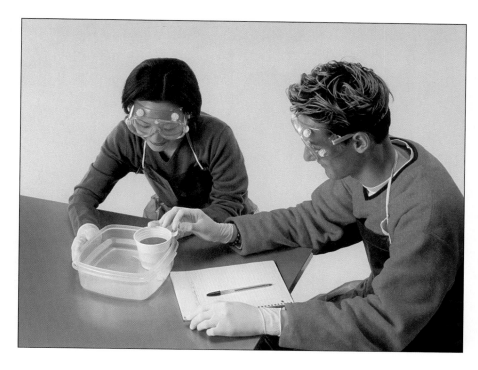

Procedure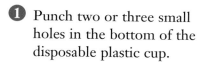

1. Punch two or three small holes in the bottom of the disposable plastic cup.

2. Put tape over the holes, inside the plastic cup. The tape must be long enough for one end to come out of the cup.

3. Tape the cup to a corner of the plastic box. The bottom of the cup should be well above the bottom of the plastic box.

4. Fill the plastic box about three-quarters full of tap water.

5. Fill the cup with salt water that contains food colouring.

6. Gently pull on the end of the tape that is above the water in the cup. Carefully remove the tape.

7. Watch patiently for several minutes. Observe any movement of the food colouring.

Analyze

1. Describe the movement of the food colouring.

2. Infer the reason why the water moved as it did.

Conclude and Apply

3. What would you predict about ocean currents, based on the movements of salt water that you observed?

Skill
P O W E R
To review the safety symbols used in this textbook, turn to page 608.

In the last investigation, you discovered that water behaves like air: cool water sinks because it is more dense than warm water. As well, salt water is more dense than fresh water, so it also sinks. These movements help to create currents in the oceans.

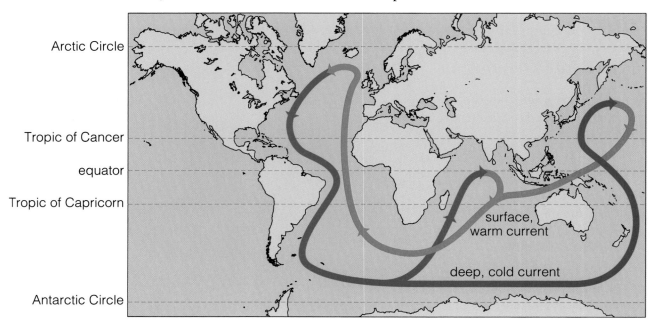

Figure 14.19 A combination of surface and deep-water currents create a conveyor belt that mixes ocean water throughout the world.

Word CONNECT

The technical name for the great ocean conveyor belt is *thermo-haline circulation*. You probably know the meaning of "thermo." Find the meaning of "haline" in a dictionary or on the Internet. Then write a paragraph to explain why the name "thermo-haline circulation" is appropriate for the great ocean conveyor belt.

The largest continuous ocean current, shown in Figure 14.19, is sometimes called the "great ocean conveyor belt." How does this "conveyor belt" work? Much of the warm water of the Gulf Stream and North Atlantic Drift evaporates on its trip across the ocean, leaving the salt behind. By the time the water reaches the Arctic Ocean, the salt concentration is quite high. The water that is already in the Arctic Ocean also has a high salt concentration due to the formation of icebergs: when water freezes to form icebergs, the salt stays behind in the liquid water. Thus the Arctic water is both cold and quite salty. When the warm water from the Gulf Stream and North Atlantic Drift combines with the Arctic water, it cools. The combined, very salty water sinks to the bottom of the ocean and starts its trek southward.

The deep ocean current flows south along the bottom of the Atlantic Ocean, all the way to Antarctica. There it turns east and splits into two branches. One branch turns north and travels along the east coast of Africa. As it moves toward the Indian Ocean, it warms and rises. At the same time, the second branch passes south of Australia and then turns north into the Pacific Ocean. When the second branch reaches the North Pacific, it also warms and rises, and then heads west. The two branches join, pass south of Africa, and eventually join the Gulf Stream again. The entire trip takes about 1000 years. Despite the length of the trip, however, this conveyor belt has an important influence on world climate. It transports thermal energy, as well as nutrients, from pole to pole.

Sailors and scientists have known about the Gulf Stream for hundreds of years. Scientists have only known that it was part of a larger, circulating conveyor belt since the early 1990s. At this time, scientists found three sites where the water was cold and salty enough to sink and start the pattern flowing. Then, just a few years later, they became concerned because one of the three sites, the Greenland branch, stopped working. Was this due to global warming? Would the Gulf Stream slow down or even stop? Would Northern Europe freeze over? Scientists, called oceanographers, intensified their research. Finally, in 1999, they discovered that the other two sites increased their flow and made up for the loss of the Greenland branch. Although their concern was relieved for the present time, oceanographers continue their research to learn more about these critical ocean currents.

El Niño

In Conduct an Investigation 14-C, you saw that cold water sinks in warmer water because it is more dense. A different set of circumstances can cause cool water to rise. If a constant wind blows out to sea from shore, it pushes the water along with it. If there is open ocean ahead of the wind and water, the water continues to move. If the water were dust, or another solid material, the wind would leave a hole in it. Water is a fluid, however. So the water below comes up to replace the water that was blown away. This process, called **upwelling,** brings up cool water from below.

Upwellings occur off the west coasts of continents that are within or near the tropical zone. This is because trade winds blow off the west coasts of Africa and parts of North and South America (see Figure 14.20) most of the time. The upwellings bring a rich supply of nutrients that have settled to the bottom of the ocean. Algae thrive in the cool, nutrient-rich waters, and fish feed on the algae. Many large commercial fisheries are located near these productive waters.

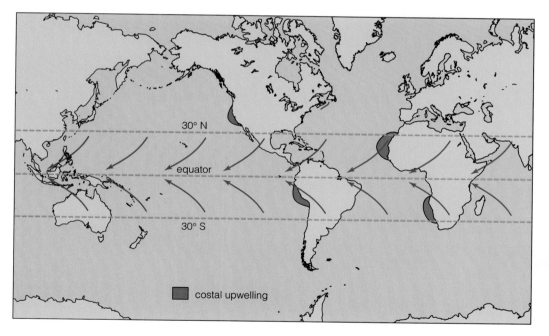

30° N

equator

30° S

costal upwelling

Figure 14.20 Upwellings are a rich source of marine fish and seafood. The lives of many fishing families are dependent on these fertile waters.

Why is a discussion of trade winds, upwellings, and fisheries found in a section titled "El Niño?" What is an El Niño, and how is this unique weather condition related to fishing? For hundreds of years, Peruvian fishers have known that a warming of the Pacific waters interrupts their excellent fishing conditions every few years. Since the warming nearly always starts in December, they named it **El Niño,** which is Spanish for "boy child." Only recently have scientists and meteorologists discovered that the changes occurring in Peru are closely tied to many other dramatic weather conditions around the world.

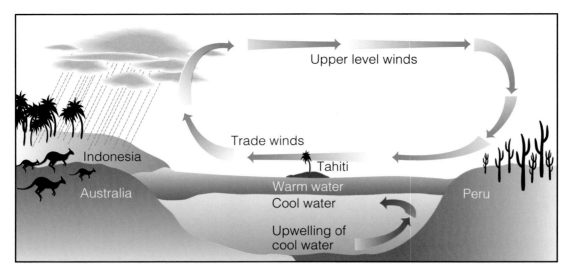

A Under normal conditions, the trade winds blow the warm, equatorial water west, toward Australia and Indonesia.

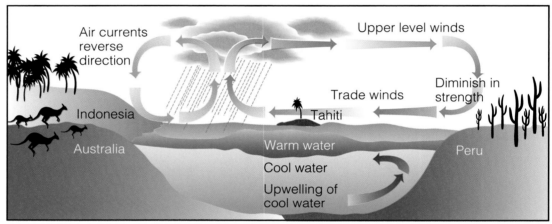

B When air pressure increases over the Indian Ocean west of Australia and Indonesia, and air pressure falls over Tahiti, winds start blowing to the east. The bulge of warm water heads east across the Pacific Ocean. El Niño is on the way.

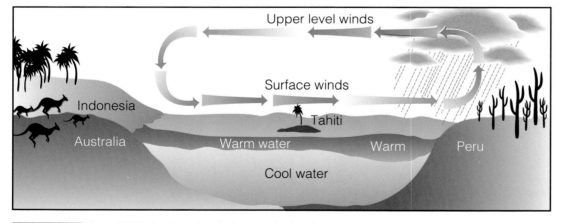

C Warm water prevents upwellings, and fishing is poor in Peru. Rains begin to flood the desert. El Niño has arrived.

Figure 14.21 As an El Niño develops, the winds reverse in direction.

Scientists are not yet certain about what triggers an El Niño. Nevertheless they understand, several events that occur while an El Niño is developing. Figure 14.21 shows some of these events, starting with the normal conditions that exist before an El Niño begins. Under normal conditions, the trade winds blow across the Pacific Ocean from east to west. With no barriers to slow or divert them, they blow for 14 000 km across open seas. They push the warm equatorial water toward

Australia and Indonesia. As the warm water is pushed westward, it piles up near Australia. The water level is 1.5 m higher near Australia than near Peru. When the warm, moist air reaches Australia or Indonesia, it rises as an ocean breeze. The rising air cools, and the moisture condenses, bringing rain. The cooler, drier air in the upper level turns back toward the east and returns to South America. It drops over Peru and warms. Because it is dry, rain is rare.

Then, for some unknown reason, the trade winds diminish. Air pressure rises over Australia and lowers over Tahiti, a small Pacific island about half way between Australia and South America. The new pressure difference causes the wind to blow to the east, off the shores of Australia (see Figure 14.21B). The "pile" of warm water begins to move eastward, toward Peru. The rising air is now out in the Pacific Ocean, and dry air is descending over Australia. El Niño is on the way.

Figure 14.21C shows the conditions that exist in a fully developed El Niño. The water level has dropped near Australia and risen near Peru. The air currents have completely reversed in direction, and the warm water has reached Peru and piled up near the shore. The warm water prevents the upwelling of cool water and nutrients. The fish population diminishes. When the moist air reaches land, it rises and cools. Soon rain begins in the desert.

Figure 14.22 El Niño is felt around the world. Cattle are nearly starving due to a draught in Australia. Relief agencies try to supply food so people can survive the draught in Ethiopia. In California, El Niño brings storms and flooding.

Figure 14.23 Working in the middle of the Pacific Ocean, these scientists are setting up one of the 70 buoys that collects meteorological and oceanographic data. The buoy radios back the data to a central location, where the data are analyzed.

INTERNET CONNECT

www.school.mcgrawhill.ca/resources/

Learn more about El Niños by going to the web site above. Go to **Science Resources**, then to **SCIENCEPOWER 10** to know where to go next. Find out how El Niños affect Canada, and write a short report on your findings.

The extraordinary changes in ocean temperatures, wind directions, and moisture in the air that occur all across the Pacific cannot help but affect the weather in many other regions of the world. In some cases, the effects are mild, causing few problems. In other cases, the effects are severe.

Probably the most damaging El Niño of the last century occurred from 1982 to 1983. The temperatures of the ocean waters off Peru were 5° to 10°C warmer than normal. Pacific islands that normally see about one typhoon every 50 years experienced five typhoons in five months. Severe flooding occurred in Ecuador, Peru, and Chile. Western North America experienced many storms and mud slides. Drought and brush fires devastated Australia. Fishing was poor from Mexico to Alaska. Droughts hit Indonesia and Southern Africa, then moved on to India, Sri Lanka, and the Philippines. The photographs in Figure 14.22 show some of the damage caused by this most devastating El Niño of the century.

Oceanographers had no way to predict the coming of the 1982–1983 El Niño, nor its intensity. The devastating aftermath of this El Niño drew attention to the need for early detection of the events leading up to an El Niño. Although it is not possible to stop or even reduce the severity of an El Niño, knowing ahead of time that one is coming will allow people to prepare and possibly prevent some of the damage that might occur. In 1985, a ten-year study, called the Tropical Ocean-Global Atmosphere (TOGA) program, began. Throughout the ten years, a series of 70 instrument buoys, like the one in Figure 14.23, were moored across the Pacific Ocean near the equator. Instruments on the buoys detected and sent back data on wind speeds, sea surface temperatures, and ocean water temperatures to a depth of 500 m, as well as other types of data. The data from these buoys were helpful in the early detection of the 1997–1998 El Niño. The instrument buoys, called the Tropical Atmosphere Ocean (TAO) array, continue to provide valuable data that scientists use to learn more about El Niño events.

Check Your Understanding

1. Name three factors that determine the speed and direction of surface currents in oceans.

2. Describe two ways that ocean currents can influence the climate of coastal regions.

3. What can cause the salt concentration of sea water to change?

4. Under what conditions will cool water rise?

5. Describe two events that occur while an El Niño is developing.

DidYouKnow?

After studying El Niños for several years, scientists realized that conditions between El Niños reached the opposite extreme. For example, waters in the Eastern Pacific near Peru became even cooler than normal. Scientists call this condition "La Nina" — which means "little girl" — to indicate the opposite of El Niño.

14.4 Over Land and Sea

Figure 14.24 You will often see quite different sky conditions above land and a large lake or ocean beside the land. These differences tell you that the land and water influence the conditions of the atmosphere above them.

At the beginning of this chapter, you learned how the spherical shape of Earth causes uneven heating. You discovered that this uneven heating causes convection currents and thus worldwide wind patterns. You also learned how the rotation of Earth creates the Coriolis effect, which causes the directions of winds to shift to the right in the Northern Hemisphere and to the left in the Southern Hemisphere. Then you learned how the tilt of Earth's axis causes the seasons to change while Earth revolves around the Sun. The first time that you compared the effects of land with the effects of water was when you looked at ocean currents. Over the next few pages, you are going to compare the effects of land and water on the air above them. This will set the stage for a detailed study of local weather events in the next chapter.

Although air is usually in motion, due to convection and the Coriolis effect, large portions of air often remain in nearly the same place long enough to take on the temperature and moisture characteristics of the land or ocean below. Since these characteristics can vary greatly, the differences between the land and ocean can have a significant influence on the properties of the air above. When this occurs, and a large portion of the air is nearly uniform in temperature and humidity, we have what is called an **air mass.**

Meteorologists use the system shown in Table 14.1 to classify air masses. First air masses are classified as continental or maritime, depending on whether they form over land or ocean. Since air that remains above land for a period of time is

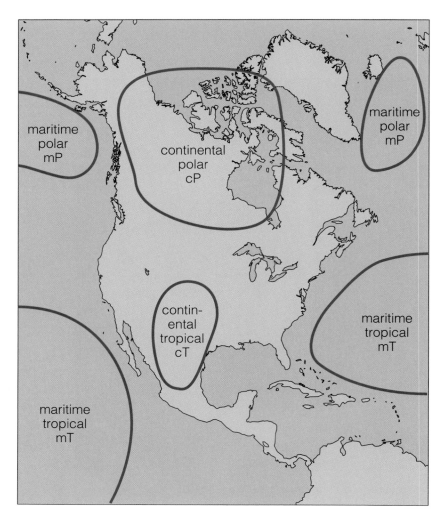

maritime polar mP

continental polar cP

maritime polar mP

continental tropical cT

maritime tropical mT

maritime tropical mT

Figure 14.25 This is an example of the way that air masses might form.

usually drier than air that remains above an ocean, this classification is an indication of the amount of moisture in the air. Air masses are further classified as polar or tropical. Cool air masses are polar, and warm air masses are tropical.

Figure 14.25 shows some typical air masses. These air masses are, of course, not stationary. Look at the figure, and then picture the prevailing wind patterns in your mind. Imagine what will happen when the air masses begin to move and collide. In Chapter 15, you will consider the results of these collisions of air masses — weather.

Table 14.1 Properties of Air Masses

Name	Symbol	Characteristics
continental polar	cP	cool and dry
maritime polar	mP	cool and moist
continental tropical	cT	warm and dry
maritime tropical	mT	warm and moist

Check Your Understanding

1. Define the term "air mass."

2. Describe the type of air mass that forms over Canada.

3. What are the characteristics of a maritime tropical air mass?

Now that you have completed this chapter, try to do the following. If you cannot, go back to the sections indicated.

Explain why the average temperature of a region far from the equator is, in general, cooler than the temperature of a region close to the equator. (14.1)

Describe the property of Earth that is responsible for the changing seasons. (14.1)

Describe the unique characteristics of the day that starts each new season: summer, fall, winter, and spring. (14.1)

Name Earth's five major zones and describe their characteristics. (14.1)

Describe wind patterns that would exist if Earth were a uniform, non-rotating sphere. (14.2)

Explain the Coriolis effect, and describe the resulting wind patterns. (14.2)

Describe the effects of prevailing wind patterns on the weather of a region. (14.2)

State where you would expect to find jet streams. Explain why they exist. (14.2)

List three patterns that you see in surface ocean currents. (14.3)

Discuss the importance of the warm Gulf Stream. (14.3)

Contrast the size and speed of cold and warm ocean currents. (14.3)

Explain why ocean currents are important to weather and climates of the world. (14.3)

Describe the conditions that create upwellings of cool, deep ocean waters. (14.3)

Name two signs that an El Niño is developing. (14.3)

Explain the way that meteorologists classify air masses. (14.4)

Summarize this chapter by doing one of the following. Use a graphic organizer (such as a concept map), produce a poster, or write the summary to include the key chapter concepts. Here are a few ideas to use as a guide:

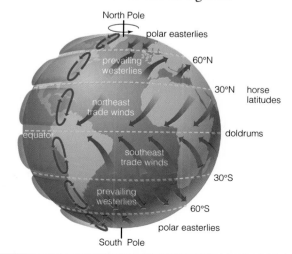

Prepare Your Own Summary

- How does the spherical shape of Earth affect the temperature of different regions?
- Why are the seasons in the Northern and Southern Hemispheres the opposite of each other?
- How does Earth's rotation affect wind patterns?
- Where would you find the trade winds?
- What is a jet stream?
- What is unique about the West Wind Drift?
- How does salt concentration affect the movement of sea water?
- Where might a maritime polar air mass develop?

Skill
POWER

For tips on making a concept, turn to page 578.

Reviewing Key Terms

If you need to review, the section numbers show you where these terms were introduced.

1. Explain the difference between longitude and latitude. (14.1)

2. Make a sketch of Earth, and label the following. (14.1)

   (a) equator

   (b) Arctic Circle

   (c) polar zones

   (d) Tropic of Capricorn

   (e) Antarctic Circle

   (f) temperate zones

   (g) Tropic of Cancer

   (h) tropical zone

Understanding Key Concepts

Section numbers are provided if you need to review.

3. Where is the reference line for longitude: that is, 0° longitude? (14.1)

4. Why is the tropical zone defined as the region between $23\frac{1}{2}$ °N and $23\frac{1}{2}$ °S latitude? (14.1)

5. Where and when could the day length be 24 h? (14.1)

6. On what day does solar radiation hit the Tropic of Capricorn perpendicular to Earth's surface? (14.1)

7. Refer to Figure 14.8. Explain why convection currents have the three closed patterns shown in diagram B rather than the single closed pattern shown in diagram A? (14.2)

8. Explain why a point on the equator is moving much faster than a point on the Arctic Circle. (14.2).

9. How can the Coriolis effect cause the prevailing westerlies to blow from west to east and, at the same time, cause the trade winds to blow from east to west? (14.2)

10. Describe the event that led to a detailed study of jet streams. (14.2)

11. Describe the development of a jet stream. (14.2)

12. Explain the property of water that allows ocean currents to distribute solar energy efficiently throughout the world. (14.3)

13. What is a gyre? How are gyres in the Northern Hemisphere different from gyres in the Southern Hemisphere? (14.3)

14. Describe one pattern that is found in most gyres. How does this pattern influence climates on the coast of nearby continents? (14.3)

15. How does water temperature affect ocean currents? (14.3)

16. Describe the path of the great ocean conveyor belt. (14.3)

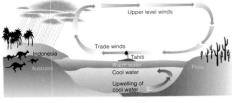
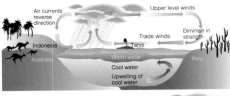
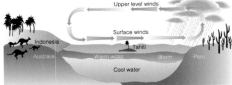

Figure 14.21

Refer to this figure when answering questions 17 through 19. Relate each answer to specific parts of the figure.

17. How do conditions on the coast of Peru change when an El Niño develops? Why? (14.3)

18. What happens in Australia during an El Niño? Why? (14.3)

19. What is the Southern Oscillation? (14.3)

20. What type of air mass sometimes forms over central Canada? (14.4)

Developing Skills

21. Make a sketch of Earth, showing the prevailing surface wind patterns. (14.2)

22. Design a test to determine which water sample is more dense than the other: sea water at 27°C or fresh water at 4°C.

23. Construct a concept map that shows how thermal energy is absorbed by Earth and distributed around Earth.

24. Estimate the longitude and latitude of point P.

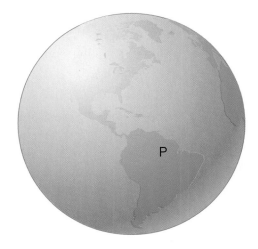

Problem Solving/Applying

25. Conduct research to find out how El Niños affect the different regions of Canada.

26. If you lived in Australia, how might you prepare for an El Niño?

27. If you know that a thunderstorm is developing to the east, should you prepare for rain? Explain why or why not.

Critical Thinking

28. How do you think different climates have affected the development of civilizations around the world?

29. Sea captains and fishers who lived hundreds of years ago learned about such things as ocean currents and El Niños. Why are expensive computers and satellites needed to study weather today?

Pause&
Reflect

1. Go back to the beginning of the chapter, on page 452, and check your original answers to the Opening Ideas questions. How has your thinking changed? How would you answer those questions now that you have investigated the topics in this chapter?

2. How does the climate in the region where you live affect your everyday life?

3. What topic in the chapter would you choose as a subject, if you were asked to prepare a class presentation? Why would you choose this topic?

15 Local Weather

- Why do clouds have so many different shapes?
- What is a cold front?
- What causes tornadoes?
- What is the difference between a cyclone and a hurricane?

Science Log

Think about the questions above. Based on what you have already learned about weather, predict answers to the questions. Write your answers in your Science Log. What is the most dangerous weather condition that has occurred in or near your community? Write down as much as you know about what happened. Also write down any questions you have about it. As you study this chapter, check your answers and ideas. Make corrections when necessary. Look for answers to your unanswered questions.

Meteorologists called it an extratropical storm when it reached Canada. The Torontonians who experienced it called it a hurricane.

On October 5, 1954, Hurricane Hazel developed in the Atlantic Ocean. It tracked east into the Caribbean Sea. Then it turned north. When Hazel passed through Haiti, the estimated death toll was 1000. Hazel continued north into the United States. Before Hazel reached Garden City, South Carolina, the town had 275 homes. After Hazel went through, there were two. When Hazel moved into the United States, it was classified as a tropical storm. Nevertheless it took 95 lives and caused $251 million worth of damage.

On October 15, Hazel moved into Ontario. When Hazel collided with a cold air mass west of Toronto, it intensified. Nearly 20 cm of rain fell in less than 24 h. This caused flooding in small rivers and creeks. Raging winds and flood waters washed out streets, destroyed bridges and homes, and caused power failures. In the end, 81 lives were lost. One entire neighborhood, on Raymore Drive, was washed away by the Humber River. There alone, 35 people were killed.

By the time Hazel ended, nearly 5000 people had lost their homes. The estimated cost was over $130 million (in 1990 dollars).

In this chapter, you will learn how hurricanes form. You will read about tornadoes, typhoons, and monsoons. You will also read about more common weather conditions, such as wind, clouds, and rain. As well, you will learn why weather changes from day to day.

Systems

A Jar Full of Clouds

What conditions are necessary for clouds to form?

Key Concepts

In this chapter, you will discover
- how clouds form
- how rain, snow, sleet, and hail form
- what happens when air masses meet
- what causes a thunderstorm
- how tornadoes and hurricanes develop

Key Skills

In this chapter, you will
- make an artificial cloud
- identify clouds
- predict weather events from clouds

Key Terms

- aerosol
- cumulus
- stratus
- cirrus
- deposition
- nimbus
- nimbostratus
- cumulonimbus
- coalesce
- sleet
- freezing rain
- hail
- front
- cold front
- warm front
- stationary front
- occluded front

- anticyclone
- cyclone
- frontal low
- updraft
- downdraft
- tornado
- wind shear
- hurricane
- typhoon
- tropical cyclone
- easterly waves
- tropical depression
- tropical storm
- storm surge
- eye (of a hurricane)
- monsoon

Starting Point ACTIVITY

What You Need

clear, glass wide-mouthed jar with lid
  (1 L or larger)
ice cubes or crushed ice
hot water
can of aerosol spray, such as air freshener
black construction paper
flashlight

What to Do

1. Prop up the black construction paper so that the glass jar can be positioned in front of it.

2. Fill the jar with hot (not boiling) water to warm the jar. Pour out all but about 2 cm of the water.

3. Turn the jar lid upside down. Fill it with ice, and place it on top of the jar.

4. Darken the room. Shine the flashlight on the jar from the side.

5. Observe the jar for at least 3 min. Record anything that you see happening inside the jar.

6. Empty the jar. Repeat step 2.

7. Spray a very small amount of the aerosol into the jar. *Very quickly* place the lid containing the ice on the jar.

8. Repeat steps 4 and 5.

What Did You Discover?

1. How did your results with the aerosol differ from your results without the aerosol?

2. Suggest reasons why the results were different.

3. Write a concluding statement that describes the criteria for cloud formation.

15.1 Rain or Shine?

Figure 15.1 What can these clouds tell you about the weather?

Both of the clouds in Figure 15.1 are made of tiny droplets of water. Yet they are very different from each other. From your own observations, you know that there are many more types of clouds than these. If all clouds are formed from water, why are there so many different types? The answer to this question lies in the variety of conditions of wind, temperature, and humidity. All of these conditions affect cloud formation. Therefore they also affect cloud size, shape, and appearance. You cannot see wind, temperature, or humidity, but you can see clouds. As you learn more about clouds, you will begin to understand what they tell you about other weather conditions.

In the Starting Point Activity, you created the conditions that are needed for cloud formation. You created water vapour by using hot water that evaporates readily. You caused the air to become saturated with water vapour by cooling it to its dew point temperature with ice. Then you added condensation nuclei with an **aerosol** spray. How are these conditions created in nature?

Condensation Nuclei

You have learned that some of the water in air can condense and form droplets. This happens, for example, if the air becomes cooler or more water evaporates. The water droplets form around tiny particles, such as dust and salt. These particles are called condensation nuclei. In this activity, you will estimate the amount of condensation nuclei in a beaker of clean snow.

CAUTION: Use care when working near a flame.

What You Need
500 mL beaker
Bunsen burner
support stand
wire gauze
clamp
support ring

What to Do

1. Imagine a 500 mL beaker of clean, white snow. Predict the amount of condensation nuclei that would be in this beaker of snow.

2. Walk to the nearest yard or field, and collect clean snow. Pack the snow firmly in the beaker.

3. Melt the snow by putting the beaker over a Bunsen burner. Follow the set-up shown in the diagram.

4. When the snow has melted, turn off the Bunsen burner. Observe the water for any particles or condensation nuclei. Also smell the water to see if you can detect any substances in it.

5. Estimate the total amount of particles. Use the following scale.

   (a) There are not enough to be visible.

   (b) The particles are about the size of a grain of sand or sugar.

   (c) They would fit on the period the end of this sentence.

   (d) They would cover up the middle of the letter "o."

   (e) They would cover up the middle of the letter "O."

6. Continue to heat the water until it evaporates. Is there any residue left on the beaker? Estimate the total amount of condensation nuclei.

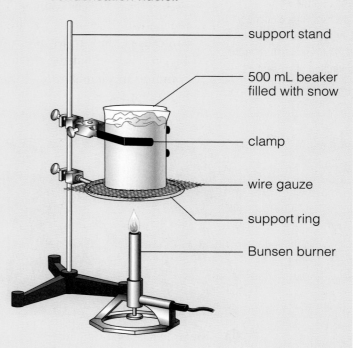

support stand

500 mL beaker filled with snow

clamp

wire gauze

support ring

Bunsen burner

What Did You Discover?

1. How closely did your final estimate compare with your initial prediction?

2. Different substances — such as salt, sulfuric acid, nitric acid, dust, and sand — can serve as condensation nuclei. Compare how much of each you would expect to find in Saskatoon, Kapuskasing, Hamilton, and Halifax.

3. How might salt from an ocean help to form clouds near the ocean? Describe a mechanism that would explain this process.

Word CONNECT

Look up the word "aerosol" in a dictionary. Find out if all condensation nuclei in nature fit the definition of an aerosol.

In nature, condensation nuclei take the form of dust, smoke, pollen, and sea salt. The average diameter of one of these particles is about 0.01 mm. The wind can carry such tiny particles thousands of kilometres. On average, every litre of air over the oceans contains about one million particles. Over the land, every litre of air contains five to six million particles!

Cool It

The most common way that air cools to its dew point temperature is by moving to a higher altitude. As you learned in Chapter 13, the temperature of the atmosphere drops as the altitude increases, until you reach the top of the troposphere. So air cools as it rises. In addition, air expands as it rises. This enhances cooling. Thus any mechanism that lifts air to higher altitudes can cause clouds to form. Study Figure 15.2 to learn about the three most common mechanisms for lifting air to higher altitudes.

A Solar radiation heats the ground. The ground heats the air by conduction. As the air becomes warm, it expands and becomes less dense. Therefore it rises.

B Two air masses of different temperatures meet. The cooler air mass slides under the warm air mass. It pushes the warm air mass to higher altitudes, where the temperature is cooler.

C A moving air mass meets a mountain range. It rises over the mountains. As it rises, it expands and cools. Often it reaches its dew point temperature.

Figure 15.2 Lifting mechanisms

Air may also be cooled by contact with very cool ground. In Chapter 13, you learned that Earth emits infrared radiation. At night, the ground is not absorbing any solar radiation. It is still emitting infrared radiation however. Thus it is still cooling. If there are clouds in the sky, they absorb much of the infrared radiation and limit the amount of cooling. On a clear, windless night, however, much of the radiation escapes. As a result, the ground cools rapidly. The ground then cools the air by conduction. If the air cools to its dew point temperature, clouds or fog form.

Cloud Shapes

Clouds come in an almost limitless variety of shapes. Meteorologists usually classify them, however, according to three general shapes: **cumulus, stratus,** and **cirrus**. The puffy clouds that often have flat bases are cumulus clouds (see Figure 15.1A). Sometimes people call them "cauliflower clouds." They may be formed by convection currents or by air masses meeting.

Stratus clouds form in seemingly endless layers (see Figure 15.1B). You cannot see shapes or forms in stratus clouds because they are flat. When stratus clouds are low and dark, they make the day seem dull and dreary. Stratus clouds can form when air masses meet or when a layer of air is pushed up the side of a mountain range. They may also form by conduction, when they come in contact with a very cool ground surface. Fog is really a stratus cloud that is sitting on the ground (see Figure 15.3).

When very little water vapour is in the air, the dew point temperature is quite low. Often it is below freezing. Under these conditions, the air must rise very high to reach its dew point temperature. The water vapour changes from a gas directly to a solid by a process called **deposition.** Crystals of ice form instead of water droplets. Cirrus clouds are made of ice crystals (see Figure 15.4).

Many clouds have features that are a combination of the three basic shapes. Their names are therefore a combination of the shape names. For example, high fluffy clouds, made of ice crystals, are cirrocumulus clouds.

Either stratus or cumulus clouds may cause precipitation. The name of a rain or snow cloud is made by combining the shape name with a form of the term **nimbus.** In other words, the name of the cloud may start with "nimbo" or end with "nimbus." For example, a **nimbostratus** cloud is a stratus cloud that brings rain. A rain- or snow-bearing cumulus cloud is called a **cumulonimbus** cloud.

Figure 15.3 This fog is caused by rapid cooling of the ground due to the emission of infrared radiation. It is often called "radiation fog."

How Far Up?

Meteorologists also classify clouds by their altitude. Low clouds form below 2000 m. Nearly all low clouds are some form of stratus cloud. However, some stratus clouds are also found above 2000 m. Middle clouds form between 2000 m and 6000 m. The prefix "alto" is combined with the shape name to identify middle clouds. High clouds form above 6000 m. Since high clouds are nearly always made of ice crystals, their names usually begin with "cirro" or end with "cirrus."

Some cumulus clouds have a very low base and a top well above 6000 m. They cannot be classified according to altitude because they continue through all the altitudes, or levels. They are sometimes called "all level clouds." Cumulonimbus clouds, for example, are all levels clouds.

Figure 15.4 Cirrus clouds are sometimes called "mares' tails." They look like horses' tails swept by the wind.

Word **CONNECT**

Find the general meaning of the prefix "alto." Where do alto voices fit in a choir or quartet? How appropriate is the prefix "alto" for middle clouds?

Guide to the Sky

Low Clouds (below 2000 m)

Stratus clouds

Nimbostratus clouds

Stratocumulus clouds

Middle Clouds (between 2000 m and 6000 m)

Altostratus clouds

Altocumulus clouds

Figure 15.5 Naming clouds

High Clouds (over 6000 m)

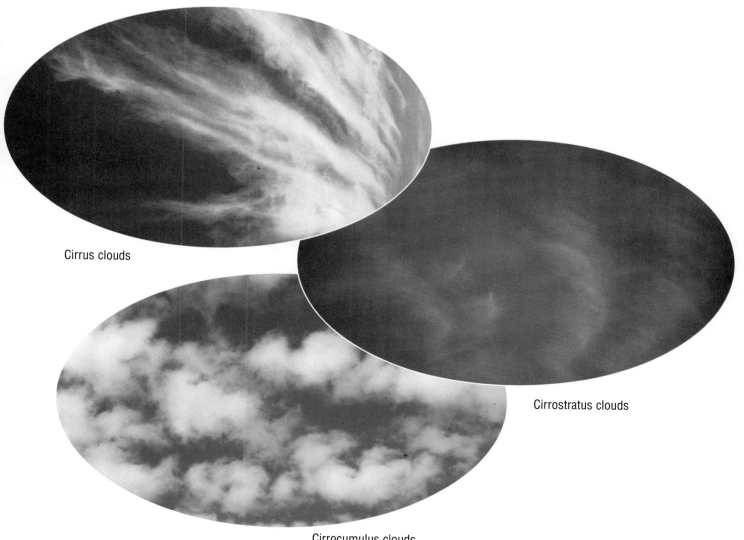

Cirrus clouds

Cirrostratus clouds

Cirrocumulus clouds

All Level Clouds

Cumulus clouds

Cumulonimbus clouds

Deceptive Clouds

Meteorologists classify clouds according to altitude, shape, and potential for precipitation. Clouds can have so many different forms that it is often difficult to classify them. In this activity, you will practise classifying clouds. Then you will compare your results with your classmates' results.

What to Do

1. Study the "Guide to the Sky." Use the guide to help you classify clouds that you observe.

2. For three days, classify and record the clouds that you see in the morning before school and in the afternoon after school. (Your class may decide to use different times, perhaps during the school day.) Do your own classifications. Do *not* discuss them with classmates.

3. Give your classifications to your teacher when they are complete. Your teacher will compile the data and create a table of the results.

4. As a class, discuss the results.

What Did You Discover?

1. What was the largest number of different classifications for any one observation time?

2. Why were the clouds at this time difficult to classify?

3. Were there any classifications that everyone in the class agreed on? If so, what made these clouds easy to classify? If not, what was the smallest number of different classifications for any one observation time?

4. Discuss the importance of observer agreement when collecting data and drawing conclusions.

Skill
P O W E R

For tips on organizing scientific data, turn to page 599.

Across Canada

"I was born in Prince Albert, Saskatchewan," says Dr. Robert (Bob) Schemenauer. "The summers were hot, and the winters cold. The sky was always beautiful." Watching the beautiful sky led Bob to study weather and climate. He worked as a cloud physicist with Environment Canada for many years. He researched acid rain and fog, weather modification, and clouds.

Bob lives in Toronto, Ontario. However, you might find him in a dry or desert community where people lack water. Using his knowledge of wind and clouds, Bob helps the people obtain water — from fog! Many dry areas get a lot of fog, but it usually rolls away without leaving its precious water behind. To catch the water, Bob and his colleagues set up nets — a bit like huge volleyball nets. They put the nets high on a foggy hill or mountain above the community. The wind blows the fog against the nets. Tiny water droplets catch on the fine plastic

mesh and trickle down. A pipeline carries the water down to the people. They use it to drink, cook, bathe their babies, water their goats, and grow vegetables and trees. The process needs no electricity. "Only wind and gravity are required to collect and deliver fog water," says Dr. Schemenauer. "It is an environmentally friendly, sustainable water resource."

Dr. Robert Schemenauer

When Bob is working with fog, he cannot always see the beautiful sky that he loves. He does not mind. The sound of water running in the desert makes up for it.

Think It Will Rain?

Why do some clouds bring rain or snow while others do not? The answer to this question is the size of the water droplets. The average water droplet in a cloud has a diameter of about 0.02 mm. These water droplets are smaller than the tiny dust particles that you sometimes see bouncing around in a beam of sunlight. The slightest whiff of air can send the droplets flying. They simply are not heavy enough to fall to Earth. A drop must have a diameter of at least 0.5 mm in order to fall. Drops this small create a fine mist. The average raindrop that makes it to the ground has a diameter of about 2 mm. This is 100 times larger than the diameter of a typical water droplet in a cloud. So how do water droplets grow from 0.02 mm to 2 mm?

Figure 15.6 The wispy trails on the bottom of this cloud are really rain starting to fall. The air is warm, however, and the raindrops evaporate before they reach the ground. The wisps are called "virga."

Math CONNECT

How much more water is in a raindrop than in a cloud droplet? The diameter of a drop does not describe the amount of water that it contains. To compare amounts, you must compare volumes. The formula for the volume of a sphere is $V = \frac{4}{3}\pi r^3$. Find the volume of a cloud droplet if $r = \frac{d}{2} = \frac{0.02 \text{ mm}}{2} = 0.01$ mm. Find the volume of an average raindrop if $r = \frac{d}{2} = \frac{2 \text{ mm}}{2} = 1$ mm. How many times larger is a raindrop than a cloud droplet?

Condensation is a slow process. A cloud droplet takes several hours to grow to raindrop size by condensation alone. Although this can happen, it is not the most common way for raindrops to form. Cloud droplets are almost constantly being tossed up, down, and around by air currents. As a result, they often **coalesce:** collide and blend together. In warm air, coalescence is the most common way that raindrops form. In temperate climates such as Canada's, however, most raindrops start out as snowflakes. In the cold upper air where clouds form, water droplets and ice crystals both exist. Vapour deposits on ice crystals more readily than it condenses on water droplets. Therefore ice crystals grow much faster than water droplets. In fact, water evaporates from the droplets and deposits on the crystals. Like droplets, the crystals collide and stick together. They become snowflakes. As the snowflakes fall through warmer air, they melt and become raindrops.

Figure 15.7 It is hard to imagine that drenching rain started out as fluffy snow.

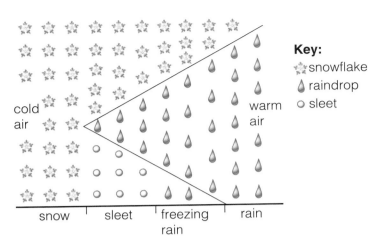

cold air

warm air

Key:
- ✻ snowflake
- 💧 raindrop
- ○ sleet

snow | sleet | freezing rain | rain

Figure 15.8 The type of precipitation that reaches the ground depends on the temperatures of the layers of air above.

Rain, Snow, Sleet, or Hail?

You have just learned how rain forms. Have you guessed what causes snow? If the air beneath the clouds is below the freezing point all the way to the ground, the crystals in the clouds stay in the form of snow. If the air is extremely cold, the crystals tend to remain small, almost like a fine powder. If the air is warmer but still below freezing, the snowflakes stick together as they fall. They form larger flakes. Sometimes a layer of air below a cloud is warm enough to melt the snow and turn it into rain. Then, closer to the ground, the air is below the freezing point. Examine the diagram below as you read about the results of rain falling through cold air.

If the air very near the ground is cold enough, the raindrops freeze again. They do not freeze as crystals, however. They freeze into ice pellets that we usually called **sleet.** A very dangerous condition occurs if the ground and objects on the ground are below the freezing point, but the air is warm enough to allow rain to fall. (**Note:** Water does not freeze until it is well below zero (about –7°C to –20°C), unless it has a solid object onto which it can freeze.)

When the rain hits the cold objects, it freezes instantly. This creates a solid coating of ice. **Freezing rain** can cause serious damage if it accumulates on trees and power lines. The residents of eastern Ontario and western Québec can tell many stories about the great ice storm of 1998 (see Figure 15.9).

Figure 15.9 The ice that formed on the power lines was so heavy that many lines fell. Thousands of homes were without power.

Hail is another dangerous form of precipitation. Hailstones start out as frozen raindrops. They do not fall directly to Earth, however. In large cumulonimbus clouds, winds swirl up and down. The wind carries the small hailstones back up into the clouds. There they collide with droplets in air that is near or below the freezing point. The droplets freeze immediately and coat the hailstones. The size of a hailstone depends on the amount of time it spends being buffeted by the wind inside the cloud. Most hailstones take at least 10 min to grow to about 0.5 cm. Imagine how long the hailstone shown in Figure 15.10 must have taken to form!

To many people, hail is just a nuisance. Sometimes the hailstones dent automobiles, break windows, or damage roofs. The damaged objects can be repaired or replaced, and the cost is often covered by insurance. Farmers look at hail differently. An entire crop can be destroyed in 10 to 20 min. Livestock have sometimes been killed by large hailstones. In Chapter 16, you will read about peoples' efforts to reduce the severity of hail by trying to reduce the size of hailstones.

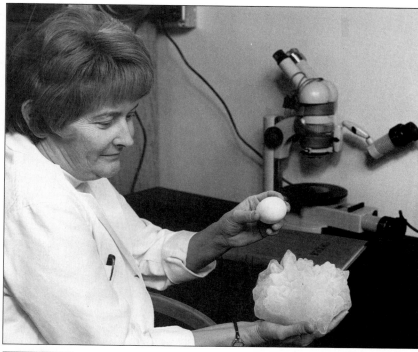

Figure 15.10 The largest hailstone ever recorded fell in Coffeyville, Kansas, in 1970. It had a mass of 0.75 kg.

Check Your Understanding

1. In the Starting Point Activity, you used an aerosol spray to provide something needed to form clouds. What serves the same purpose in nature?

2. Name two ways that cirrus clouds differ from stratus clouds.

3. Describe one way that cloud droplets can become raindrops.

4. How does sleet differ from hail?

5. **Apply** Would you expect hail to fall from nimbostratus clouds? Explain the reasoning behind your answer.

15.2 Highs, Lows, and Fronts

We live in comfortable, heated homes that protect us from most bad weather conditions. Our lives are still affected by the weather nearly every day. Imagine the following scenario.

It is a beautiful weekend day, however. The Sun is shining, and the temperature is pleasantly warm. You have a softball practice in the late afternoon, and you are planning to spend the evening with friends. You are trying to finish your homework before the practice. You are working so hard that you do not notice the change in the weather. Suddenly you realize that the windows are rattling. You look outside and see dark rain clouds coming. The wind picks up, and the sky gets darker.

Figure 15.11 Sometimes drizzling rain lasts for days. At other times, the rain seems to fall in buckets, but it is over very quickly. When you see rain clouds in the west, can you predict which type of rain is coming?

Then the rain comes pelting down. "Oh no, the softball practice is really important! The tournament starts tomorrow." Dejected, you continue with your homework. Then, as fast as it came, the storm is gone. The wind has died down, and the Sun is trying to shine. You get dressed for the practice and head out the door. Oops! You need a much warmer jacket. The temperature has dropped a lot since the storm passed. At the softball practice, the coach comments on the passing cold front. "Oh, is that what it was — a cold front? What is a cold front?"

Frontal Systems

In Chapter 14, you learned about air masses. An air mass is a parcel of air that spends enough time over a region to take on the temperature and humidity of the region. An air mass can remain in the same place for some time. It eventually begins to move, however, due to the worldwide wind currents. What happens when one moving air mass overtakes another with different characteristics? The air masses interact, sometimes violently. The zone between the air masses is called a **front.** Meteorologists define four general types of fronts: cold, warm, stationary, and occluded.

Cold Fronts

When a moving cold air mass overtakes a warmer air mass, the zone where they meet is called a **cold front.** The cold air is more dense than the warm air. It moves in below the warm air and pushes the warm air upward (see Figure 15.12). Because the warm air is pushed up rapidly, a cumulus cloud usually forms. The vapour in the rising air condenses. It releases the energy that was originally used to convert

Did You Know?

Vilhelm Bjerknes (1862–1951) led a team of meteorologists in Bergen, Norway, from 1918 to 1923. Bjerknes, often called the father of modern meteorology, developed the theory of fronts and frontal systems. Since the team was working during World War I, they used the term "front" for a clash between two air masses because it seemed similar to a "battle front," which is a clash between two armies.

it into a vapour. The latent energy reverts back into thermal energy. This reduces the rate of cooling of the air. Therefore the rising air often remains warmer than the surrounding air. It continues to rise. If the upward motion and condensation continue long enough, the cumulus cloud becomes a cumulonimbus cloud. Rain quite frequently comes with a cold front.

Some cold air masses move very slowly. Others can move as fast as 100 km/h. Fast-moving fronts can cause intense thunderstorms. The thunderstorms are often accompanied by hail and sometimes by tornadoes. You will read about these severe weather conditions in the next section.

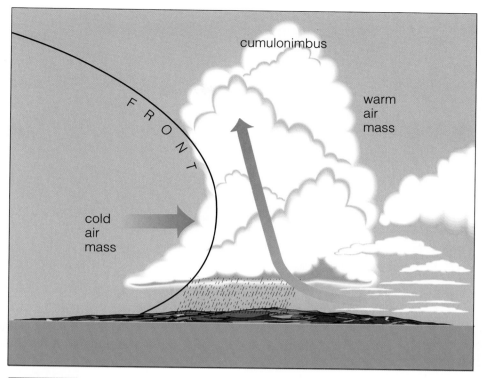

Figure 15.12 A cumulonimbus cloud usually forms just ahead of a cold front. Rain may be intense, but it usually only lasts a short time.

Warm Fronts

When a warm air mass overtakes a cooler one, a **warm front** is created. The warm air gently rides up over the trailing end of the cold air mass, as shown in Figure 15.13. The zone of contact between the two air masses is a gentle slope. Therefore stratus clouds usually form. As the warm air climbs higher up onto the cold air mass, altostratus and cirrus clouds form. Close to the front, nimbostratus clouds often bring light rain or snow. The precipitation may last much longer than it does at a cold front. It eventually passes, however. It leaves the temperature warmer than before the warm front arrived.

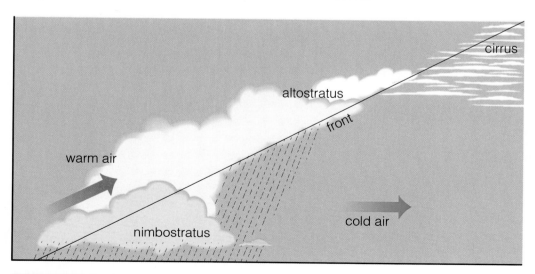

Figure 15.13 Clouds may form far ahead of the location of the front on the ground. They bring warning of a gentle rain.

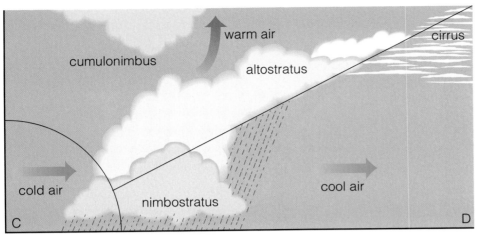

Figure 15.14 Cold fronts nearly always move faster than warm fronts. Due to this difference in speeds, a cold front can sometimes catch up with a warm front and create an occluded front.

Stationary and Occluded Fronts

A **stationary front** is just what its name indicates. A cold air mass and a warm air mass are in contact, but neither is moving. Some warm air drifts up and over the cold air mass. The zone of contact remains in the same place, however. The rising warm air condenses and forms stratus clouds and often rain. The front may remain stationary for several days. The result is a dreary, gloomy sky.

Sometimes a cold front catches up with a slower-moving warm front. This creates an **occluded front.** The approaching cold front pushes all the warm air up, away from the ground, and makes contact with the leading cold air mass. As shown in Figure 15.14, many types of clouds are present, one after the other. The cold front brings cumulus clouds. The warm front brings several types of stratus clouds, as well as cirrus clouds. Occluded fronts often cause a period of steady precipitation.

Highs and Lows

You can rarely watch a weather report or look at a weather map without seeing high pressure or low pressure systems. What are these systems? How are they related to fronts?

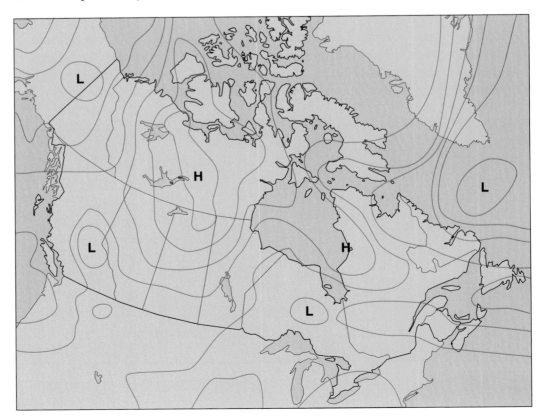

Figure 15.15 The H and L represent the centres of high and low pressure systems. The lines that encircle these symbols are called *isobaric lines*. They are drawn by connecting points of equal atmospheric pressure.

Any region where air is descending (and therefore exerting more pressure on the region below) is a high pressure system. For example, when an air mass forms over cold ground, the air cools by conduction and convection. As the air cools, it becomes more dense and settles lower to the ground. This creates more pressure. As the air continues to settle, the system draws in more air from above. Figure 15.16 shows that the high pressure system also pushes air out, toward lower pressure areas at the perimeter. Recall that the Coriolis effect causes moving air to veer to the right in the Northern Hemisphere. Therefore all the air that is pushed outward from a high pressure cell, in all directions, curves to the right. The overall result of the Coriolis effect on a high pressure cell is a clockwise rotation of air, called an **anticyclone.**

Off the Wall

The Coriolis effect is the reason why large storms spin counterclockwise in the Northern Hemisphere and clockwise in the Southern Hemisphere. Many people claim that water spins down a drain (or toilet bowl) in a different direction in each hemisphere, but this has not been proved. In reality, to see the Coriolis effect in action you have to poke a pinhole in the bottom of a cylindrical water tank, 2 m in diameter. However, the water takes about 10 000 s to start spinning.

High pressure systems create a clear sky because the air is descending instead of rising. Since the temperatures are cold high in the atmosphere, the descending air has little moisture. Thus clouds do not form. High pressure systems are usually located within a single air mass. They may be hundreds of kilometres across. Because of their size, they may cause weather conditions to stay the same for several days.

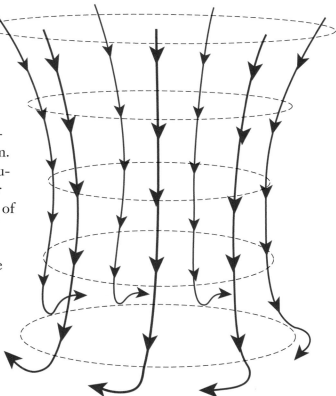

Figure 15.16 Weather conditions are usually quite stable in a high pressure cell. The air settles to the ground. This reduces the chances that clouds will form and prevents most turbulence.

A low pressure system exists where rising air is leaving less dense air below. In desert-like areas, for example, very intense heating of the ground by the hot summer Sun can create a low pressure system. The hot ground heats the air by conduction. The hot air rises, creating a zone of low pressure. As the air rises, it pulls in more air beneath it. Once again, the Coriolis effect causes the air to curve to the right. This results in rotation of the rising air (see Figure 15.17). In the Northern Hemisphere, the air in a low pressure system rotates in a counterclockwise direction, forming a **cyclone.**

You have also learned that warm air rises in a frontal system. The rising warm air creates a low pressure system. Figure 15.18 shows the steps in the development of one type of **frontal low.** Read the captions to find out, in more detail, how this system develops.

Figure 15.17 Low pressure systems usually bring unstable weather conditions. The rising air creates clouds. Precipitation often follows.

Low pressure systems are generally smaller than high pressure systems. They are most likely to occur between air masses. They bring unstable conditions, which cause changing weather, precipitation, and often storms.

DidYou**Know**?

Dust devils, such as the one shown here, are the result of very small low pressure systems. They usually occur in very hot, arid regions. The Sun heats the ground intensely. The hot ground heats the air just above it. As the air rises, it swirls and carries dust upward. On hot summer days in Canada, you can see small dust devils in sandy baseball fields or dusty parking lots. Most dust devils last only a few seconds to a few minutes. A few have been observed to last several hours, however. The wind speeds are typically below 80 km/h. Dust devils rarely cause damage, but some are strong enough to knock over a fence or even a vehicle.

A A stationary front forms between a cold air mass and a warm air mass.

B Movements within the air masses, or winds high above, disturb the front. Cool air begins to push under the warm air in a small part of the front. A small cold front forms. The darker areas in the diagrams indicate the locations of clouds.

C The cold front continues to push under the warm air. This causes the warm air to rise and form a cumulus cloud. As well, the warm air moves as a warm front. It moves up, over the cold air adjacent to the cold front. The warm front also forms clouds.

D The cold front moves about twice as fast as the warm front. It pushes more and more warm air upward.

E Eventually the cold front overtakes the warm front. It pushes all the warm air upward. Rising and rotating warm air forms a low pressure cell.

F Finally the warm air disappears. The front becomes a stationary front again.

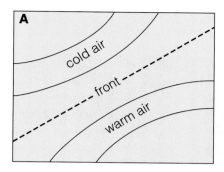

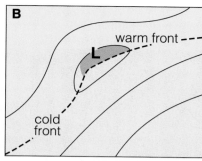

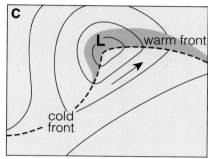

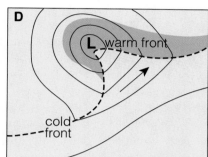

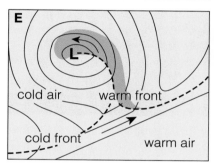

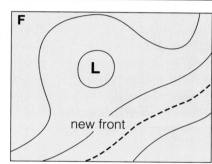

Figure 15.18 The development of a frontal low pressure system

Check Your Understanding

1. Describe the circumstances that create a cold front.

2. Name two ways in which a warm front differs from a cold front.

3. Which type of front is likely to bring a long, steady rain?

4. Compare high pressure and low pressure systems. Consider their size and the type of weather they bring.

Pause&
Reflect

Think about what you have learned about the water capacity of air, and warm and cold fronts. Provide reasons for the following observations:

When the air is cold, the sky is often clear and sunny. When the air is warm, however, the sky is likely cloudy. There may be rain.

15.3 Severe Weather

Figure 15.19 One thundercloud can produce rain, hail, lightning, and a tornado — all at almost the same time.

Looking at the photograph above, it is hard to believe that the relatively tiny tornado is the most destructive of all weather phenomena. Tornadoes do not come out of a clear blue sky. They always come from huge thunderclouds. So to learn about tornadoes, first you need to understand thunderstorms.

Figure 15.20 There is something eerily beautiful about a thunderstorm — as long as you are not out in it.

Thunderstorms

Thunderstorms themselves can be quite destructive. They bring lightning and strong gusting winds. They also bring torrential rains that can cause flash floods. Thunderstorms can form "out of the blue" in a very short time. They form from cumulus clouds that continue to grow and develop into cumulonimbus clouds. So the conditions that create thunderstorms are much the same as the conditions that create cumulus clouds. Only a small percentage of cumulus clouds ever develop into thunderclouds, however.

Meteorologists usually describe the development of a thunderstorm in three stages. The first stage is the formation of a cumulus cloud. In section 15.1, you learned that a cumulus cloud forms when warm air rises upward rapidly. This may happen because very warm ground is heated quickly by the Sun and starts the process of convection. A cold front can also cause a cumulus cloud to form. Often, in fact, many cumulus clouds form in a line along a cold front.

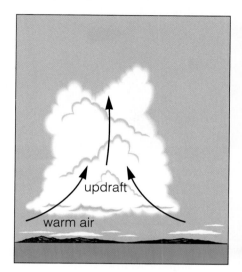

A In the first stage of a thunderstorm, a cumulus cloud forms.

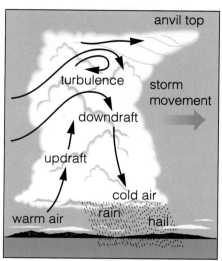

B In the second, or mature, stage, cloud droplets coalesce into snowflakes and then raindrops. The raindrops fall to Earth.

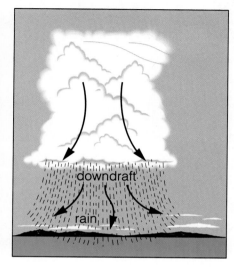

C In the final stage, warm air is no longer drawn up into the cloud. Rain continues to fall, however.

Figure 15.21 Stages in the development of a thunderstorm

How does the small, fluffy cumulus cloud develop into a cumulonimbus, or storm, cloud? As shown in Figure 15.21, a large amount of warm, moist air must be available to feed the cumulus cloud. In the second stage of thunderstorm development, more warm air rises up into the cloud and condenses. The condensation releases latent energy. The latent energy becomes thermal energy. Still warmer than the surrounding air, the warm air continues to rise. This creates an **updraft** that pulls in more air from below. Soon so many cloud droplets are rising and colliding in the turbulence that they grow larger. The cloud rises so high that the temperature at the top drops below freezing. Ice crystals form. The process of coalescence speeds up. Then rain begins. The rain cools the air and pulls it along. This creates a **downdraft.** At the peak of a thunderstorm, rain and a downdraft of cool air are at the leading edge of the cloud. An updraft of warm, moist air is at the trailing edge. The top of the cloud reaches the top of the troposphere. There strong winds are blowing, usually out of the west. These winds blow the top of the cloud forward, forming the familiar anvil shape. If the updrafts and turbulence in this stage are strong enough, hail can form.

It is during the second, or mature, stage that the thundercloud produces lightning. The extreme turbulence in the cloud causes ice crystals, snow particles, and water droplets to collide with great force. This strips electrons from some particles and leaves them on others. Positively charged particles accumulate at the top of the cloud. Negatively charged particles accumulate at the bottom. The negative bottom of the cloud drives negative charges away from the surface of the ground,

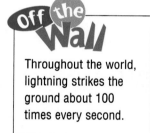

Off the Wall

Throughout the world, lightning strikes the ground about 100 times every second.

DidYouKnow?

The top of a thunder-cloud can grow upward at a rate of 10 m/s!

Figure 15.22 A lightning bolt produces the highest temperatures that occur on Earth. The source of the energy for lightning comes from the collisions of ice and snow particles in a cloud. These collisions cause positive and negative charges to separate.

Did You Know?

Approximately 90 percent of all lightning occurs between clouds.

leaving the surface of the ground positively charged. As the amount of charge separation increases, the attractive forces intensify between the positive and negative charges. Eventually the attraction is so great that a tremendous electrical discharge occurs. The charged particles race through the air, creating a bolt of lightning. The energy of the collisions of the charged particles is so great that the temperature of this thin strand of air rises to over 30 000°C — five times hotter than the surface of the Sun. Due to the intense heat, the air expands with a tremendous force. It collides with the surrounding air particles. The collisions of air particles continue outward from the lightning bolt. This forms the sound wave that we hear as thunder.

Eventually the rain and the downdraft of cool air cut off the updraft of warm, moist air — the source of energy for the storm. This is the third stage of a thunderstorm. The rain continues until the supply of moisture runs out. Then the storm is over.

Did You Know?

A tornado has enough energy to drive a piece of wood through a wall.

Tornadoes

Throughout the world, there are nearly 40 000 thunderstorms every day. Each one releases an enormous amount of energy. The largest thunderstorms deliver as much energy as a nuclear bomb. Sometimes this energy is released in the form of a **tornado.**

A tornado is a swirling funnel, or vortex, of air. It destroys nearly everything in its path. Until recently, tornadoes were very difficult to study. They destroyed any instruments that were close enough to take measurements. Currently meteorologists use Doppler radar to measure the wind speeds within a funnel cloud. They have found that these wind speeds can vary from 60 km/h to as high as 500 km/h. No wonder tornadoes are so destructive! What can possibly generate such incredible speeds?

You have probably heard the phrase "raining cats and dogs." Have you ever heard of raining fish and frogs? Some people claim that this has happened. When a tornado moves out over a lake, it may suck up the water and the animals in the water. Then drops everything on the land. This kind of tornado is called a *tornadic waterspout*. True waterspouts form directly over the warm water of oceans or large lakes. Waterspouts are similar to tornadoes. They rarely reach the intensity of severe tornadoes, however.

Meteorologists are not in full agreement about how a tornado forms. However, most tornadoes have three similar stages. The first stage is common to nearly all thunderclouds. In low pressure systems, where thunderclouds develop, a condition called **wind shear** usually exists. Wind shear means that the wind is blowing in different directions at different altitudes. As the air in the updraft of a thundercloud rises to higher altitudes, it encounters these winds blowing in different directions. The air begins to rotate. A small cyclone forms inside the thundercloud. Read the captions in Figure 15.23 to see how this cyclone can develop into a tornado.

A Nearly all thunderclouds have small cyclones of rotating air in the updraft. The wind shear that starts or intensifies the rotation is usually greater in thunderclouds that generate tornadoes.

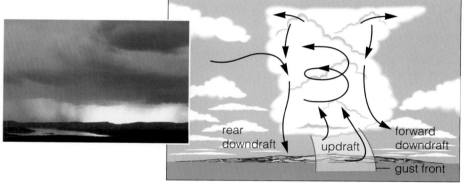

B The air pressure in the centre of the cyclone, and below it, is lower than the air pressure in the surroundings. This causes the cyclone to become narrower and stretch downward. When any rotating object becomes narrower, it spins faster. For example, ice skaters often go into a spin with their arms outspread. When they draw their arms inward, they spin much faster. As the cyclone spins faster, a wall cloud becomes visible at the base of the thundercloud.

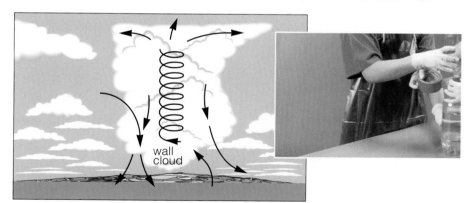

C The cyclone becomes very narrow and stretches more. A funnel cloud becomes visible below the wall cloud. When the funnel cloud touches the ground, it is a fully developed tornado.

Figure 15.23 Stages in the development of a tornado

Tornado in a Bottle

As you have learned, the Coriolis effect is important for creating spinning air in a cyclone and
anticyclone. In the next section, you will study
the importance of this effect on hurricanes.
Tornadoes spin, as well. So does the Coriolis
effect also play a role in tornadoes? In a tornado,
the energy and matter (warm air) are quickly
transferred from the ground to the cloud. You are
now going to consider the spinning of tornadoes.
You will also consider the possible role of the
Coriolis effect.

What You Need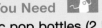

2 plastic pop bottles (2 L)
duct tape
plastic cement
stopwatch or watch with a second hand

What to Do

1. Work with a partner. Fill one of the bottles
   about three-quarters full of water.

2. Place the other bottle on top, opening to
   opening. Use a small amount of plastic
   cement to glue the bottles together.
   Reinforce the joint with duct tape.

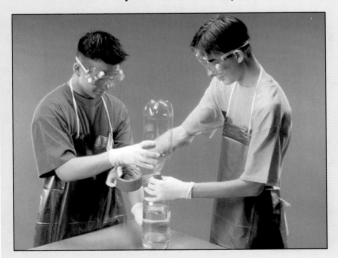

3. Invert the bottles so that the one with water
   is on top.

4. Observe and record
   (a) how the water drains
   (b) the time it takes for the water to drain

5. Repeat step 4 three times.

6. Swirl the bottles in one direction until the
   water is rotating rapidly. Invert the bottles.
   Repeat steps 4 and 5.

7. Swirl the bottles in the opposite direction,
   and invert them. Repeat steps 4 and 5.

What Did You Discover?

1. Describe the differences when the bottles
   were just inverted and when the water was
   rotated before the bottles were inverted.
   Consider both qualitative and quantitative
   differences. Relate the differences to the efficiency of the two systems.

2. Did rotating the water in the opposite direction have an effect on the time it took for the
   water to drain?

3. Compare your answers with those of other
   students.

4. What is the analogy between the swirling water
   in the bottle and the spinning air of a tornado?

5. Is the water transferred faster when it is spinning or when it is not spinning? Explain why.

6. What does your simulation of a tornado
   indicate about the efficiency of moving air
   masses and energy?

7. Infer, from your evidence, whether the
   Coriolis effect plays a role in tornadoes. Give
   two possible reasons why or why not.

DidYou**Know**?

In the early twentieth century, the residents of Codell, a small town in western Kansas, thought
they might be able to predict tornadoes. For three years in a row — 1916, 1917, and 1918 — a
tornado hit the town on the same day, May 20.

Meteorologists still have a lot to learn about predicting tornadoes. The damage and destruction they leave behind is vivid, however. Meteorologist Theodore Fujita learned how to estimate the wind speed of tornadoes by studying their damage. He developed a scale to classify tornadoes according to their wind speed and damage. His scale is shown in Table 15.1. Nearly 70 percent of all tornadoes lie in the two lowest categories. Only 2 percent are in the two highest categories.

Table 15.1 Fujita Scale for Tornadoes

Category	Wind speed (km/h)	Damage
F0	65–116	light (sheds blown over and small trees uprooted)
F1	117–180	moderate (roofs damaged and mobile homes damaged)
F2	181–253	considerate (roofs torn off houses but walls remain)
F3	254–332	severe (cars picked up off the ground)
F4	333–419	devastating (houses and large frame structures demolished)
F5	420–515	incredible (steel structures destroyed)

The average funnel cloud of a tornado varies from 30 to 60 m in diameter. Tornadoes usually travel over land at speeds of 30 to 50 km/h. They cover a distance of about 14 km. A few tornadoes have been reported to travel at speeds of from 65 to 95 km/h and to be as wide as 1.5 km. In rare cases, a tornado may travel several hundred kilometres.

Hundreds of tornadoes are reported every year. They are reported on every continent except Antarctica. The majority of tornadoes occur in North America, however. Most of these occur in the United States. A large percentage are concentrated in a region of the central plains known as "tornado alley," around the states of Oklahoma, Kansas, and Missouri. The excessively large number of tornadoes in one region is not a coincidence. Cold, arctic air reaches south into "tornado alley." Dry desert air flows in from the west. Moist tropical air moves up from the Gulf of Mexico. The interaction of extremely different air masses is ideal for creating tornadoes. Do you think the residents of "tornado alley" would use the word "ideal" to describe their situation?

Hurricanes

A tornado may be more destructive to everything in its path, but a **hurricane** is much larger and lasts much longer. Thus hurricanes leave as much or more damage than tornadoes. Like tornadoes, hurricanes are related to thunderstorms.

One large thunderstorm can release about as much energy as a nuclear bomb. A hurricane can be described as a gigantic, 500 km wide, whirling, roving thunderstorm. Where does all this energy come from?

Figure 15.24 Satellite photographs of hurricanes are very distinct. This is because they are nearly always surrounded by clear air. Here you can clearly see the swirls and central eye that are unique to hurricanes.

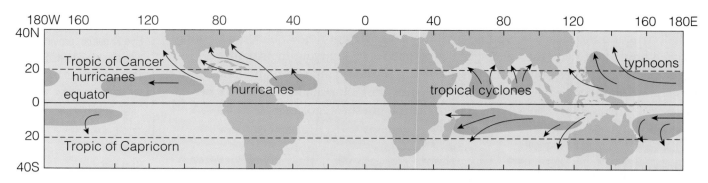

Figure 15.25 The dark areas show where hurricanes are likely to form. The arrows show which direction they travel.

A hurricane gets its energy from the thermal energy of warm, tropical, ocean water. Recall, from the discussion of El Niño, that the trade winds blow warm ocean water toward the west. They cause the water to "pile up" when it approaches a continent. This deep, warm water is what fuels hurricanes. Meteorologists have found that the water temperature must be at least 26°C, to a depth of at least 60 m, for a hurricane to develop fully and be sustained. In the Atlantic Ocean, waters reach this temperature in the late summer. As a result, most of the hurricanes in this region occur in August, September, and October. Figure 15.25 shows where hurricanes are likely to form and which direction they move. Notice that hurricanes are called **typhoons** in the West Pacific. They are called **tropical cyclones** in the Indian Ocean.

Hurricanes do not occur directly over the equator. The reason is that the Coriolis effect is absent directly over the equator. The Coriolis effect is needed to give hurricanes their spin. So hurricanes are rarely found closer to the equator than 7°N or S latitude. The majority develop between 10° and 25°N or S latitude.

Thus the following conditions are necessary to generate a hurricane:
• the conditions needed to develop a thunderstorm
• deep, warm, ocean water for energy to keep the thunderstorm going
• the Coriolis effect to give it spin

Most hurricanes that affect North America start as waves of disturbances in the trade winds over the Atlantic Ocean, west of the African coast. These easterly waves are the source of several, unorganized thunderstorms. In order for the thunderstorms to grow tall enough and strong enough to develop into a hurricane, there must be little or no wind shear. That is, the winds at the top of the clouds must be similar in strength and direction to the winds at sea level. Wind shear could tear apart the clouds and prevent their growth. The warm, moist air rises until it cools enough to condense and form clouds. As it condenses, it releases the latent energy. The latent energy keeps the air warm so that it rises higher and higher. The warm ocean water provides an almost endless supply of water vapour. The water vapour continuously adds energy to the growing storms.

As the storms grow stronger, the updrafts draw air inward. They help to pull several thunderclouds together. The Coriolis effect helps them organize and begin to rotate. When wind speeds within the storm reach about 37 km/h, the storm is classified as a **tropical depression.** When the wind speeds grow to 65 km/h, the classification changes to **tropical storm.** If the storm takes on the form shown in Figure 15.26, and the wind speeds reach 120 km/h, the storm earns the classification of hurricane.

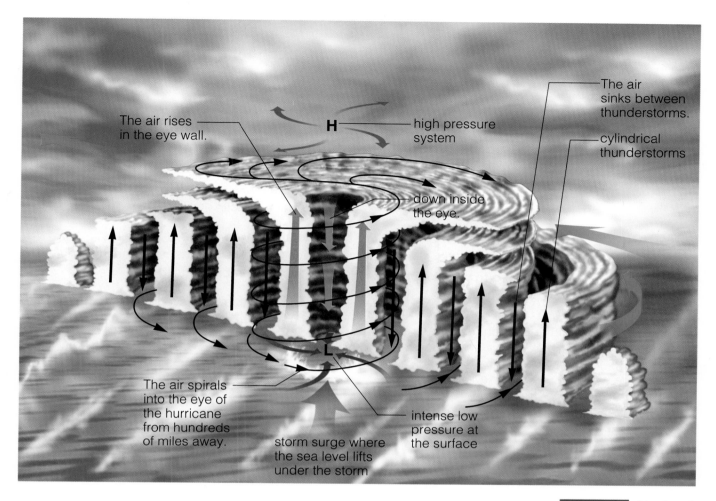

The air rises
in the eye wall.

H

high pressure
system

The air
sinks between
thunderstorms.

cylindrical
thunderstorms

down inside
the eye.

The air spirals
into the eye of
the hurricane
from hundreds
of miles away.

L

intense low
pressure at
the surface

storm surge where
the sea level lifts
under the storm

In a hurricane, the entire system is whirling around. At the same time, strong updrafts draw air into the thunderclouds. Then some air flows back down between the clouds. The rapidly rising air creates a low pressure zone at sea level. It creates a high pressure zone above the clouds. As the air moves outward from the high pressure zone,

Figure 15.26 A hurricane is made of many cylindrical thunderstorms, with spaces between the clouds.

the Coriolis effect causes it to curve to the right — opposite to the direction of the hurricane's spin. The high winds and low pressure at the centre of a hurricane draw the ocean surface upward. This ridge of sea water is called the **storm surge.** It may be as high as 5.5 m. In the middle of the hurricane, there is a calm clear central zone called the **eye.** The eye averages about 30 km wide. Sometimes tropical birds become trapped in the eye. They must move with the hurricane until it dissipates.

Hurricanes have an overall width of 300 to 800 km. The strongest winds are usually in the centre, surrounding the eye. The winds in this eye wall may vary from 120 km/h to 250 km/h. When a hurricane moves over land, it looses its speed and intensity for two reasons. First, the landforms and structures create friction for the wind. Second, there is no ocean water to feed more energy into the hurricane. Even though a hurricane looses energy over land, it is still fierce. Figure 15.27 shows an example of the type of damage a hurricane can cause.

Figure 15.27 The high winds in a hurricane can tear apart buildings and uproot trees. The water, however, is often the most damaging part of the hurricane in coastal areas. The storm surge may bring nearly 6 m of water over the land. The torrential rains can cause flooding.

Storm Surges

In coastal areas, the most damaging part of a hurricane is the storm surge. When intense winds and huge waves are already battering the shore, a storm surge can raise the sea level by several metres. In this activity, you will simulate the conditions that might lead to a storm surge.

CAUTION:

- This activity must be performed with a test tube that has been designed to withstand sudden temperature changes, such as a Pyrex™ test tube. An untreated glass test tube might shatter with the sudden temperature change.

- Use care when working near a flame.

What You Need
Pyrex™ test tube
large flat tray
china pencil
Bunsen burner
tongs

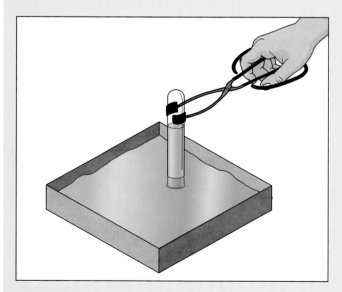

Skill
P O W E R

To review the safety symbols used in this textbook, turn to page 608.

Science Inquiry **ACTIVITY**

What to Do

1. Fill the tray with water.

2. Invert the test tube. Insert its open end just under the surface of the water.

3. Observe the level of the water. Mark it with the china pencil.

4. Add about 1 cm of water to the test tube. Place the bottom of the test tube in the flame of the Bunsen burner for 1 min.

5. Quickly but carefully invert the test tube over the tray of water. Insert its open end just under the surface of the water.

6. Observe the level of the water. Mark it with the china pencil.

7. Add about 1 cm of water to the test tube. Place the bottom of the test tube in the flame of the Bunsen burner until most of the water has evaporated.

8. Quickly but carefully invert the test tube over the tray of water. Insert its open end just under the surface of the water.

9. Observe the level of the water. Mark it with the china pencil.

What Did You Discover?

1. Describe the qualitative differences you observed in the three different situations.

2. Relate these differences to the conditions that might cause a storm surge during a hurricane.

3. Hypothesize why the water level rises to different heights. (Hint: High temperatures imply that molecules are moving more quickly. This means that the local pressure decreases.)

Monsoons

A **monsoon** is a system of winds that causes torrential rain and extensive flooding in the summer. It causes very dry conditions in the winter. Southern Asia is the only region of the world that has the unique positioning of land and oceans to create intense monsoons (see Figure 15.28). The flooding causes serious damage in the summer. The absence of monsoons for even one season, however, would result in crop losses and famine due to lack of water.

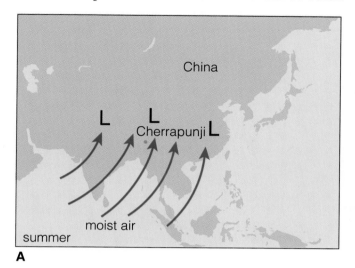

A

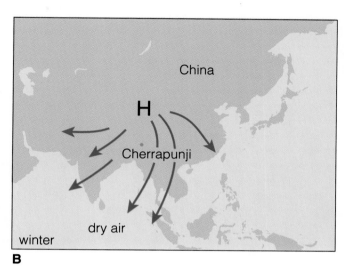

B

Figure 15.28 Monsoon winds are like huge sea breezes in the summer (A). They are like land breezes in the winter (B).

The Tropic of Cancer runs through southern India and southeast Asia. It causes the land to become intensely hot in the summer Sun. The hot air rises, drawing strong winds from over the Indian Ocean. The warm, moist air passes over the land. It generates rains that are unimaginable to those who have not experienced them. For example, the average rainfall in the town of Cherrapunji, India, in July is nearly 2.5 m. Flooding is unavoidable.

In the winter, the situation is completely reversed. The direct sunlight shines on the ocean to the south. The land cools. The wind is drawn from the land to the sea. All the wind that blows toward southern Asia passes entirely over the land, where there is little chance to pick up moisture. As well, the land to the north is cooler. Therefore the wind is very dry. In fact, a high pressure system all the way up in Siberia directs cold, dry air toward southern Asia. To get a sense of the extreme contrast between summer and winter, consider the fact that the average rainfall in the town of Cherrapunji, India, in January is only 0.2 cm.

DidYou**Know**?

At one time, female names were given to hurricanes and typhoons. Meteorologists began to name these weather events during World War II, when it became important to keep track of storms that could affect flight missions over oceans. Meteorologists decided to use female names for all hurricanes that began between the Tropic of Cancer and the Tropic of Capricorn. They decided to use male names for those that began between the tropics and the poles. Of course, this was before they realized that all hurricanes and typhoons developed in the tropics. As you have learned, the conditions that are required for these events to begin occur only in the tropics.

Weather affects the lives of every single human being. Some people experience much more severe weather than others, however. How does weather affect your life? What can you do to be prepared for the difficulties that weather may cause? What do you need to know so that you can be prepared for coming weather conditions?

What impact do you think global warming might have? Most predictions warn of coastal cities being affected by rising sea levels. Other drastic changes may also occur, however. Use the Internet or print resources to research the current rainfall patterns in India during January and July. Compare these with the projected rainfall patterns if global warming continues for 50 years or 100 years. Given that most of the rainfall happens because of the monsoons, why do you think the precipitation pattern would change? In other words, what would happen to the monsoons? What would probably happen to the region that India occupies?

Check Your Understanding

1. How can updrafts and downdrafts exist in the same thundercloud?

2. What causes thunder? Explain in detail.

3. Describe one thing that is happening inside a thundercloud just before a tornado develops.

4. Describe the weather conditions that are most likely to generate a tornado.

5. What is the source of energy that causes a hurricane to develop?

6. Why do hurricanes not form close to the equator?

Now that you have completed this chapter, try to do the following. If you cannot, go back to the sections indicated.

Describe the conditions that make it possible for clouds to form. (15.1)

Explain the three mechanisms for lifting air, which result in cloud formation. (15.1)

State the name of very high, wispy clouds. Describe conditions that might cause these clouds to form. (15.1)

Name two different types of rain clouds. (15.1)

Describe the process of coalescence in the formation of rain. (15.1)

Explain how hail forms. (15.1)

Describe the appearance of the sky when a cold front is coming through. (15.2)

Explain how a warm front develops. (15.2)

Describe one type of frontal system that is likely to cause a long period of steady rain. (15.2)

Explain why high pressure systems tend to rotate in a clockwise direction. (15.2)

Explain why thunderclouds are able to grow to such extreme heights. (15.3)

Describe the relationship between ice crystals, hailstones, and lightning. (15.3)

Explain the importance of wind shear to the formation of a tornado. (15.3)

Compare and contrast the destructiveness of a tornado and a hurricane. (15.3)

Explain why hurricanes occur only over tropical oceans. (15.3)

State the two names that apply to developing hurricanes. (15.3)

Explain how monsoons can be both beneficial and destructive. (15.3)

Summarize this chapter by doing one of the following. Use a graphic organizer (such as a concept map), produce a poster, or write the summary to include the key chapter concepts. Here are a few ideas to use as a guide:

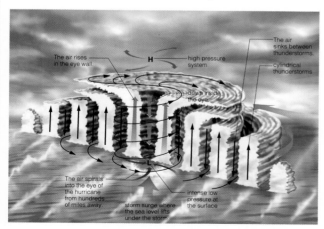

The air rises in the eye wall.

high pressure system

The air sinks between thunderstorms.

cylindrical thunderstorms

down inside the eye.

The air spirals into the eye of the hurricane from hundreds of miles away.

storm surge where the sea level lifts under the storm

intense low pressure at the surface

Prepare Your Own Summary

- What conditions are required for cloud formation?
- What does a nimbostratus cloud look like?
- If a weather forecast says that a warm front is coming through, what kind of weather can you expect?
- If the sky is clear and the forecaster says that the weather will not change for several days, what type of pressure system is probably present?
- How might a thunderstorm develop?
- What weather conditions make it likely that a tornado will develop?
- Why are there never any hurricanes directly over the equator?
- What are the characteristic shapes and locations of land and sea that are "ideal" for the formation of a monsoon?

Reviewing Key Terms

If you need to review, the section numbers show you where these terms were introduced.

1. In your notebook, indicate whether each statement is true or false. Correct each false statement by replacing the italicized term with another term.

   (a) Small raindrops grow into large raindrops by the mechanism of *deposition*. (15.1)

   (b) A *stationary front* may bring several days of steady, gentle rain. (15.2)

   (c) A *cyclone* is a large mass of air that is rotating in a clockwise direction. (15.2)

   (d) A *cold front* is likely to cause cirrus clouds to form a long distance ahead of the location of the front on the ground. (15.2)

   (e) A *typhoon* is the same as a hurricane. (15.3)

2. In your notebook, match each description in column A with the correct term in column B.

A
• thundercloud
• featureless layers of cloud
• weather condition caused by a cold air mass overtaking a warm air mass
• weather condition caused by wind moving in different directions at different altitudes
• first stage of a developing hurricane
• raindrops that freeze while passing through very cold air
• giant land breeze and sea breeze that changes direction with the seasons
• clouds made of ice crystals
• weather condition caused by warm air rising inside a thundercloud
• meeting of two air masses

B	
• cumulus (15.1)	• occluded front (15.2)
• cirrus (15.1)	• updraft (15.3)
• stratus (15.1)	• downdraft (15.3)
• nimbostratus (15.1)	• tornado (15.3)
• cumulonimbus (15.1)	• wind shear (15.3)
• coalesce (15.1)	• hurricane (15.3)
• sleet (15.1)	• typhoon (15.3)
• hail (15.1)	• monsoon (15.3)
• freezing rain (15.1)	• tropical storm (15.3)
• cold front (15.2)	• tropical depression (15.3)
• warm front (15.2)	• easterly wave (15.3)
• front (15.2)	

Understanding Key Concepts

Section numbers are provided if you need to review.

3. Describe the function of dust, pollen, smoke, or sea salt in the formation of clouds. What is the term that describes this function? (15.1)

4. Describe conditions in which clouds would be very high. (15.1)

5. State the three general characteristics for classifying clouds. (15.1)

6. Describe the most common process that produces raindrops in the temperate zone, where Canada is located. (15.1)

7. What conditions are likely to produce freezing rain? (15.1)

8. Sketch a cross section of a cold front. Explain each part of your sketch. (15.2)

9. Describe the sky conditions that you would expect to see before, during, and after the passing of a warm front. Include types of clouds and precipitation. (15.2)

10. What causes an occluded front? (15.2)

11. State the direction that air rotates around a high pressure system. Explain why. (15.2)

12. Compare the average sizes of high and low pressure systems. (15.2)

13. Describe the process that causes cumulonimbus clouds to grow extremely tall. (15.3)

14. Sketch a thundercloud at its second (mature) stage. Include labelled arrows to show all the winds that are involved in the storm. Use + and − signs to show where charged particles accumulate. Show where rain is falling. (15.3)

15. What role does wind shear play in the formation of a tornado? (15.3)

16. Why is "tornado alley" ideal for creating tornadoes? (15.3)

17. Explain the conditions that are necessary for
    (a) initiating a hurricane
    (b) sustaining a hurricane
    (c) causing a hurricane to spin (15.3)

18. Describe the eye of a hurricane. (15.3)

19. Explain the negative and positive aspects of monsoons. (15.3)

Developing Skills

20. Name the following clouds. State the conditions that might cause each cloud to form.

21. Construct a concept map with the terms and phrases below.

    In boxes:
    - Random thunderstorms form.
    - Thunderstorms group together.
    - tropical depression
    - tropical storm
    - hurricane
    - Hurricane does not develop.

    On arrows between boxes:
    - on equator
    - 10°N latitude
    - high wind shear
    - no wind shear
    - sea water at 25°C
    - sea water at 27°C

Skill POWER

For tips on making a concept map, turn to page 578.

Problem Solving/Applying

22. Some people ignore tornado warnings. Use your knowledge of tornadoes to prepare a convincing argument that people must go to a basement. Either make your presentation in class or write out your argument.

23. Your family has been invited to visit friends in Fort Lauderdale, Florida. You have a choice between the first week in June or the third week in September. Based on your new understanding of severe weather, which time would you suggest for your family to go? Explain why.

Critical Thinking

24. Why do you think people live in areas where it is likely that a severe weather event will damage or destroy their property at some time in the future?

25. You are planning a hike in the mountains in the fall. The chances of a heavy blizzard are small but not zero. How will you prepare for the hike?

Pause& Reflect

1. Go back to the beginning of the chapter, on page 484, and check your original answers to the Opening Ideas questions. How has your thinking changed? How would you answer those questions now?

2. What was your greatest misconception about weather before you studied this chapter? Where did you get the incorrect information? How will you attempt to correct any misconceptions that your friends or family members have?

16 Humans and Weather

Science
Log

In your Science Log, write possible answers to the questions above. Compare your answers with those of your classmates. Which answers could you and your classmates not agree on? As you study this chapter, compare what you learn with the answers you wrote.

Weather satellites, such as the one you see here, are commonplace today. Weather satellites peer down on every square metre of Earth's surface. They send back an abundance of information continuously. At the same time, hundreds of automatic weather stations send weather data to central offices. Weather radar penetrates clouds to search out rain or snow. Weather balloons rise through the atmosphere, gathering data as they climb.

Meteorologists use computers to try to make sense of all the data that flood in. People cannot seem to get enough weather information. Some radio stations report weather more frequently than every 30 min. You can log on to the Internet at any

moment, and check weather conditions anywhere in the world. It is hard to imagine that weather satellites have been orbiting Earth for less than 50 years. It is even harder to imagine that, just over 160 years ago, scientific weather forecasting was not possible at all! How did people decide what to wear? How did they protect themselves from dangerous storms?

In this chapter, you will learn about the instruments that collect weather data. You will find out how meteorologists use the data to make forecasts. You will explore the influence of weather on history when forecasting was not possible. As well, you will see how humans unintentionally influence weather.

Key Concepts

In this chapter, you will discover

- how meteorological instruments measure properties of the atmosphere
- how meteorologists use data to create weather maps
- how meteorologists use weather maps to make a forecast
- what some ancient societies believed about weather
- how weather affected the lives of people in the past
- how weather affects our lives today
- what challenges the future holds for weather and climate

Key Skills

In this chapter, you will

- build instruments to measure properties of the atmosphere
- measure wind speed and direction
- measure humidity
- interpret weather maps

Key Terms

- psychrometer
- hygrometer
- aneroid barometer
- bar
- Beaufort wind scale
- anemometers
- wind vanes
- Doppler radar
- isotherms
- isobars
- Coordinated Universal Time (UTC)
- trends
- analog method
- Numerical Weather Prediction (NWP)
- temperature inversion

Play the Part

Weather affects everyone's life. For example, you make decisions based on the weather nearly every day. What will you wear on the way to school? Do you need an umbrella? Do you need snow boots? Some people, however, must make more critical decisions based on the weather. How fast is the storm moving? Should we reroute the airplane to avoid the storm?

What information do people need in order to make these decisions?

What to Do

1. Play the role of one of the people in the list below.
   - owner of a construction company
   - banker
   - farmer
   - captain of a Caribbean cruise ship
   - pilot
   - mayor
   - minister of agriculture
   - ski lodge operator
   - manager of a fishing fleet

2. In the role of the person you chose, answer the following questions.
   a) What type of weather information will you need?
   (b) How far in advance will you need this information?
   (c) How will your needs change with the season of the year?

3. Form a group with three or four other students. Discuss your answers.

What to Discover?

1. Contrast the needs of people in different jobs.

2. Discuss similarities in peoples' needs for weather information. Is there one type of weather information that nearly everyone uses? If so, what is it?

16.1 Collecting Weather Data

Figure 16.1 How many different types of data have these friends just shared?

Crickets make good thermometers. When the temperature increases, crickets chirp faster. When the temperature drops, they chirp slower. It is possible to count the number of times that a cricket chirps in 1 min and use this to estimate the temperature.

The friends on the telephone have just exchanged a lot of information about the weather. How many different measurements were needed to report this information? How were these measurements taken?

Measuring Temperature

Galileo Galilei (1564–1642) invented the first thermometer more than 400 years ago. The most common method for measuring temperature today is based on the same principle that Galileo used. This principle is that a change in the temperature of a fluid causes a change in the density of the fluid. In previous science courses, you learned that the buoyancy of a solid object depends on the density of the fluid in which it is placed. When a solid object is less dense than a fluid, it will float in the fluid. When the solid is more dense than the fluid, it sinks.

To build his thermometer, Galileo placed sealed, glass balls in a cylinder. The cylinder was filled with a special fluid. The densities of the sealed balls do not change with temperature. The density of the fluid does change, however. Therefore the balls sink or float, depending on the density and thus the temperature of the fluid. The lowest ball that is still floating indicates the temperature.

If the density of the fluid changes with temperature, then the volume must also change. Convince yourself that this is true by completing the MathConnect on the left.

Figure 16.2 This modern Galileo thermometer is very much like the one that Galileo invented in 1596.

Math CONNECT

Recall that the formula for density (D) is

$D = \dfrac{m}{V}$

The density of water at 4°C is 1.000 g/mL. What is the volume of 500 g of water at 4°C?

The density of water at 95°C is 0.961 g/mL. What is the volume of 500 g of water at 95°C?

In today's common thermometers, either mercury or alcohol is sealed in a glass tube. (The alcohol contains a dye, so that it can be seen.) The volume of the mercury or alcohol increases with an increase in temperature. A scale on the glass tube shows the exact temperature.

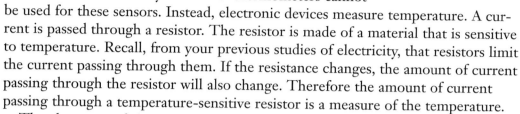

Temperature sensors are sometimes placed in remote locations or sent aloft in weather balloons. They must be read automatically. The data are then radioed back to a central location. Mercury or alcohol thermometers cannot be used for these sensors. Instead, electronic devices measure temperature. A current is passed through a resistor. The resistor is made of a material that is sensitive to temperature. Recall, from your previous studies of electricity, that resistors limit the current passing through them. If the resistance changes, the amount of current passing through the resistor will also change. Therefore the amount of current passing through a temperature-sensitive resistor is a measure of the temperature.

The placement of a temperature sensor is critical. If it is placed too near the ground, the temperature of the ground will influence the reading. If it is placed in direct sunlight, the thermometer will absorb radiant energy. The thermometer will become much warmer than the air. Therefore temperature sensors are put in boxes, such as the one in Figure 16.3.

These boxes are placed 1.2 m above ground level. They are always painted white so they reflect radiant energy rather than absorbing it. This prevents the temperature inside from increasing. No matter how good an instrument is, it needs to be placed correctly. Otherwise the readings will not be valid.

Figure 16.3 This "weather shack" has slats that allow air to flow freely through it. They also protect the instruments inside from direct sunlight and rain.

Pause&
Reflect

Have you noticed that concepts you studied in previous science courses are important for understanding weather? Write down at least four concepts you studied previously that are helping you understand weather.

Measuring Humidity

In Chapter 13, you calculated relative humidity. You did this when you measured the dew point temperature in the activity on page 432. The method you used, however, is not the most common method for measuring humidity. Instruments called **psychrometers** are generally used. They measure relative humidity based on the effects of evaporation.

If the relativity humidity is 100 percent, then no water can evaporate into the air. At any relative humidity lower than 100 percent, evaporation occurs. As the humidity drops lower and lower, the rate of evaporation increases. Therefore the rate of evaporation is a measure of relative humidity.

What happens when water evaporates from a surface? Evaporation removes thermal energy from the surface. This cools the surface. Therefore the temperature of a moist surface, when evaporation is as rapid as possible, should lead to the relative humidity. If the surface is the bulb of a thermometer, the temperature is easy to measure.

A psychrometer has two identical thermometers. One thermometer has a bulb that is open to the air (dry bulb). The other has a bulb that is covered by a wet cloth (wet bulb). When water begins to evaporate from the wet bulb, the air near the bulb becomes more humid than the surrounding air. This would soon cause the evaporation rate to decrease. Therefore you must move the air rapidly past the wet bulb. This will ensure that the air near the bulb has the same humidity as the surrounding air.

The instrument in the photograph is called a sling psychrometer. It has a handle with thermometers attached to a joint. To measure humidity, you hold the handle and rapidly swing the thermometers in a circle. Then you compare the temperature readings. To find out how to convert the readings to relative humidity, complete the following activity.

Another instrument for measuring humidity is the **hygrometer.** Hygrometers are based on the principle that certain materials, such as human hair, bind water from the air and change in length. A measure of the change in length reflects a change in humidity.

Figure 16.4 To use a sling psychrometer, hold the handle and rapidly swing the thermometers in a circle.

Some hygrometers are located in remote areas or carried high into the atmosphere by weather balloons. These hygrometers use an electronic measuring device. An electric current is passed through a solid, hygroscopic salt. (A hygroscopic salt is a salt that tends to bind water.) As water binds to the salt, the electrical resistance of the salt changes. The amount of current that flows through the circuit containing the salt is a measure of the relative humidity of the air.

How Humid Is It?

How do you interpret the temperature readings on a psychrometer? What can humidity values tell you about the air around you? You will answer these questions by building and testing a psychrometer.

What You Need

2 identical laboratory thermometers
2 pieces of stiff cardboard
cellophane tape
support stand
2 clamps
gauze pad (2 cm x 2 cm)
string
water

What to Do

1. In your notebook, make a data table with the following headings: Location, Dry bulb temperature (°C), Wet bulb temperature (°C), Difference in temperatures (°C), Relative humidity (%). Leave at least four rows for data.
2. Wrap the gauze pad around the bulb of one of the thermometers. Tie on the gauze pad with the string.
3. Securely fasten both thermometers onto one piece of stiff cardboard. The bulbs should extend below the edge of the cardboard. Have your teacher check your apparatus before you lift it upright.
4. Clamp the cardboard to a support stand. Make sure that the thermometers are upright.
5. Soak the gauze pad with water.
6. Fan the thermometers briskly with the second piece of cardboard. Read the temperatures on the thermometers every 5 s (while fanning). Stop when the temperature of the wet bulb thermometer stays the same for at least two readings. Record the temperatures.
7. Repeat steps 5 and 6 in at least two other locations. For example, take readings in the hallway and outside (if the temperature is not below freezing).
8. Calculate the difference between the two readings. Record it in your table.
9. Determine the relative humidity. Find the dry bulb temperature in the top row of the table below. Find the temperature difference in the first column. Then find the square where the row and the column meet. The number in this square is the relative humidity. Record the value.

What Did You Discover?

1. In your table, find the location with the lowest relative humidity. Then find the location with the highest relative humidity.
2. In what other way(s) did these two locations differ?
3. Write a statement to explain why the relative humidities were different at these locations.
4. Write down any questions you have about this activity or your results. Discuss these questions as a class.

Relative Humidity

Dry Bulb Temperature (°C)

Difference Between Dry Bulb and Wet Bulb Temperature (°C)	5	6	7	8	9	10	11	12	13	14	15	16	17	18	19	20	21	22	23	24	25	26	27	28	29	30	31	32	33	34	35
1	86	86	87	87	88	88	89	89	90	90	90	90	90	91	91	91	92	92	92	92	92	92	92	93	93	93	93	93	93	93	94
2	72	73	74	75	76	77	78	78	79	79	80	81	81	82	82	83	83	83	84	84	84	85	85	85	86	86	86	86	87	87	87
3	58	60	62	63	64	66	67	68	69	70	71	71	72	73	74	74	75	76	76	77	77	78	78	78	79	79	80	80	80	81	81
4	45	48	50	51	53	55	56	58	59	60	61	63	64	65	65	66	67	68	69	69	70	71	71	72	72	73	73	74	74	75	75
5	33	36	38	40	42	44	46	48	50	51	53	54	55	57	58	59	60	61	62	62	63	64	65	65	66	67	67	68	68	69	69
6	20	24	26	29	32	34	36	39	41	42	44	46	47	49	50	51	53	54	55	56	57	58	58	59	60	61	61	62	63	63	64
7	7	11	15	19	22	24	27	29	32	34	36	38	40	41	43	44	46	47	48	49	50	51	52	53	54	55	56	57	57	58	59
8				8	12	15	18	21	23	26	27	30	32	34	36	37	39	40	42	43	44	46	47	48	49	50	51	51	52	53	54
9						6	9	12	15	18	20	23	25	27	29	31	32	34	36	37	39	40	41	42	43	44	45	46	47	48	49
10									7	10	13	15	18	20	22	24	26	28	30	31	33	34	36	37	38	39	40	41	42	43	44
11											6	8	11	14	16	18	20	22	24	26	28	29	31	32	33	35	36	37	38	39	40
12														7	10	12	14	17	19	20	22	24	26	27	28	30	31	32	33	35	36

Word CONNECT

The term "barometer" is derived from two Greek words: *baros,* meaning "weight," and *metron,* meaning "measure." What weight are you measuring with a barometer?

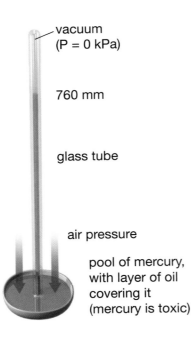

vacuum
(P = 0 kPa)

760 mm

glass tube

air pressure

pool of mercury, with layer of oil covering it (mercury is toxic)

Measuring Atmospheric Pressure

Barometers measure atmospheric pressure. In some laboratories today, you may still see mercury barometers much like the first one invented by Evangelista Torricelli (1608–1647) in 1644. Examine Figure 16.5 to review the principle behind mercury barometers.

Figure 16.5 A barometer has a glass tube that is sealed at one end and filled with mercury. The tube is inverted. The open end is placed in a pool of mercury, without letting any air inside. The mercury column in the tube drops down. It stops dropping when the pressure that the atmosphere exerts on the surface of the mercury in the pool equals the pressure that the column of mercury in the tube exerts on the pool. When standard atmospheric pressure is acting on the pool of mercury, the height of the column of mercury is 760 mm. When atmospheric pressure goes up, it pushes on the pool of mercury. The column of mercury goes up.

Off the Wall

Why is mercury used in a barometer instead of water? If water were used, the barometer would have to be more than three stories high. Try to reason why.

The **aneroid barometer** is another common instrument for measuring atmospheric pressure. Some air is removed from a flexible container called an **aneroid cell.** Then the aneroid cell is sealed. When atmospheric pressure increases, it compresses the cell. When atmospheric pressure drops, the cell expands. Any change in the volume of the cell causes the needle to move on the scale (see Figure 16.6).

Recently scientists have developed electronic sensors that can measure atmospheric pressure. These sensors con-

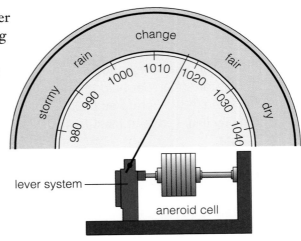

lever system

aneroid cell

Figure 16.6 The aneroid barometer is designed so that a slight change in the size of the aneroid cell causes a significant change in the position of the needle on the scale.

tain thin silicon membranes. The membranes show a change in electrical resistance when exposed to different pressures. Once again, the amount of current that flows through the silicon is a measure of the pressure on the membrane.

In previous science courses, you learned that the unit for pressure is a pascal (Pa). A pascal is equal to a force of one newton (N) exerted over an area of one square metre. Meteorologists usually report atmospheric pressure in units of millibars (mb), or thousandths of a **bar.** One bar is 100 000 Pa or 100 kPa. The bar is a convenient unit because it is almost the same as standard atmospheric pressure. (Standard atmospheric pressure is 1.013 bar or 1013 mb.)

Math CONNECT

Example

Convert 1024 mb to pascals (Pa).

$$1024 \text{ mb} \times \frac{1 \text{ b}}{1000 \text{ mb}} \times \frac{100\,000 \text{ Pa}}{\text{b}} = 102400 \text{ Pa or } 102.4 \text{ kPa}$$

Problem

Convert 983 mb to pascals (Pa).

Building a Better Barometer

Home weather stations are becoming quite popular. Suppose that an instrument company is planning to design kits for people to build their own weather instruments. You work for this company. Your assignment is to design a kit for building an accurate pressure-tendency barometer. **Note:** A pressure tendency barometer only measures changes in pressure. It does not measure actual pressures.

Challenge

Design and test a kit for building a pressure-tendency barometer. The barometer must measure the direction of changes in atmospheric pressure. Include written directions for assembling the barometer.

Safety Precautions

Be careful when using scissors and other objects that have sharp edges.

Materials

variety of containers, such as a coffee can, jar, and bottle
rubber from a variety of balloons
elastic bands
string
tape or glue
straw or another material for a pointer
paper
scissors
thermometer
other materials of your choice

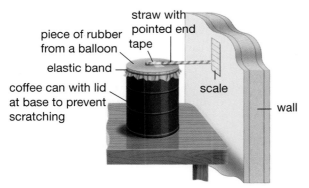

piece of rubber from a balloon
straw with pointed end
tape
elastic band
coffee can with lid at base to prevent scratching
scale
wall

Design Criteria

A. The materials should be inexpensive and easy to obtain.

B. The barometer must be well-sealed so that no air leaks in or out, and it should respond to small changes in atmospheric pressure.

C. Your directions for assembling the barometer should be easy to follow.

Plan and Construct

① Some members of your group may have built a barometer like the one in the illustration. Discuss how it works and how you could improve the design.

② Discuss whether atmospheric pressure and other factors will affect the barometer. Decide how to make correctors to eliminate errors caused by these factors.

③ Make a list of test criteria. Choose the criteria that you will use.

④ Check your design with your teacher. Then build and test your barometer. Write directions for assembling your barometer, using materials in your kit.

⑤ Find someone who is not in your group. Ask them to follow your written directions and build the barometer.

Evaluate

1. How sensitive was your barometer? That is, how small a pressure change could your barometer detect?

2. How appropriate were your design criteria? If you wanted to test more barometer designs, would you use another criteria?

3. How clear were your directions? Did your volunteer tester have any trouble following your directions?

4. What changes would you make in your design if you were to start again? What changes would you make in the testing process?

Table 16.2 Beaufort Wind Scale

Beaufort number	Description	Observations	Wind speed (km/h)
0	calm	Smoke rises vertically. Sea is like a mirror.	0–2
1	light air	Smoke drifts. Wind vanes do not move. There are ripples on sea.	3–6
2	light breeze	Wind can be felt on face. Leaves rustle. Winds vanes move. There are small wavelets in sea.	7–11
3	gentle breeze	Leaves and twigs move. Small flags are extended. There are wavelets and scattered whitecaps at sea.	12–19
4	moderate breeze	Dust and loose paper rise. There are small waves and many whitecaps.	20–29
5	fresh breeze	Small trees sway. There are moderate ocean waves.	30–39
6	strong breeze	Large branches move. Whistling can be heard in power lines. There are large waves and ocean spray.	40–50
7	near gale	Trees bend. It is hard to walk. There is white foam on breaking waves.	51–61
8	gale	Twigs break off trees. Walking is extremely difficult. There are very long, moderately high waves.	62–74
9	strong gale	Slight damage to buildings may occur. Crests of waves roll over. Ocean spray reduces visibility.	75–87
10	storm	Trees are uprooted. Buildings are damaged. Sea is white with foam, and tumbling of sea is observed.	88–101
11	violent storm	This is very rare. There is widespread damage and very high waves.	102–119
12	hurricane	This is very rare. There is severe damage to structures. Sea is heavy and foaming. Ocean spray drastically reduces visibility.	120 and higher

Figure 16.7 Canadian meteorologist John Patterson developed the three-cup anemometer. Patterson was the director of Canada's weather service from 1930 to 1946.

A The propeller type of anemometer must point into the wind to measure wind speed correctly. The wind vane keeps the propeller pointed in the right direction.

B The cup anemometer responds equally to winds from any direction.

Measuring Wind Speed and Direction

The environment contains many natural wind speed detectors: things that move in the wind. Wind speed was very important to sailors in the days before steam-powered ships. In 1805, British Commander Francis Beaufort developed a system that allowed sailors to estimate wind speeds. The sailors only needed to observe the motion of the sea and the motion of objects on the ship. This system is called the **Beaufort wind scale.** The scale has now been expanded to include objects on land. It still provides good estimates for experienced observers.

Meteorologists need much more accurate wind speed and direction monitors than trees and oceans. Instruments called **anemometers** measure wind speed. **Wind vanes** show wind direction. Two common combinations are shown in Figure 16.7. Wind speed can be determined from the rotation rate of either the propeller or the cups. A wind vane has a large tail. The tail makes the arrow point in the direction from which the wind is coming. When using a propeller type of anemometer, the wind vane keeps the anemometer pointed into the wind. To get accurate data, the anemometer should be placed at a height of about 10 m. It must be located in an open area so that buildings and trees do not alter wind direction or speed. You will build your own wind vane and anemometer in the following investigation.

Note: Meteorologists usually report wind speeds in knots. "Knots" is short for nautical miles per hour. One knot equals 1.85 km/h.

Measure the Wind

Two of the most important measurements in meteorology are wind direction and wind speed. In this investigation, you will build and test a wind vane and an anemometer. Then you will use your instruments to determine right and wrong ways to measure wind speed and direction.

Part 1
Determining Wind Direction

Problem

How can you determine the direction from which the wind is blowing?

Safety Precautions

- Use care when cutting plastic.
- Be very careful when hammering nails.

Apparatus

compass or magnetic direction finder
hammer
scissors
compass
protractor

Materials

thin, stiff plastic
plastic straw
wood block (5 cm × 5 cm × 50 cm)
wood sticks (approximately 1 cm × 2 cm × 30 cm)
9 nails (1 very fine, 8 others small)
tape
washer
stiff paper

Procedure

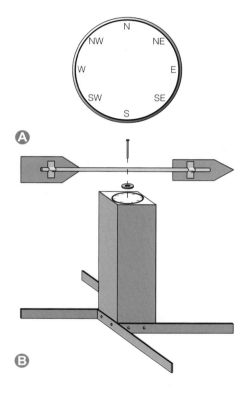

A

B

1 Use the compass to draw a circle on the stiff paper. The circle should have a diameter of 5 cm.

2 Write symbols for the compass directions, as shown in diagram A above. Use the protractor to determine the 45° angles between each symbol.

3 Cut out the circle. Attach it to the end of the wood block.

4 Nail the "feet" onto the wood block, as shown in the diagram.

5 Cut a small arrow (tip of wind vane) and a large arrow (tail of wind vane) out of the stiff plastic. Estimate sizes from the diagram.

6 With the scissors, cut small slits (one 3 cm and the other 5 cm) in each end of the plastic straw. Be sure that the slits are aligned.

7 Insert the tip and tail of the arrow into the slits in the plastic straw. Secure them with tape.

8 Find the point along the straw where it balances on your finger. Mark this point. Hold the straw so that the tip and tail of the arrow are vertical. Push the fine nail vertically through the straw at this point. Twist the nail to enlarge the hole. Make sure that the straw will turn freely on the nail.

9 Put the nail through the washer. With the hammer, pound the nail into the block at the centre of the paper compass.

10 Wait for a day when the wind is blowing. Place your wind vane in an open area. (If the wind is blowing too hard, you may need to put weights on the "feet" of your instrument.)

CONTINUED ▶

⑪ Use your magnetic compass to orient the N on your wind vane toward magnetic north. Test your wind vane at two different heights above the ground. Observe and record the wind direction.

⑫ Choose four other locations, near trees, buildings, or steep hills. Observe and record wind directions in each location.

Analyze

1. What direction does the arrow point, into the wind or in the direction of the wind? What makes it point in that direction?

2. Describe the accuracy and effectiveness of your wind vane.

Conclude and Apply

3. Write a paragraph that explains the best method for obtaining accurate wind direction measurements. In your paragraph, include a description of the effect of trees, buildings, or any other large objects on the direction of the wind.

Part 2

Determining Wind Speed

Problem

How can you measure the speed of the wind?

Safety Precautions

Be careful when using the scissors and the needle.

Apparatus

scissors
compass
protractor
ruler
wind vane (from Part 1)
needle that is long enough and strong enough to go through the Ping-Pong™ ball
thimble
coloured marker

Materials

stiff cardboard
Ping-Pong™ ball
40 cm nylon line
glue

Procedure

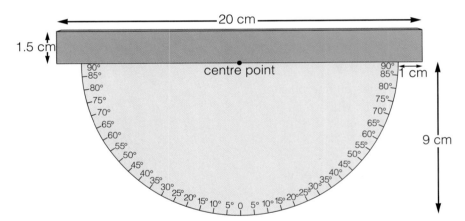

❶ Use a ruler and compass to draw an angle measuring scale similar to the one shown above. Use to the dimensions in the diagram. Use a protractor to mark off every 5°. Mark the centre point. Cut out the device.

❷ Thread the nylon line through the needle. With great care, use a thimble to push the needle through the centre of the Ping-Pong™ ball. (If you have trouble getting the needle through the ball, ask your teacher for help.) Tie a knot in the end of the nylon line. Pull the thread through the ball until the knot almost reaches the ball. Glue the knot to the ball.

❸ Push the needle through the centre point on the cardboard scale. (The needle should be treaded with the nylon line.) Remove the needle. Tie a large knot in the end of the nylon line. Glue the knot to the cardboard scale.

❹ Colour the nylon line with the marker to make it easier to see. This completes your anemometer.

5 Wait for a day when the wind is blowing. Take your wind vane and anemometer to an open area. Use your wind vane to determine the wind direction.

6 Hold the anemometer so that the cardboard scale is parallel to the wind direction. Hold it away from your body, as shown in the photograph. This ensures that you do not disturb the wind. Read and record the angle on the scale.

7 Immediately after reading the angle, observe the effects of the wind on leaves, trees, smoke, dust, or any other objects that the wind might be moving. Use the Beaufort wind scale on page 524 to estimate the wind speed.

8 Choose four other locations, near trees, buildings, or steep hills. Observe and record the wind direction and angle on your anemometer in each location. Also estimate the wind speed using the Beaufort scale.

9 For each angle you measured with the anemometer, use the table below to convert the angle into a wind speed.

Wind Speeds

Angle (°)	Speed (km/h)
0	0
5	10
10	13
15	16
20	19
25	21
30	24
35	27
40	29
45	32
50	35
55	38
60	42
65	46
70	53

Analyze

1. Compare the wind speeds you determined using your anemometer with the wind speeds you estimated using the Beaufort scale. How similar are the values?

2. How do large objects, such as trees and buildings, affect the wind speed?

3. How might you improve the accuracy of your anemometer?

Conclude and Apply

4. How accurate do you believe your hand-held anemometer is?

5. Write a paragraph to summarize the way that large barriers affect wind speed.

Measuring Precipitation

What could be difficult about measuring rain or snow? Just put out a bucket, and measure the amount of water or snow in it. Think for a moment about how difficult 1 mm or 2 mm would be to measure. The measurement is much easier if you collect the rain with a funnel directed to a small cylinder as shown in the figure on the left. You must be sure that trees or buildings do not shelter the rain gauge. You must be sure that wind does not cause the readings to be inaccurate.

Some automatic instruments have funnel-shaped buckets that tip over when they are full. These instruments are called *tipping bucket gauges*. The buckets are attached to an electric circuit. The circuit sends a signal when the bucket tips. The number of times that the bucket tips is a record of the amount of rain that fell.

Snow is difficult to measure due to wind and to settling of the snow. A board should be placed in an area where wind is least likely to disturb the snow. The snow on the board should be measured and brushed off every few hours during a long snowfall. This prevents the lower levels of snow from being packed by the snow that accumulates on top.

Figure 16.8 Rain gauge made from a funnel connected to a cylinder with a tubing.

Figure 16.9 Twice a day, at about 150 sites around North America, helium-filled or hydrogen-filled weather balloons are released.

A World of Weather Data

Most countries have weather agencies that are similar to Environment Canada. These agencies collect and share data. Environment Canada's Automated Weather Observation System (AWOS) includes approximately 100 units placed throughout the country. Each unit collects a variety of data. It automatically radios the data to a central location. At least once an hour, the data are organized and sent to other agencies throughout the world. Many other countries also have automated systems. Much data are still collected by individuals, however, and relayed to a central location.

Weather Balloons

As you have learned, temperature, pressure, and humidity all change with altitude. To have a complete data set of weather data, upper air data are needed. These data are usually obtained with weather balloons, such as the one shown in Figure 16.9. Each balloon carries a "mini weather station," called a *radiosonde*. Electronic sensors detect temperature, pressure, and humidity. A tiny radio sends the data back to the ground. Tracking the balloon itself provides information about wind direction and speed at different altitudes.

A typical balloon rises to an altitude of nearly 25 km. It sends back data continuously. Eventually the density of the atmosphere becomes so low that the balloon expands and bursts. A small parachute carries the instruments back to the ground. A card on the balloon asks the finder to return the balloon to a specific address.

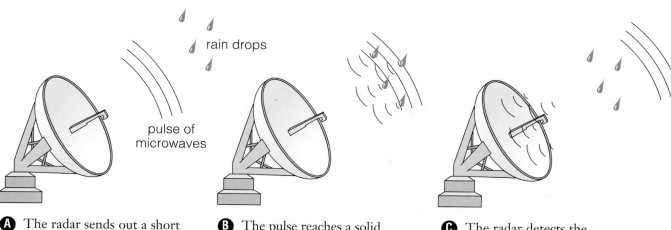

A The radar sends out a short pulse of microwaves.

B The pulse reaches a solid or liquid object, such as a raindrop. The object reflects some of the microwave energy.

C The radar detects the reflected pulse.

Figure 16.10 Radar instruments send out microwaves in pulses. In between pulses, the antenna "listens" for reflected pulses.

Weather Radar

Radar can detect solid objects or liquid drops that are larger than approximately 1 mm. Therefore radar cannot see cloud droplets. It can detect rain, snow, sleet, or hail, however. One of the great advantages of radar is that it can penetrate a cloud to see if raindrops are forming inside. The main function of weather radar is to detect precipitation and thus track storms.

Radar emits microwaves that are reflected back when they hit a solid or liquid object (see Figure 16.10). The radar instrument emits pulses of microwaves. Between pulses, it detects any reflected signals. Radar can determine the distance from the object by measuring the length of time between sending a pulse and receiving the reflected signal. The intensity of the reflected signal indicates the amount of precipitation that is falling. Computers convert the intensity of the signal into different colours. This makes the images easier to interpret (see Figure 16.11).

About ten years after radar had become a common tool of meteorologists, a new technique was developed. This technique was named **Doppler radar**. At first, Doppler radar collected so much data, so fast, that the computers could not handle the data. Today's computers, however, can process huge amounts of data very rapidly. Thus Doppler radar has become an excellent tool. Doppler radar can locate a storm. It can also determine the direction and speed with which the storm is moving. In fact, if two Doppler radar systems are tracking the same storm at the same time, computers can combine the data. Then the computers can create a three-dimensional image of the storm. To learn how Doppler radar works, read the captions in Figure 16.12 on the next page.

Figure 16.11 The various colours on the radar image show the different amounts of precipitation.

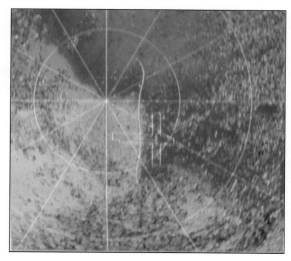

A Raindrops are moving toward the radar system. Every time a wave hits a raindrop, the raindrop is closer than it was when the last wave reached it. Therefore the reflected waves are closer together. This makes the frequency of the reflected waves higher than the frequency of the outgoing wave. Computers can calculate the speed of the raindrops from the difference in the frequencies of incoming and outgoing waves.

B The opposite is true of raindrops that are moving away from the radar system. The reflected waves are farther apart. This makes their frequency lower than the frequency of the outgoing waves.

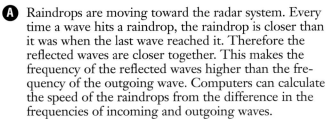

Figure 16.12 Doppler radar detects differences in the frequencies of transmitted and reflected waves.

Doppler radar can even distinguish between types of precipitation. A special technique allows the radar to detect the shape of the drops. Large raindrops are round and flat, like a hamburger. Since hail is nearly spherical, Doppler radar can tell the difference. The use of Doppler radar allows meteorologists to warn residents of the coming of severe thunderstorms, hailstorms, and tornadoes.

Weather Satellites

The field of meteorology took a giant step forward with the launching of satellites. For the first time, meteorologists could see the world as a whole. Satellite images fill gaps in meteorological data. They fill gaps especially over oceans, where it is difficult to get information.

Two general types of satellites can provide data about every part of Earth. Geostationary satellites orbit Earth at the same rate that Earth rotates. Therefore they remain above the same point on Earth at all times. These satellites orbit over the equator, as shown in Figure 16.13A. Polar orbiting satellites move north and south as Earth rotates beneath them. They complete one orbit in just under 2 h. Therefore they can generate an image of the entire globe in about 6 h. An example of the path of a polar orbiting satellite is shown in Figure 16.13B.

Satelite moving at same speed that Earth is moving.

satellite

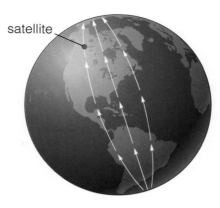

satellite

Earth is rotating beneath it.

A One geostationary satellite can see most of the Western Hemisphere. It remains over the same point on Earth. Therefore it can observe changes, such as storm movements, as they are occurring.

B Earth is turning below a polar orbiting satellite. Its path appears to wrap around Earth, as shown here.

Figure 16.13 Meteorologists use both types of weather satellites. This allows them to collect data for every point on Earth.

Unlike radar, satellites do not emit any electromagnetic waves. Satellites only detect light and infrared radiation coming from Earth and the atmosphere. Most weather satellites have at least three separate detectors. One detector senses visible light that is scattered or reflected by Earth, clouds, and other gases or particles in the atmosphere. The other two sensors detect two different ranges of wavelengths of infrared radiation.

Visible light sensors detect clouds, haze, and pollution. They also identify severe storms. These sensors can distinguish between thick and thin clouds. Thin clouds do not appear as bright as thick clouds. They cannot determine how high the clouds are located, however. Infrared sensors detect heat. For this reason, they can distinguish between high and low clouds. Low clouds have higher temperatures than high clouds. Infrared sensors can also distinguish between water, snow, and ice crystals. As well, they can detect forest fires and volcanoes, and they can determine sea surface temperatures. Longer wavelength infrared sensors detect upper-level water vapour and winds. By comparing images from all three types of sensors, meteorologists can collect an abundance of information.

Check Your Understanding

1. Explain the principle on which common thermometers are based.

2. Why must you swing a sling psychrometer in the air?

3. Explain how an electric circuit can be used to measure humidity.

4. What can Doppler radar detect that common radar cannot detect?

5. Compare and contrast the information obtained by visible light detectors and infrared detectors on weather satellites.

16.2 Weather Maps and Forecasting

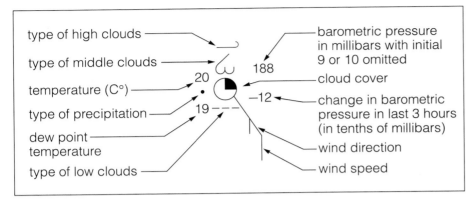

type of high clouds

type of middle clouds

temperature (C°)

type of precipitation

dew point temperature

type of low clouds

barometric pressure in millibars with initial 9 or 10 omitted

cloud cover

change in barometric pressure in last 3 hours (in tenths of millibars)

wind direction

wind speed

Figure 16.14 Nearly a dozen bits of weather data are displayed in this small station model.

Pause&Reflect

Predicting weather in 30 min and 3 h is called "nowcasting." Who would need exact data from nowcasts?

How would you predict the weather half an hour from now? Would you use the same approach to predict the weather three hours, three days, three weeks, three months, or three years from now? Most likely you would not. To predict the weather in half an hour, you could look out a window and check the sky to the west. What if the Sun was shining, but you saw trees blowing in the wind and a storm cloud in the west? You would probably predict that it would be raining in half an hour. The best method for predicting the weather in three months or three years is to use climate information. You would base your prediction on the average of the data for the particular time of year, over a period of several years. The challenge comes in trying to predict the weather in three hours, three days, or three weeks.

Suppose that you wanted to prepare a short-term forecast. You would need to collect and analyze weather data from the past several days, over a wide area. You would have difficulty, however, if you tried to analyze lists of numbers for temperature, atmospheric pressure, wind speed, and precipitation data. For this reason, meteorologists organize the data on a weather map.

Model Problem

The following values for atmospheric pressure were taken from a station model: 029, 863. Express these values in millibars (mb).

Given Numbers from station models: 029, 863

Required Atmospheric pressure in units of millibars (mb)

Analysis 029 is lower than 500, so the prefix is 10.
863 is higher than 500, so the prefix is 9.
To convert to millibars, use one decimal place.

Solution With the prefix 10, 029 is 10029.
With one decimal place, 10029 becomes 1002.9 mb.

With the prefix 9, 863 becomes 9863.
With one decimal place, 9863 becomes 986.3 mb.

Paraphrase The atmospheric pressure is 1002.9 mb at the first station and 986.3 mb at the second station.

Weather Maps

There is a lot data to put on a weather map. Therefore meteorologists use symbols to condense the data. All the information from one station can be expressed in symbols, similar to those shown in Figure 16.14. Appendix E lists the symbols with their meanings. Only two of the symbols need an additional explanation. From Figure 16.14, it is hard to tell if the wind is blowing from the southeast or from the northwest. Think of wind direction as an arrow. The wind speed barbs are the feathers. The circle is the tip. The arrow points in the direction toward which the wind is blowing. Remember, however, that wind direction is reported as the direction *from* which the wind is blowing. Therefore Figure 16.14 indicates that a southeasterly wind is blowing.

All atmospheric pressure (barometric pressure) values at Earth's surface start with 9 or 10. In an effort to conserve space, the 9 or 10 is omitted in the station models. If the reported number is below 500, you may assume that a 10 was omitted. If the number is above 500, assume that a 9 was omitted. To interpret the number in units of millibars (mb), you must also put a decimal point before the last digit. For example, the value 188 in the figure means 1018.8 mb.

Meteorologists combine information from dozens of weather stations. They create a map, such as the one in Figure 16.15. Then the analysis begins. The first step is often to draw lines called **isotherms.** These lines connect points of equal temperature, as shown in Figure 16.16A. Isotherms are especially useful for locating air masses, since the temperatures within an air mass should be quite similar.

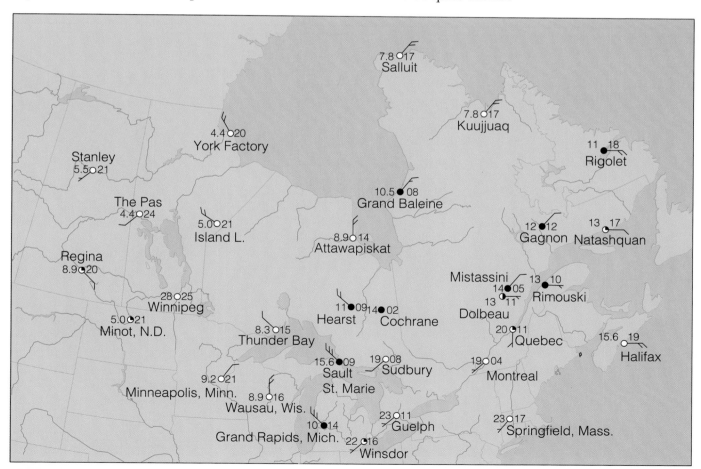

Figure 16.15 Data such as these are collected every hour at many weather stations. The data are entered into computers that produce these maps.

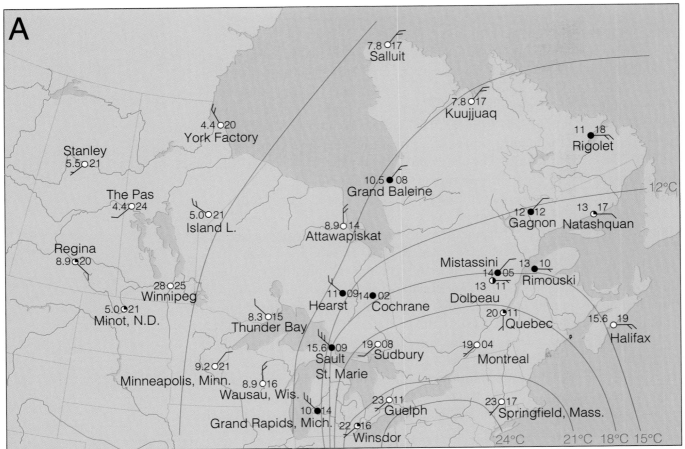

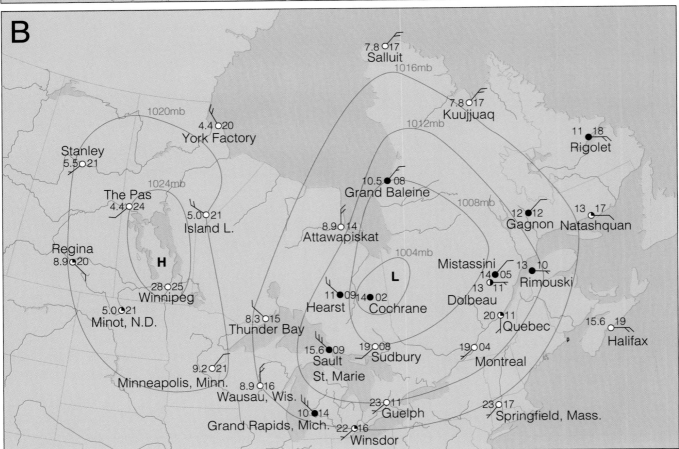

Figure 16.16 These isotherms and isobars look much like the lines that show equal altitude on a topographical map.

Isotherms are also useful for locating frontal systems. Look for isothermal lines that are close together. These closely spaced lines show that temperatures are changing significantly over a short distance. This is what you would expect for a frontal system.

Next you would probably draw **isobars.** These lines connect all points that have the same atmospheric pressure. The isobars often produce closed loops within loops (see Figure 16.16 B) that help to identify high and low pressure systems. What if a region of rapidly changing temperature overlaps with a low pressure system? You can be quite sure that a front is located in the area.

Examine the lower middle part of the map. Notice where the isotherms are very close together. You also see strong winds, overcast skies, and a thunderstorm. Unquestionably this is a cold front. Now start at the centre of the low pressure system. Look to the east. Here the isotherms are somewhat close together. When you look north of these isotherms, you see overcast sky for many kilometres. This indicates the presence of a warm front. Consult Figure 16.17 to see the symbols that represent cold fronts, warm fronts, and occluded fronts.

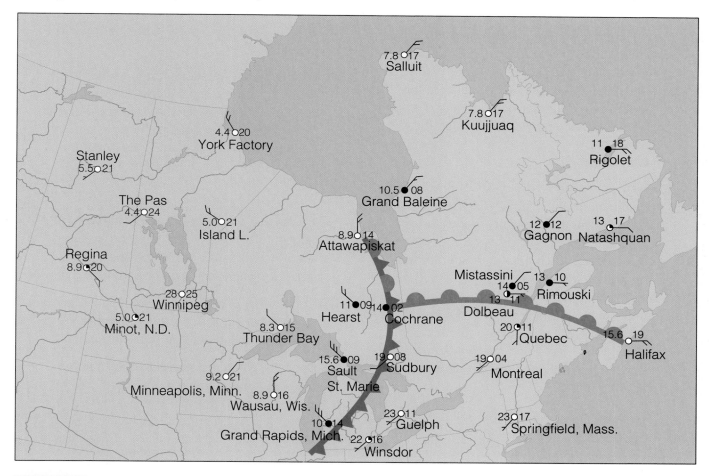

Figure 16.17 The blue lines represent cold fronts. The triangles point in the direction that a front is moving. The red lines represent warm fronts. The half circles show the direction of motion. Combine the two types of lines, and you have the symbol for an occluded front.

Interpreting Weather Maps

Organizations, such as Environment Canada, that prepare weather maps use computers to analyze them. You can develop a stronger understanding of weather maps by analyzing one yourself.

What You Need

2 copies of a weather map
highlighter (optional)
pencil
black, red, and blue pencils or markers

What to Do

1. Your teacher will provide you with two copies of a weather map. (The weather map will be similar to the one in Figure 16.14.) Study the weather map. Look for patterns of temperatures. You may want to highlight the temperature data on one copy of the map. Before starting to write on the map think carefully about where you might draw isotherms.

2. Draw isotherms for every 3°C. For example, draw lines at 0°C, 3°C, 6°C, 9°C, and so on. Draw your isotherms with a pencil, so you can erase them if you discover that you are on the wrong track. Pick a temperature at one of the extremes on the map. Then make small marks every place that you see this temperature. In many cases, your selected temperature will be between two temperatures on the map. Estimate the distance between the stations that your temperature might be found.

3. Sketch a smooth line to connect your marks.

4. Follow the same procedure for other temperatures at 3°C intervals. If you feel confident that your lines are correct, you may wish to trace over them with a black pencil or marker.

5. On the second copy of the map, use the same approach to draw isobars. Draw your isobars 4 mb apart. When you have completed your isobars, label the centres of high (H) and low (L) pressure systems.

6. Study both maps. Look for characteristics of fronts. Look at the temperatures behind and ahead of possible fronts. Consider the sky conditions.

7. When you find possible fronts, sketch them in pencil. Review them again. Do you feel confident that they fit what you know about fronts? If so, draw cold front symbols with the blue pencil or marker. Draw warm front symbols with the red pencil or marker.

What Did You Discover?

1. Was it easy or difficult to draw isotherms and isobars? Discuss any problems you encountered. How difficult or easy was finding frontal systems by analyzing the isobars and isotherms?

2. Compare your map with your classmates' maps. How similar or different are the weather maps drawn by your classmates?

3. Describe what you learned about meteorology by analyzing a weather map.

DidYou**Know**?

Meteorologists and pilots have a saying that helps them remember the location of high and low pressure systems with respect to wind direction. They say "Keep the low on your left and the wind at your back." Think about what you learned about wind circulating around high and low pressure systems. Can you see why the saying is correct?

What Time Is It?

You just analyzed a weather map for one specific time. Your map covered at least four time zones. How would you label your map so that anyone, anywhere in the world, would know the time at which these conditions existed? You need a universal time reference.

In Chapter 13, you learned that the zero degree longitudinal line is called the prime meridian. It runs through Greenwich, England. The time zone that contains the prime meridian has long been the reference time for all navigation and weather communications. For many years, the reference time was called Greenwich Mean Time (GMT). GMT is based on the position of the Sun with respect to the prime meridian. More recently, however, an atomic clock has been adopted as the standard. At times, it is a few seconds different from GMT. The reference time that is based on the atomic clock is called **Coordinated Universal Time (UTC).**

Weather Maps and Forecasting

Suppose that someone asked you what you thought was the biggest breakthrough in weather forecasting. What would you say? Many people would say satellites or computers. It is true that satellites have provided a huge source of data that was not available before. Computers can manage such large amounts of data very rapidly. Thus they have improved forecasting. Nevertheless, fairly good forecasting was possible before these technologies were introduced.

Forecasting was not possible at all, however, before the invention of the telegraph. Think about this. You have to know the current weather conditions at least several hundred kilometres in all directions, especially to the west, in order to forecast the weather in your area. Before the telegraph, weather systems travelled faster than messages. The telegraph made rapid communication possible for the first time. Therefore forecasting became a science in 1844, when Samuel Morse (1791–1872) invented the telegraph.

DidYou**Know**?

The telegraph was the first method of communication that was faster than a horse and rider. The telegraph carried electrical signals over a wire. Samuel Morse developed a code for all the letters of the alphabet. The letters were represented by dots and dashes. The sender "tapped out" a message on a key. An operator on the other end of the line received the message. The operator listened to the long and short signals and decoded the message. Soon the telegraph was improved. The sender could type a message on an instrument that was similar to a typewriter. Each key sent a unique signal. A similar instrument on the other end of the line typed the message that was received.

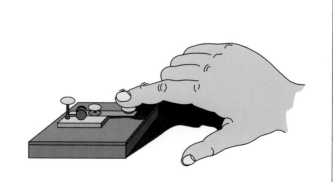

The biggest drawback to the telegraph was the need for wires, or lines, to carry the signals. Thousands of kilometres of lines had to be built and maintained. Then, in the 1920s, Marconi invented the "wireless" telegraph, or radio. The telegraph started down the road to obsolescence.

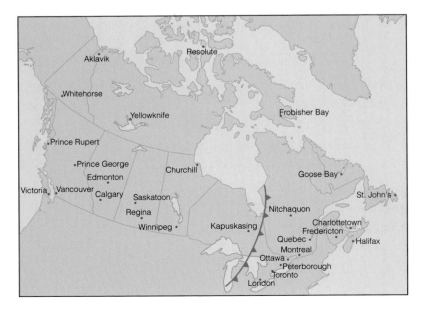

You how know what frontal systems and pressure systems are, and how they interact. You can use your knowledge to prepare forecasts based on the **trends.** You need to collect weather maps for several days. Then analyze the motion of the fronts, highs, and lows, and any other information on the maps. Determine how fast and in what direction systems are moving. Notice whether the trend continues. That is, notice whether the systems continue to move with the same speed and direction. If they do, you can predict where fronts and pressure systems will be in one day, two days, or more.

Consider the movement of the front shown in Figure 16.18. Notice that the cold front has moved about 400 km on each of the last two days. The last map gives data at midnight UTC, or 7:00 p.m. Eastern Standard Time the night before. (Eastern Standard Time is five time zones from the prime meridian. Therefore it is 5 h before midnight.) If the fronts continue to move as they have been for three days, the cold front should hit Peterborough at about 1:00 p.m. EST. Now it is your turn to use these methods to make a forecast.

DidYou**Know**?

Do you know why the weather forecast is always near the end of local television newscasts? News program producers know that the main reason most people tune in to the news is to hear the weather forecast. People will leave the television on through the entire newscast and, of course, the commercials, in order to hear the weather forecast.

Figure 16.18 These weather maps show the locations of a cold front on three successive days. Each map represents the conditions at 0000 UTC. Observing trends, or the direction and speed in which weather systems are moving, allows you to predict where the systems will be. It also allows you to predict what will happen over the next few days.

Forecast the Weather

Here is your chance to put your knowledge to work. You will use current newspaper or Internet weather maps to predict the weather for two days. Notice that the newspaper weather maps do not contain the detailed station models. Instead, the maps summarize data and often use special icons. As well, some weather maps do not use symbols that are the same as those in Appendix E. Each newspaper weather map has a key, however. The key tells you what the symbols and icons mean.

Problem

What will the weather conditions be tomorrow and the following day?

Materials

5 weather maps for 5 consecutive days (ending the day of or the day before this investigation is done)

Procedure

❶ Your teacher asked you to find and save weather maps for five consecutive days, ending yesterday or today (if you used a morning newspaper). Lay out the weather maps so that you can see all of them.

❷ Pick three communities for which you will make forecasts. One should be the community where your school is located. The other two should be at least 200 km from your community and from each other. Pay special attention to the locations of these communities while you are carrying out the following steps.

❸ Locate the warm, cold, occluded, and stationary fronts on the maps. Identify fronts that appear to be the same but have moved from one day to the next. Determine how fast and in what direction they have been moving.

❹ Predict and record where you expect these fronts to be tomorrow and the following day.

❺ Identify high and low pressure systems that appear to be the same, having moved from day to day. Determine the speed and direction in which they are moving.

❻ Predict and record where you expect the high and low pressure systems to be tomorrow and the following day.

CONTINUED ▶

7 Compare temperatures on the two sides of each frontal system. Notice how they are changing (or not changing) from day to day.

8 Look for patterns in sky conditions and precipitation, such as clear, cloudy, rain, or snow. Note how these patterns move from day to day.

Analyze

1. Where do you expect the frontal systems to be tomorrow and the following day, with respect to the three communities you identified in steps 1 and 2 of the Procedure?

2. Will the three communities be in a high or a low pressure system tomorrow and the next day?

3. Will cloud cover, rain, or snow move into the three communities tomorrow or the following day?

Conclude and Apply

4. Think about your answers to the Analyze questions. Prepare forecasts for tomorrow and the following day for the three communities. Include temperature, sky conditions, wind (calm or windy), atmospheric pressure trends (increasing or decreasing), and precipitation.

5. Compare your forecasts for your own community with a television, newspaper, or web site forecast.

6. Put aside your results for two days. Record the actual weather conditions in your community tomorrow and the next day. Compare the weather conditions in your community with your forecasts. Also compare them with the forecasts you used in question 5.

7. How accurate was your forecast? How have your ideas about forecasting changed? Write a paragraph to summarize the ease or difficulty of using trends for forecasting.

Extend Your Skills

8. Think about the concepts you have learned in this unit. Use these concepts to answer the following questions about forecasting. Give reasons for your answers.

   (a) In comparison with a clear sky, how will cloud cover affect daytime temperatures? How will cloud cover affect nighttime temperatures?

   (b) In comparison with bare ground, how will snow cover affect daytime temperatures? How will snow cover affect nighttime temperatures?

   (c) On a very clear night, would you expect the temperature to be cooler if the wind is blowing or if the air is completely still?

Computers and Forecasting

Figure 16.19 Weather computers such as this one, can link up with other computers around the world. These connections give meteorologists up to the minute information.

Meteorologists have been using computers to help them make forecasts for over 50 years. The improvements have been tremendous. Today computers, such as the one in Figure 16.19, can make billions of calculations every second.

When computers were originally used in forecasting, many meteorologists believed that the **analog method** would be the best method to use. For this method, enormous amounts of weather station data had to be stored in a computer. Then the current conditions were entered. The computer searched for as many days as possible with conditions similar (analogous) to the current conditions. Then the computer looked at the weather on the days that followed all of the analogous days it had found. The forecast was based on what happened in the past. Forecasts that were made in this way could be quite good. No two days are identical, however. Sometimes small differences in weather conditions caused large errors in a forecast.

Today computers rely mostly on a method called **Numerical Weather Prediction (NWP).** Meteorologists enter many elaborate equations into a computer. They start with the most fundamental principles of science. These principles include equations of force and motion and equations describing the conservation of energy. Then they add complex equations that describe interactions occurring within the atmosphere. You have learned about many of these interactions. For example, heat is transferred from matter at a higher temperature to matter at a lower temperature. Air moves from a region of higher pressure to a region of lower pressure. Anything that is moving on Earth's surface curves to the right in the Northern Hemisphere and to the left in the Southern Hemisphere. Finally meteorologists enter current data. Then the computer goes to work. It predicts data for such conditions as wind, pressure, temperature, and precipitation. Meteorologists scrutinize the data to see how these conditions will interact and produce weather.

Forecasting has improved tremendously with technology and with experience. It is certainly not perfect, however. The equations can still be improved. Current data may be flawed or missing. Nevertheless forecasts help us prepare for each day. More importantly, forecasts have saved many lives by warning people about severe weather, such as tornadoes, hurricanes, monsoons, and even El Niños.

Skill
P O W E R

To find out more on Organizing and Communicating Scientific Results turn to page 599.

Career **CONNECT**

"And Now the Weather . . ."

Weather forecasters with television stations must combine two very different skills. They must understand the weather information they are describing to viewers. They must also be able to present it well.

In Canada, weather forecasters usually complete a program, such as broadcast journalism, at a post-secondary institution. They also complete a first-year university course in meteorology. There are no rules that say what education or credentials a Canadian weather forecaster must have in order to do the job. Generally applicants just have to prove that they are qualified.

The job of a weather forecaster combines communication skills with science skills. In reality, very few jobs are either pure science or pure arts. For example, research scientists need the skills to communicate their test results effectively. Artists need to know about such things as the viscosity of different types of paints.

Think about a job you have had or would like to have some day. List the different responsibilities that are involved in this job. Consider the skills that would help you meet these responsibilities. Which responsibilities require mathematics or science skills? Which responsibilities require arts or humanities skills? On your list, indicate which responsibilities require which skills. Compare your list with other students' lists.

Check Your Understanding

1. The following values for atmospheric pressure were taken from a station model. Express these values in millibars (mb).

   (a) 895   (b)   117   (c)   083

2. Describe the method for drawing isobars on a weather map.

3. What pattern of isotherms and isobars indicates the presence of a cold front?

4. Why are giant supercomputers needed in order to use the Numerical Weather Prediction method of forecasting?

5. **Apply** There are cirrus clouds in the sky. Later in the day, altostratus clouds move in. What would you predict about the weather over the next few days?

6. What is Greenwich Mean Time? Why is it important?

16.3 Past, Present, and Future

For as long as humans have lived on Earth, weather has been on the mind of nearly everyone. Early humans were dependent on rain to water their crops. They had no irrigation. Extreme heat or cold could devastate their herds of cattle, sheep, or goats. Thunderstorms and hail were not only frightening but also dangerous. No one could escape weather.

We can be quite sure that weather was extremely important to these early people because the most powerful gods in their mythology were gods of weather. In the unit opener, you read about the Greek god Zeus, the controller of the sky. Perhaps you have also read about the Egyptian Sun god, Ra. Thor was the Norse god of thunder and lightning. Quetzalcoatl was the Aztec wind god. The list goes on and on.

Figure 16.20 Quetzalcoatl, the Aztec god of wind.

Early Mythology About Weather

Societies that did not worship gods nevertheless passed on many myths about weather. For example, a myth of the Micmac people tells about a great leader named Glooskap. One severe winter, he became troubled because his people were suffering from cold and famine. He went out in search of the cruel giant, Winter. When Glooskap found Winter, the giant's charm put him to sleep. Glooskap was strong, however, and he awoke. Then a loon came to him. The loon told him about a country far to the south where it was always warm. Glooskap went to the seashore. He rode south on the back of a whale until the air and water grew warm. When he went ashore, he found a beautiful woman dancing with some children. He saw the flowers in her long, brown hair. He immediately knew that she was Summer. He persuaded her to go north with him to visit Winter's home. When she saw the distress that Winter was causing Glooskap's people, she was moved. Summer was stronger than Winter, so she melted his icy wigwam. She told Winter that he could rule Glooskap's land for six months of every year. At the end of the six months, she would return and bring warmth and comfort to the land. This is the story of how Glooskap found summer.

The written records and the oral stories of nearly every ancient society include mythology about weather. Often the high priests or witch doctors were believed to have the power to predict weather. Some societies, such as the Aztecs, offered sacrifices to their gods so that their gods would provide rain for their crops. In Nigeria and medieval Europe, people performed ceremonies that they believed would prevent thunderstorms and hailstorms. All in all, weather is one of the most universal topics in mythology.

DidYouKnow?

North American First Nations were not the only societies that performed rain dances. The Aboriginal people of Australia performed rain dances for the Rainbow Serpent. They believed that the Rainbow Serpent had the power to send rain.

INTERNET CONNECT

www.school.mcgrawhill.ca/resources/

If you want to read more about mythology and gods of weather, go to the web site above. Go to **Science Resources**, then to **SCIENCEPOWER 10** to know where to go next. Share your favourite myth with your class.

The Scientific Approach to Weather

The Greek philosopher Aristotle (384–322 B.C.E.) was the first person to attempt to explain weather as a natural occurrence. In *Meteorologica*, Aristotle portrayed weather events as natural interactions among what he believed to be the four basic elements: Earth, Air, Fire, and Water. Many of Aristotle's ideas were inaccurate, but he "started the ball rolling." For several centuries, no one questioned Aristotle's ideas. Then, in the sixteenth century, scientists added to a growing base of scientific knowledge about weather. Table 16.3 lists some leading scientists and their contributions to the science of studying weather.

Word CONNECT

The modern term "meteorology" comes from the name of Aristotle's book, *Meteorologica*. Look up this term in a dictionary. Find the meanings of the Greek words that form the core of "meteorology" and "meteorologica."

Table 16.3 Scientists and the Science of Meteorology

Scientist	Contribution to meteorology
Leonardo da Vinci	invented the hygrometer for measuring humidity
Galileo Galilei	invented the thermometer for measuring temperature
Evangelista Torricelli	invented the barometer for measuring atmospheric pressure
Blaise Pascal	discovered that air pressure decreases with altitude
Isaac Newton	explained the colours of the rainbow (see Figure 16.21)
Robert Boyle	discovered the relationship between the pressure and volume of a gas
Antoine Lavoisier	discovered that air contains nitrogen, oxygen, and carbon dioxide
John Dalton	discovered that the amount of water in saturated air varies with temperature
Gustave-Gaspard de Coriolis	showed, mathematically, how moving objects are affected by Earth's rotation

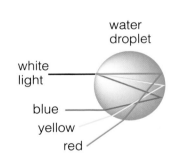

Figure 16.21 When white light enters a water droplet in the air, it refracts or bends. The shorter wavelengths (blue) bend more than the longer wavelengths (red). This causes the colours to separate. The light reflects off the back of the droplet. It refracts again when exiting the droplet. When the light reaches your eyes, the colours are separated into a rainbow.

DidYou**Know**?

As you may recall, John Dalton is famous for his theory that the atom is the smallest particle of matter. He proposed that compounds are formed from combinations of atoms. Dalton developed his atomic theory when he was studying the evaporation of water. His experiments led him to the idea that water vapour and air must be made of particles of different sizes that mix together. He then focussed on the concept of particles and developed his theory.

Folklore About Weather

Scientists gradually developed a scientific understanding of weather. As this happened mythology lost its place in most societies. A knowledge of the way that weather works, however, does not replace the need for forecasting. The livelihood, and even the lives, of people such as sailors and farmers depend on weather. Therefore many of these people developed the ability to make reasonable predictions based on their experiences. An abundance of folklore grew out of their experiences. Although some truth can be found in the folklore, predictions based on folklore are not very reliable!

Pause&
Reflect

Reread the last few paragraphs about weather folklore. Can you think of any reasons why one of these ideas might be valid? Do you know any present-day folklore?

Figure 16.22 Bright-red sunsets are sometimes caused by dust in the air, indicating that conditions are dry in the west.

The most frequently quoted rhyme from weather folklore is probably this: "Red sky in the morning, sailors take warning. Red sky at night, sailors' delight." A lot of folklore centres on the coming of rain. Some people believe that bees return to their hive before it rains. Others believe that birds fly higher just before a thunderstorm. Ants build little barriers around their nests if it is going to rain. When cattle lie down in a pasture, some people predict rain. Sport-fishing enthusiasts tell us that fish jump more just before it rains.

The coming of spring is a very important event, especially if the winter has been severe. One familiar piece of folklore, based on spring, is Groundhog Day. If a groundhog comes out of its burrow on February 2 and sees its shadow, some people say that there will be another six weeks of winter. If the groundhog does not see its shadow, then spring is on the way.

Figure 16.23 The sky is overcast, and the groundhog does not see its shadow. Is spring "just around the corner?"

Weather and Historical Events

In Chapter 14, you learned about the effects of the Gulf Stream. The Gulf Stream makes the climate in northern Europe much warmer than the climate in other parts of the world that lie at the same latitude. Greenland also benefits from the warmth that the Gulf Stream brings. During the tenth century, the Norse people built a thriving colony in Greenland. Then the climate cooled between 1450 and 1850. Scientists do not fully understand why. This "Little Ice Age," as it is sometimes called, destroyed the Norse colony in Greenland.

Some complex societies, such as the Mayans in Central America, have disappeared. Although descendants are still living, the organized governmental system is gone. No one knows for sure why. It is possible, however, that drought and famine were responsible. Several years of high temperatures and very little rain could possibly devastate a small, isolated nation.

Weather has turned the tide of several wars throughout history. During the thirteenth century, the Mongols ruled much of Asia. In 1274 and again in 1281, the Mongol leader, Kublai Khan, sent fleets of ships to invade Japan. In both cases, his fleets were destroyed by hurricanes. Kublai Khan never ruled Japan.

You may have heard the story of Hannibal attempting to cross the Alps with his army, using elephants for transport. Hannibal lost so many soldiers in the blizzards that he never conquered the Roman Empire.

Russian winters have taken their toll on armies from other nations. In 1812, Napoleon sent 600 000 troops to invade Russia. Along the way, Napoleon lost 35 000 troops. Nevertheless his army continued. The troops entered Moscow on September 14. They found the city deserted and without supplies. Napoleon's advisors urged him to withdraw. He waited until it was too late. A month later, the troops headed toward home. They did not have enough supplies and horses. A typical Russian winter made the retreat nearly impossible. Historians estimate that no more than 100 000 troops made it home. This was only one sixth of the number that started out on the mission.

In 1941, Hitler made a mistake similar to Napoleon's. He attempted to invade Russia in the fall. By the time the German soldiers approached Moscow, the weather was so cold that their soup froze before they could eat it. They had tanks instead of horses, but their motor oil and antifreeze did not work in −50°C temperatures. Hitler's soldiers fought long and hard. They were no match for the Siberian soldiers who defended Moscow. The Siberian soldiers were used to Siberian winters and prepared for the intense cold.

Weather has affected nearly every war that has ever been fought. Battles have been won or lost due to dust storms, thunderstorms, or other weather conditions.

German soldiers, unprepared for the extreme cold of a Russian winter in 1941.

Then and Now

In the past, humans were at the mercy of the weather. Today disasters still occur, but organized help is usually available. With our modern communication and transportation, help often comes from distant parts of the world. As well, with weather satellites and radar, meteorologists can detect the coming of severe weather. Their forecasts give people time to flee from disasters. Property damage cannot be avoided, but many lives are saved.

Canada has had a weather service for over 100 years. In 1871, Professor George Kingston at the University of Toronto, with a $5000 grant, established the Canadian Meteorological Service. Two years later, the Toronto meteorologists knew that a hurricane was heading toward Cape Breton. The telegraph lines to

Halifax were down, however. They could not send a warning. The hurricane drove steamships aground, destroyed bridges, and smashed hundreds of homes. It left nearly 1000 people dead. This disaster prompted the Canadian government to fund a national weather warning system.

In the 1920s, wireless radio was invented. By 1935, Canada's weather service was providing daily weather reports and forecasts for the Canadian Radio Commission's Trans-Canada network. (This network eventually became the CBC.) In 1952, Percy Saltzman became the first television weather broadcaster. In 1971, the weather service joined Canada's new Department of the Environment. In 1983, the weather service installed their first supercomputer in the Canadian Meteorological Centre in Montréal. In 1992, Canada became the first country to establish a daily, nationwide UV (ultraviolet) index. Today Environment Canada provides detailed, up-to-the-minute weather forecasts. As well, its scientists carry out research to study and improve Canada's air, land, and water quality.

Where Are We Today?

In the past, the world seemed so big and the sky seemed so vast. No one could imagine humans having any impact on the environment. Today we know that we have begun to alter the air, land, and water we depend on. The population of Earth is growing rapidly. With the sheer numbers of people, we cannot avoid interacting with the environment. What are these interactions? How is weather involved?

In Unit 1, and again in Chapter 13, you studied the greenhouse effect and global warming. You completed an activity to predict the effects that global warming might have on weather in the future.

In Chapter 8, you learned about the chemical reactions that cause acid rain. In the 1970s, scientists in both Europe and North America began to see the effects of acid rain on the environment. At first, building taller smokestacks seemed to be the answer. Industrialists believed that the gases would be dispersed if they were released at high altitudes. By the time they reached the ground, they would be dilute. Therefore they would do no harm. This proved not to be the case. Forests and lakes were damaged at locations that were distant from the tall smokestacks. Scientists used their knowledge of the movements of air masses and prevailing wind patterns to find out why. They traced the path of the pollution and found the source. Strict regulations have now been established to reduce the release of the gases that cause acid rain.

Figure 16.24 Tall smokestacks cause pollutants to be carried to locations distant from the source. They do not solve the problem of acid rain.

Figure 16.25 Smog appears as a yellowish-brown haze hanging over a city. Nitrogen dioxide causes the yellow colour. Incompletely burned hydrocarbons make the haze thick.

The Effects of Smog in Canada

In Chapter 8, you also learned about nitrogen oxides and particulate matter — the pollutants that lead to smog. The following two chemical equations summarize the reactions that produce ozone. These reactions require sunlight. They also require nitrogen dioxide from automobile exhaust.

$$NO_2 + \text{Sunlight} \rightarrow NO + O$$

The oxygen atom that forms is called a free radical because it has an unpaired electron. Free radicals are highly reactive. The oxygen atom usually reacts rapidly with a molecule of oxygen to form ozone (O_3):

$$O + O_2 \rightarrow O_3$$

Volatile organic compounds (VOCs) from partially burned fuel are not shown in the equations. They are a necessary ingredient of smog. As well, the air temperature must be above 18°C for these reactions to proceed fast enough for ozone to accumulate. Although Canada is often considered to be a cold country, the temperature in the summer becomes sufficiently warm in many cities to support the formation of smog. Ozone levels are used as an indicator of the amount of smog. Environment Canada has set a national objective to keep ozone levels below 82 ppb (parts per billion). The figure below shows the number of days that cities in Canada have had ozone levels above the national objective.

Figure 16.26 These graphs show the average number of days per year that the cities have ozone levels above 82 ppb. The averages were taken over a period of six years, between 1987 and 1992.

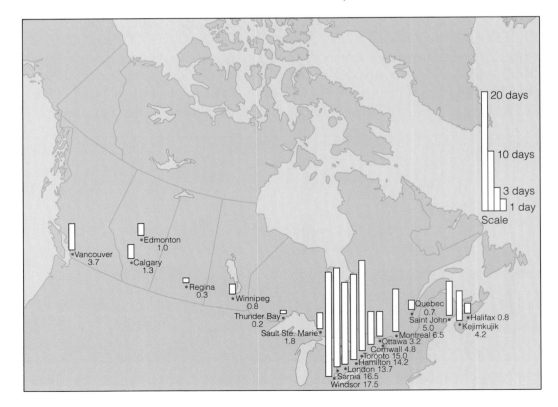

You may wonder why there is so much smog in the Atlantic provinces. This area has the unfortunate situation of "inheriting" air from the west. Approximately 80 percent of the smog in New Brunswick blows in with air from southern Ontario, Québec, and the Ohio Valley in the United States.

Smog is harmful for more than aesthetic reasons. Ozone causes irritation of the eyes, nose, and throat. It is very hard on people who have sensitive respiratory systems. For example, smog increases the number of attacks for people with asthma. Ozone is also harmful to plants. The cost of crop damage is estimated to be as high as $70 million in Ontario and $9 million in British Columbia. Ozone damages materials, as well. For example, it causes rubber to harden and crack. It increases the rate that dyes fade, it causes paints to deteriorate, and it damages synthetic fabrics, such as nylon, polyester, and acetate. As a result, ozone can cause serious economic problems.

A unique weather condition complicates the situation in cities where smog tends to occur. This weather condition is called a **temperature inversion**. Vancouver, British Columbia, offers an excellent example. If the air at ground level is cooled by ocean breezes and warm air remains over it, the mountains may block further movement of air for a time. Thus the warm air puts a cap on the smog. It traps the smog over the city. As you know, cool air is more dense than warm air. Therefore cool air cannot rise through warm air. Figure 16.27 illustrates a temperature inversion.

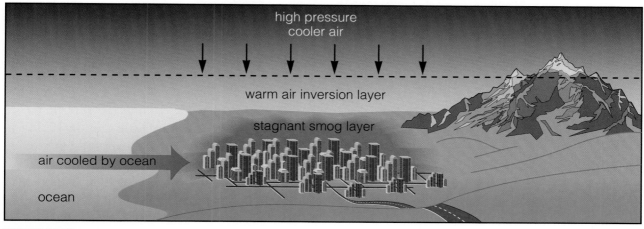

Figure 16.27 A temperature inversion

Ozone: Good or Bad?

While you were reading about the hazards of ozone and smog, did you wonder why scientists are concerned about the hole in the ozone layer? Is there good ozone and bad ozone? No, ozone is all the same. When ozone comes in contact with living organisms and non-living materials, though, it causes damage. The ozone that is high in the stratosphere is needed for life on Earth. It absorbs the harmful ultraviolet radiation from the Sun. A class of chemical compounds, called chlorofluorocarbons (CFCs), has caused a thinning of the ozone layer. CFCs have been used as refrigerants and as aerosol propellants because they are chemically inert: that is, they undergo few chemical reactions.

For many years, people in rural areas of the Fraser Valley, east of Vancouver, British Columbia, have noticed a white haze in the air about 200 m above ground level. During a temperature inversion, the haze may remain in place for several days. Recently scientists from Environment Canada studied the haze and found relatively large amounts of two salts — ammonium sulfate and ammonium nitrate — in the air at ground level. They also discovered that large amounts of ammonia escape into the air from the manure of dairy cattle, hogs, and poultry. They believe that the salts form in the air when ammonia from the manure reacts with oxides of sulfur and nitrogen in pollutants that blow out to the rural areas from Vancouver. You might call this a form of rural smog.

When CFCs come in contact with living organisms and non-living materials, they cause no harm because they do not react. Scientists have discovered a problem when CFCs diffuse high into the atmosphere, however. The ultraviolet light breaks down the CFCs into chemicals that react with and destroy ozone.

Shortly after this problem was discovered, leaders of many countries met in Montréal. They drew up an agreement called the Montréal Protocol. They agreed to reduce and, eventually, completely ban the use of CFCs. Unfortunately the concentration of these chemicals in the atmosphere is very high. It will take several years for the thinning of the ozone layer to slow and hopefully stop.

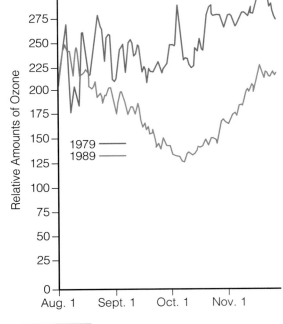

Figure 16.28 The graph shows the relative amounts of ozone in the stratusphere over Antarctica. Conditions in September and October are "ideal" for ozone depletion. Note the change in just ten years.

Canadians and Weather Extremes

Weather has affected our government in some unusual ways. Canada's social systems were greatly influenced by the "dust bowl" of the 1930s. This decade brought the most severe drought that the Prairie provinces had ever endured. Year after year, summer brought extremely high temperatures and very little rain. In 1936, temperatures reached 44.4°C. Nearly 800 people died from heat-related illnesses. Figure 16.29 shows what happened to the Prairie farmlands. With no crops and starving animals, the people were in great need. Many farmers lost their lands and their homes. Many residents of the Prairies believed that the government had a responsibility to help Canadians survive these times of crisis. To pursue this goal, they formed the Cooperative Commonwealth Federation (CCF). The CCF developed into the New Democratic Party (NDP).

Montréal is at the opposite extreme. Montréal has more snow, on average, than any other major city in the world. The city spends around $45 million for snow removal every winter. Surprisingly the economic benefits of snow are much greater than the costs in Québec. The province receives more funds from tourism and winter recreation, such as skiing, than it spends on snow removal.

Heavy winter snow not only affects the economy, it also affects the environment. To make driving safer, government workers spread salt on the streets and highways. Melting snow carries this salt into streams and ponds. The dense salt water sinks to the bottom of ponds. It creates potentially toxic conditions for organisms that live in the water. Environment Canada and Transport Canada are co-operating to study the effects of road salt on the aquatic environment. They are searching for solutions to the problem.

Figure 16.29 Parched Prairie farmlands left farmers with no crops and many debts.

Let It Snow (or Rain)

For thousands of years, humans have tried to influence the weather. You have probably heard about rain dances, for example. People have also tried shooting arrows and even cannon balls into the clouds to cause rain. Has anyone ever been successful? Currently many people believe that a process called *cloud seeding* can promote rain.

What is cloud seeding? It involves injecting condensation nuclei into clouds in an attempt to cause rain. The seeding may be carried out by shooting rockets into the clouds or by releasing substances from airplanes. Dry ice (solid carbon dioxide) and silver iodide are the two most commonly used substances. Silver iodide crystals are shaped a lot like ice crystals. They stimulate water to crystallize on their surfaces. Many attempts at cloud seeding over the last 50 years appear to have been successful. Rain or snow did fall. Some people argue, however, that it is not possible to determine whether the same amount of rain or snow would have fallen without the seeding. Nevertheless many experiments and projects continue. There are three common reasons to seed clouds:

Figure 16.30 The pilot of this cloud-seeding airplane lights flares that release silver iodide crystals. The updrafts draw the crystals into the clouds. There they act as condensation nuclei.

- to clear fog at airports
- to increase snow in mountains and thus increase the amount of water in spring run-offs
- to prevent hail or reduce the size of hailstones

In most cases, government agencies support the research or projects. A unique situation arose in west-central Alberta — the "hail capital" of North America.

On September 7, 1991, a severe hailstorm occurred. In less than half an hour, it dented cars, broke windows of cars and homes, and damaged roofs with hailstones the size of golf balls. Nearly 60 000 customers submitted claims to their insurance companies. By the time all the repairs had been made, the insurance companies had paid out $342 million. This amount was three times as much as they received in premiums in a year. A group of insurance companies formed an association to look for a solution, other than raising insurance premiums. They decided to hire a private company to carry out a five-year study of cloud seeding. They wanted to find out the effects of increasing the number of condensation nuclei in the clouds. Would it make the moisture fall as rain before hail formed? Would it reduce the size of the hailstones by making more, smaller hailstones? During the first year of the study, insurance claims for hail damage cost the companies $150 million. During the second year, there were no claims. At the end of the five years, the companies will compare the cost of cloud seeding with the cost of insurance claims. Then they will decide whether to continue with the cloud seeding.

Some people still question whether we can cause rain to fall. There is evidence, however, that we affect it unintentionally. Consider a study done by Environment Canada. It showed that thunderstorms are more frequent and more severe when wheat crops are at the peak of their growing season. How are these events related? At the peak of their growth, transpiration in crop plants is very high. Large amounts of water evaporate from the plants. The evaporation adds moisture to the air. This creates conditions that are favourable for thunderstorms. Imagine, then, how the burning of thousands of hectares of trees in rain forests, to clear the land for farming, can influence the weather.

You Are on the Team

START HERE ▶

Think About It

SOFTWARE GENIE

Scientists with Environment Canada have developed a software package called "Georeference Environmental Network for Information Exchange," or "GENIE." Information about any type of environmental or meteorological emergency is entered into a computer. GENIE automatically sends the information, over the Internet, to government agencies and other experts. For example, information about an oil spill goes to agencies such as Fisheries and Oceans Canada, weather service offices, and the coast guard. When the experts receive the information, they send back data to help with the emergency response.

GENIE then evaluates the data and establishes priorities. For example, in a recent ice storm, GENIE compared requests for fuel and shelter with predictions about when and where power would become available. Relief workers were then able to help those who would be without power for the longest time.

RECOVERING USEFUL GAS FROM LANDFILLS

Organic waste materials in landfills degrade into a gas. Nearly half of the "landfill gas" is methane, a greenhouse gas. Methane is also the major component of natural gas. Recovering landfill gas for use as a fuel reduces the release of greenhouse gases into the atmosphere. It also helps to conserve non-renewable resources. Environment Canada and Natural Resources Canada are encouraging the recovery and use of landfill gas. In workshops, they present research and technologies for recovering and purifying the gas. Currently about 300 000 t (tonnes) of methane are recovered from landfill sites in Canada. This, however, is only one fourth of the methane produced in landfills throughout the country.

SEVERE WEATHER CAUSES OIL SPILL AND COMPLICATES RESPONSE

Gale-force winds drove an oil tanker into a dock at Havre-St-Pierre, Québec, on March 23, 1999. The crash cut a gash in the hull of the ship. This caused 50 t of crude oil to leak into the Gulf of St. Lawrence near the Mingan Archipelago National Park Reserve. The reserve includes 40 islands and 2000 islets and reefs. It is a delicate ecosystem that provides food for whales, dolphins, seals, and sea birds. Oil contamination could cause untold damage. To add to the crisis, freezing rain and waves, nearly 2 m high, made it very difficult for response teams to reach the spill. As soon as conditions allowed, helicopters and snowmobiles carried workers to the site. Soon 140 workers were there, cleaning as fast as possible. GENIE software produced maps of the spill and maps of the progress on a daily basis. As well, GENIE established priorities for the clean-up process. When winds caused blocks of ice to start moving, Fisheries and Oceans Canada used another computer model. This ice-movement model predicted where the ice would encounter and affect the oil spill. The Wildlife Service set up a centre to clean oil-covered birds. Although the shores of 15 islands were contaminated, 80 percent of the oil was removed within a month. Pre-planning and prepared teams prevented the spill from causing much more serious damage.

SENSOR DETECTS OIL SPILLS

Environment Canada, along with other agencies, has developed a laser sensor to detect oil spills. The sensor is carried in a DC-3 airplane that flies at 600 m above the ground. The sensor can scan an area 200 m wide. It sends a beam of ultraviolet laser light to the ground. A certain compound in crude oil absorbs the laser light. When it does this, it emits fluorescent light. The sensor detects the intensity and wavelength of the fluorescence. Then it identifies the type of oil in the spill. Clean-up crews can go directly to the site, with the right kind of equipment. The quick response can prevent excessive spreading of the oil and contamination of large areas.

Imagine that your group is a team that specializes in a specific weather-related issue. Your team is going to submit a proposal for a grant to Environment Canada. In this investigation, you will prepare your proposal. Your proposal will include

- a description of the issue in which your team specializes
- the qualifications (education and experience) of each member of your team
- the goals you wish to achieve with the funds from the grant

What to Do

1 Review the articles shown here. Note all the different teams that contributed to solving each problem. Look back in the textbook to find descriptions of teams working together to solve a weather-related environmental problem. Within your group, discuss the type of team you would like to role-play. Your team might choose to develop a new or improved instrument or software program. You might want to be a frontline response team that is first to arrive at the scene of a crisis. You might want to develop a process for dealing with an oil spill or a toxic chemical spill in a remote region with severe weather conditions. Decide on the type of team you will role-play.

2 Discuss the types of experts your team will need. Will you need a computer programmer, a chemist, a mountain climber, a mechanic, a meteorologist, and/or a doctor? Assign a role to each member of your group.

3 Each member of your group will, individually, research his or her own role. Find out what type of education and experience you will need to best perform this role.

4 Write your proposal. Be sure to cover, in detail, each of the three points listed above. Each member will write about his or her own "education and experience." Each member will then outline a paragraph to fulfill the first and third points listed above. Together, discuss the outlines and finalize your proposal.

Analyze

1. Each group will present their proposal to the entire class. If possible, invite a representative from Environment Canada to your class to hear your presentations. Ask the representative to describe the types of real proposals that have been submitted to Environment Canada.

2. During the presentations, make a list of the different roles of the members of the teams. Discuss the need for each member to have a different role. How well would a team function if each member had the same qualifications?

3. After listening to the presentations, make a list of all the careers that interest you, personally.

Skill
POWER

For tips on working in a group effectively turn to page 584.

What the Future Holds

The condition of the environment in the future depends on decisions made today. Scientists at Environment Canada have evaluated the trends and conditions that affect the atmosphere. They have made predictions about events up to the year 2010. Some of their predictions are listed below.

- Greenhouse gas emissions will be reduced to below the levels in 1990. Nevertheless global average temperatures will continue to rise.
- Stratospheric ozone levels will be at their lowest levels. Canadians will have to use more sunscreen to protect themselves from skin cancer. The scientists do not expect the ozone layer to begin to recover until after 2010.
- Natural disasters will increase. Economic losses, due to this increase, will rise.
- Acid rain and the conditions that cause it will continue to affect lakes and forests. This will be a problem especially in eastern Canada. Chemical changes, leading to harmful, long-term effects on the environment, will continue.
- Ground-level air pollution will continue to affect thousands of people. It will contribute to respiratory problems and cancer. Thus it will add billions of dollars to the cost of the health-care system.

The scientists believe that Canada is headed in the right direction. However, the work has only begun.

Check Your Understanding

1. Weather has always had a significant impact on the lives of humans. What evidence do we have to support this?

2. Discuss one example of the way that weather has affected historical events.

3. Describe the weather conditions that are needed for smog to form.

4. Ozone can be harmful to living organisms. It is necessary for life to exist on Earth, however. Explain.

5. Give one example of the way that weather affects the Canadian economy.

Now that you have completed this chapter, try to do the following. If you cannot, go back to the sections indicated.

Explain the function of a common thermometer. (16.1)

Explain the function of an electronic thermometer used in a remote location. (16.1)

Compare the basic principles behind the functioning of a hygrometer and a psychrometer. (16.1)

Describe three different ways to measure atmospheric pressure. (16.1)

Discuss the critical factors in the placement of meteorological instruments. (16.1)

Explain the importance of using weather balloons to collect data. (16.1)

Explain how Doppler radar can determine the direction and speed of movement of a rain storm. (16.1)

Contrast the types of data collected by radar and by weather satellites. (16.1)

Describe a station model for weather maps. (16.2)

Explain how to draw isotherms and isobars on a weather map. (16.2)

Explain the trends method for making a forecast. (16.2)

Describe the types of equations that make up the Numerical Weather Prediction method. (16.2)

Summarize some of the beliefs of ancient societies about weather. (16.3)

Explain why folklore continued to grow even after people began to understand the scientific basis of weather. (16.3)

List the "ingredients" that are necessary for smog to form. (16.3)

Explain why scientists believe that the ozone layer will eventually be restored. (16.2)

Summarize one way in which weather has shaped Canadian history. (16.3)

List four major weather-related environmental challenges. (16.3)

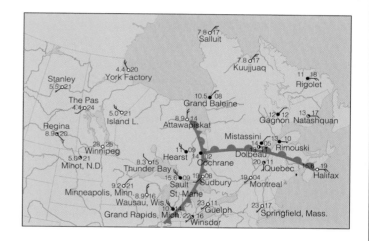

Prepare Your Own Summary

Summarize this chapter by doing one of the following. Use a graphic organizer (such as a concept map), produce a poster, or write the summary to include the key chapter concepts. Here are a few ideas to use as a guide:

- Why must you swing a sling psychrometer in the air to get an accurate measurement of relative humidity?
- How is the three-cup anemometer an improvement over the propeller anemometer?
- Why is it difficult to measure snowfall accurately?
- What can radar "see" that weather satellites cannot "see"?

- How do geostationary satellites stay over the same point on Earth at all times?
- What features do you look for on a weather map if you want to find a cold front?
- A weather map includes many time zones. How do meteorologists report the time at which the weather conditions on the map were observed?
- What is causing the stratospheric ozone layer to become thinner?
- What is one logical reason for the creation of folklore about weather?

Reviewing Key Terms

If you need to review, the section numbers show you where these terms were introduced.

1. Use the list of key terms at the beginning of the chapter to fill in the blanks.

   (a) Meterologists usually report atmospheric pressure in units of ▊▊▊▊▊. (16.1)

   (b) Lines of constant temperature are called ▊▊▊▊▊. (16.2)

   (c) Human hairs were originally used in instruments called ▊▊▊▊▊. (16.1)

   (d) When you make a forecast based on weather maps for several previous days, you have used the ▊▊▊▊▊ method of forecasting. (16.2)

   (e) A ▊▊▊▊▊ turns a propeller anemometer in the right direction for measuring wind speed. (16.1)

   (f) A ▊▊▊▊▊ puts a cap of warm air over a layer of cooler air, preventing the cooler air from moving. (16.3)

Understanding Key Concepts

Section numbers are provided if you need to review.

2. How does an aneroid barometer differ from a mercury barometer? (16.1)

3. What is the function of the box in the photograph below? Describe the features that are critical to its function. (16.1)

4. Explain how an electric circuit can be used to measure temperature. (16.1)

5. What kind of weather data can be obtained *only* by weather balloons? (16.1)

6. How do weather satellites determine the heights of clouds? (16.1)

7. Describe the path of a polar orbiting weather satellite. (16.1)

8. Which instrument made forecasting possible? Why was forecasting not possible before this instrument was invented? (16.2)

9. How does a station model convey wind direction and speed? (16.2)

10. Review Figure 16.15. Look closely at the stations that indicate rain was falling. How does this pattern of rainfall support the presence of the cold and warm fronts in Figure 16.16?

11. What types of equations are included in the computer models used in the Numerical Weather Prediction method of forecasting? (16.2)

12. How did the people in some ancient societies attempt to influence the weather? Give one example. (16.3)

13. What did Aristotle contribute to the field of meteorology? (16.3)

14. Describe two examples of folklore about weather. (16.3)

15. Choose and discuss, in detail, one example of weather affecting a historical event. (16.3)

16. Which characteristic of CFCs made scientists believe that they were safe to use as refrigerants and aerosol propellants? (16.3)

17. Why did industries build extremely tall smokestacks? (16.3)

18. Which pollutant from automobiles reacts with sunlight to start the formation of smog? (16.3)

19. What is a temperature inversion? (16.3)

20. What is the purpose of cloud seeding? (16.3)

Developing Skills

21. Imagine that you are designing a barometer that functions on the same principle as an aneroid barometer. What factor, other than atmospheric pressure, might affect the measurements? How can you correct for this factor?

22. How might you adapt the instrument in the photograph so that it could measure much higher wind speeds?

23. Make a concept map that shows the process of creating a weather forecast. Start with data collection.

Problem Solving/Applying

24. Imagine that you are in a large, open area. A steady wind is blowing toward your back. What type of pressure system is probably on your right?

25. Go back to Figure 16.14. Study the station model for Windsor, Ontario. State the temperature, atmospheric pressure, amount of cloud cover, wind direction, and wind speed.

26. Imagine that it is February. You are in Halifax, Nova Scotia. You are asked to predict the weather six months from now. What steps would you take to make a good prediction?

27. Imagine that you are reading about past explorers. One explorer found the ruins of an ancient civilization on the east coast of South America, at about 20°S latitude. The explorer found no evidence for any decendants of the people who built the civilization. Give a plausible explanation for the demise of this civilization.

Critical Thinking

28. Leaders of many nations have agreed to work toward decreasing the release of greenhouse gases into the atmosphere. We might be able to slow the process of global warming. It is still likely to occur, however. How might the government and people of Canada prepare for possible global warming and prevent potential disasters?

29. Decreasing the release of greenhouse gases and gases that cause acid rain involves costs. The cost to some industries is much greater than the cost to others. In your opinion, who should be responsible for covering the costs?

Pause& Reflect

1. Go back to the beginning of the chapter, on page 516, and check your original answers to the Opening Ideas questions. How has your thinking changed? Revise your original answers as needed.

2. Has your attitude toward weather forecasters changed in any way? If so, how?

3. Suppose that you were asked to write a research paper about a topic in this chapter. What topic would you choose? Why?

Meteorologists at the Maritimes Weather Centre (MWC) in Dartmouth, Nova Scotia, provide weather information to fishers, the navy, and the public. If a tropical storm or hurricane is headed toward their region, a special division of the MWC, called the Canadian Hurricane Centre, springs into action. Ted McIldoon, a senior meteorologist at MWC, is experienced in predicting the movement of hurricanes that are approaching Canadian shores.

Q What, exactly, do meteorologists do?

A We study changes in Earth's atmosphere in order to forecast the weather. By interpreting atmospheric data, we can fairly accurately predict weather conditions for the near future. We also issue weather warnings for such things as strong winds, storm surges, and freezing sprays.

Q What are the "atmospheric data" that you interpret?

A We look at current weather conditions, such as temperature and air pressure. Our data come from surface observation sites and weather balloons. We collect data from eastern North America, other countries bordering on the North Atlantic, and the Caribbean. We also receive computer-forecast data from the Canadian Meteorological Centre (CMC) in Montréal. Meteorologists enter current atmospheric data from across Canada into CMC's computer. They also enter information on past weather system movements. The computer then produces maps. These maps show predicted weather patterns for 12 to 120 h into the future. In addition to the data, we receive images from two radar stations in the Maritimes and from two different satellites. Having this wide range of data helps us assess local conditions.

Q Why do you need both radar and satellite images? How are they different?

A Satellites look down on the clouds. They produce images such as this one of Hurricane Hortense. These images tell us about the amount of solar radiation that is reflected back to space. As well, they tell us the temperatures at the tops of the clouds. From these data, we determine the heights and types of clouds.

Satellite images cannot tell us whether precipitation is falling from those clouds. Radar images give us this information. Radar instruments send a signal toward the clouds. If the signal hits raindrops, snowflakes, or hailstones, some of the signal is reflected back to the radar receiver. The strength or intensity of the reflected signal tells us the amount of precipitation.

Q **Does Canada get very many hurricanes?**

A On average, three tropical storms pass through the Maritimes Weather Centre's response zone each year. They are rarely strong enough to cause much concern. Hurricanes depend on warm water for their energy. A hurricane that is approaching our region over water loses its strength as it moves over progressively colder water. Sometimes strength isn't even a factor. Many hurricanes bypass us completely.

Q **Why is that?**

A Hurricanes, like all weather systems, are steered by prevailing upper level winds. Most Atlantic hurricanes form in the tropics. The easterlies, or trade winds, blow them toward North America. As they cross the Atlantic, they often turn northwest and then north. At this point, they reach the westerlies. They begin to change direction. The westerlies guide them to the east, back out to sea. The track of Hurricane Bonnie is typical for Atlantic hurricanes. Whether or not a hurricane reaches Canada depends on when it changes its direction.

Even though Canada gets few hurricanes, we continue to monitor them. They are rarely capable of causing damage here, but they do affect our weather.

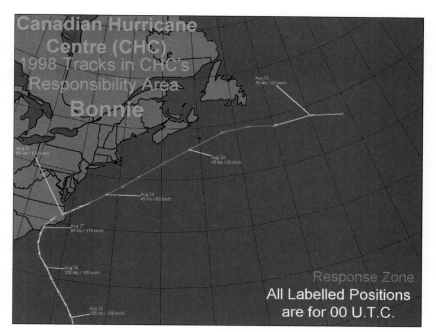

EXPLORING Further

What Do You See?

Compare this radar image of Hurricane Hortense with the satellite image shown on the previous page. What extra information does the radar image give that the satellite image does not? How can information from both images be used to make a weather forecast?

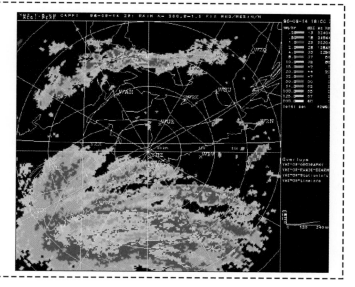

A SIMULATION

Cooling the Driving Habit

Think About It

From 1980 to 1999, Canada experienced 17 of the 20 hottest years ever recorded. The Canadian government is becoming increasingly concerned about global warming and greenhouse gas emissions. In this activity, you will consider the following plan to limit the use of gasoline-powered personal vehicles. The plan is intended to control emissions of greenhouse gases, particularly carbon dioxide.

- All vehicles with odd-numbered licence plates (that is, ending with an odd number) can be driven only on Mondays, Wednesdays, Fridays, and the first and third Sunday of the month.
- All vehicles with even-numbered licence plates can be driven only on Tuesdays, Thursdays, Saturdays, and the second and fourth Sunday of the month.

Your provincial government is sponsoring a forum to invite public input into this plan.

Plan and Act

① The following people are attending the forum:
- a climatologist from Environment Canada
- a stockholder in Alberta Oil and Gas Company
- a city transit official in charge of buses
- a businesswoman who lives on a farm in the country and commutes to work
- a bicycle courier who rides through heavy urban traffic to deliver parcels
- a parent who is concerned about creating a clean environment for his three children
- a CEO from Ballard Fuel Cells, a Canadian company that powers vehicles with hydrogen-driven fuel cells

② Think about the likely point of view of each person. What concerns will each person emphasize? Which people do you expect to hold on to their points of view? Which might be convinced to see other sides of the issue?

③ Your teacher will assign your group the role of one of these people. You will receive some background information. As a group, research your role. Come prepared to make a strong but short presentation. Use posters and models if you wish. You will have to assume the role of your person. This means that you will have to defend her or his probable point of view, even if you personally disagree.

④ Your teacher may ask you to form part of the jury for the forum. As a juror, your task will be to look at all sides of the issue. Make sure that nobody can mislead you with irrelevant or incorrect "facts."

Analyze

1. Based on the simulation, would you support or oppose the plan? Give reasons for your decision.

2. Were you convinced by the researched facts or by the eloquence of the presentations?

3. Did any of the participants say something that you would not have expected them to say in their roles?

4. What if you had decided differently? What might the world look like by the time your children are sitting in the same classroom doing the same activity? Would they make the same decision that you did? Explain your answers.

5. Can you suggest a different plan that would be more effective for reducing automobile emissions? Can you suggest a more practical plan that would be fair to everyone?

Preparing for a *Really* Rainy Day

In most of the world, including Canada, people are affected by severe weather. There are few, if any, places in Canada that do not see a weather-related emergency at least once a century. Here are four examples:

- a hurricane dumping 50 cm of rain in a single day (Toronto, 1954)
- a flooding river (Winnipeg, May 1997)
- An ice storm knocking out power lines for weeks (Québec and eastern Ontario, January 1998)
- blizzards paralyzing a city (Halifax, January 2000)

Other, more common weather-related emergencies include whiteouts and tornadoes. In addition, forest fires are more likely to occur after a very dry winter and spring.

Preparation is the key to surviving and minimizing damage in a weather emergency. People need to be told, *quickly* and *clearly*, what to do.

Challenge

Develop and present a plan to help people prepare for a sudden weather-related emergency. Prepare a one-page pamphlet and a 2 min television broadcast to explain and show emergency preparation procedures. Use visuals in your broadcast.

Materials

art and construction materials of your choice (for example, a cardboard box, modelling clay, toy cars, felt markers, paper, and papier-mâché paste)

Design Criteria

A. The information and instructions in the pamphlet should be clear and concise.

B. The pamphlet will be distributed to households well ahead of an emergency. Therefore it must be "eye-catching" so that people will keep it in a convenient place.

C. The 2 min (120 s) emergency broadcast will be repeated throughout the emergency. It will begin a few hours before, if possible. Focus on what people can do, assuming that they can no longer leave their homes safely.

Plan and Construct

1 Choose a weather emergency to research. Find out what people who regularly experience this type of emergency do to deal with it. Discard ideas that clearly would not be helpful in the Canadian climate.

2 Design your pamphlet, based on what you have learned. Although "a picture is worth a thousand words," remember that a few well-written words can be the clearest way to present information. Use a font that is large enough to be easily read. A bulleted list of step-by-step instructions is often better than full sentences. Do not make your pamphlet look intimidating. (A single-spaced typed page, without a break, is overwhelming!)

3 Design your broadcast. Remember that every second counts in an emergency. Also remember that you need to grab the viewers' attention. You do not want them to flip to another channel! (Assume that you have about 10 s to do this.) Use any visual aids that you think will be helpful. Focus on what people can do with household items, since they will not be able to leave their homes to buy additional materials.

4 Distribute your pamphlets to the class. Present your broadcast.

Evaluate

1. After all the presentations have been given, assess your own work. What part of your presentation do you feel was the most effective? What could you have done differently? Did another group do something that you wish you had tried?

2. Rank the media you used (model/diorama, pamphlet, broadcast) from most to least efficient.

Now that you have completed Chapters 13, 14, 15, and 16, you can assess how much you have learned about weather by answering the following questions. Before you begin, you may find it useful to return to each Chapter at a Glance and each Chapter Review.

True/False

In your notebook, indicate whether each statement is true or false. Correct each false statement.

1. In convection, energy is transmitted when high-energy molecules move to low-temperature areas.

2. Solar radiation contains a complete spectrum of all forms of electromagnetic radiation.

3. Thirty percent of the solar radiation reaching Earth's atmosphere is reflected back into space.

4. White objects absorb more light than deep-blue objects do.

5. Water is always at a constant temperature while it is boiling.

6. Water has a relatively large heat of fusion.

7. Absolute humidity is reported as a percentage.

8. Nitrogen and oxygen in the air absorb infrared radiation from Earth.

9. There is no physical significance about the location of the line called the Arctic Circle.

10. The tilt of Earth's axis causes the Coriolis effect.

11. Weather systems usually come from the west.

12. Winds in the polar jet stream can move as fast as 300 km/h.

13. Wind and water currents tend to curve to the right in the Northern Hemisphere.

14. There are no ocean currents that encircle the world.

15. During an El Niño, the trade winds in the South Pacific reverse their direction. The reversed winds prevent ocean upwellings off the coast of Peru.

16. Nimbostratus clouds are thunderclouds.

17. The most common mechanism for cloud formation is radiative cooling.

18. Warm fronts often bring thunderstorms.

19. The air in a lightning bolt is hotter than the surface of the Sun.

20. The wind in a hurricane is stronger than the wind in a tornado.

21. A hygrometer and a psychrometer measure the same property of air.

22. An anemometer measures wind direction.

23. Radar detects rain, snow, and hail.

24. On a weather map, a frontal system is shown by many isotherms lying close together.

Completion

In your notebook, complete each statement with the correct term or phrase.

25. To form clouds, ▨▨▨▨▨▨ and ▨▨▨▨▨▨ are needed.

26. Fog occurs when a ▨▨▨▨▨▨ cloud comes down to the ground or when the air cools past the ▨▨▨▨▨▨ temperature.

27. Rain that evaporates before it hits the ground is called ▨▨▨▨▨▨ .

28. When cloud droplets combine and grow, they are said to ▨▨▨▨▨▨ .

29. A meteorologist uses ▨▨▨▨▨▨ ▨▨▨▨▨▨ to check the location of clouds and precipitation, a ▨▨▨▨▨▨ to measure temperature, a ▨▨▨▨▨▨ to measure pressure, and a ▨▨▨▨▨▨ to measure dew point temperature.

30. If a fast-moving ▨▨▨▨▨▨ front catches up to a slow-moving ▨▨▨▨▨▨ front, an ▨▨▨▨▨▨ front might be formed.

31. In an area of ▨▨▨▨▨▨ pressure called a ▨▨▨▨▨▨ , the air spirals into the middle, in a ▨▨▨▨▨▨ direction.

Matching

32. In your notebook, copy the descriptions in column A. Beside each description, write the term from column B that best fits the description. A term may be used once, more than once, or not at all.

A	B
• distance, in degrees, north or south of the equator	• radiation
• area where day and night are equally long	• longitude
• distance, in degrees, east or west of the prime meridian	• solar constant
• border between two air masses with different characteristics	• gyre
• scientist who studies long-term weather patterns	• hurricane
• energy that is spread out by waves	• tornado
• ability of a surface to reflect sunlight	• frost
• circular ocean current	• meteorologist
• huge storm system developing over a warm ocean	• front
	• latitude
	• climatologist
	• equinox
	• solstice

Multiple Choice

In your notebook, write the letter of the best answer for each of the following questions.

33. Which of the following does *not* contribute to Earth's constant average temperature?
    (a) water's large specific heat capacity
    (b) water's large heat of fusion
    (c) water's high boiling and freezing points
    (d) water's high surface tension
    (e) water's large heat of vaporization

34. Where does most weather occur?
    (a) stratosphere
    (b) mesosphere
    (c) troposphere
    (d) thermosphere
    (e) magnetosphere

35. Which of the following has the *least* influence on global weather patterns?
    (a) The equator is hotter than the poles.
    (b) Earth is rotating.
    (c) Warm air rises.
    (d) Cold air can hold less moisture than warm air.
    (e) Days last longer in the summer.

36. The jet stream
    (a) was discovered by jet pilots.
    (b) is caused by the contact of cold and warm air masses high in the atmosphere.
    (c) always moves in a straight east-west direction.
    (d) does not affect the motion of ground-level air systems, such as fronts.
    (e) can be found everywhere on Earth if you reach a certain height in the atmosphere.

37. Ocean currents are *not*
    (a) always the same temperature as the surrounding water.
    (b) affected by the shapes of the continents.
    (c) started by the wind.

    (d) influenced by the Coriolis effect.
    (e) one of the ways that heat is transferred from the tropics to the poles.

38. Which type of air mass would likely be warm and dry?
    (a) continental arctic, cA
    (b) continental polar, cP
    (c) continental tropical, cT
    (d) maritime tropical, mT
    (e) maritime polar, mP

39. Which of the following is *not* true of hurricanes?
    (a) They require energy from warm water.
    (b) They never occur over the equator.
    (c) They start between 7° and 42°N or S latitude.
    (d) They start as random thunderstorms.
    (e) They whirl in opposite directions.

40. Hygroscopic salts are used in electric circuits that are designed to measure
    (a) atmospheric pressure.
    (b) wind speed.
    (c) precipitation.
    (d) relative humidity.
    (e) temperature.

Short Answer

In your notebook, write a sentence or a short paragraph to answer each of the following questions.

41. Air at 26°C can hold ten times as much water as air at −8°C. Use this fact to explain why we need to use a humidifier in the winter and a dehumidifier in the summer, in the same room. Assume that temperature in the room is kept at 20°C year-round.

42. How much might global warming raise the average temperature of Earth if the amount of carbon dioxide in the atmosphere doubled?

43. If Earth were flat and stationary, how would global weather patterns be different?

44. The planet Epsilon Eridani IV rotates on its axis in the opposite direction that Earth rotates. Draw a picture for Epsilon Eridani IV, similar to the one below for Earth. Show how the Coriolis force would operate on Epsilon Eridani IV.

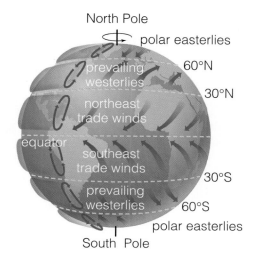

North Pole
polar easterlies
60°N
prevailing westerlies
30°N
northeast trade winds
equator
southeast trade winds
30°S
prevailing westerlies
60°S
polar easterlies
South Pole

45. The Gulf Stream can be explained by the analogy of an ocean conveyor belt. It can also be explained in terms of wind-driven currents. What are the differences between these two explanations?

46. What is El Niño? How does it affect the weather in Canada?

47. Draw a diagram to explain the steps in the creation of a sea breeze.

48. What is happening, in terms of fronts, when hail turns into freezing rain? What would you expect to happen next?

Problem Solving

Show complete solutions for all problems that involve equations and numbers. Use the GRASP problem-solving model or a model suggested by your teacher.

49. How much energy is needed to heat 200 g of water from a refrigerator (4°C) to the boiling point?

50. A cold front pushes 20 000 kg of water upward. This causes the temperature of the water to drop by 30°C. How much energy is released? (Assume that the water does not freeze.)

51. The temperature of the air is 17°C. The relative humidity is 74 percent.
 (a) How much water is present in each kilogram of air?
 (b) What is the dew point temperature of the air?

Critical Thinking

52. Why does the temperature sometimes get warmer during a rainstorm and cooler as the rain evaporates?

53. Why does the temperature get warmer as snow falls at the beginning of winter? Assume that a front is not passing by.

54. Hurricane Hazel killed about 1000 people in Haiti alone in 1954. All the hurricanes that struck North America in the 1990s, combined, did not kill as many people. Explain why.

Applications

55. Global warming is thought to be caused by the addition of greenhouse gases to the atmosphere. This is not believed to be a key factor in ending the last ice age, however. What other factors could have affected the global climate at that time?

56. December 21 is the shortest day of the year. Why does the temperature generally get colder in the month or two following December 21, even though the days are getting longer?

57. Deserts are typically hot places. Cool air usually descends in desert weather systems, however. This means that the ground may be colder than the ground in a rain forest at the same latitude. Explain why. (There is more than one correct answer.)

58. (a) How could the loss of one of Earth's major rain forests affect local weather conditions?
 (b) How could this affect the climate in Canada?

59. When would you expect to see a yellow haze over a large city? Would you expect to see it during several days of sunny, clear weather or several days of overcast weather? Explain.

60. The temperature is 20°C. The dew point temperature is 18°C. Would you expect to see low, middle, or high clouds? Explain.

Classifying Living Things

Over 2000 years ago, the Greek philosopher Aristotle developed a system of classification that grouped organisms according to whether they were plant or animal. Scientists used Aristotle's system for hundreds of years. As more and more living things were discovered, however, the system did not work well because it did not show probable relationships between similar organisms.

In 1735 Carolus Linnaeus produced a new system. His system also classified all organisms as plant or animal, but it was very different in other ways from Aristotle's system.

Linnaeus' system gives a two-word name to each type of organism. (This system of naming organisms is still used today.) The two-word name is the organism's scientific species name. It is given in Latin, a language that is no longer

spoken. The first word of the organism's name is its genus, and the second word is its specific epithet. A **genus** is a group of organisms that are very closely related. A **species** is the smaller, more limiting classification grouping. The black bear, shown on the left, and the brown bear, shown on the right, are members of the same genus, *Ursus*, but they are different species. The black bear is the species *Ursus americanus*, and the brown bear is *Ursus arctos*.

In the twentieth century, knowledge about the great diversity of organisms on Earth exploded. It became clear that separating organisms into only two kingdoms, plant and animal, was inadequate. For example, bacteria are just too different from either plants or animals to be grouped with either. During the 1960s, new information supported the subdivision of organisms into the five different kingdoms shown in the following table. Prokaryotic cells (monerans) lack a true cell nucleus, whereas eukaryotic cells have a nucleus.

	Monera	Protista	Fungi	Plantae	Animalia
Type of cells	prokaryotic	eukaryotic	eukaryotic	eukaryotic	eukaryotic
Number of cells	one-celled	one- and many-celled	one- and many-celled	many-celled	many-celled
Movement	some move	some move	don't move	don't move	move
Nutrition	Some members make their own food; others obtain it from other organisms.	Some members make their own food; others obtain it from other organisms.	All members obtain food from other organisms.	Members make their own food.	Members eat plants or other organisms.

Over the last two decades, most scientists have adopted the use of an additional approach in classifying organisms, called *cladistics*. This approach helps to classify organisms based on how closely related they are. For example, humans and dogs share a more recent common ancestor than either does with an alligator. Therefore they are grouped together (as mammals) due to their closeness of ancestry. The alligator, which shares a more remote ancestry with mammals, is not included in the same group. Thus cladistics is based on relationships. Many of the older classifications were based mainly on similarities.

Cladistics has led to different classifications for some organisms. A few years ago, scientists realized that monerans did not belong in a single group. They discovered that one group of monerans (see the table above) is more closely related to the organisms in the other kingdoms than to the other monerans. This is true even though all the monerans share many similarities and even look the same under a microscope.

Scientists now recognize three main higher categories of life, known as *domains*. These are the Domains Bacteria, Archaea, and Eukarya. Bacteria includes the Kingdom Eubacteria ("true bacteria"), Archaea includes the Kingdom Archaebacteria ("ancient bacteria"), and Eukarya include four kingdoms: Protista, Fungi, Plantae, and Animalia. The diagram below shows this new classification of organisms.

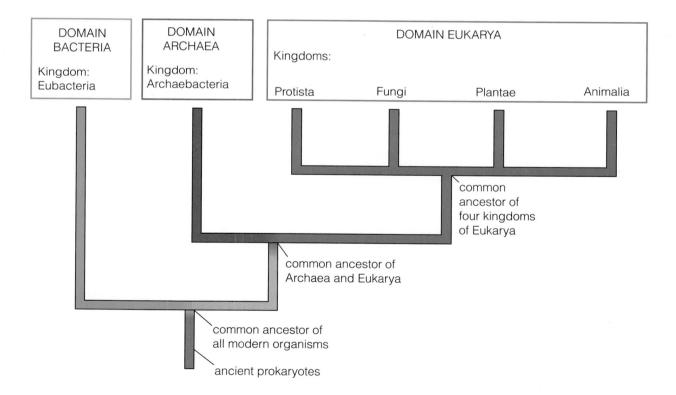

Using Resources and the Internet Effectively

Using Resources Effectively

You probably have some books and periodicals in your classroom that you can use to find out more about certain topics. For much of the information you need, however, you will want to use the library in your school or a branch of your local library.

A library can be overwhelming if you are not prepared. If you are prepared, you can quickly and efficiently find what you need.

First, be aware of the huge amount of material you can access at a library: general and specialized encyclopedias, directories (telephone, city, and postal code), almanacs, atlases, handbooks, periodicals, newspapers, government publications, pamphlets, tapes, videos, CD-ROMs, databases, and the ever-changing store of information on the Internet.

To make the best use of your time and the resources that are available, ask yourself these questions before you start your research:

* *What* information do I need? How much detail do I need?

* *When* is the assignment due? (This might help you decide how much detail you need.)

* *Why* do I need the information? Am I preparing something for an audience (my teacher, another group, or another class)?

* *How* will I be presenting the information (as a written report, a poster, an oral presentation, or a multimedia presentation)?

Next, identify which kinds of resources will give you what you need. Librarians are extremely knowledgeable and helpful. Consider them an initial resource, and ask them questions about library use when you cannot find what you need.

What Is the Internet?

The Internet is an extensive network, or "web," of interlinked yet independent computer networks. Today the network includes
* educational and government computers
* computers from research institutions
* computerized library catalogues
* businesses
* homes
* community-based computers (called *freenets*)
* a diverse range of local computer bulletin boards
Anyone who has an account on one of these computers can send electronic mail and access resources from hundreds of other computers on the network. The spider map shows some of the ways you will find the Internet most useful as a learning tool.

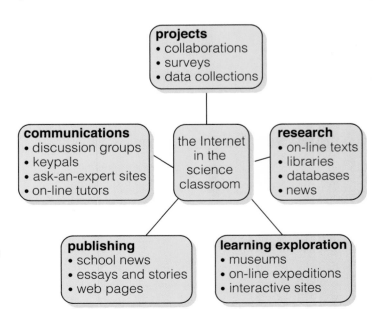

projects
* collaborations
* surveys
* data collections

communications
* discussion groups
* keypals
* ask-an-expert sites
* on-line tutors

the Internet in the science classroom

research
* on-line texts
* libraries
* databases
* news

publishing
* school news
* essays and stories
* web pages

learning exploration
* museums
* on-line expeditions
* interactive sites

Web sites can be a valuable source of information. When "surfing" the Internet yourself, however, remember that anyone, anywhere, can develop a web site or post information on the Internet. Anyone can use the Internet to "publish" personal opinions. Sometimes it is difficult to distinguish accurate scientific information from these opinions. Always check the source of the information. Be wary of an individual who is publishing alone. Government sites and educational association sites tend to contain much more reliable information. Follow your own school's guidelines for "surfing" the Internet to do your research. As well, make good use of McGraw-Hill Ryerson's School Division web site *www.school.mcgrawhill.ca/resources/*, to streamline your search.

Using the Internet Effectively

There are several navigation programs that allow you to access the Internet. Once you have done this, where do you go next? The following steps can help you find information quickly and efficiently.

If you know the web site address, you can go directly to the site. The web site address is called the "Universal Resource Location," or "URL." The URL for the publisher of this textbook is *http://www.mcgrawhill.ca* It will take you to the headquarters of McGrawHill-Ryerson Limited in Whitby, Ontario. You can use the McGraw-Hill Ryerson site to obtain information about specific topics in this textbook.

If you do not know a specific URL, you can search for information by using search engines. These search engines locate sites based on key words that you enter for the search. Key words can include phrases or single words that relate to a subject.

INTERNET CONNECT

www.school.mcgrawhill.ca/resources/

How are satellites being used to monitor changes on Earth? Visit the web site above. Go to **Science Resources**, then to **SCIENCEPOWER 10** to know where to go next. Select a major satellite project to investigate. Who is involved in the project, and what data are being collected? How will these data help us understand and predict how Earth's environment is changing? Prepare a poster about the satellite project you have chosen. Use your poster to present your findings to the class.

Basic Search

For a basic search, type in one or a few key words. The search engine will respond with a list of web sites that are related to the key words. A basic search usually results in many web sites, or "hits." For example, you can enter the word "energy" if you are interested in gases. This will result in about 125 000 hits! The number of hits usually depends on how specific the key words are. General key words tend to result in many hits.

Advanced Search

Most search engines use methods based on Boolean logic to narrow the field of search. These methods combine key words with other words (such as "AND," "NOT," and "OR"), symbols (such as "+" and "−"), or various letters. For example, adding "AND" between "gases" and "greenhouse" will narrow the search to web sites that contain *both* key words (about 54 400 hits). You can further refine the search by adding "NOT carbon monoxide" (about 605 hits). This will disregard web sites on carbon monoxide. Your searches will be more efficient if you familiarize yourself with the advanced search methods of the search engine you use.

Periodic Table of the Elements

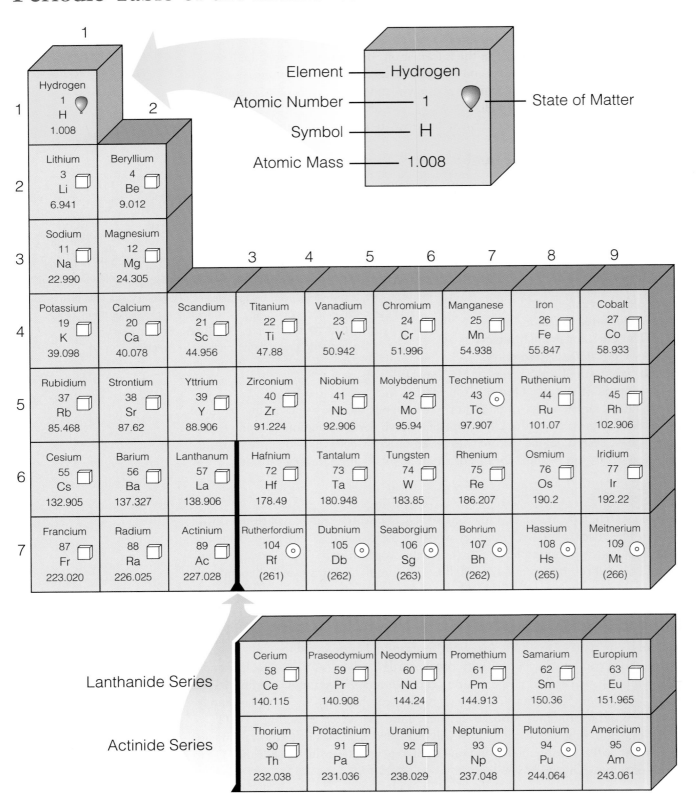

Element —— Hydrogen
Atomic Number —— 1 — State of Matter
Symbol —— H
Atomic Mass —— 1.008

| 1 | 2 | 3 | 4 | 5 | 6 | 7 | 8 | 9 |

1 | Hydrogen 1 H 1.008 |

2 | Lithium 3 Li 6.941 | Beryllium 4 Be 9.012 |

3 | Sodium 11 Na 22.990 | Magnesium 12 Mg 24.305 |

4 | Potassium 19 K 39.098 | Calcium 20 Ca 40.078 | Scandium 21 Sc 44.956 | Titanium 22 Ti 47.88 | Vanadium 23 V 50.942 | Chromium 24 Cr 51.996 | Manganese 25 Mn 54.938 | Iron 26 Fe 55.847 | Cobalt 27 Co 58.933 |

5 | Rubidium 37 Rb 85.468 | Strontium 38 Sr 87.62 | Yttrium 39 Y 88.906 | Zirconium 40 Zr 91.224 | Niobium 41 Nb 92.906 | Molybdenum 42 Mo 95.94 | Technetium 43 Tc 97.907 | Ruthenium 44 Ru 101.07 | Rhodium 45 Rh 102.906 |

6 | Cesium 55 Cs 132.905 | Barium 56 Ba 137.327 | Lanthanum 57 La 138.906 | Hafnium 72 Hf 178.49 | Tantalum 73 Ta 180.948 | Tungsten 74 W 183.85 | Rhenium 75 Re 186.207 | Osmium 76 Os 190.2 | Iridium 77 Ir 192.22 |

7 | Francium 87 Fr 223.020 | Radium 88 Ra 226.025 | Actinium 89 Ac 227.028 | Rutherfordium 104 Rf (261) | Dubnium 105 Db (262) | Seaborgium 106 Sg (263) | Bohrium 107 Bh (262) | Hassium 108 Hs (265) | Meitnerium 109 Mt (266) |

Lanthanide Series

| Cerium 58 Ce 140.115 | Praseodymium 59 Pr 140.908 | Neodymium 60 Nd 144.24 | Promethium 61 Pm 144.913 | Samarium 62 Sm 150.36 | Europium 63 Eu 151.965 |

Actinide Series

| Thorium 90 Th 232.038 | Protactinium 91 Pa 231.036 | Uranium 92 U 238.029 | Neptunium 93 Np 237.048 | Plutonium 94 Pu 244.064 | Americium 95 Am 243.061 |

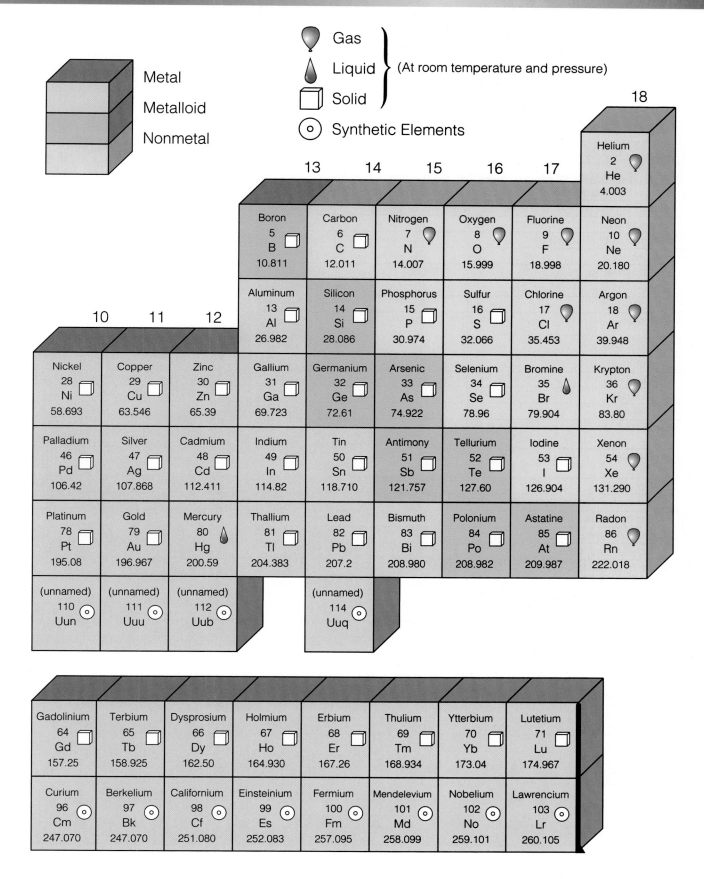

Properties of Common Substances

KEY TO SYMBOLS:

Common names of substances are enclosed in parentheses.

(*) water solution of a pure substance   (e) element   (c) compound   (n) not a pure substance

Name	Formula	Melting point (°C)	Boiling point (°C)	Density (g/cm³ or g/mL)
acetic acid (vinegar) (c)	CH_3COOH	16.6	118.1	—
alcohol (see ethanol) (c)				
aluminum (e)	Al	659.7	2519	2.7
aluminum oxide (alumina) (c)	Al_2O_3	2015	—	—
ammonia (c)	NH_3	−77.8	−33.4	less dense than air
ammonium nitrate (c)	NH_4NO_3	169.6	210	
antimony (e)	Sb	631	1587	6.70
argon (e)	Ar	−189	−185	denser than air
arsenic (e)	As	—	—	5.727 (grey) 4.25 (black) 2.0 (yellow)
barium (e)	Ba	727	1897	3.62
berkelium (e)	Bk	1050	—	14.78
beryllium (e)	Be	1280	2471	1.85
bismuth (e)	Bi	271	1560	9.7
boron (e)	B	2075	4000	2.37 (brown) 2.34 (yellow)
bromine (e)	Br	−7.2	58.8	3.12
calcium (e)	Ca	845	1484	1.55
calcium carbonate (limestone) (c)	$CaCO_3$	decomposes at 900°C	—	2.93
calcium hydroxide (slaked lime) (c)	$Ca(OH)_2$	decomposes at 522°C	—	2.24
calcium oxide (lime) (c)	CaO	2580	2850	3.3
carbon (diamond) (e)	C	3500	3930	3.51
carbon (graphite) (e)	C	4492	4492	2.25
carbon dioxide (c)	CO_2	—	—	—
chlorine (e)	Cl_2	−101.6	−34.6	denser than air
chromium (e)	Cr	1907	2671	7.2
cobalt (e)	Co	1480	2927	8.9
copper (e)	Cu	1084	2562	8.95
copper (II) nitrate (c)	$Cu(NO_3)_2$	—	—	—
copper (II) sulfate (bluestone) (c)	$CuSO_4 \cdot 5H_2O$	decomposes at 150°C	—	2.28
diamond (see carbon) (e)				
ethanol (ethyl alcohol) (c)	C_2H_5OH	−114.5	78.4	0.789
ethylene (ethene) (c)	C_2H_4	−169	−103.9	—
fluorine (e)	F_2	−270	−188	—
gold (e)	Au	1063	2856	19.3
glucose (c)	$C_6H_{12}O_6$	146	decomposes before it boils	1.54
graphite (see carbon) (e)				
helium (e)	He	−272.2	−268.93	—
hematite (c)	Fe_2O_3	1565	—	5.24

Appearance (at room temperature: 20°C)	Comments
colourless liquid with pungent smell	used in the manufacture of cellulose ethanoate; vinegar is a 5 to 7 percent solution in water
silver-white metal	used in aircraft, cooking utensils, and electrical apparatus
white, crystalline substance	used in refining of aluminum and in cement
very soluble gas with pungent smell	used as refrigerant and in manufacture of resins, explosives, and fertilizers
white, soluble, crystalline salt	used in explosives and as a fertilizer
silver-grey solid	used in infrared detectors
inert gas	used in electric lights
grey, black, or yellow solid	used in semiconductors and alloys; compounds are very poisonous and are used in medicine and as pesticides
silver-white solid	used in X-ray diagnosis
—	—
hard, white metal	used for corrosion-resistant alloys
brittle, white, crystalline metal with reddish tinge	used in alloys, catalysts, nuclear reactors; compounds used in medicine
brown amphorous powder or yellow crystals	used for hardening steel and for producing enamels and glasses
red-brown liquid	used to make certain pain-relieving drugs; liquid causes severe chemical burns; vapour is harmful to lungs
soft, white metal that tarnishes easily	very abundant; essential to life
white solid	main ingredient in chalk and marble
white solid	aqueous solution used to test for CO_2
white solid	used in cement and for marking lines on playing fields
colourless, solid crystals	very hard; used for drilling through rock
grey-black solid	very soft; used in lubricants, pencil leads, and electrical apparatus
colourless gas with a faint tingling smell and taste	does not support combustion and is denser than air; used in fire extinguishers and as a refrigerant at −78.5°C
green gas	poisonous; used to kill harmful organisms in water
shiny, silvery solid	very hard metal; used to make stainless steel
hard, silver-white, magnetic metal	used in alloys; compounds used to produce the colour blue in glass and ceramics
shiny, reddish solid	soft metal; good conductor of heat
blue, solid crystals	used in pesticides
colourless liquid	derived from fermentation of sugar; used as solvent or fuel; found in wine
colourless, inflammable gas with a sweetish smell	made from petroleum; used in manufacture of ethanol and other organic chemicals
greenish yellow gas	similar to chlorine
shiny, yellow solid	very soft metal; highly resistant to tarnishing
white solid	simple sugar; human body converts most sugars and starches to glucose
nonflammable inert gas	used as refrigerant; provides inert atmosphere for welding; used to fill air ships and balloons
rusty red colour	found in iron ore; rusty iron

Name	Formula	Melting point (°C)	Boiling point (°C)	Density (g/cm³ or g/mL)
hydrochloric acid (*)	HCl	varies	varies	varies
hydrogen (e)	H_2	−259	−253	much less dense than air
hydrogen peroxide (c)	H_2O_2	−0.4	150.2	1.45
iodine (e)	I	114	184	4.95
iron (e)	Fe	1535	2861	7.86
lead (e)	Pb	327.4	1750	11.34
lead (II) nitrate (c)	$Pb(NO_3)_2$	—	—	—
limestone (see calcium carbonate) (c)				
lithium (e)	Li	179	1340	0.534
magnesium (e)	Mg	651	1107	1.74
magnesium chloride (c)	$MgCl_2$	708	1412	2.3
magnetite (c)	Fe_3O_4	—	—	5.18
manganese (e)	Mn	1246	2061	7.43
mercury (e)	Hg	−38.9	356.6	13.6
methane (c)	CH_4	−182.5	−161.5	—
molybdenum (e)	Mo	2623	4679	10.28
neon (e)	Ne	−248	−246	—
nickel (e)	Ni	1455	2913	8.90
nitrogen (e)	N_2	−209.9	−195.8	slightly less dense than air
nitrogen dioxide (c)	NO_2	—	—	—
oxygen (e)	O_2	−218	−183	slightly denser than air
ozone (e)	O_3	−192.5	−112	denser than air
phosphorus (e)	P	44 / —	280 / —	1.82 (white) / 2.20 (red)
platinum (e)	Pt	1769	3824	21.41
polyethylene (polythene) (c)	$(C_2H_4)_n$	—	—	—
potassium (e)	K	63.5	759	0.86
propane (c)	C_3H_8	—	−42.17	—
selenium (e)	Se	217	684.9	4.81
silicon (e)	Si	1410	3265	2.33
silicon dioxide (silica) (c)	SiO_2	1600	—	—
silver (e)	Ag	961	2162	10.5
sodium (e)	Na	97.5	892	0.971
sodium chloride (table salt) (c)	NaCl	801	1465	2.16
sodium fluoride (c)	NaF	988	1695	2.56
steel (n)	varies	varies	varies	varies
strontium (e)	Sr	777	1412	2.6
sucrose (sugar) (c)	$C_{12}H_{22}O_{11}$	170	decomposes at 186°C	1.59
sulfur (brimstone) (e)	S	112.8	444.6	2.07
technetium (e)	Tc	2157	4265	11.5
tellurium (e)	Te	450	990	6.25
tin (e)	Sn	231.9	2602	7.31
titanium (e)	Ti	1666	3287	4.5
tungsten (e)	W	3422	5555	19.25
uranium (e)	U	1130	4131	19.05
water (c)	H_2O	0	100	1.00
xenon (e)	Xe	−111.9	−107.1	—
zinc (e)	Zn	419	907	7.14
zirconium (e)	Zr	1852	4400	6.51

Appearance (at room temperature: 20°C)	Comments
colourless liquid	corrosive acid; properties vary according to concentration
colourless gas	highly inflammable; liquid form used as rocket fuel
colourless liquid	thick and syrupy when pure; an antiseptic
violet-black, solid crystals	crystals sublime readily to form poisonous violet vapour
shiny, silver solid	rusts readily; soft when pure
shiny, blue-white solid	soft metal; forms poisonous compounds
white or colourless crystals	easily decomposed by heat; soluble in water
silver-white metal (least dense solid known)	used in alloys; its salts have various medical uses
light, silvery white metal that tarnishes easily in air	used in alloys and photography; compounds used in medicine; essential to life
white, deliquescent substance	
shiny, black crystalline solid	strongly magnetic
grey-white solid	used in alloys with special magnetic properties
shiny, silvery liquid	only liquid metal; forms poisonous compounds
odourless, inflammable gas formed from decaying organic matter	main constituent in natural gas
silver-white solid	used in high-strength steel alloys
colourless, odourless gas	discharge of electricity at low pressures through neon produces an intense orange-red glow
silvery white, magnetic metal that resists corrosion	used for nickel plating and coinage, in alloys, and as a catalyst
colourless gas	will not burn or support burning; makes up 80 percent of air
brown gas	causes reddish-brown colour in smog
colourless gas	must be present for burning to take place; makes up 20 percent of air
bluish gas	used for purifying air and water and in bleaching; atmospheric layer blocks most of Sun's ultraviolet light
dark red powder	highly poisonous, inflammable
white, waxy, luminous in the dark	nonpoisonous, less inflammable; compounds used in fertilizers and detergents; occurs only in combined state, mainly calcium phosphate $Ca_3(PO_4)_2$; essential to life
silver-white solid	used in jewellery; alloyed with cobalt, used in pacemakers
tough, waxy, thermoplastic material	polymer of ethylene; used as insulating material; flexible and chemically resistant
silvery white, soft, highly reactive, alkali metal	essential to all life; found in all living matter; salts used in fertilizers
colourless gas	inflammable; used as fuel
non-metal resembling sulfur; silvery grey, crystalline solid	used in manufacture of rubber and ruby glass; used in photoelectric cells and semiconductors
steel-grey metalloid similar to carbon in its chemical properties	used in pure form in semiconductors and alloys and in the form of silicates in glass
hard, granular powder; insoluble in water	main constituent of sand; used in clocks and watches as quartz
shiny, white solid	soft metal; best-known conductor of electricity
soft, silvery-white metal; very reactive	used in preparation of organic compounds, as coolant, and in some types of nuclear reactors
white, crystalline solid	used to season or preserve foods
colourless, crystalline substance	used in water fluoridation and as an insecticide
metallic grey solid	used in alloys of iron with carbon and other elements; widely used as structural material
silver-white solid	used in the manufacture of colour television tubes
white solid	made from sugar cane or sugar beets
yellow solid	used to make dyes, pesticides, and other chemicals
silver-grey solid	used in gamma ray diagnosis of bone abnormalities
silver-white solid	used in semiconductors
shiny, slightly yellow solid	soft metal; rust resistant
lustrous white solid	alloys are widely used in the aerospace industry
grey-white solid	used in light bulb filaments
metallic grey solid	used as a nuclear fuel (usually converted into plutonium)
colourless liquid	good solvent for non-greasy matter
inert gas	used in fluorescent tubes and light bulbs
hard, bluish-white metal	used in alloys such as brass and galvanized iron
silver-white solid	used in the chemical industry as anti-corrosive material

Properties of Common Substances **575**

Weather Map Symbols

Sample Plotted Report at Each Station

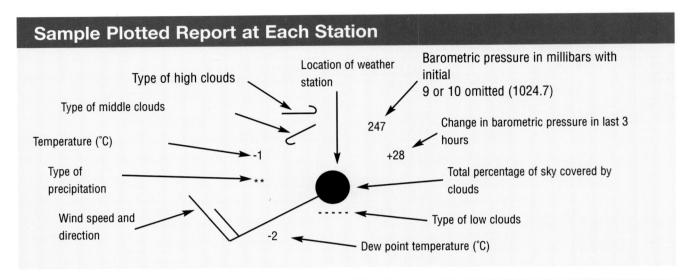

Symbols Used in Plotting Report

Precipitation	*Wind Speed and direction		Sky coverage		Some types of high clouds	
≡ Fog	◯	0 calm	◯	No cover	⌐⌐ Scattered cirrus	
★ Snow		1-2 knots		1/10 or less		
● Rain		3-7 knots		2/10 to 3/10	⌐⌐ Dense cirrus in patches	
		8-12 knots		4/10		
Thunder-storm		13-17 knots		1/2	⌐⌐ Veil of cirrus covering entire sky	
		18-22 knots		6/10		
' Drizzle		23-27 knots		7/10	⌐⌐ Cirrus not covering entire sky	
▽ Showers		48-52 knots		Overcast with openings		
	1 knot = 1.852 km/h		●	Complete overcast		

Some types of middle clouds		Some types of low clouds		Fronts and pressure systems	
∠ Thin altostratus layer		⌒ Cumulus of fair weather		(H) or High	Centre of high- or
∥ Thick altostratus layer		⌣ Stratocumulus		(L) or Low	low-pressure system centre
Thin altostratus in patches		----- Fractocumulus of bad weather		▲▲▲▲ Cold front	
Thin altostratus in bands		— Stratus of fair weather		●●●● Warm Front	
				▲●▲● Occluded front	
				●⌒●⌒ Stationary front	

*Knots are the standard units for reporting wind speed.

SCIENCE SKILLS GUIDE

USING GRAPHIC ORGANIZERS TO IMPROVE YOUR LEARNING

An efficient way to organize information you are learning is to represent it visually by using a **graphic organizer**. One kind of graphic organizer you will find helpful is a **concept map**. A concept map is a diagram that visually represents how science concepts, or ideas, are related. Since a concept map shows the relationships among concepts, it can clarify the meanings of these concepts, and related terms, and help you understand what you are studying.

Look at the construction of the concept map below, called a **network tree**. Notice how some words are circled while others are written on connecting lines. The circled words are concepts. The lines in the map show related concepts, and the words written on the lines describe the relationships between the concepts. This network tree shows how the parts of an ecosystem can be categorized.

As you learn more about a topic, your concept map will grow and change. Remember that concept maps are a tool for you to use. There is no one "correct" concept map; it represents the connections that make sense to *you*. Make your map as neat and clear as possible, and be sure that you have good reasons for suggesting the connections between its parts.

When you have completed a concept map, you may have dozens of interesting ideas. Your map is a record of your thinking. Although it may contain many of the same concepts as other students' maps, your concepts may be recorded and linked differently. You can use your map for study and review. You can refer to it to help you recall concepts and relationships. At a later date, you can use your map to see what you have learned and how your ideas have changed.

Here are other types of concept maps that you will find useful.

An **events chain** is used to describe events in order. In science, an events chain can be used to describe a sequence of happenings, the steps in a procedure, or the stages of a process. When making an events chain, you first must find out the one event that starts the chain. This event is called the initiating event. You then find the next event in the chain and continue until you reach an outcome. Here is an events chain showing the events that occur when a ball is thrown.

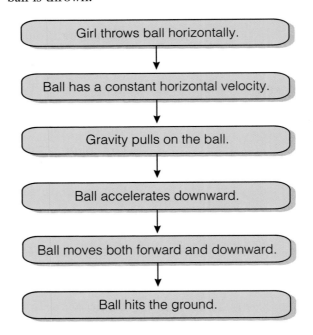

A **cycle concept map** is a special type of events chain map. In a cycle concept map, the series of events do not produce a final outcome. There is no beginning and no end to a cycle concept map.

To construct a cycle map, you first decide on a starting point and then list each important event in order. Since there is no outcome and the last event relates back to the first event, the cycle repeats itself. You can see this in the following cycle map of the generalized life cycle of a moth.

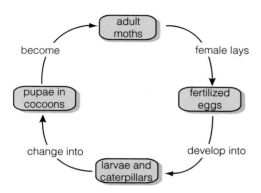

A **spider map** is a concept map that you may find useful for brainstorming. You may, for example, have a central idea and a jumble of related ideas, but these ideas may not be related to each other. By placing the related ideas outside the main idea, you may begin to group them so that their relationships become easier to understand. Examine the following spider map of motion to see how various ideas relating to motion may be grouped to provide clearer understanding.

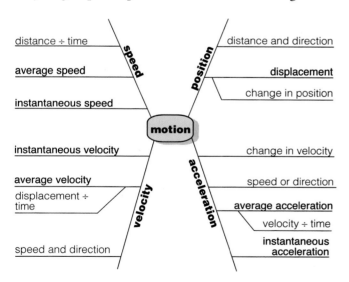

Another method to help you solidify your learning is comparing and contrasting. When you compare, you look for similarities between two things. When you contrast, you look for differences. Thus comparing and contrasting can involve listing the ways in which two things are similar and the ways in which they are different. You can also use a graphic organizer, called a **Venn diagram**, with two circles

to do this. The following Venn diagram can help you distinguish the similarities and differences between sharks and dolphins.

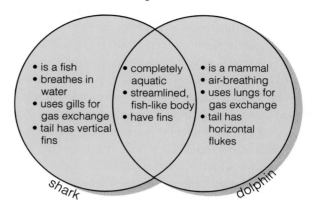

Instant Practice

1. Complete the following concept map on the categories of science.

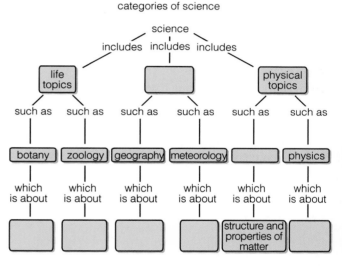

2. Use the following terms to produce a network tree concept map: musical instruments, orchestral music, tuba, electric, cello, wind, percussion, rock and jazz, French horn, string, drum kit, brass, guitar, flute, oboe, trumpet, kettle drums, xylophone, cymbals, violin, bass, double bass, organ, clarinet, trombone.

3. Produce an events chain concept map that shows the steps for preparing yourself a cup of tea.

4. Make a Venn diagram to compare and contrast a bicycle and a car.

5. Examine the cycle map of the generalized life cycle of a moth. Change it into an events chain concept map.

HOW TO USE A SCIENCE LOG

Scientists keep logs, or detailed records, of their observations, new data, and new ideas. This helps them organize their thinking and keep track of the progress of their research. You can keep a *Science Log* (or *Science Journal*) also, to help you organize your thinking.

Your *Science Log* is a place where you can record what you already know about a topic and add what you learn as you continue through this course. Your *Science Log* can be a special booklet or a marked-off section of your science notebook. Your teacher can advise you on which approach to take.

You will find that recording something you have learned will help you solidify it in your own mind and will often help you clarify ideas and concepts. It is also very useful to indicate what you already know about a topic. You may discover that you know more than you realized. On the other hand, you might discover that a particular topic needs close attention because you do not know very much about it. The value of a *Science Log* is that you find out for yourself how clear your understanding is and, like scientists, keep track of the progress of your learning. You do not have to wait until your teacher assesses your knowledge through a formal test or examination.

Here are some ways in which **SCIENCEPOWER™ 10** makes sure that you can add to your *Science Log* effectively. Each chapter begins with a set of questions called "Opening Ideas... ."

Are you able to answer any of these questions from your previous studies? You can write, draw a sketch, or use whatever method suits you best, to explain what you know. This is *your* log, so you can feel free to record that you know very little about a particular topic. Your *Science Log* is an important study tool because learning and understanding become easier when you have an idea of what you do and do not know.

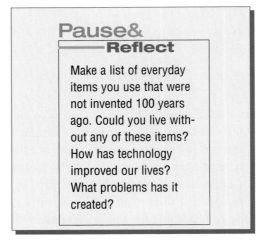

Pause&
——— Reflect

Make a list of everyday items you use that were not invented 100 years ago. Could you live without any of these items? How has technology improved our lives? What problems has it created?

Throughout each chapter, *Pause & Reflect* features help you keep thinking about what you now know. They are designed to help you make connections and organize your thoughts. Your teacher will guide you on your use of the *Pause & Reflect* questions.

At the end of each Chapter Review, a *Pause & Reflect* question asks you to look back over the new concepts you have learned. A question may ask you to review your original answers to the *Opening Ideas* questions. Some questions may direct your thinking to *Key Concepts* in the chapter. You may be amazed at how much your original ideas have changed, based on the new knowledge you have gained by studying the chapter.

Here are some other things that you might want to include in your *Science Log:*

- questions that you would like to be able to answer
- sketches and notes about models and processes in science
- graphic organizers (see *SkillPower 1* for a few examples)
- thoughts on what you find difficult or how you might overcome the barriers to learning a new topic

Opening
Ideas...

- How is your brain powered by the Sun?
- Why are rabbits more common than foxes?
- Why might overfishing of herring lead to an increase in populations of sea urchins?

- ideas on how you might answer a scientific question or solve a problem using technology
- notes about interesting items in the news that involve a chapter topic and that spark more questions or answer some existing questions
- profiles of leading Canadian scientists or technologists that you learn about in the media, or profiles of careers related to science and technology that you find interesting
- connections between science and other subject areas that occur to you in the course of your learning

Your *Science Log* will help you become a better learner, so take the time to make entries on a regular basis.

Instant Practice

1. Examine the graph below. It shows the general relationship between the pressure and volume of a gas enclosed in a cylinder, at a constant temperature.

   (a) In your *Science Log*, explain what you think the graph indicates.

   (b) Suggest at least one way that the data in the graph could be obtained. Is this an example of science or technology? Explain.

   (c) In part (b), if you answered that it is an example of science, is technology also involved? (Hint: How would you measure values of pressure and volume?)

   (d) Think of an example of a simple technology that follows the principle shown in the graph. Would you need to know this principle to produce the technology? Explain why, or why not.

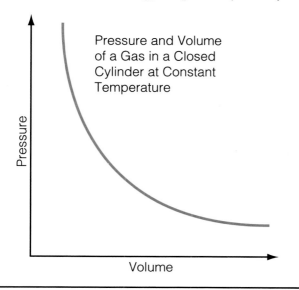

Pressure and Volume of a Gas in a Closed Cylinder at Constant Temperature

2. Examine the graph below. It compares the concentration of atmospheric carbon dioxide in the atmosphere with changes in temperature over the last 150 000 years. At first glance, the graph seems to be relevant only for the past. Answer the following questions to see if this is true.

   (a) Describe the general patterns for temperature change and the levels of carbon dioxide. What is the general relationship between these two variables?

   (b) Identify a current issue that relates to the data in the graph.

   (c) How can the data in the graph be applied to this issue?

   (d) Why is it useful to have scientific input on societal issues?

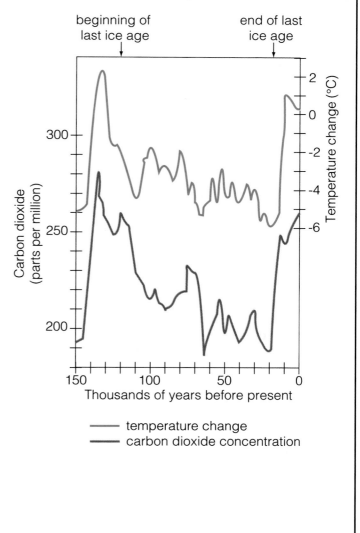

Atmospheric Carbon Dioxide and Temperature

temperature change
carbon dioxide concentration

NOTE-TAKING AND STUDY SKILLS

Note-Taking

Having good class notes is one key to being successful in this science course. Your notes should summarize the topics you learn in class each day. They should be concise and easy to read — you will need to refer to them when you are studying. You may also want to review them on a daily basis. It is important to realize that you do not have to write down everything that is said or written by your teacher. You should strive to be selective in taking notes. Good note-taking skills will enable you to filter out the unimportant from the important information.

Listening and Observing

Note taking is not difficult, but you need to be prepared and to concentrate on what you are learning. Here are some of the methods you can use to listen and observe well during class:

- Focus on the topic being considered.
- Listen for key words and ideas given by your teacher.
- Listen for information that is repeated or accompanied by a visual aid. This information is often the most important and will help you to understand the concept that you are learning.
- Listen carefully to any questions that your teacher asks. These questions often indicate specific information that your teacher wants you to understand.
- Observe the different ways that your teacher is explaining an idea. By doing this, you will have a better understanding of the important aspects.
- Observe any words or ideas that are highlighted or shown in different colours. These techniques are used to emphasize words or ideas that are important.
- Write down any examples that are used to explain a concept. These examples will help you understand the information and recall it later when you review your notes.

Being Prepared

Here are some of the tools you will need for taking effective notes:

- Lined and unlined paper: You need enough so that you do not have to ask your neighbour for more.
- At least two pens: You may wish to have different colours for different purposes.

- Highlighters and coloured pencils: Use these to emphasize important words and ideas.
- Ruler: You should underline any key words, ideas, and definitions.

Note-Taking Do's and Don'ts

Do
- Write legibly.
- Date and title the notes for each class.
- Highlight or underline important words, definitions, and ideas.
- Write down examples your teacher uses to explain what you are learning.
- Write in point form. Writing in sentences takes too long, and you will not be able to keep up with the information.
- Use your own words. You will be able to understand the information more easily this way.

Do Not
- Write down every bit of information. This takes too long and is unnecessary.
- Write down ideas that you do not understand. Ask for clarification before you make a note.

Instant Practice

Choose a section in one of the chapters of *SCIENCEPOWER™ 10*. Summarize the information in the section using the guidelines above. Turn to the *Check Your Understanding* questions at the end of the section. Answer these questions using the notes you have made. Your ability to answer these questions will reflect the quality of your notes.

Study Skills

In this science course, you will be presented with information that you will need to understand and apply to similar and new situations. The methods that you use to study will depend on the type of information.

There are many different methods that you can use to study. One such method is a picture page. A picture page consists of a diagram or drawing that describes a particular concept, as shown in the diagram on the next page.

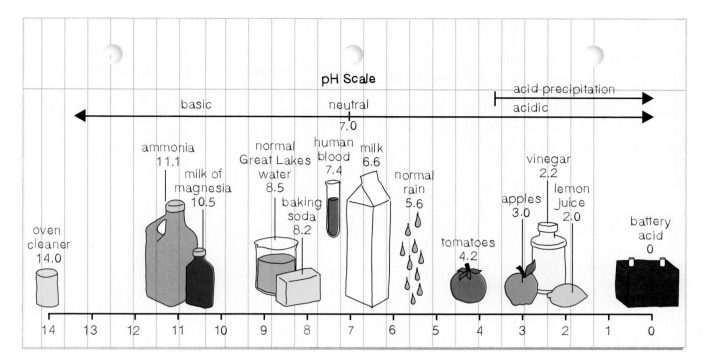

Use symbols and drawings that are meaningful to you, instead of words, in order to help you understand and remember a specific idea. Picture pages work well for people who learn and remember things visually. They should not and cannot be applied, however, to all the information you will need to learn. Picture pages are best used for information that can be easily described through diagrams and symbols, such as cellular reactions (such as photosynthesis) and the components of ecosystems. Another method is note taking. Each chapter that you cover should have its own set of notes. They should be easy to read and understand, and include important information, examples, and ideas. Good notes will enable you to study more easily and effectively.

Study Habits

In addition to the study skills used to understand and remember the information you will learn in this course, you should also try to develop good study habits. Good study habits will allow you to use your time and mental energy effectively and successfully. These are some of the study habits you should keep in mind when studying:

- Study in a cool, quiet work space, away from noise and distractions.

- Organize your work space, and keep it neat and tidy. A messy space can distract you and prevent you from focussing.

- Have all the materials (such as your notebook, pen, paper, and textbook) you will need in your work space. Being prepared means that you can sit and study rather than having to get up continually.

- Study small amounts of information at a time. Quality study is more important than quantity study.

- Use picture pages, study notes, flash cards, or other methods to help you remember important ideas.

- Study when your mind is alert. If you are too tired, you will not be able to study effectively.

- Take breaks. Small breaks (5 to 10 min) will help you stay alert and allow you to remember information more easily.

- Review a little bit each night. Do not try to cram all your studying into one or two days because you will not retain much information.

Instant Practice

In pairs, create notes for one of the chapters in *SCIENCEPOWER™ 10*. Follow the note-taking skills you have just learned. Then study your chapter using only the notes that you and your partner have created. Individually, make up four different questions about the information in the chapter. Try to answer your partner's questions. You may be surprised at your success!

WORKING IN GROUPS

In this course, you are often asked to work in a group to complete a task. Studies have found that students improve their problem-solving and critical-thinking skills when co-operative groups are used. As well, students retain learned material for a longer period of time than they do when working individually or competitively. You need to follow some important rules, however, for effective learning in groups.

In a co-operative group, each of you will have one or more assigned tasks for which you are responsible. This allows the group to make the best use of each member's special skills, and to help each member develop new skills. Groups often develop a special ability to work together, so that each presentation or project completed together is an improvement over the last.

Working well in a group is not always easy. The best way to develop your skills is to consider carefully what makes a group succeed at a task.

Assessing Group Performance

These are some behaviours that you should aim toward when doing group work in this course and other courses:

- Share your ideas with others in the group.
- Show others respect, even if you disagree with them.
- Listen to another group member when this person is speaking.
- Encourage others to speak.
- Stay on the group's task.
- Help the group to stay on task.
- Do not allow yourself to be distracted.
- Keep your voice low so that you will not distract other groups.
- Allow others to present their ideas, even when you think you know the answers.

Instant Practice

1. The first time you are asked to work in a group in this course, assess yourself on how well you did. Your teacher will provide a *Performance Task Self-Assessment* form for you to use. Before you begin your assessment, read over the form to note how you will be assessed.

2. Use the *Performance Task Group Assessment* form provided by your teacher to assess your whole group.

3. Identify three main reasons for your group's success or lack of success in working well together.

UNITS OF MEASUREMENT AND SCIENTIFIC NOTATION

Sometimes, when you are working with numbers, you need an approximate idea about a quantity. At other times, you need to be very precise. Imagine that you are building a cupboard in your home. You need to take precise measurements to make sure that it will be square. In science, measuring quantities precisely is often needed because we cannot rely solely on our senses. For example, which inner circle would you say is larger in the diagrams below? Use a ruler to find out if you are right.

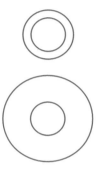

The Metric System

When you take measurements in science, you use the **metric system**. The metric system is a decimal system of measurement.

In the metric system, all units are multiples of 10. Therefore, if you need to express a quantity using a larger unit, you multiply by a multiple of 10. To express a quantity using a smaller unit, you divide by a multiple of ten. For example, the prefix *kilo-* means multiplied by 1000. Thus one kilogram equals one thousand grams:

$$1 \text{ kg} = 1000 \text{ g}$$

The prefix *milli-* means divided by 1000. Thus one milligram equals one one-thousandth of a gram:

$$1 \text{ mg} = \frac{1}{1000} \text{ g}$$

The table on the right lists some frequently used units of measurement in the metric system.

Frequently Used Metric Quantities, Units, and Symbols

Quantity	Unit	Symbol
length	nanometre	nm
	micrometre	μm
	millimetre	mm
	centimetre	cm
	metre	m
	kilometre	km
mass	gram	g
	kilogram	kg
	tonne	t
area	square metre	m²
	square centimetre	cm²
	hectare	ha (10 000 m²)
volume	cubic centimetre	cm³
	cubic metre	m³
	millilitre	mL
	litre	L
time	second	s
temperature	degree Celsius	°C
force	newton	N
energy	joule	J
	kilojoule	kJ
pressure	pascal	Pa
	kilopascal	kPa
electric current	ampere	A
quantity of electric charge	coulomb	C
frequency	hertz	Hz
power	watt	W

The following table shows the most commonly used metric prefixes. (Adding metric prefixes to a base unit is a way of expressing powers of ten.)

Metric Prefixes

Prefix	Symbol	Relationship to the base unit
giga-	G	10^9 = 1 000 000 000
mega-	M	10^6 = 1 000 000
kilo-	k	10^3 = 1 000
hecto-	h	10^2 = 100
deca-	da	10^1 = 10
–	–	10^0 = 1
deci-	d	10^{-1} = 0.1
centi-	c	10^{-2} = 0.01
milli-	m	10^{-3} = 0.001
micro-	μ	10^{-6} = 0.000 001
nano-	n	10^{-9} = 0.000 000 001

Example 1

Canada's national highway network has about 24 500 km of highway. How would you express this distance in metres?

Solution

24 500 km = ? m

$$24\ 500\ \text{km} \times \frac{1000\ \text{m}}{1\ \text{km}} = 24\ 500\ 000\ \text{m}$$

Example 2

The mass of a piece of thread is 0.1 mg. How would you determine its mass in g?

Solution

0.1 mg = ? kg

$$0.1\ \text{mg} \times \frac{1\ \text{g}}{1000\ \text{mg}} = 0.000\ 1\ \text{g}$$

Instant Practice

1. 992 mL = ? L
2. 2 850 000 mm = ? m
3. 12 ms = ? s
4. 11.2 daL = ? L
5. 1.2 kg = ? g
6. 0.5 g = ? mg
7. 102 μm = ? mm
8. 28.3 kg = ? g

SI Units

In science classes, you will often be instructed to report your measurements and answers in **SI** units. The term SI is taken from the French name *Le système international d'unités*. SI uses the metre as the base unit of length, the kilogram as the base unit of mass, and the second as the base unit of time. Most of the other units are related to the base units.

Example

Convert 54.8 cm to SI base units.

Solution

$$54.8\ \text{cm} \times \frac{1\ \text{m}}{100\ \text{cm}} = 0.548\ \text{m}$$

Instant Practice

Convert each measurement to SI units.

1. 3 h
2. 2300 mg
3. 0.01 mm
4. 31 min
5. 1 230 000 μm
6. 12 g

Exponents of Scientific Notation

An **exponent** is the symbol or number denoting the power to which another number or symbol is to be raised. The exponent shows the number of repeated multiplications of the base. In 10^2, the exponent is 2 and the base is 10. The table below shows the powers of 10 as numbers in standard form and in exponential form.

	Standard form	Exponential form
ten thousands	10 000	10^4
thousands	1000	10^3
hundreds	100	10^2
tens	10	10^1
ones	1	10^0
tenths	0.1	$\frac{1}{10^1} = 10^{-1}$
hundredths	0.01	$\frac{1}{10^2} = 10^{-2}$
thousandths	0.001	$\frac{1}{10^3} = 10^{-3}$
ten thousandths	0.0001	$\frac{1}{10^4} = 10^{-4}$

Why use exponents? Consider the number 602 000 000 000 000 000 000 000. If a zero were accidentally added to this number, it would appear to be ten times larger than it actually is. To avoid making mistakes when writing zeros, scientists express large numbers in scientific notation.

Example 1

Write 602 000 000 000 000 000 000 000 in scientific notation.

Solution

In scientific notation, a number has the formula $x \times 10^n$, where x is greater than or equal to 1 but less than 10, and 10^n is a power of 10.

602 000 000 000 000 000 000 000. ⟵ The decimal point starts here. Move the decimal point 23 places to the left.

$= 6.02 \times 100\ 000\ 000\ 000\ 000\ 000\ 000\ 000$
$= 6.02 \times 10^{23}$

This number may now be more easily recognizable as Avogradro's number, a familiar quantity in chemistry. It gives the number of particles in a mole.

Example 2

The average diameter of a human mitochondrion is about 0.000 0023 m. Write 0.000 0023 in scientific notation.

Solution

To write this number in the form $x \times 10^n$, move the decimal point to the right until there is one non-zero number to the left of the decimal point.

The decimal point starts here. Move the decimal point 6 places to the right.   0.000 0023

$= 2.3 \times 0.000\ 001$
$= 2.3 \times 10^{-6}$

When you move the decimal point to the left, the exponent of 10 is positive. When you move the decimal point to the right, the exponent of 10 is negative. The number of places that you move the decimal point is the number of the exponent.

Instant Practice

1. Express each number below in scientific notation.

   (a) A bond between water molecules in liquid water (hydrogen bond) lasts about $\frac{1}{100\ 000\ 000\ 000}$ s.

   (b) The frequency of X-rays is approximately 1 000 000 000 000 000 000 Hz, whereas their wavelength is about $\frac{1}{10\ 000\ 000\ 000}$ m.

   (c) The average distance of Saturn from the Sun is about 1 427 000 000 km.

   (d) 56×10^6

   (e) The mass of one water molecule is about 0.000 000 000 000 000 000 000 000 03 kg.

   (f) In one year, light travels approximately 9 500 000 000 000 km.

2. Change each of the following to standard notation.

   (a) 7.28×10^8 kg

   (b) 1.03×10^{-6} m

   (c) 5.2×10^{-4} s

   (d) 6.1×10^{12} L

USING A MICROSCOPE

Part 1 Parts of a Microscope

A **light microscope** is an optical instrument that greatly increases our powers of observation by magnifying objects that are usually too small to be seen with the unaided eye. The microscope you will use is called a compound light microscope because it has a series of lenses (rather than only one as in a magnifying glass) and it uses light to view the object. A microscope is a delicate instrument, so proper procedure and care must be practised. This *SkillPower* reviews the skills that you will need to use a microscope effectively.

Before you use a microscope, you need to know its parts and their functions. Do the *Instant Practice* below to familiarize yourself with the parts of a microscope.

Instant Practice

1. Study the photograph of the compound light microscope. Learn the names and functions of its parts.

2. Now close this book. Draw and label as many parts of a microscope as you can.

3. Explain to a classmate the function of each part.

A. Eyepiece (or ocular lens)
You look through this part. It has a lens that magnifies the object, usually by 10 times (10×). The magnifying power is engraved on the side of the eyepiece.

B. Tube
The tube holds the eyepiece and the objective lenses at the proper working distance from each other.

C. Revolving nosepiece
A revolving nosepiece holds two or more objective lenses. Turn it to change lenses. Each lens clicks into place.

D. Objective lenses
The objective lenses magnify the object. Each lens has a different power of magnification, such as 4×, 10×, or 40×. (Your micro-scope may instead have 10×, 40×, and 100× objective lenses.) For convenience, the objective lenses are referred to as low, medium, and high power. The magnifying power is engraved on the side of each objective lens. Be sure that you can identify each lens.

E. Arm
The arm connects the base and the tube. Use the arm for carry-ing the microscope.

F. Coarse-adjustment knob
This knob moves the tube up and down to bring the object into focus. Use it only with the low-power objective lens.

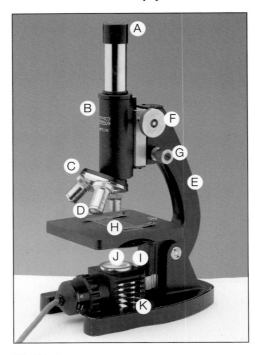

G. Fine-adjustment knob
Use this knob with medium-power and high-power magnification to bring the object into sharper focus.

H. Stage
The stage supports the microscope slide. Stage clips hold the slide in position. An opening in the centre of the stage allows light from the light source to pass through the slide.

I. Condenser lens
The condenser lens directs light to the object being viewed.

J. Diaphragm
The diaphragm controls the amount of light reaching the object being viewed.

K. Light source
Shining a light through the object being viewed helps you to see the details. Your microscope might have a mirror instead of a light. If it does, it must be adjusted to direct the light source through the lenses.
CAUTION: Use an electric light, not sunlight, as the light source for focussing your mirror.

Part 2 Now Practise!

You are now ready to practise the proper use of a microscope to view an object. In this activity, you will also practise calculating magnification and the **field of view**: the size of the area that can be seen using a microscope. By doing these calculations, you will be able to estimate the actual sizes of the objects you have magnified with your microscope.

What You Need

microscope
lens paper
prepared microscope slide
plastic ruler

Safety Precautions

- Be sure that your hands are dry when you plug in or disconnect the cord of the microscope.
- Handle microscope slides carefully so that they do not break or cause cuts or scratches.

What to Do

1. Obtain a microscope, and carry it to your work area. Use both hands to carry the microscope upright and support it properly. One hand should hold the arm of the microscope firmly, and the other hand should support the base.

   (a) Do not turn any knobs until you have read through the rest of this procedure.

   (b) If the microscope has an electric cord for the light source, make sure that the cord is properly connected and plugged in.

   (c) Use lens paper to clean the lenses and the light source (or mirror). Do not touch the lenses with your fingers.

2. The microscope should always be left with the low-power objective lens in position. If your microscope has not been left this way, look from the side and rotate the revolving nosepiece until the low-power objective lens clicks into place.

   (a) Use the coarse-adjustment knob to lower the objective lens until the lens is about 1 cm above the stage, as shown in the photograph.

   (b) Look through the eyepiece (ocular lens). Adjust the diaphragm until the view is as bright as you can get it.

Once you are sure that the low-power objective is clicked into place, you can lower the objective using the coarse-adjustment knob.

3. Place a prepared slide on the stage. Make sure that the object to be viewed is centred over the opening.

   (a) Look through the eyepiece. Slowly turn the coarse-adjustment knob until the object is in focus.

   (b) Use the fine-adjustment knob to sharpen the focus.

4. View the object under higher magnification. **CAUTION:** Do not use the coarse-adjustment knob with the medium-power or high-power objective lens.

   (a) While watching from the side, rotate the revolving nosepiece to the medium-power objective lens. Do not change the focus first.

   (b) After the medium-power objective lens has clicked into place, adjust the focus using only the fine-adjustment knob.

   (c) Next view the object under the high-power objective lens. Rotate the nosepiece (while watching from the side) until it clicks into place. Focus only with the fine-adjustment knob.

(d) When you have finished viewing the object, remove the slide. Return the slide to the proper container before proceeding to step 5.

(e) If you do not continue to step 5, carefully unplug the microscope. Click the low-power objective lens into place, and return the microscope to its storage area.

5. To calculate the total magnification of the object on your slide, multiply the number on the eye-piece by the number on the objective lens. For example, a 10× eyepiece and a 4× objective lens give a total magnification of 40×.

6. You are now ready to calculate the size of the field of view. Set your microscope to the low-power objective, and place a clear plastic ruler on the stage.

7. Focus on the ruler. Position it so that one of the centimetre markings is at the left edge of the field of view.

The diameter of the field of view under low power illustrated here is 2.5 mm.

8. Measure and record the diameter of the field of view in millimetres (mm). If the field of view is 2.5 mm in diameter, then an object that occupies about half the field of view would be about 1.25 mm in diameter.

9. The millimetre markings are too far apart to permit direct measurement of the field of view for lenses with magnifications higher than 10×. If you know the diameter of the field of view for the low-power lens, however, you can calculate the field of view for the other lenses. Before doing so, unplug the microscope by pulling out the plug. **CAUTION:** Never tug on the electrical cord to unplug it.

Use the following formula to calculate the field of view for the medium-power objective lens:

Troubleshooting

You may encounter some problems when using your microscope. The following list gives the more common problems and how you can deal with them.

- *Is everything dark?* Make sure that the microscope is plugged in and the light is on. If the microscope has no light, adjust your mirror.

- *Are you having trouble finding anything on the slide?* Be patient. Follow all of the steps outlined in this procedure, from the beginning. Make sure that the object being viewed is in the middle of the stage opening. While watching from the side, lower the low-power objective lens as far as it will go. Then look through the ocular lens and slowly raise the objective lens using the coarse-adjustment knob.

- *Are you having trouble focussing, or is the image very faint?* Try closing the diaphragm slightly. Some objects that you will examine are almost transparent. If there is too much light, a specimen may be difficult to see or will appear "washed out."

- *Do you see lines and specks floating across the slide?* These are probably structures in the fluid of your eyeball that you see when you move your eyes. Do not worry; this is normal.

- *Do you see a double image?* Check that the objective lens is properly clicked into place.

- *Do you close one eye while you look through the microscope with the other eye?* You might try keeping both eyes open. This will help prevent eye fatigue. It also lets you sketch an object while you are looking at it.

- *Did you "lose" the image when you changed lenses?* Always place the part of the slide you are interested in at the centre of the field of view before changing to a higher-power objective lens. Otherwise, when you turn to medium or high power, you may not see the object that you were viewing under low power. Do you know why?

Medium-power field of view = Low-power field of view × $\dfrac{\text{Magnification of low-power objective lens}}{\text{Magnification of medium-power objective lens}}$

If, for example, your low-power objective lens is a 4× lens with a field of view of 4 mm, and your medium-power objective lens is a 10× lens, then the field of view for the medium-power lens would be

$$\text{Medium-power field of view} = 4 \text{ mm} \times \frac{4}{10}$$
$$= 4 \text{ mm} \times 0.4$$
$$= 1.6 \text{ mm}$$

Do a similar calculation to determine your high-power field of view. Record the value.

Instant Practice

A **scale drawing** is a drawing in which you keep constant the proportions of what you see through the microscope. It is important because it allows you to compare the sizes of different objects and helps you form an idea of the actual size of an object. Also, a scale drawing helps you explain what you see to someone else. Follow the steps below to make a scale drawing.

1. Draw a circle (the size does not matter) in your notebook. The circle represents the microscope's field of view.

2. Imagine that the circle is divided into four equal sections, as shown below. Use a pencil and a ruler to draw these sections in your circle.

3. Using low or medium power, locate a sample that interests you on the prepared slide. Imagine that the field of view is also divided into four equal sections.

4. Notice in what part of the field of view the object lies. Also notice how much of the field of view the object occupies.

5. Draw the object in the circle. Position it so that it is in the same part of the circle as it appears in the field of view. Draw the object to scale. This means that it should take up the same proportion of space on the circle as it does in the field of view.

6. Label your drawing.

7. Estimate the size of the object in your drawing.

microscope's field of view

drawing made to scale

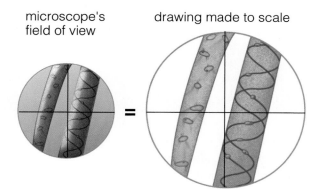

Part 3 Preparing a Wet Mount

Now that you have learned how to use a microscope properly, you are ready to prepare and view slides of your own, using a variety of materials.

What You Need

microscope
microscope slides
cover slips
medicine dropper
tweezers
small piece of newspaper and other samples
tap water
lens paper

Safety Precautions

- Be careful when using sharp objects, such as tweezers.
- Handle microscope slides and cover slips carefully so that they do not break or cause cuts or scratches.

What to Do

1. To prepare a wet mount, begin with a clean slide and cover slip. Wash the slide and cover slip with water. Dry them carefully with lens paper. **CAUTION:** The cover slip is very thin. It is safest to dry both of its surfaces at the same time by holding the lens paper between your thumb and forefinger. Once cleaned, hold the slide and cover slip by their edges to avoid getting fingerprints on their surfaces.

2. Tear out a small piece of newspaper containing a single letter. Use an *e*, *f*, *g*, or *h*. Pick up the letter with the tweezers and place it in the centre of the slide.

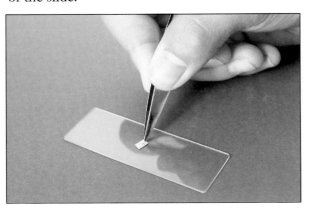

3. Use the medicine dropper to place a very small drop of tap water on the newspaper sample. Pick up a cover slip gently by its edges. Place it, at an angle of 45°, on the surface of the slide near the edge of the newspaper sample.

4. Slowly and carefully lower the cover slip over the sample. Make sure that there are no air bubbles trapped underneath the cover slip. This type of sample preparation is called a **wet mount**.

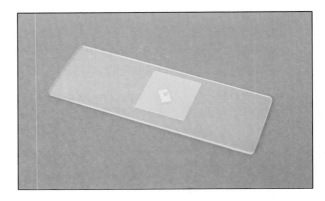

5. Set your microscope on the low-power objective lens. Place the slide on the microscope stage. Centre the sample over the opening in the stage.

   (a) Look through the eyepiece. Move the slide until you can see the letter. Adjust the coarse-adjustment knob until the letter is in focus.

   (b) Move the slide until you can see the torn edge of the newspaper. Slowly move the fine-adjustment knob about one eighth of a turn either way. Do you see the whole view in sharp focus at one time?

6. View the letter under the medium-power objective lens. Remember to watch from the side while you rotate the nosepiece into position. Use only the fine-adjustment knob to focus.

7. Examine the letter. Notice that it is made up of many small dots. To reveal the structure of small objects, the microscope must do more than magnify. It must also reveal detail. The capacity to distinguish detail is called **resolution**, and the measure of resolution is known as **resolving power**. The resolving power of a microscope is defined as the minimum distance that two objects can be apart and still be seen as separate objects.

Troubleshooting

* *Do you see round or oval shapes on the slide?* These are likely to be air bubbles. Move the cover slip gently with your finger to get rid of them, or study another area of the slide.

* *Do you see a straight line?* This could be the edge of your cover slip.

Instant Practice

1. Before rotating the nosepiece to a higher magnification, it is best to have the object you are examining at the centre of the field of view. Why?

2. To view a letter torn out of a newspaper (such as *e*) through the microscope the right way up, how would you position the slide on the stage?

3. The black letters in a newspaper are composed of numerous small dots. What do you think the colour photographs are composed of? Prepare a wet mount using a piece of a colour print from a newspaper, and find out how the colour print is made.

4. Prepare and examine microscope slides of different samples of materials, such as strands of hair, cotton, Velcro™, and grains of salt or sand. Obtain your teacher's approval of the material you select.

ESTIMATING AND MEASURING

The gathering of scientific data often involves the measurement of different quantities. Special tools and techniques have been developed to take accurate measurements. **Accuracy** refers to how close a measurement is to the true value of a particular quantity, such as the length or mass of an object. Some of the measurements that scientists need to make are more complex than others. Whether complex or simple, measurements must be taken properly. In this *SkillPower*, you will learn and practise some measuring techniques, so that you can gather your own data.

Estimating

In some cases, it may not be essential or possible to take exact measurements. In such cases, scientists make estimates. For example, suppose that you are an ecologist and you need to know the number of rabbits living in a grassland habitat. You cannot count every rabbit in the habitat because it would take too much time and money. This is also not necessary, since you do not need to know the exact number. You can obtain an estimate of the population size by surveying the rabbits in a smaller study area, say a 1 km² area of the habitat. You can then multiply the number of rabbits in this study area by the total number of km² in the grassland habitat to obtain an estimate of the size of the rabbit population.

Instant Practice

1. Suppose that you are trying to determine the number of unicellular organisms in 1 L of pond water. You have determined how many are in one drop of water. What do you need to do to estimate the number in 1 L? How will you determine the relationship between the drop and 1 L?

2. The distance between Vancouver and Ottawa is 3550 km. If you are flying in an airplane that averages 450 km/h, estimate how long the flight will take.

Sampling

As mentioned above, it is impractical for a scientist to count each individual in a large population of organisms. Instead, scientists count or study the number of individuals in one or a few smaller areas within the larger region where the organisms live. This method of investigation is known as **sampling**: a sample of the population is studied to give scientists an idea of the population as a whole. For a sample to be a good representation of the population, the individuals in the sample must be randomly chosen. Also, the sample should not contain too few individuals: 10 to 30 is usually appropriate.

For example, suppose that you want to know the average height of the students in your school. Your school has 1000 students, so you cannot measure all of them. You will be able to get a good estimate of height by calculating the average height of a sample of students. You will need about 30 students in your sample. You will have to ensure, however, that you use a random sample. You cannot choose 30 of your closest friends because all of them will probably be in your grade, and this will not be a representation of the students in your school. How can you ensure a random sample? One way is to obtain a list of all the students and assign a number to each student. Then you write down each number on a small slip of paper, throw the slips into a hat, mix them up, and pull out 30. This is random because each name has the same chance of being drawn from the hat.

Instant Practice

1. Suppose that you want to estimate the number of paramecia in a lake. Should you determine the number of paramecia in 1 L of water and then multiply this number by the total litres in the lake? Explain.

2. Suppose that you want to estimate the population of a species of fish in a lake. How would you ensure that you take random samples from the lake? Examine the diagram to help you answer this question.

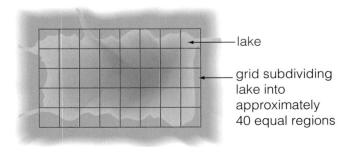

lake

grid subdividing lake into approximately 40 equal regions

Measuring Area

As you know, length is the distance between two points. **Area** is the number of square units required to cover a surface. Area can be calculated easily for a square or rectangular shape: measure the lengths of two neighbouring sides (in other words, the length and width) and multiply them together. For example, the area of a rectangle with a length of 7 cm and a width of 3 cm is

$$7 \text{ cm} \times 3 \text{ cm} = 21 \text{ cm}^2$$

Notice that the values for area are expressed in square units.

The area of a triangle is obtained by multiplying the base and height, and dividing by 2. In other words,

$$\text{Area of triangle} = \frac{1}{2} \times \text{Height} \times \text{Base}$$

A parallelogram is a four-sided shape with opposite sides parallel, as shown below.

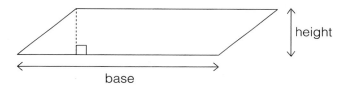

The area of this shape is

$$\text{Area of parallelogram} = \text{Height} \times \text{Base}$$

A special formula is required to calculate the area of a circle. Measure the radius, r (the distance between the centre of the circle and its circumference), and square this value. Then multiply by the special number pi (3.14), which is symbolized by π.

$$\text{Area of a circle} = \pi r^2$$

Instant Practice

1. What is the area of a parallelogram with a height of 3 cm and a base of 6 cm?

2. Suppose that you are helping to renovate the foyer of your school. The centrepiece of the floor is to be a mosaic of tiles. The main form of the mosaic is a circle with a diameter of 3 m, set in a square with sides of 4 m. Your job is to order the appropriate amount of each kind of tile. What is the minimum area of each tile that you will need?

Measuring Volume

The **volume** of an object is the amount of space that the object occupies. Volume involves three dimensions: height, length, and width. The units that are used to measure the volume of a solid are called **cubic units** (for example, cm³). The units that are used to measure the volume of a liquid are called **capacity units**. The base unit for liquids is the litre (L). In this course, however, you will probably be working in millilitres (mL). Cubic units and capacity units are interchangeable, as indicated below:

$$1 \text{ cm}^3 = 1 \text{ mL}$$
$$1 \text{ dm}^3 = 1 \text{ L}$$
$$1 \text{ m}^3 = 1 \text{ kL}$$

To measure the volume of a liquid, you need a graduated cylinder. Once you have poured in the liquid, place the cylinder on a flat surface. Read the level at the top of the column of the liquid, but make sure that your eye is level with the top — do not measure from above or below. Finally you need to consider the **meniscus**: the slight curve at the top of the liquid where the liquid meets the sides of the cylinder. For most liquids, such as water, the sides curve slightly upward, so you measure at the lowest level of the meniscus (see the diagram below). In a mercury thermometer, the edges of the mercury curve slightly downward, so you measure at the top of the meniscus.

The volumes of solids can be measured in several ways, depending on their shape and form. A solid that pours, such as sugar, can be measured like a liquid. Its surface must be as flat as possible, however.

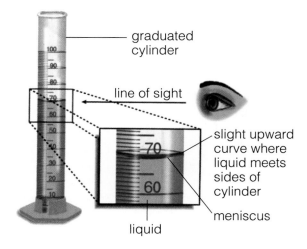

Take a reading from the bottom of the meniscus with your line of sight at the level of the meniscus.

For the volume of a rectangular solid, measure the length, width, and height, and then multiply these measurements together. For the volume of a cylinder, calculate the area of its circular base (see the formula on the previous page) and multiply this area by the height of the cylinder.

The volume of irregularly shaped objects may be determined by the amount of liquid they displace. The displacement for a small object, such as a coin or a pebble, may be determined with a graduated cylinder. The water that is displaced equals the volume of the object, as shown in the diagram below.

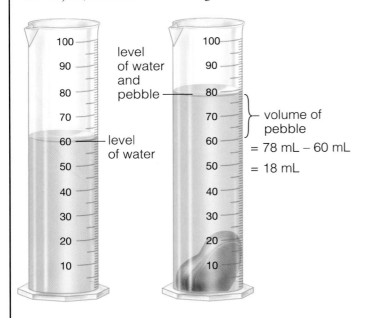

level of water and pebble

level of water

volume of pebble
= 78 mL − 60 mL
= 18 mL

The volume of larger objects can be determined by displacement as well, using an overflow can. The spout allows water that is displaced by an object to be caught and measured in a graduated cylinder, as shown in the following two diagrams.

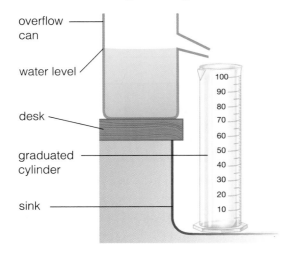

overflow can

water level

desk

graduated cylinder

sink

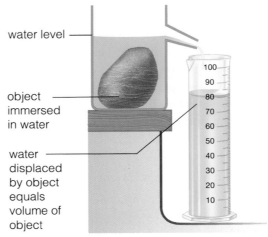

water level

object immersed in water

water displaced by object equals volume of object

Instant Practice

Refer to the diagrams below.

1. What is the volume of each graduated cylinder?

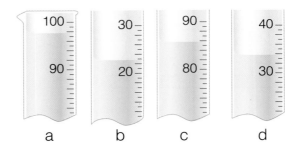

a   b   c   d

2. Calculate the volume of the following object.

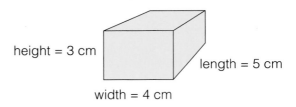

height = 3 cm

length = 5 cm

width = 4 cm

3. Calculate the volume of the following cylinder.

radius = 4 cm
height = 5 cm

4. To measure the volume of a small object, follow these steps:

   (a) Place a carefully measured amount of water, say 50 mL, into a 100 mL graduated cylinder. To do this, fill the cylinder to just under 50 mL and use a medicine dropper to bring the level to 50 mL.

   (b) Tilting the cylinder slightly, gently immerse the object. The object will displace an amount of water that is equal to its volume. The level of the water (50 mL) in the cylinder will rise by this amount.

   (c) Read the new volume level. Subtract the original amount of water from this new amount. This will give you the volume of the object.

5. You can use an overflow can and a graduated cylinder to measure the volume of a large object.

   (a) Place your finger over the spout, and fill the can to above the level of the spout. Put the can on a level surface. Remove your finger to allow the excess water to drain into a sink.

   (b) Place a graduated cylinder beneath the spout. Carefully immerse the object in the water. Be careful that you do not immerse your fingers. The volume of the water that is displaced into the cylinder equals the volume of the object.

Measuring Mass

The **mass** of an object is the measure of the amount of material that makes up the object, but not the space occupied by the object. For example, which has more mass, a cube of wood or a cube of lead of the same size? In this case, you know that the cube of lead has more mass because lead is much denser than wood. What about a marble and a quarter? This comparison is not as easy to make. To measure the mass of each object accurately, you need to use a balance or a scale.

You can use an electronic balance, similar to the one shown on this page. An electronic balance is relatively easy to use. "Zero" the balance, place the object on the balance, and read off the mass of the object in the display.

You can also use a triple beam balance, similar to the one in the photographs on the next page. A triple beam balance has a pan on one side and a set of three beams on the other. Each of the beams has a scale

marked off and a rider or weight that can be moved along the beam. You can find the mass of an object by placing it directly on the pan. What if you need to determine the mass of a quantity of salt? There is an easier way than dumping the salt on the pan! Learn how by doing the following *Instant Practice*.

Instant Practice

1. Before you begin, set the balance to zero by sliding all three riders back to their zero points, at the left side of the beams. The pointer at the right side of the beams should swing slowly an equal amount above and below the zero. If it does not, turn the adjusting screw until it does.

   (a) Place your object on the pan. The pointer will rise above the zero mark.

   (b) Slide along the largest rider until the pointer falls below zero. Then move it back one notch.

   (c) Repeat with the next heaviest rider, and then with the lightest rider. Adjust the last rider until the pointer swings equally above and below zero.

   (d) Add the readings of the three beams to find the mass.

2. What is the mass of half a beaker of salt?

   (a) Place an empty beaker (or cup) on the pan of the balance. Determine the mass of the beaker, and record it.

   (b) Remove the beaker, and half-fill it with salt. Place the beaker on the pan of the balance. Determine the mass of the salt and the beaker together.

   (c) Determine the mass of the salt only.

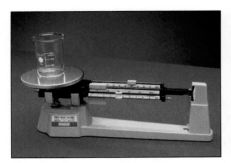

A Determine the mass of the empty beaker.

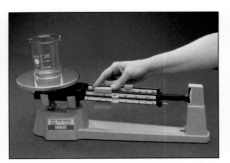

B Add 100 g to the mass measurement by moving the appropriate rider along the beam.

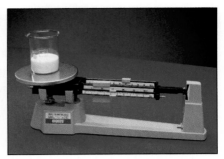

C Carefully add the solid to the beaker on the pan of the balance. The scales will be balanced again when 100 g of the solid have been added to the beaker.

3. You may also use the balance "in reverse." Suppose that you need to measure 100 g of salt to use in an activity. Refer to the photographs above as you go through the following steps.

   (a) Place an empty beaker on the pan, and determine its mass.

   (b) Now move the appropriate slider along, and add 100 g to the right side of the scale. The pointer will fall below zero.

   (c) Carefully pour salt into the beaker until the pointer begins to move. You need to add exactly 100 g of salt to balance the scales again.

Error and Percentage Error Calculations

Every investigation that has numerical results has a degree of uncertainty. This uncertainty is due to the limited accuracy of the measuring apparatus or slight errors on the part of the investigators. It is impossible to remove this uncertainty as a source of error, but you can often assess how serious your errors are. Then you can decide how much to take them into account in your conclusions.

Example

Several students are conducting an investigation to find the value of the acceleration due to Earth's gravity. They are using a ticker timer and a mass that is held at rest and then dropped through about 2 m. They know that the "official" value (determined by careful, repeated experiment) is -9.8 m/s^2 (the negative sign represents a downward acceleration). After completing their procedure, the students calculate a value of -9.6 m/s^2 (downward).

To assess the accuracy of their findings, the students calculate the percentage error between their observed value and the expected value. (The vertical bars show that any negative sign at the end is ignored, so the answer is positive.)

$$\text{Error} = \left| \frac{\text{Observed value} - \text{Expected value}}{\text{Expected value}} \right| \times 100\%$$

$$= \left| \frac{(-9.6 \text{ m/s}^2) - (-9.8 \text{ m/s}^2)}{-9.8 \text{ m/s}^2} \right| \times 100\%$$

$$= \left| \frac{0.2 \text{ m/s}^2}{-9.8 \text{ m/s}^2} \right| \times 100\%$$

$$= |-0.0204| \times 100\%$$

$$= 2.04\%$$

So the group's percentage error is 2.0% (to 2 significant digits; see page 605 for significant digits).

Instant Practice

1. What do you think are likely causes of error in the students' investigation?

2. Based on the students' percentage error, do you think their experimental design is flawed? Do you think they were sloppy in carrying out their procedure? Explain your answers.

3. Another group of students performed the same investigation and recorded a value of -10.7 m/s^2 for the acceleration due to Earth's gravity. Repeat the error and percentage error calculations for this value. What mistake do you think these students might have made in their investigation? Do they need to repeat their procedure to correct this mistake?

4. A third group obtained a value of -7.6 m/s^2. What is this group's percentage error? Do you think this group's procedure was well-designed and carried out correctly? Explain your answer.

ORGANIZING AND COMMUNICATING SCIENTIFIC RESULTS

Scientific results have little value unless they are reported clearly and concisely. While learning about science, you will also learn to communicate scientific results so they are easy to follow. To do this, you must first organize them in an appropriate way. When your results include numerical data, you may report the data in the form of a table, bar graph, circle graph, or line graph.

Tables

Regardless of the final form in which the data are presented, they are often arranged in a table first. Tables also provide a convenient way to organize data for use in further calculations.

Example

Table 1 contains the data needed to determine the per capita consumption of crude oil in selected countries. To find out how to construct such a table, read the following steps while examining the completed table.

1. Decide on the number of columns and rows for your table. Remember to leave one row for column headings.

2. Gather data on population and crude oil consumption for the countries. Place the data in your table.

Table 1 Per Capita Consumption of Crude Oil in Selected Countries (1997)

Country	Population	Crude oil consumption (t)	Per capita consumption (t)
Australia	18 613 000	28 415 000	1.53
Belgium	10 174 400	32 723 000	3.22
Canada	30 675 000	79 510 000	2.59
France	58 804 900	88 947 000	1.51
Germany	82 079 400	101 739 000	1.24
Italy	56 782 800	84 311 000	1.48
Japan	125 931 500	225 783 000	1.79
Mexico	98 552 800	67 534 000	0.69
Netherlands	15 731 100	57 286 000	3.64
United Kingdom	58 970 100	86 612 000	1.49
United States	270 311 700	755 068 000	2.79

3. Calculate the values for the last column by dividing the consumption by the population. For example, the per capita oil consumption for Australia is 28 415 000 ÷ 18 613 000 = 1.53 t. Repeat this calculation for every country.

4. Which country has the highest per capita consumption of crude oil? Which country has the lowest per capita consumption?

Instant Practice

1. **(a)** Organize the following data into a table. In the table, include one column that gives the actual change in population and another column that gives the percent change between 1961 and 1996 for each province and territory. For example, Alberta's population increased by 2 696 826 − 1 331 944 = 1 364 882. The percentage increase was

$$\frac{1\ 364\ 882}{1\ 331\ 944} \times 100\ \% = 102.5\%$$

Population sizes of the provinces and territories for 1961: Alberta, 1 331 944; British Columbia, 1 629 082; Manitoba, 921 686; New Brunswick, 597 936; Newfoundland, 457 853; Northwest Territories, 22 998; Nova Scotia, 737 007; Ontario, 6 236 092; Prince Edward Island, 104 629; Québec, 5 259 211; Saskatchewan, 925 181; Yukon Territory, 14 628.

Population sizes of the provinces and territories for 1996: Alberta, 2 696 826; British Columbia, 3 724 500; Manitoba, 1 113 898; New Brunswick, 738 133; Newfoundland, 551 792; Northwest Territories, 64 402; Nova Scotia, 909 282; Ontario, 10 753 573; Prince Edward Island, 134 557; Québec, 7 138 795; Saskatchewan, 990 237; Yukon Territory, 30 766.

(b) Which province or territory experienced the largest actual increase in population size? Which experienced the lowest increase? Which province or territory experienced the greatest rate of increase? Which experienced the lowest rate of increase?

2. (a) Given below are the names of the top ten career scorers in the National Hockey League up to April 1999, followed by games played and total points. Organize the data into a table. Include a column for points per game. Top ten career scorers: Wayne Gretzky, 1487, 2857; Gordie Howe, 1767, 1850; Marcel Dionne, 1348, 1771; Mark Messier, 1413, 1660; Phil Esposito, 1282, 1590; Mario Lemieux, 745, 1494; Paul Coffey, 1322, 1487; Ron Francis, 1329, 1484; Steve Yzerman, 1178, 1483; Ray Borque, 1453, 1467.

(b) Re-order the players from highest to lowest points per game.

Graphing

Graphs communicate data in a visual way. When designing a graph, your goal is to communicate a large amount of information in a simple, clear manner.

Constructing a Bar Graph

Bar graphs are most useful when you have numerical values associated with categories of places or things. In the following example, the categories are Canadian rivers.

Example

Table 2 gives the data for the bar graph at the right, which shows the length of some of Canada's principal rivers. To learn how the bar graph was prepared, read the following steps while examining the graph.

1. Draw an *x*-axis and a *y*-axis on a sheet of graph paper. Label the *x*-axis "River" and the *y*-axis "Length." Remember to include units.

2. Select an appropriate scale. Write the numerical values of the scale on the *y*-axis.

3. Decide on a width for the bars that will make the graph easy to read. Leave the same amount of space between each bar.

4. To draw the bar that represents the Churchill River, move along the *x*-axis the width of your first bar. Then go up the *y*-axis to just above 1500 to represent 1609. Use a pencil and ruler to draw in the first bar lightly. Repeat the procedure for all the other rivers.

5. When you have drawn all the bars, you might wish to colour them so that they stand out. If you decide to use different colours, you may need to make a key, or legend, to explain the meanings of the colours.

6. Give your graph a title.

Table 2 Length of Principal Rivers of Canada

River	Length (km)
Churchill	1609
Columbia	2000
Fraser	1370
Mackenzie	4241
Nelson	2575
Peace	1923
Saskatchewan	1939
South Saskatchewan	139
St. Lawrence	3058
Yukon	3185

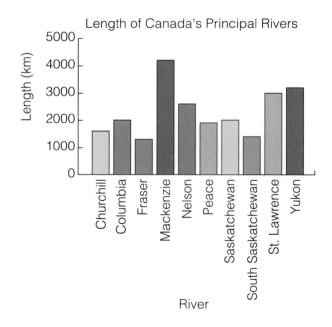

Length of Canada's Principal Rivers

Instant Practice

Make a bar graph that shows the land area, in thousands of km², of Canada's provinces and territories. Use the following data: Alberta, 642 317; British Columbia, 925 186; Manitoba, 553 556; New Brunswick, 71 450; Newfoundland and Labrador, 373 872; Northwest Territories, 1 183 085; Nova Scotia, 53 338; Nunavut, 1 936 113; Ontario, 917 741; Prince Edward Island, 5660; Québec, 1 365 128; Saskatchewan, 591 670; Yukon Territory, 474 391.

Constructing a Histogram

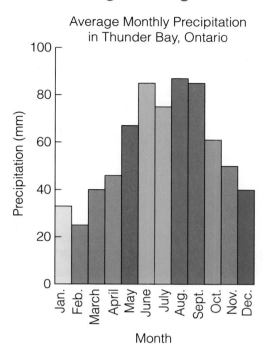

Average Monthly Precipitation in Thunder Bay, Ontario

The x-axis in this histogram represents time, which is a continuous variable. The precipitation data have been grouped by the month.

How does a histogram, such as the one shown above, differ from a bar graph? You probably noticed that there is no space between the bars. The reason for placing the bars in contact with each other is that the x-axis represents a continuous quantity. In this histogram, the continuous quantity is time and each group is one month. The total of the data is represented by the height of a bar. In this case, the height of each bar represents the total precipitation during a month. The steps for making a histogram are the same as the steps for making a bar graph.

Instant Practice

The following data represent the heights of 40 students. Make a histogram to display the heights of the students. Use height groupings of 0.1 m for the bars along the x-axis. Choose an appropriate scale on the y-axis for the number of students in each group.

Heights of students, in metres: 1.65, 1.31, 1.56, 1.54, 1.71, 1.66, 1.64, 1.52, 1.44, 1.79, 1.86, 1.27, 1.75, 1.56, 1.36, 1.44, 1.68, 1.82, 1.51, 1.28, 1.67, 1.38, 1.71, 1.46, 1.55, 1.66, 1.45, 1.68, 1.75, 1.65, 1.48, 1.56, 1.55, 1.91, 1.56, 1.78, 1.61, 1.41, 1.77, 1.61

Constructing a Circle Graph

Circle graphs are an excellent way to communicate categories as percentages of a whole.

Example

To learn how to construct a circle graph, follow the steps below while examining the circle graph that shows the percentage of cropland by province.

Table 3 Percentage of Canada's Cropland by Province

Province	Percentage of total	Degrees (°) in "piece of pie"
Alberta	27	97
Atlantic provinces	1	4
British Columbia	2	7
Manitoba	12	43
Ontario	8	29
Québec	4	14
Saskatchewan	46	166

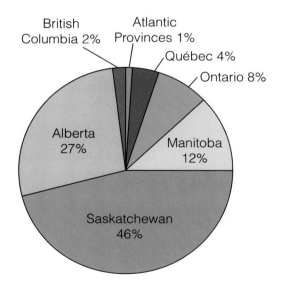

1. Make a large circle on a piece of paper. Put a dot in the centre.

2. To determine the number of degrees in each "piece of the pie," which represents each section, use the following formula:

$$\text{Degrees for "piece of pie"} = \frac{\text{Percentage of total}}{100\%} \times 360°.$$

Round your answer to the nearest whole number. For example, the degrees in the "piece of pie" that represents the cropland in Alberta are

$$\text{Degrees for Alberta} = \frac{27\%}{100\%} \times 360°$$

3. Draw a straight line from the centre of the circle to the circumference. Place a protractor on this line. Use the protractor to mark a point on the circumference at 97°. Connect the point to the centre of the circle. This is the "piece" that represents the cropland in Alberta.

4. Repeat steps 2 and 3 for the remaining provinces.

Instant Practice

Make a circle graph using the following data for the wheat production of the continents: North and Central America, 18%; Europe, 24.5%; Oceania, 3.5%; Africa, 3%; Asia, 47%; South America, 4%.

Drawing a Line Graph

Line graphs, or co-ordinate graphs, show relationships between two variables, such as time and distance. You can use a line graph to predict the value of one variable at any desired value of the other variable. The following examples will show you how to create line graphs from data tables, as well as how to use the line graphs.

Example 1

A land survey across a 1000 km tract of land reported the altitudes at 100 km intervals. The data is shown in Table 4, and the graph is shown below the table. Examine the table and the graph as you read the following steps, describing how the graph was made.

1. With a ruler, draw an x-axis and a y-axis on a piece of graph paper.

2. Label the x-axis " Distance" and the y-axis "Altitude." Include units.

3. Decide on a scale to use. Here the scale on the x-axis will go from 0 to 1000, and the scale on the y-axis will go from 0 to at least 347. It is usually convenient to use a round number, such as 400, to end a scale. Choose the scales so that the height and width of the graph are similar.

4. To plot your graph, carefully move a pencil up the y-axis to 26 m. This is the altitude at the beginning of the survey. Make a mark on the y-axis. The co-ordinates for this point are (0, 26). Repeat the procedure for each pair of values in the table.

5. Since there is no information on the altitudes between 100 km intervals, you do not know where the line should go between data points. Therefore draw a straight line from one data point to the next.

6. Give your graph a title.

Table 4 Altitude Across a Tract of Land over 1000 km

Distance (km)	Altitude (m)
0	26
100	47
200	71
300	131
400	177
500	347
600	332
700	298
800	174
900	149
1000	76

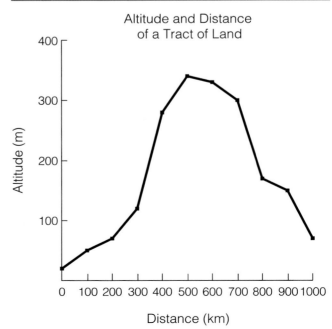

Altitude and Distance of a Tract of Land

Example 2

Table 5 shows the distance covered per second in a 110 m hurdle race. The points on the line graph were taken from the table and plotted by following the steps in Example 1. The line on this graph is not drawn straight from point to point, however. The difference between these two examples is the fact that we know the race was run in a smooth continuous motion. Therefore the lines between data points should be drawn as a smooth curve connecting the points.

A graph like this is useful for making predictions. For example, if you want to know how much distance the runner has covered in 7.5 s, you can find out from the graph. Find where 7.5 falls on the *x*-axis, and draw a line straight up to the curve. Then draw another straight line from this point to the *y*-axis. The line reaches the *y*-axis at 50 m.

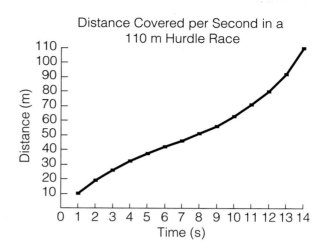

Distance Covered per Second in a 110 m Hurdle Race

Table 5 Distance Covered per Second in a 110 m Hurdle Race

Time (s)	Distance (m)
0	0
1	10
2	20
3	28
4	34
5	40
6	45
7	47
8	53
9	58
10	64
11	71
12	80
13	93
14	110

Instant Practice

During a rowing event, a group of students monitored the progress of one pair of rowers. The students recorded the distance every 50 s. Make a graph of distance covered with time from the data in Table 6. Use your graph to estimate the distance covered after 75 s.

Table 6 Distance Covered in a Rowing Event

Time (s)	Distance (m)
0	0
50	221
100	430
150	701
200	940
250	1190
300	1410
350	1680
400	1920

Straight Line Graphs

When a graph is a straight line, you can obtain important information by determining the slope of the line.

Example

A group of students used an instrument called a spark timer to make measurements of the position of a cart on an air track at 0.1 s intervals. The points on the graph below were plotted from the group's data. Draw a line of best fit, and determine the speed of the cart from the slope of the line. Examine the graph while you read the steps in the procedure below.

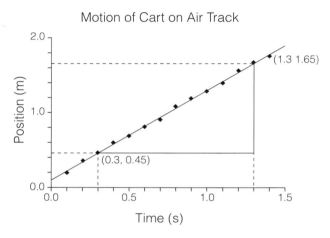

Motion of Cart on Air Track

1. Since the data points do not lie on a straight line, you must estimate the best place for the line. Place a ruler on the graph. Move the ruler around until there are about as many data points above the edge of the ruler as there are below it. Draw the line. This is the line of best fit. Do *not* simply connect the first and last points. Do *not* assume that the line must go through the origin.

2. The slope of a straight line is defined as the "rise" over the "run." To find this ratio, pick any two points on the line. Do *not* use two data points. None of them really lie on the line. Your calculation will be more accurate if you pick points that are relatively far apart. Write the co-ordinates of these points. Their co-ordinates are (0.3, 0.45) and (1.3, 1.65). This system of representing position is sometimes known as Cartesian co-ordinates.

3. The rise is the vertical distance between the points. You can calculate the rise by subtracting the *y* co-ordinate of the first point from the *y*

co-ordinate of the second point. The value is $1.65 - 0.45 = 1.2$. Since the units on the *y*-axis are metres, the rise is 1.2 m.

4. The run is the horizontal distance between the points. You can calculate the run by subtracting the *x* co-ordinate of the first point from the *x* co-ordinate of the second point. The value is $1.3 - 0.3 = 1.0$. Since the units on the *x*-axis are seconds, the run is 1.0 s.

5. Calculate the slope of the line by using the following equation:

$$\text{Slope} = \frac{\text{Rise}}{\text{Run}}$$
$$= \frac{1.2 \text{ m}}{1.0 \text{ s}}$$
$$= 1.2 \text{ m/s}$$

6. The units of the slope are metres per second. These are the units of speed. The slope of any straight line graph of time against distance is the speed. If the line is not straight, you cannot determine a slope. A curved line would mean that the speed of the object is changing.

7. Sometimes you may need to work out a mathematical formula that describes the relationship between the two variables on a graph. As you may recall from your mathematics studies, one useful form of the equation of a straight line is

$$y = mx + b$$

where *m* is the slope of the line, and *b* is the *y*-intercept (the *y*-value where the line crosses the *y*-axis). In this example, position is plotted on the *y*-axis, and time is plotted on the *x*-axis. You have already calculated a value for the slope:

$$m = 1.2 \text{ m/s}$$

Looking back at the graph, you can read off the *y*-intercept value. (Notice the units.)

$$b = 0.1 \text{ m}$$

Finally you must change *y* into the position variable and *x* into the time variable. This gives you the equation that relates position and time for the students' air track data.

$$d = 1.2 \times t + 0.1$$
$$\text{or} \quad d = 1.2t + 0.1$$

Instant Practice

Table 7 gives data for the vertical velocity of a baseball that has been thrown into the air. The upward direction is taken to be positive, so a negative velocity means that the ball is travelling downward.

1. Plot the data on a velocity-time graph, with velocity on the vertical axis. Draw a line of best fit.
2. Does one of the values fall a long way from your line of best fit? Why do you think it does?
3. Work out an equation that relates the baseball's velocity to the time it has been in the air.
4. What quantity does the slope of the graph represent? Why is this quantity negative? Hint: You may wish to return to this question after reading Chapter 12, section 12.1.

Table 7 Velocity-Time Data for Baseball Thrown in Air

Time (s)	Velocity (m/s)
0.0	23.0
0.5	17.5
1.0	12.5
1.5	8.0
2.0	3.0
2.5	−2.0
3.0	−7.0
3.5	−11.5
4.0	−17.0
4.5	−22.0
5.0	0.0

Reporting Significant Digits

A measurement is often thought of as a definite, absolute quantity. However, any measurement has uncertainty associated with it. For example, suppose that you measured the length of a desk as 1.12 m, using a metre stick with millimetre markings. The actual length of the desk will probably be either slightly more or slightly less than this value — it is *very* unlikely that the length will fall *exactly* in the middle of the 1.12 m marking! However, the ruler you used does not allow you to be more precise — you cannot say with certainty that the length is 1.124 m. Thus, the length of 1.12 m is actually an estimate. You are sure that the desk is at least 1.1 m long, plus about (but not exactly) 0.02 m. The last number you report is

therefore an estimate. Each measurement includes digits that are certainly known and one digit that is estimated. All of these digits are termed significant digits. In the example of 1.12 m, there are 3 significant digits.

The number of significant digits is important because it indicates the uncertainty in the results of experiments. Thus it is important to know how to determine significant digits. Also, measurements are often used in other calculations. In such cases, you must keep track of the number of significant digits because a final answer cannot have more significant digits than are initially reported. For example, consider the area of a table measuring 1.2 m by 2.16 m. Multiplying these values gives 2.592 m^2, which has 4 significant digits. However, the value of a quantity cannot be more precise than the values used to calculate it. In this case, the area would be rounded off to two significant digits, 2.6 m^2. Use the following rules to help you decide on the use of significant digits.

1) Count as a significant digit:
   - any non-zero digit (e.g., 1.323 has 4 significant digits)
   - any zero between non-zero digits (e.g., 1.30201 has 6 significant digits)
   - any zero following a non-zero digit and to the right of the decimal point (e.g., 1.300 has 4 significant digits)
2) Note, though, that any zero after a significant digit and to the left of the decimal point is ambiguous (if there is no decimal point explicitly written, assume it falls after the last zero). Do not attempt to assign significant digits for such cases. For example, 43 000 has 3 zeros to the left of the decimal point, but the number of significant digits is unclear. To report the number of significant digits for such numbers, you must use scientific notation: 4.3×10^4 has 2 significant digits, but 4.3000×10^4 has 5 significant digits.
3) Do not count leading zeros as significant (e.g., 0.23 and 0.022 have two significant digits).
4) For a value obtained by addition or subtraction, the number of significant digits is equal to the value having the fewest decimal places (e.g., 2.03 mm + 1.1 mm = 2.1 mm, not 2.13 mm; 13.5 g + 1.07 g + 0.135 g = 14.7 g, not 14.705 g).
5) For a value obtained by multiplication or division, the number of significant digits is equal to the value with the fewest significant digits (e.g., 3.2 m $\times$ 2.041 m $\times$ 0.03 m = 0.19 m^3, not 0.18913 m^3).

USING MODELS IN SCIENCE

Engineers and architects often make a model of the structure they are designing, such as a bridge or a building. The model helps them uncover any design flaws and determine how the actual structure will respond to stresses before it is built. Similarly, a model of an airplane may be tested in a wind tunnel so that engineers can study its flight capabilities.

In science, a model does not have to be a scaled representation of an object. A model can be a picture, a mental image, a structure, or a mathematical expression. In fact, a model can be anything that represents an object or a process to help you better visualize and understand how it works.

Sometimes you need a model because the object being investigated is too small or too large to envision. In some cases, the object is hidden from view, such as the landforms of the ocean floor or the inside of a living organism.

Examples

The great distances of space make it impossible for celestial events to be viewed directly. Astronomers can model the paths and positions of Earth, the Moon, and the Sun, however, to help them describe what happens in a lunar eclipse.

$$2H_2O(g) + O_2(g) \rightarrow 2H_2O(\ell)$$

You can describe the chemical reaction that forms water by saying that hydrogen gas combines with oxygen gas to produce liquid water. This is fine for simple chemical reactions, but most reactions are quite involved. Instead of words, you can use a shorthand, called a chemical equation, to represent a chemical reaction. A chemical equation, such as the one above, is a model that describes a chemical reaction using chemical formulas and other symbols, such as plus signs and arrows.

An atom's valence electrons are the electrons in its outer shell. Valence electrons determine an atom's ability to bond with other atoms. Scientists often use a model, called an electron dot diagram, to represent an atom's valence electrons. The electron dot diagram shown below represents the four electrons of carbon.

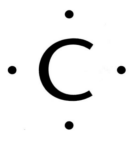

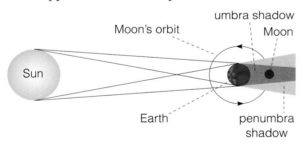

Scientists have used many techniques to probe Earth's internal dynamics and the positions of the continents. By combining the results of many experiments and observations, they have been able to create the model at the right to show the subdivisions of Earth's crust. This model helps us understand the concept of plate tectonics.

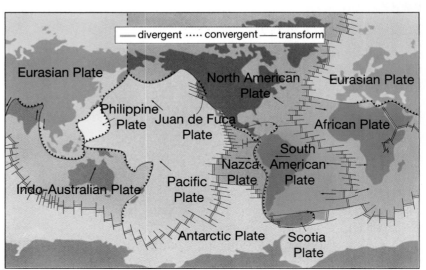

Instant Practice

The changes caused by the Industrial Revolution in nineteenth-century England produced a notable change in the frequency of two forms of the peppered moth. Before the effects of industry, the light form of this moth was much more common than the dark form. As industrial pollution increased, the dark form replaced the light form as the more common moth. The main reason for the frequency change in the two forms was that the trees on which the moths lived were affected by pollution. The main predators of the moths were birds. Depending of the colour of the trees, the birds were able to spot one form more easily than the other.

1. With this knowledge, you can construct a model that simulates how the colour and pattern of an organism can affect its survival. Working with a partner, consider the kinds of materials that you can use to represent both the colour and the pattern of the moths and the trees on which the moths lived. Make 20 of each of the two forms of moth. You can make one of the forms from lightly speckled wrapping paper or newspaper print and the other form from dark-coloured construction paper. Use the moth outline here to make a template from a thin piece of cardboard.

2. Next choose two large sheets of paper, each similar to one of the two forms of moth. Produce two different models, one simulating the effects before the Industrial Revolution and another simulating the effects once the Revolution was well underway. Decide who will be the "bird" and who will be the timer. You will need a stopwatch or a watch with a second hand. Have the timer spread out two or three different sheets of newspaper on a table or the floor. Distribute all the moths randomly on the newspaper. When the moths have been arranged, the "bird" uses one hand to pick up as many moths (one at a time) as possible in 10 s. After the 10 s are over, determine how many of each form of moth remain.

SAFETY SYMBOLS

The following safety symbols are used in the *SCIENCEPOWER™ 10* program to alert you to possible dangers. Make sure that you understand each symbol in an activity or investigation before you begin.

	Disposal Alert This symbol appears when care must be taken to dispose of materials properly.
	Biological Hazard This symbol appears when there is danger involving bacteria, fungi, or protists.
	Thermal Safety This symbol appears as a reminder to be careful when handling hot objects.
	Sharp Object Safety This symbol appears when there is a danger of cuts or punctures caused by the use of sharp objects.
	Fume Safety This symbol appears when chemicals or chemical reactions could cause dangerous fumes.
	Electrical Safety This symbol appears as a reminder to be careful when using electrical equipment.
	Skin Protection Safety This symbol appears when the use of caustic chemicals might irritate the skin or when contact with micro-organisms might transmit infection.
	Clothing Protection Safety A lab apron should be worn when this symbol appears.
	Fire Safety This symbol appears as a reminder to be careful around open flames.
	Eye Safety This symbol appears when there is a danger to the eyes and safety glasses should be worn.
	Poison Safety This symbol appears when poisonous substances are used.
	Chemical Safety This symbol appears when chemicals could cause burns or are poisonous if absorbed through the skin.
	Animal Safety This symbol appears when live animals are studied and the safety of the animals and the students must be ensured.

WHMIS Symbols

Look carefully at the WHMIS (Workplace Hazardous Materials Information System) safety symbols shown here. The WHMIS symbols are used throughout Canada to identify dangerous materials in all workplaces, including schools. Make sure that you understand what these symbols mean. When you see these symbols on containers in your classroom, at home, or in a workplace, use safety precautions.

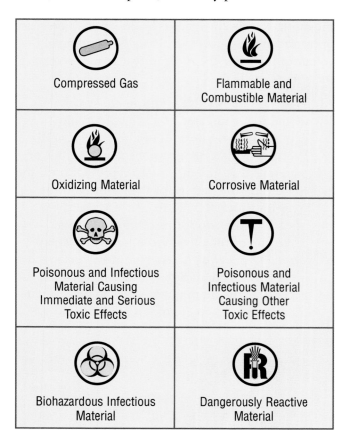

Instant Practice

1. Find four of the *SCIENCEPOWER™ 10* safety symbols in activities or investigations in this textbook. For each symbol, identify the possible dangers in the activity or investigation.

2. Find any two WHMIS symbols on containers in your school, or ask a parent or guardian to look for WHMIS symbols in a workplace. Record the name of the substance in each container. What dangers are associated with this substance?

SCIENTIFIC AND TECHNOLOGICAL DRAWING

A clear, concise drawing can often illustrate or replace words in a scientific explanation. Drawings are especially important when you are trying to explain difficult concepts or describe something that contains a lot of detail. It is important to make scientific drawings clear, neat, and accurate.

Making a Scientific Drawing

Follow these steps to make a good scientific drawing.

1. Use unlined paper and a sharp pencil with an eraser.

2. Give yourself plenty of space on the paper. You need to make sure that your drawing will be large enough to show all the necessary details. You also need to allow space for labels. Labels identify parts of the object you are drawing. Place all of your labels to the right of your drawing, unless there are so many labels that your drawing looks cluttered.

3. Carefully study the object that you will be drawing. Make sure that you know what you need to include.

4. Draw only what you see, and keep your drawing simple. Do not try to indicate parts of the object that are not visible from the angle you are observing. If you need to show another part of the object, do a second drawing. Make sure that you indicate the angle on each drawing.

5. Shading or colouring is not usually used in scientific drawings. If you want to indicate a darker area, you can use stippling (a series of dots). You can use double lines to indicate thick parts of the object.

6. If you do use colour, try to be as accurate as you can. Choose colours that are as close as possible to the colours in the object you are observing.

7. Label your drawing carefully and completely, using lower-case (small) letters. Pretend that you know nothing about the object you are observing. Think about what you would need to know if you were looking at it for the first time. Remember to place your labels to the right of the drawing, if possible. Use a ruler to draw a horizontal line from each label to the part you are identifying. Make sure that none of your label lines cross.

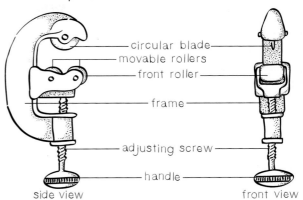

Pipe Cutter in Front and Side Views

circular blade
movable rollers
front roller
frame
adjusting screw
handle

side view   front view

8. Give your drawing a title. **Note:** The drawing of onion skin cells shown below is from a student's notebook. The student used stippling to show darker areas, horizontal labels for the cell parts viewed, and a title — all elements of an excellent scientific drawing.

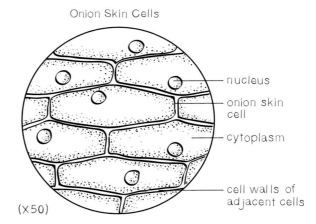

Onion Skin Cells

nucleus
onion skin cell
cytoplasm

cell walls of adjacent cells

(X50)

The stippling on this drawing of onion skin cells, as observed under a microscope, shows that some areas are darker than others.

Instant Practice

1. Make a drawing of an object in your classroom. Use stippling to indicate that it has three dimensions.

2. Draw the top view and side view of a bowl. Show how you can use stippling to give the impression of the concave and convex surfaces of the bowl.

3. Select any mechanical system in your classroom or at home: for example, a door hinge or the gears of a bicycle. Show two different views of the system, to help someone else understand how the system works.

SOLVING NUMERICAL PROBLEMS (GRASP)

Problem-solving skills are important in everyday life, in school and in the workplace. Whether you realize it or not, you solve many problems every day. For example, one of the first problems you solve every day is deciding what to wear. The "given" information that you use to make your decision is a knowledge of what items of clothing you own and which ones are clean. Then you have to think about what is required of you on that day. If you are going to a job interview, you dress differently than you would if you were going to play soccer or softball. After you have analyzed all of the information, you make a decision, get dressed, and go out to start your day!

Although solving numerical problems seems more difficult than deciding what to wear, you can use the same method to solve both types of problems. Solving any problem is easier when you establish logical steps. One excellent method for solving numerical problems includes five basic steps: Given, Required, Analysis, Solution, and Paraphrase. You can easily remember these steps because the first letter of each word spells the word **GRASP**. These steps will help you get a "grasp" on quantitative or numerical problem solving.

The GRASP method

Given

The first step in solving a numerical problem is to organize the given data. Read the problem carefully. Make a list of all of the numerical quantities given in the problem statement, as well as any other important qualitative information. Include the symbols, numerical values, and units for each numerical quantity. For example, if you are told that the mass of a rock is 3.5 kg, you would list "Mass of rock, m = 3.5 kg."

Required

The second step in the GRASP method is to identify exactly what information the problem requires you to find. Write the name of the quantity, the symbol, and the units. For example, if you are asked to find the velocity of an object, write "Velocity, v (m/s)."

Analysis

To carry out the third step, analyze the problem statement by breaking it down into individual phrases. A single phrase may contain important

information. You can use the following strategies to help you analyze the problem:

- Look at the given data and the required value. Write down any relationships between these quantities. For example, if you are given values for the area and pressure and you need to determine the force, write down "$P = \dfrac{F}{A}$."

- If possible, make a diagram. A good diagram can often provide the key to solving a problem.

- Ensure that the units in the given data are consistent with each other and with the units you will use in your final answer. If the units are not consistent, make the necessary conversions.

- Analyze the problem statement to determine if you need any information that can be found in a table, appendix, or other reference. For example, the densities of many substances are listed in tables in science textbooks. The masses of many objects, from an electron to the Sun, can be found in reference materials, both print and electronic. Look up and record any numerical values that you need.

- Write down any assumptions you will have to make in order to solve the problem.

Solution

In the fourth step, use all the data and information that you have accumulated to find the solution. Convert all the units to the units required in your final answer. Then substitute the given values into the relationships you have written down, and carry out the mathematical operations. Include units in your calculations, but leave your answers unrounded.

Paraphrase

The purpose of the fifth and final step is to clarify the meaning of the calculations you have done. The word "paraphrase" means to restate in a different way. Paraphrase your solution, including the quantity, value, and units, in the form of a sentence. Round your answer(s) to the appropriate number of significant digits. See page 605 for tips on reporting significant digits.

Choosing and Rearranging Formulas

Solving a numerical problem often involves choosing a standard mathematical formula and then rearranging it so that the variable you want is isolated on the left side of the equation. The first two steps of the GRASP method remind you to identify the variables that you are given and the variables that you need to find. (Remember that a problem sometimes gives you an extra variable "in disguise." A phrase such as "from a standstill" or "starting from rest" tells you that the starting velocity in the problem is 0 m/s.) In the *Analysis* step, you need to choose a formula that includes these variables. (If you cannot find the right formula, check that you have identified the right variables.) You can now use techniques of algebra to rearrange the formula and isolate your "required" variable. Only then, in the *Solution* step, should you start to replace variables with numerical data.

For example, suppose that the average velocity of an airplane over a 10 s time interval was 200 m/s, and you want to know how far the airplane travelled in this 10 s interval. The formula that relates average velocity, displacement, and time interval is

$$\vec{v}_{av} = \frac{\vec{\Delta d}}{\Delta t}$$

As this formula stands, you cannot work out the displacement. If you multiply both sides by Δt, however, and then reverse the equation, you get

$$\vec{\Delta d} = \vec{v}_{av} \times \Delta t$$

$$\text{or} \quad \vec{\Delta d} = \vec{v}_{av} \Delta t$$

This rearrangement allows you to do the calculation.

$$\vec{\Delta d} = \vec{v}_{av} \Delta t$$
$$= (200 \text{ m/s}) \times (10 \text{ s})$$
$$= 2000 \text{ m}$$

In your Grade 10 science studies, most of the formulas that you will need will be similar to the one above. You will occasionally have to use slightly more complex formulas, such as

$$\vec{\Delta d} = \vec{v}_i \times \Delta t + \frac{\vec{a} \times (\Delta t)^2}{2}$$

or

$$\vec{v}_{av} = \frac{\vec{d}_f - \vec{d}_i}{t_f - t_i}$$

For these formulas, you should think carefully about which variable you need to isolate, and which techniques from your mathematics studies you need to apply.

Example of the GRASP Problem-Solving Method

The Model Problem below and the Instant Practice problems at the end of this section use formulas, symbols, and variables that you can find in Unit 3: The Physics of Motion. You do not have to know exactly what each symbol or variable means, however, to work through these problems.

Notice the special box that is used for the Model Problem. This box is also used in the main part of the textbook, to help you focus on worked model problems when you encounter them.

Model Problem

A car accelerates at 5.0 m/s² forward for 3.0 s, starting from rest.

(a) What velocity, in metres per second (m/s), does the car reach at the end of the acceleration?

(b) How far, in metres, does the car travel in this time?

Given

Starting velocity, $\vec{v}_i$ = 0 m/s

Time interval, Δt = 3.0 s

Acceleration, $\vec{a}$ = +5.0 m/s²

Required

(a) Final velocity, $\vec{v}_f$ (m/s)

(b) Displacement, $\vec{\Delta d}$ (m)

Analysis

$\vec{v}_i$ = 0 m/s $\vec{v}_f$ = ? m/s

Δt = 3 s $\vec{\Delta d}$ = ? m

$\vec{a}$ = 5 m/s²

(a) The formula that includes acceleration, initial velocity, final velocity, and time interval is

$$\vec{a} = \frac{\vec{v}_f - \vec{v}_i}{\Delta t}$$

You need to rearrange this formula to isolate v_f:

$$\vec{a} \times \Delta t = \vec{v}_f - \vec{v}_i \qquad \text{(Multiply both sides by } \Delta t.)$$

$$\vec{a} \times \Delta t + \vec{v}_i = \vec{v}_f \qquad \text{(Add } \vec{v}_i \text{ to both sides.)}$$

$$\vec{v}_f = \vec{v}_i + \vec{a} \times \Delta t \qquad \text{(Reverse the equation.)}$$

(b) You could use either of two formulas:

$$\Delta \vec{d} = \frac{(\vec{v}_i + \vec{v}_f) \times \Delta t}{2} \quad \text{with your value for } v_f \text{ from part (a)}$$

or $\quad \Delta d = v_i \times \Delta t + \dfrac{a \times (\Delta t)^2}{2} \quad$ with the original given information

The first formula is probably the simpler one to use.

Solution

(a) $v_f = v_i + a\,\Delta t$

$\qquad = 0 \text{ m/s} + (5.2 \text{ m/s}^2) \times (3.0 \text{ s})$

$\qquad = 15.6 \text{ m/s}$

(b) $\Delta \vec{d} = \dfrac{(\vec{v}_i + \vec{v}_f)\,\Delta t}{2}$

$\qquad = \dfrac{(0 \text{ m/s} + 15.6 \text{ m/s}) \times (3.0 \text{ s})}{2}$

$\qquad = 23.4 \text{ m}$

Paraphrase

(a) The car reaches a velocity of 16 m/s forward (to 2 significant digits) after 3.0 s.

(b) The car travels 23 m (to 2 significant digits) during the acceleration.

In the *Solution* step, notice that all the calculated digits are left in, to ensure accuracy. In the *Paraphrase* step, however, the answers are rounded to 2 significant digits because this was the accuracy of the given data.

Instant Practice

1. A cyclist travels a distance of 430 m in a straight line at an average velocity of 25 km/h. How long, in seconds, does this take? Hint: The formula you need can be found on the previous page. Remember to change the units of velocity.

2. A downhill skier, travelling at a steady 45.0 m/s, passes a "split time" marker on the course at 26.3 s. If the marker is 945 m from the start line, and the whole course is 2990 m long, what time can the skier expect to record for the run? Hint: The information you are given includes three variables — initial time t_i = 26.3 s, initial distance d_i = 945 m, and final distance d_f = 2990 m. If you assume that the skier's speed does not change in the second part of the race, you can also get a value for the average speed, v_{av}. The formula you need can be found on the previous page.

Glossary

This Glossary defines each key term found in **bold face** type in the units of this textbook. It also includes additional helpful terms.

A

abiotic non-living part of the environment (e.g. water, elements)

absolute humidity the actual quantity of water vapour in the air, in grams of water vapour per kilogram of air

accelerated motion motion with changing speed, or direction, or both; hence, motion in which the velocity is changing

acceleration due to gravity acceleration produced by the force of gravity on Earth, often represented by the letter g; about 9.8 m/s^2 in a downward direction

acceleration how much an object's velocity changes in a certain time; that is, rate of change of velocity; a vector quantity

accelerometer a device that measures acceleration

accuracy how free from error a measurement is (e.g., a micrometer could be precise to 0.01 mm, but inaccurately set with an error of 0.5 mm); *see also* precision

acid sour-tasting compound that produces hydrogen ions when it dissolves in water, H$^+$(aq)

acid precipitation precipitation that contains higher than normal levels of acid; commonly know as *acid rain*, which refers to deposition of acid solutions in several forms, such as rain and snow

acid rain see *acid precipitation*

activity series a list of metals organized according to their chemical reactivity; the most reactive metal appears at the top and the least reactive metal appears at the bottom

aerosol a suspension of solid or liquid particles in a gas, such as air

air brakes parachutes or surfaces that can turn or pivot to increase drag

air mass a large portion of air that is nearly uniform in temperature and humidity

algal bloom population explosion of algae due to increased levels of nutrients in the water system

analog method weather forecasting based on weather patterns in enormous amounts of past weather station data

analysis program software that graphs the videotaped motion of objects, after the user marks the position of a selected point in each frame of a digitized video

anemometer an instrument that measures wind speed

aneroid barometer an instrument that measures atmospheric pressure based on volume changes of a sealed, partly evacuated cell

anion a negatively charged ion that results when a neutral atom gains an electron

Antarctic Circle latitude of 66.5°S; above this latitude, the Sun does not rise in (southern) midwinter and does not set in (southern) midsummer

anticyclone a clockwise rotation of air

aquaculture cultivation of organisms that live in water (e.g., salmon farm)

Arctic Circle latitude of 66.5°N; above this latitude, the Sun does not rise in midwinter and does not set in midsummer

area the number of squared units (e.g., m^2) required to cover a surface

atmosphere a gaseous envelope surrounding a planet

atmospheric pressure the pressure exerted by air on its surroundings due to the weight of the air; see also *standard atmospheric pressure*

atomic structure the configuration of subatomic particles within an atom (e.g., a hydrogen atom has the structure of one proton in its nucleus surrounded by one electron in its shell

aurora spectacular natural light display, created by clusters of extremely high energy charged particles, coming mainly from the Sun, and colliding with molecules in the atmosphere near the north and south poles

Automated Weather Observation System (AWOS) a weather data system created by Environment Canada, with approximately 100 automatic data collection units throughout Canada

average acceleration acceleration measured over a certain time interval; symbol is a_{av}

B

balanced chemical equation a chemical equation in which there are equal numbers of atoms for each element on both sides of the equation

bar graph diagram consisting of horizontal or vertical bars representing data

base bitter-tasting, slippery-feeling compound that produces hydroxide ions, OH$^-$(aq), when it dissolves in water

Beaufort Wind Scale originally a system that allows sailors to estimate wind speeds on a 0–12 scale, based only on the motion of the sea and of objects on the ship; has been adapted for observations on land

binary compound a compound such as water (H$_2$O) and sodium chloride (NaCl) that contains two different elements

bioaccumulation see *biological magnification*

biodiversity variety of living organisms that inhabit Earth

biological magnification the process whereby substances (e.g., toxic compounds, chemicals) collect in the bodies of organisms in progressively higher concentrations towards the top of a food chain

biomass weight of living things, often expressed as dry weight of an organism, population, or community per unit area

biosphere the life zone of Earth, including the lower part of the atmosphere, hydrosphere, and upper part of Earth's crust

biotechnology using or modifying living organisms to produce marketable goods

biotic living part of the environment (e.g., plant and animal organisms)

bob (of a pendulum) a small mass which hangs from the end of a taut string to form a pendulum

bog a plant community found in acidic, wet areas; spongy ground formed from partly decomposed mosses, which form peat

Bohr-Rutherford atom a scientific model of the atom, dating from about

1913; electrons orbit in fixed shells around a small, dense nucleus which contains protons and neutrons

C

capacity units the units that are used to report the volume of liquid (e.g., L)

carbohydrate any of a group of compounds made of carbon, hydrogen, and oxygen (e.g., sugars and starches)

carbon cycle the flow of carbon through an ecosystem, from the atmosphere to organisms and back to the atmosphere; in aquatic ecosystems, much carbon dioxide is in solution in the water

Carboniferous Period approximately 300 million years B.C.E.; a time when plant material accumulated in swamps and was eventually converted to coal

carnivore an animal that consumes other species of animals (e.g., lynx, wolf, hawk)

carrying capacity the maximum number of organisms in a population that can survive on the resources available in an ecosystem

Cartesian co-ordinates two numbers giving the exact location of a point on a graph; the first number of the pair is read off the horizontal axis, and is usually called the x co-ordinate; the second number is read off the vertical axis, and is usually called the y co-ordinate

catalyst a substance that speeds up a chemical reaction but is not itself used up or changed by the reaction

cation a positively charged ion that results when a neutral atom gives up an electron

cellular respiration the conversion of carbohydrates (sugars) by organisms into energy

chemical equation a method or model for describing what happens to reactants and products during a chemical reaction, using chemical formulas of the chemicals involved

chemical property a characteristic of a substance that describes its ability to enter into a chemical reaction (e.g., an acid's capacity to be neutralized by a base; the tendency or iron to rust)

chemical reaction a process in which new substances with new properties are formed (e.g., the reaction between sodium metal — a highly

reactive substance — and chlorine gas — a highly poisonous substance — produces safe and edible sodium chloride or table salt)

chemosynthesis the use of certain chemicals by some bacteria to produce sugars, which the bacteria then use for food

Cherenkov radiation radiation caused by particles travelling faster than light in a refractive medium which slows light down; the optical equivalent of a sonic boom

chlorofluorocarbons (CFCs) a class of chemical compounds once used as refrigerants and aerosol propellants because they are chemically inert; at high altitudes, however, they are broken down by ultraviolet light into chemicals that react with and destroy ozone

cirrus high-level clouds made of ice crystals, formed by deposition

cladistics a method of classifying organisms based on ancestry

classical system an older system for naming compounds that have elements with more than one valence; the Latin name of the metal in the compound is used, with the suffix "ic" added to indicate the ion with the higher charge and the suffix "ous" added to indicate the ion with the lower charge (e.g., $FeCl_2$ is ferrous chloride; $FeCl_3$ is ferric chloride)

classify in biology, to group together organisms based on genealogical descent

clearcutting a forestry practice in which all the trees are harvested from an area of forest

climax community the last stage of succession in which communities of organisms are most complex (e.g., a mature forest)

closed system an environment in which substances do not enter or leave (e.g., Earth is often referred to as a closed system)

coalescence a process in which cloud droplets collide and blend together, forming raindrops

coefficient a number placed in front of the formula of a compound in a chemical equation to show the number of units of the compound that are involved in a reaction; you add coefficients, when necessary, to balance the equation

cold front a zone created when a cold air mass overtakes a warmer air mass;

the cold air moves in below the warm air and pushes it upward

commons any resource shared by a group or population of people (e.g., the oceans, forests, atmosphere)

community groups of different species of organisms that interact together (e.g., a community of soil or stream organisms)

competition the struggle among individual organisms for access to a limited resource, such as food or territory

complete combustion an exothermic synthesis reaction in which hydrocarbons are burned in a plentiful supply of oxygen; the products of complete combustion are carbon dioxide and water

compound a pure substance made up of two or more elements that are chemically combined (e.g., water is a compound consisting of two elements, hydrogen and oxygen)

computer spreadsheet software that helps to organize information, using rows and columns

concentration the amount of substance that is present in a given volume

concept map a diagram that shows relationships among concepts

condensation nuclei tiny particles, such as dust or salt, which stimulate droplet formation

conduction the mechanism of thermal energy transfer in which highly energetic atoms or molecules collide with less energetic atoms or molecules, giving them energy

conservation to control or regulate how a natural resource, such as a forest or river, is used; to manage a resource so that it is available for present and future users

convection the mechanism of thermal energy transfer in which highly energetic molecules move from one place to another, carrying thermal energy with them

conventions agreements among scientists to measure and calculate using the same units and symbols

co-ordinate graph a grid that has data points named as Cartesian pairs, such as (4,3)

Coordinated Universal Time (UTC) the current standard reference time, based on the atomic clock; UTC can be up to a few seconds different from Greenwich Mean Time (GMT)

copepod a small type of crustacean living in either fresh or salt water

Coriolis effect changes in the motion of objects moving on Earth's surface caused by Earth's rotational motion

cost-benefit analysis a process that weighs the advantages (costs) and disadvantages (benefits) of different courses of action

covalent bond the force of attraction between atoms that share one, two, or three pairs of electrons

cubic units the units used to report the volume of a solid (e.g., cm^3)

cumulonimbus rain- or snow-bearing cumulus clouds, also known as storm clouds

cumulus all-level, puffy clouds that often have flat bases; formed by convection currents or by the meeting of air masses

cycle (of a pendulum) single motion of a pendulum that is completed as the bob moves (a) from a starting point slightly to one side of the equilibrium position, (b) through the equilibrium position to a position opposite the starting point, and (c) back through the equilibrium position, returning to the starting point

cycle concept map an events chain map in which a series of events does not produce a final outcome; this type of concept map has no beginning and no end

cyclone a counterclockwise rotation of air

D

Dalton's atomic theory a theory to explain the nature of matter: all matter is made up of small particles called atoms, which can neither be created nor destroyed

decomposers various bacteria and fungi that break down dead material and animal wastes and extract the remaining nutrients

decomposition reaction a chemical reaction in which a compound breaks down (decomposes) into two or more simpler compounds or elements

denitrification the conversion of nitrates to form nitrogen gas

denitrifying bacteria bacteria that can convert nitrates to form nitrogen gas

density-dependent factors variables that affect a population based on the degree of crowding within the population (e.g., disease, food supply)

density-independent factors variables that affect a population that are not based on the degree of crowding within the population (e.g., floods, temperature)

deposition a process in which water vapour changes from a gas directly to a solid

derailleur gears a set of bicycle gears in which the chain moves from one gear wheel to another

desertification the change of arable land (farmland or potential farmland) into desert through natural processes and/or human activities

detergent a cleansing substance which, unlike soap, remains soluble in "hard" water and does not form a "scum"

detritivore organism that consumes dead material and animal wastes; includes decomposers

diatomic molecule a molecule that contains two identical atoms

displacement the change in position of an object; a vector quantity

distance the total length of a journey along every twist and turn of the path

DNA deoxyribonucleic acid; a molecule that determines the inherited characteristics of an organism; chromosomes contain DNA

domain one of the three main subdivisions of life (Bacteria, Archaea, and Eukarya)

Doppler effect a change in the observed frequency of a wave, due to the motion of the source of the waves towards or away from the observer

Doppler radar a device that uses the Doppler effect to measure velocity

double displacement reaction a chemical reaction in which the cations of two different compounds exchange places, resulting in the formation of two new compounds

downdraft an air movement created by the cooling effect of rain, particularly in a storm cloud

drag forces of air resistance that act to slow down a moving object

E

easterly wave a wave of disturbance in the trade winds over the Atlantic Ocean, west of the African coast; the source of thunderstorms that may develop into a hurricane

ecological footprint a measure of an individual's or a population's impact on the environment, including land needed for living, to produce food, and discard waste

ecological perspective a view of societal issues concerned with relationships between living things and their environment

ecology the study of all the interactions that occur within the biosphere

economic perspective a view of societal issues focussing on money

economics the study of how wealth is created and distributed

ecosystem all the interacting parts of a biological community and its environment; a group of living organisms that, along with their abiotic (non-living) environment, form a self-regulating system through which energy and materials are transferred

El Niño a warming of eastern Pacific waters off the coast of South America, occurring every few years, caused by a reversal of the direction of the trade winds between South America and Australia and Indonesia; affects weather throughout the world

electrolyte a substance that dissolves in water, producing a solution that is able to conduct electricity

electron dot diagram a model that represents an atom and its valence electrons by substituting an element's symbol for its nucleus and inner-shell electrons, and placing dots around the symbol to show the number of valence electrons

element a pure substance that cannot be broken down into simpler substances by ordinary means, such as a chemical reaction (e.g., iron, sulfur, oxygen are elements)

emigration movement of a number of organisms from an area or region during a specific period of time

endothermic a physical or chemical change that results in an absorption of energy

Environment Canada federal government agency that provides detailed, up to the minute weather forecasts and also carries out research to study and improve Canada's air, land, and water quality

environment surroundings of an organism, including the biotic and abiotic parts

Environmental Impact Assessment (EIA) an inquiry that identifies and predicts the effects of a proposed development on the environment, economy, and people's health and well-being

enzyme a naturally occurring catalyst found in the body, enabling cellular chemical reactions to occur at body temperatures

equilibrium position the position in which a pendulum bob hangs directly below the pendulum's support

error the difference between a single experimental observation and the expected (or average) value for that observation

ethical perspective a view of societal issues that tries to determine whether a technological change is right or wrong according to generally accepted beliefs and values

eutrophication a water system that has been enriched by nutrients needed by plants; often nutrients from sewage and run-off over-enrich the water system causing an increase in bacterial growth and oxygen depletion

events chain map a concept map that describes a sequence of events, the steps in a procedure, or the stages of a process

exothermic a physical or chemical change that results in a release of energy

experiment an investigation or procedure that is designed to test a hypothesis

eye (of a hurricane) the calm, clear central zone of a hurricane, averaging 30 km wide

F

fact a verifiable statement or event known to have happened

fair test investigation carried out under strictly controlled conditions to ensure accuracy

fecal coliform the bacteria *E. coli* found in the solid waste (feces) of animals

field of view the area seen through the eyepiece of a microscope or other optical instrument

fossil fuel a source of energy (e.g., coal, petroleum) formed from the remains of organisms that lived in a previous geological time period

freezing rain a dangerous weather condition, created when the ground temperature is below freezing, but the air is warm enough to allow rain to fall; the rain freezes instantly, creating a solid coating of ice

front (or *frontal system*) a zone created when two air masses with different characteristics meet

frontal low a low pressure system created by rising warm air created by a disturbance in a stationary front

G

gene a segment of DNA on a chromosome that encodes a particular protein

genetically alter to artificially combine or modify genes in a cell

genus a biological group of closely related species (e.g., the genus *Ursus* includes species such as the brown bear and the black bear)

geodimeter an instrument that uses a laser gun to detect changes in position of points around a volcano

Global Positioning System (GPS) a system in which a receiver uses precisely timed signals from a network of satellites to calculate position; GPS receivers can calculate position to an accuracy of 15 m anywhere on Earth

global village a metaphor coined by Marshall McLuhan to describe our interconnected, communication-dependent society; a society based on electronic forms of communication, such as satellites and the Internet

global warming increase in average global temperature due to increasing levels of atmospheric CO_2 and other pollutants, which trap in radiant energy from the Sun

graphic organizer a visual learning tool that helps clarify the relationship between a central concept and related ideas or terms

greenhouse effect a natural process caused by a planet's atmosphere in trapping thermal energy from the Sun

greenhouse gas a gas that traps thermal energy in the atmosphere and prevents it from escaping into outer space (e.g., carbon dioxide, dinitrogen oxide, chlorofluorocarbons, and methane)

Greenwich Mean Time (GMT) the time at the prime meridian in Greenwich, England, long used as a reference time for all of Earth's time zones; Canada's time zones lie between 3.5 h (Newfoundland) and 8 h (British Columbia) behind GMT; *see also* Coordinated Universal Time

groups vertical columns in the periodic table

G-suit a body suit worn by jet pilots and astronauts, which applies hydraulic pressure to the legs and lower torso, maintaining blood pressure to the chest and brain during high-acceleration manoeuvres

gyres circular ocean currents that flow clockwise in the Northern Hemisphere, and counterclockwise in the Southern Hemisphere

H

habitat the place where an organism lives

hail ice pellets that grow through contact with droplets in air that is near or below freezing

heat of fusion the amount of energy required to melt 1.0 g of a solid into a liquid

heat of vaporization the amount of energy required to convert 1.0 g of a substance from the liquid state into the gaseous state

herbivore an organism that consumes only plant material (e.g., moose, beaver, grasshopper)

high pressure system a region where air is descending and therefore exerting more pressure on the region below; high pressure systems create clear skies

histogram a type of bar graph in which each bar represents a range of values and in which the data are continuous

horizon a layer of soil distinguished by its chemical and physical properties

humidity the amount of water vapour in the air; see also *absolute humidity*, *relative humidity*

hurricane a vast, rotating thunderstorm system, up to 500 km wide, generated by deep, warm water in the mid-Atlantic Tropics; wind speeds exceed 120 km/h

hydrocarbon an organic compound that is made up only of carbon and hydrogen

hydroponics the growing of plants in nutrient-rich solutions and without soil

hygrometer an instrument that measures relative humidity based on the absorption of water by certain materials

hypothesis a testable proposal that is an explanation for an observation or a question

I

immigration the movement of a number of organisms into a new area or region during a specific period of time

incomplete combustion an exothermic synthesis reaction in which hydrocarbons are burned in a poor supply of oxygen; the products of incomplete combustion are carbon dioxide, water, and other substances such as carbon monoxide and soot (carbon)

indicator a chemical that changes colour in response to changes in the concentration of hydrogen ions or hydroxide ions

inertial guidance system a navigation device that uses gyroscopes, rather than compasses, to sense changes in direction

input in ecology, energy consumed by an organism or ecosystem

insolation incoming solar radiation; may be reflected or absorbed by Earth's atmosphere, hydrosphere, or land surface

instantaneous the value of a quantity (e.g., velocity) at a specific moment; on a graph, the instantaneous slope is measured from a tangent line

instantaneous acceleration acceleration measured at a specific instant in time; symbol is a_{inst}

interspecific competition competition among individuals of different species (see *competition*)

intraspecific competition competition among individuals of the same species (see *competition*)

ion an atom or group of atoms that carries an electrical charge; positively charged ions are called cations, and negatively charged ions are called anions

ion drive a space transport technology that uses electricity to ionize gas particles, which are driven magnetically out of the back of the drive at high speed

ionic bond the force of attraction between the oppositely charged ions in an ionic compound

ionic compound a substance that is composed of cations and anions

ionosphere a layer of charged particles lying within the thermosphere and upper mesosphere; created when atoms and molecules in the atmosphere absorb high-energy ultraviolet radiation from the Sun

isobars lines that connect points with the same atmospheric pressure

isotherms lines that connect points of equal temperature

IUPAC International Union of Pure and Applied Chemistry; a body that specifies rules for chemical names and symbols

J

jet stream a ribbon of extremely rapidly moving air near the top of the troposphere, caused by contact between cold and warm air masses; jet streams are found at the boundaries between the polar and temperate zones and between the temperate and tropical zones; wind speeds in a jet stream vary from 100 km/h to 300 km/h

K

kingdom a main subdivision of organisms; Eubacteria, Archaebacteria, Protista, Fungi, Plantae, and Animalia are currently recognized

L

latent heat of fusion see *heat of fusion*

latent heat of vaporization see *heat of vaporization*

latitude a measure, in degrees, of distance north or south from the equator

law an action or condition that has been observed so consistently that scientists are convinced it will always happen

law of conservation of energy the law stating that, in a physical or chemical reaction, energy may be converted from one form to another, but the total amount of energy remains constant

law of conservation of mass the law stating that, in a chemical reaction, the total mass of the products is always the same as the total mass of the reactants

legal perspective a view of societal issues focussing on responsibilities and fair treatment according to current laws and past decisions

light year the distance a ray of light travels in one year, about 9460 billion km

lightning a tremendous electrical discharge in which charged particles race through the air towards each other; the temperature of the air in a lightning bolt may exceed 30 000°C

linear motion motion forward or backward along a straight-line path; directions for position, displacement, velocity, and acceleration can be indicated using + and − signs; also called *one-dimensional motion*

Little Ice Age a cooling of the climate between 1450 and 1850

longitude a measure, in degrees, of distance east or west from a reference line called the prime meridian, which passes through Greenwich, England

low pressure system a region where rising air is leaving less dense air below

Lyme disease a bacterial disease transmitted by feeding ticks; characterized at first by skin rash, headache, fever, and later by heart damage and arthritis

M

mass the amount of matter in a substance; often measured with a balance

meniscus the slight curve at the top of a liquid where the liquid meets the sides of a container

mercury barometer an instrument that measures atmospheric pressure using a column of mercury

mesosphere the region of the atmosphere between 50 km and 90–100 km above Earth's surface

metaphor a figure of speech in which a word or a phrase used to describe one thing is applied to another (e.g., global village, food for thought)

meteorology the study of Earth's atmosphere and weather systems

metric system a system of measurement based on multiples of ten

metronome and marker a simple way to record motion: set a musical metronome to 60; stretch a paper tape along the object's path; walk beside the object, marking its position each time the metronome clicks

microgravity a near-weightless environment in orbit, caused by free fall but not by any absence of gravity

model a verbal, mathematical, visual, or mental representation that attempts to explain a scientific concept or hypothesis

molecular compound a substance that is composed of molecules

molecule a neutral particle that is made up of two or more atoms that are joined together by covalent bonds

monoculture the use of land for growing only a single variety of a crop

monsoons a system of winds, found in southern Asia, that generate torrential rain and extensive flooding in the summer and very dry conditions in the winter

motion formula formula relating average velocity to displacement and time:

$$\vec{V}_{av} = \frac{\Delta \vec{d}}{\Delta t}$$

motion sensor *see* ultrasonic motion sensor

multi-speed gear system a set of bicycle gears enclosed inside the rear wheel hub

mycorrhizal fungi fungi that live in or on the roots of plants and help the plants to draw nutrients from the soil

N

network tree a concept map in which ideas or concepts are circled while other terms are written on connecting lines

neutralization the reaction between an acid and a base, which results in a salt and water; neutralization reactions are double displacement reactions

nimbostratus cloud a stratus cloud that brings rain

nimbus cloud rain-bearing or snow-bearing cloud

nitrification the conversion of ammonia to form nitrates

nitrifying bacteria bacteria that can convert ammonia to nitrates

nitrogen fixation the conversion of nitrogen gas in the atmosphere to ammonia

nitrogen-fixing bacteria bacteria that can convert nitrogen gas in the atmosphere to compounds that plants can use, such as ammonia

non-renewable a term applied to resources that cannot be replaced or that are being used much faster than they are forming (e.g., coal, oil)

null hypothesis a hypothesis that predicts there will be no difference between two different situations

Numerical Weather Prediction (NWP) weather forecasting based on current weather data and complex equations that describe interactions within the atmosphere

nutrient any substance needed by an organism for proper growth, repair, and function

nutrient cycle the path of an element (nutrient) through an ecosystem

O

occluded front a zone created when a cold front catches up with and overtakes a slower-moving warm front

ocean currents giant rivers in Earth's oceans, created by surface winds and density and temperature differences in the ocean water; also influenced by the Coriolis effect; some carry warm waters from the Tropics to the Arctic; others carry cool Arctic or Antarctic waters toward the equator

omnivore an animal that consumes other species of animals and plant material (e.g., bear, raccoon, humans)

one-dimensional motion see *linear motion*

operational definition a way of defining physical quantities, which shows how they are observed and measured

orbital plane the plane in which Earth and the other planets (except Pluto) move around the Sun

ordered pair see *Cartesian co-ordinates*

organic chemistry a branch of chemistry that studies carbon-containing compounds and their properties

output in ecology, unused energy released by an organism or ecosystem

oxide a compound that is made up of any element that is chemically combined with oxygen

P

paradigm a model or concept that is accepted by most people in a society; it may explain a complex process, idea or set of data

parts per billion (ppb) a measure of small amounts of a chemical or element, usually a toxin, in body tissues or the environment; one part per billion is equivalent to 1: 1 000 000 000.

parts per million (ppm) a measure of small amounts of a chemical or element, usually a toxin, in body tissues or the environment; one part per million is equivalent to 1: 1 000 000.

peat partly decomposed, moisture-absorbing moss found in ancient swamps and bogs; may form a thick mat

percent error error expressed as a percentage proportion; calculated as

percent error =
$$\pm \frac{(\text{observed value} - \text{expected value})}{\text{expected value}} \times 100\%$$

percent ionization the number of molecules of a substance that will ionize for every 100 molecules that dissolve

periodic table a graphic arrangement that organizes elements into rows and columns on the basis of their atomic numbers; the resulting arrangement displays patterns and relationships among the elements

periods horizontal rows in the periodic table

pesticide a chemical used for killing insects

pH meter a device that provides a precise measurement of the pH of a substance when it is in solution

pH scale a scale that measures the relative acidity or alkalinity of a substance

photogate a timing device, used in motion experiments, in which light-sensitive photocells are attached to a computer

photosynthesis the conversion of energy from the Sun to chemical energy (sugars) by green plants

physical property a characteristic of a substance that can change without forming a new substance (e.g., the density of water changes when water turns from a liquid to a gas)

phytoremediation the use of plants, which can accumulate toxic compounds in their tissues, to clean soil of contaminants

picket fence a device with alternating white (or clear) and black stripes, which can be attached to a moving object such as a lab cart; the stripes trigger a photocell repeatedly as they pass

pioneer organism an organism that can move onto a new area of land (e.g., lichens, various weeds)

planimeter a mechanical computer that calculates area; a stylus on the planimeter arm is traced completely around the boundary of a region on a graph or map, which moves a rotating disk on the planimeter to display the area of the region

polar molecule a molecule in which the sharing of electrons is unequal, so that one end has a slight positive charge and the other end has a slight negative charge

polar zones the regions of Earth's surface above the Arctic Circle (66.5°N) or the Antarctic Circle (66.5°S)

political perspective a view of societal issues focussing on the role of government

polyatomic ion an ion that consists of two or more different non-metal atoms that are joined by covalent bonds

population all the individuals of one species that occupy a certain geographical area during a certain time

population density the number of individuals in a given area or volume

position an object's location as seen by an observer from a particular viewpoint; a vector quantity, with both distance and direction

position-time graph a graph in which an object's position is plotted on the vertical axis, and time on the horizontal axis

precipitate an insoluble solid formed in a chemical reaction between aqueous solutions

precision the amount of information (by significant digits) a measuring instrument provides

prediction a statement of the expected outcome of an experiment

prescribed burn a controlled fire started by people in order to remove accumulated dead plant material in an area; a wildlife management practice to maintain certain types of habitat

preservation to keep a natural resource, such as a forest or river, in its original condition, free of any harm or damage caused by human activity

prevailing westerlies winds blowing from west to east in the temperate zones

primary consumer first consuming organism in a food chain (a herbivore or an omnivore); occupies the second trophic level

primary succession succession that begins in an area of bare rock

prime meridian a reference line for longitude, running from the North Pole to the South Pole and passing through Greenwich, England

producer green plants and some species of bacteria, such as cyanobacteria, that carry out photosynthesis to produce food

productivity the amount of plant growth in a given area within a given period of time; often expressed as biomass/area/time

products the substance(s) that result from a chemical change in a chemical reaction

protozoan aquatic organism made up of one or more cells that contain a nucleus (e.g., alga, paramecium, diatom)

psychrometer an instrument that measures relative humidity based on the difference in temperature readings of a dry bulb and a wet bulb thermometer

pyramid of biomass the concept that the mass of all the organisms in each trophic level decreases as one progresses towards the top of a food chain

pyramid of energy flow the concept that the energy available to organisms at each trophic level decreases as one progresses towards the top of a food chain

pyramid of numbers the concept that numbers of organisms decrease as one progresses towards the top of a food chain

Q

qualitative data information gathered in observations in which no measurement takes place

qualitative description a scientific explanation in words, rather than numbers or mathematics

qualitative observation an observation that can be described using words

qualitative physical property a characteristic of a substance that can be described but not measured

quantitative data data that consist of numbers and/or units of measurements; obtained through measurement and mathematical calculations

quantitative description a scientific explanation using mathematics and numerical measurements

quantitative observation an observation that is described using numbers

quantitative physical property a characteristic of a substance that can be measured (e.g., density)

R

radar ranging technique for finding distances by sending out short pulses of electromagnetic radiation and timing how long they take to return

radiation the mechanism of thermal energy transfer in which atoms or molecules emit electromagnetic waves; the energy carried by these waves is converted back to thermal energy only when the waves interact with some form of matter

rate of change how fast a quantity is changing over time; calculated as

average rate of change =

$$\frac{\text{total change}}{\text{time taken}} = \frac{\text{final state} - \text{initial state}}{\text{final time} - \text{initial time}}$$

rate of reaction how fast a chemical change takes place

reactants the substance(s) that undergo a chemical change in a chemical reaction

reaction rate the length of time it takes for a chemical reaction to occur (e.g., the time for a given amount of product to form or a given amount of reactant to react); reaction rate is affected by factors such as particle size, concentration, and temperature

readability an instrument's greatest possible precision of measurement

relative humidity the amount of water vapour in the air expressed as a percentage of the amount of vapour that the air would have if it were saturated

remediate to restore a disturbed or contaminated area of land to a natural state

renewable a term applied to resources that can be replaced as fast or faster than they are being used (e.g., energy from the Sun, wind)

residence time (of atmospheric water) the time it takes for all of the water in Earth's atmosphere to fall to Earth as rain or snow and to be replaced by evaporation (approximately 9 days)

resolution the power of an optical device, such as a microscope, to produce separate images of objects that are very close to each other

Rhizobium bacterium that lives in association with the roots of some legumes (pea family) and can fix nitrogen; see *nitrogen fixation*

S

salt an ionic compound that results from the reaction between an acid and a base

sampling a method of investigation that studies only a portion of a population as a representation of the population as a whole

satellite a small body that orbits a larger one; it may be a natural satellite such as Earth's moon, or an artificial satellite sent into orbit for communications or research

saturated of air; state in which, at any given temperature, there is as much water vapour in the air as the air can hold

scalar a physical quantity that has magnitude (size), but not direction (e.g., distance, time, speed)

scale drawing a drawing in which the objects appear in the same proportions as they are in reality

scientific perspective a view of societal issues that tries to understand, explain, and predict the effects of a technological change

scientific investigation an investigation that involves the systematic application of concepts and procedures (e.g., experimentation and research, observation and measurement, analysis and communication of data and results) that require skill and habits of mind which are fundamental to the development of scientific knowledge and that have been proven over time to be useful in advancing scientific knowledge

scrubber an anti-pollution device for removing polluting gases such as sulfur dioxide from industrial smokestack emissions

secondary consumer second consuming organism in a food chain (a carnivore or an omnivore); occupies the third trohpic level

secondary succession succession that begins in an area where there was a previous ecosystem (e.g., arrival of plants and animals to an area burned by fire)

shells regions around the nucleus of an atom that may be occupied by electrons

SI the international system of measurement units, including such terms as kilogram, metre and second (from the French *Le Systéme international d'unités*)

simulation program software that has the user construct a situation that will produce a certain motion graph

single displacement reaction a chemical reaction in which one element takes the place of another element in a compound

skeleton reaction summary of a chemical reaction using symbols; may be incomplete or unbalanced (e.g., $H_2 + O_2 \rightarrow H_2O$)

sleet raindrops that refreeze into ice pellets

slope the steepness of a line graph, calculated as slope = rise/run; a line with positive slope rises as you move to the right, a line with negative slope falls as you move to the right

soil the surface layer of Earth that supports life

solar constant the amount of radiant energy hitting one square metre of Earth's outer atmosphere every second; defined for the case in which the Sun's rays are arriving perpendicular to Earth's surface

solar wind streams of extremely high energy charged particles ejected by the Sun

species a group of organisms that can interbreed and produce fertile offspring

specific heat capacity the amount of heat required to raise the temperature of 1.0 g of a substance by 1°C

speed how fast something is moving; a scalar, which does not give the direction of motion

spider map a concept map used to organize a central idea and associated ideas that are not necessarily related to each other

standard atmospheric pressure the atmospheric pressure of dry air at sea level when the temperature is 25°C, equal to 101 300 Pa

stationary front a zone created when cold and warm air masses are in contact but neither is moving

Stock system the current system for naming compounds having elements with more than one valence; roman numerals are used to indicate the charge on the cation (e.g., $FeCl_2$ is iron(II) chloride; $FeCl_3$ is iron(III) chloride)

storm surge a ridge of sea water as high as 5.5 m, created at the centre of a hurricane

stratosphere the region of the atmosphere between 10 km and 50 km above Earth's surface

stratus cloud a low-level, flat, shapeless cloud that forms in many layers; formed when air masses meet, when a layer of air is pushed up the side of a mountain range, or by conduction when in contact with a very cool ground surface (e.g., fog)

stroboscope a camera with a rapidly blinking light that records a series of pictures on the same piece of photographic film

strong acid an acid, such as sulfuric acid, that ionizes completely in water (has a high percent ionization)

strong base a base, such as sodium hydroxide, that ionizes completely in water (has a high percent ionization)

subsoil the soil beneath the uppermost layer of soil (topsoil); usually identified as the B horizon

succession changes in the structure of a community of organisms; the replacement of existing species by more recently arriving species

sustainability the ability to meet the needs of the present generation without compromising the ability of future generations to meet their needs

sustainable development the use of renewable resources in a way that will not harm the environment and, at the same time, increase the standard of living for people

synthesis reaction a chemical reaction in which two or more reactants combine to produce a new product

T

table an orderly arrangement of facts set out for easy reference

tachyon a particle not known to exist for certain, but suspected to exist by some physicists; tachyons would travel faster than the speed of light

tangent line a straight line that just touches the curve of a graph; the slope of the tangent matches the steepness of the curve at that point

technological perspective a view of societal issues focussing on manufacturing processes or devices

technology the application of knowledge and/or experience in the designing and use of devices, processes, and materials to solve practical problems and satisfy human needs and wants

telegraph the first long-distance, rapid communication device which carries coded messages as electrical pulses along cables; invented in 1844

temperate zones the regions of Earth's surface from 23.5°N–66.5°N latitude, and from 23.5°S–66.5°S latitude

temperature inversion a weather condition in which a "cap" of warm air traps a layer of cooler air below it

terminal velocity constant downward velocity reached by a falling object, when the forces of air friction (or drag) balance the force of gravity

theoretical physics the search for patterns and relationships, and for productive ways to express them, in data obtained from observation and experiment; often expressed in mathematical forms such as graphs and formulas

theory an explanation of an event that has been supported by consistent, repeated experimental results and has therefore been accepted by a majority of scientists

thermal energy the total energy of the random motions of particles making up a substance

thermometer an instrument that measures temperature

thermosphere the outer region of the atmosphere, starting at 90–100 km above Earth's surface

throughput in ecology, energy used by an organism or ecosystem

thunderstorm a violent weather condition associated with cumulonimbus clouds; the build up in charge separation results in lightning and the associated thunder, accompanied by rain

ticker timer a timing device which makes a series of dots on a paper tape as it is pulled through a timer

tiltmeter an instrument for measuring changes in the slope of the sides of a volcano

time describes when an event occurs

time interval the duration of an event, calculated as (final time − initial time)

tipping bucket gauge an instrument that measures rainfall using a funnel shaped bucket that tips over when full; the number of tips indicates the amount of rainfall

topsoil the uppermost layer of soil; usually identified as the A horizon

tornado a swirling, destructive funnel of air, created by wind shear in high-energy thunderstorms; wind speeds in tornadoes vary from 60 km/h to 500 km/h

trade the movement of goods among nations

tragedy of the commons the destruction of a shared resource by individual greed (e.g., Atlantic cod fisheries, whaling)

transect to travel across an area, often in a straight line; biologists often transect a study area in order to survey numbers of organisms there

trends method weather forecasting based on several days' observation of fronts, highs, lows, and other data

trophic level feeding level of one or more organisms in a food web (e.g., producers, primary consumers, secondary consumers)

Tropic of Cancer latitude of 23.5°N; at this latitude, the Sun is directly overhead on the first day of summer, June 21 in the Northern Hemisphere

Tropic of Capricorn latitude of 23.5°S; at this latitude, the Sun is directly overhead on the first day of winter, December 21 in the Northern Hemisphere

tropical cyclone the term for a hurricane in the Indian Ocean

tropical depression a storm that may become a hurricane, with wind speeds of 37–65 km/h

tropical storm a hurricane-like storm, but weaker, with wind speeds of 65–120 km/h

tropical zone the region of Earth's surface between the Tropics of Cancer and Capricorn (23.5°N–23.5°S latitude)

troposphere the region of the atmosphere from Earth's surface up to an altitude of 10 km

typhoon the term for a hurricane in the western Pacific Ocean

U

ultrasonic motion sensor a timing device which emit short bursts or "clicks" of high-frequency sound waves and detects the returning echo; often connected to a computer

uniform motion motion at constant velocity, with no change in speed or direction

universal indicator paper an indicator that contains various chemicals that turn different colours depending on the pH of a solution; it is also known as pH paper

updraft an air movement created by rising warm air, particularly in a storm cloud (cumulonimbus)

upwelling a process in which cool water flows up from deep in the ocean to replace surface water driven on by the wind; provides a rich supply of nutrients from the bottom of the ocean

V

valence electron one or more of the electrons occupying the outer electron shell of an atom

valence shell the outer electron shell of an atom

variable a factor that can influence the outcome of an experiment

variable pitch propeller an airplane propeller with blades that can change their "*pitch*" — the angle at which the blades are set into the central hub (invented by Wallace Turnbull in 1916)

vector a physical quantity that has both magnitude (size) and direction (e.g., position, displacement, velocity, acceleration)

vector diagram a diagram of two or more vectors, arranged so that the end of one vector is the starting point for the next vector ("tip-to-tail"); used to find vector sums

vector sum the result of adding two or more individual vectors together, "tip-to-tail"

velocity how fast an object's position is changing, that is the rate of change of position; a vector quantity, with both speed and direction

velocity-time graph a graph in which an object's velocity is plotted on the vertical axis, and time on the horizontal axis

venn diagram a graphic organizer consisting of overlapping circles; used to compare and contrast concepts or objects

volume the measurement of the amount of space occupied by a substance

W

warm front a zone created when a warm air mass overtakes a cooler one; the warm air gently rides up over the trailing end of the cold air mass

water cycle cyclic movement of water from Earth's surface to the atmosphere, via evaporation and transpiration, and then back to Earth's surface via precipitation

weak acid an acid, such as acetic acid, that only partially ionizes in water (has a low percent ionization)

weak base a base, such as ammonia, that only partially ionizes in water (has a low percent ionization)

weather balloon a hydrogen or helium filled balloon that carries a "mini-weather station" or radiosonde up through the atmosphere

weather satellite an orbiting instrument for observing Earth's weather from space, detecting visible and infrared light

wet mount a type of sample preparation using a microscope slide, a cover slip, and water

wetland a general term used to describe seasonally or permanently water-covered areas of land (e.g., lakes, rivers, estuaries, marshes, swamps, bogs)

WHMIS an acronym that stands for Workplace Hazardous Materials Information System

wildfire a very destructive fire

wildlife management manipulation of populations of wild organisms (especially game animals) and areas in which they live for the benefit of people; preservation of threatened and endangered wildlife

wind shear a condition in which the wind blows in different directions at different altitudes

wind vane an instrument that indicates the direction from which the wind is blowing

word equation a method or model for describing what happens to reactants and products during a chemical reaction, using words to name the chemicals involved

Index

The page numbers in **boldface** type indicate the pages where the terms are defined.
Terms that occur in investigations (*inv.*) and activities (*act.*) are also indicated.

Photo Credits

Text Permissions

106-111 A portion of this material adapted and used with permission from William J. Webb III; **420** Adapted text excerpt from article "An Easy Cell" by Douglas Sharp, appeared in The Hamilton Spectator, Wednesday, January 12th, 2000.

Illustration Credits

IS-3 From Glencoe Science Interactions Course 2 by Bill Aldridge, © 1998 Glencoe/McGraw-Hill; **18** "Food web illustration" News Services Division/The New York Times; **86** "Frequency of Wildfires in Eastern Canada". Reprinted with permission of Thomson Learning; **203** From Map Source: Environment Canada, *The State of Canada's Environment, 1996.* Reproduced with the permission of the Minister of Public Works and Government Services Canada, 2000; **248** From Physical Science by Charles W. McLaughlin and Marilyn Thompson, © 1999 Glencoe/McGraw-Hill; **256 top** From Science Voyages Level Blue by Alton Biggs, © 2000 Glencoe/McGraw-Hill; **256 middle** From Physical Science by Charles W. McLaughlin and Marilyn Thompson, © 1999 Glencoe/McGraw-Hill; **258** From Physical Science by Charles W. McLaughlin and Marilyn Thompson, © 1999 Glencoe/McGraw-Hill; **265** From Science Voyages Level Blue by Alton Biggs, © 2000 Glencoe/McGraw-Hill; **435** From Meteorology by Danielson, © WCB McGraw-Hill; **440** From Earth Science by Emiliant © HBJ; **441** From Science Voyages Level Red by Alton Biggs © 2000 Glencoe/McGraw-Hill; **442** From Science Voyages Level Red by Alton Biggs © 2000 Glencoe/McGraw-Hill; **468** From Earth Science by Ralph Feather, Jr. and Susan Leach Snyder © 1999 Glencoe/McGraw-Hill